YEARBOOK OF SCIENCE
AND THE FUTURE
1999

YEARBOOK OF SCIENCE AND THE FUTURE
1999

Encyclopædia Britannica, Inc.

Chicago·London·Paris·Rome·Seoul·Sydney·Tokyo

1999
YEARBOOK OF SCIENCE AND THE FUTURE

FOREWORD

"If anything characterized the year in science," writes historian and philosopher Robert P. Crease in this year's OVER-VIEW article, "it was how many key developments evoked particularly extreme reactions." "From awe and wonder to fear and terror" is how he describes the range of our responses to such events as the visitation of the spectacular Comet Hale-Bopp in early 1997, the images returned of the Martian landscape by the successful Mars Pathfinder mission and from the cosmic depths by the Hubble Space Telescope, the harrowing mishaps that plagued the crew of the Russian space station *Mir* for much of the year, the news of yet more ways in which we are jeopardizing our own health and that of the Earth's environment, the birth of human septuplets, and, of course, the announcement of the cloning of a sheep from a single cell taken from an adult ewe—arguably the single most controversial technological revelation of the year.

These provocative developments and hundreds of others are comprehensively reported in Encyclopædia Britannica's *1999 Yearbook of Science and the Future*. In some of its nearly 50 specially commissioned review articles, experts in their respective fields report on the confirmation of the existence of water molecules on the Sun's surface, discuss a theory that the legendary Bronze Age civilizations of Troy, Jericho, and Mycenae may have been doomed by swarms of earthquakes, cite two studies that attempt to put a price tag on the services that the Earth's ecosystems provide us free of charge, describe a test rocket propelled by a laser beam, and recount genetic research that clarifies the evolutionary relationship between dogs and wolves. Complementing these reviews are RECENT BOOKS OF SCIENCE, a selection of recently published titles that have been judged significant contributions to scientific learning, and SCIENTISTS OF THE YEAR, which comprises accounts of the latest Nobel Prize-winning researchers and their work and of prominent scientists, such as Jacques-Yves Cousteau and Eugene Shoemaker, who died in 1997 and early 1998.

Because no event or achievement can be fully appreciated outside of its context, the yearbook also presents 12 colorfully illustrated feature articles that probe the stories behind the stories, taking an in-depth look at some of the most important research efforts and contentious topics in science today. In WARMING UP TO THE OUTER SOLAR SYSTEM, for example, a noted planetary scientist describes the ongoing work to explore the edge of the solar system, where comets like Hale-Bopp originate. Two of the most pressing environmental issues on the eve of the millennium—the massive die-offs of coral reefs being reported around the world and the observed decline in the natural pollinators on which agriculture depends—are covered in WHAT IS KILLING THE REEFS? and THE BIRDS AND THE BEES, THE FLOWERS AND THE TREES. Another pair of features offer penetrating examinations of two long-contested questions of modern science: the nature of human consciousness and the prehistoric origins of the modern people of Japan. Still other features deal with the evolution of feathers and bird flight, the contribution of plastics to modern society, and the state-of-the-art research being conducted by the U.S. Army in a facility devoted to a scientific understanding of the battlefield environment. Finally, a special photo essay and an accompanying commentary showcase the work of a sculptor who creates ephemeral outdoor artworks from materials at hand to suggest not only the forces of nature at work but also something subtly more.

As in past years, all of us at Britannica who have been involved with the production of this edition hope that its content engages not only your intellect but also your passions. As Professor Crease observes, scientific and technological events and achievements often provoke strong reactions from us because "science affects not just what we know but how we understand ourselves." Please feel free to share, by mail or in electronic form, your own reactions to the book and your suggestions on ways to improve it. Our E-mail address is <yearbook@eb.com>.

—Charles Cegielski, Editor

CONTENTS

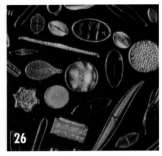

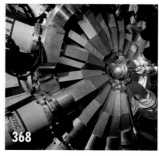

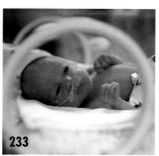

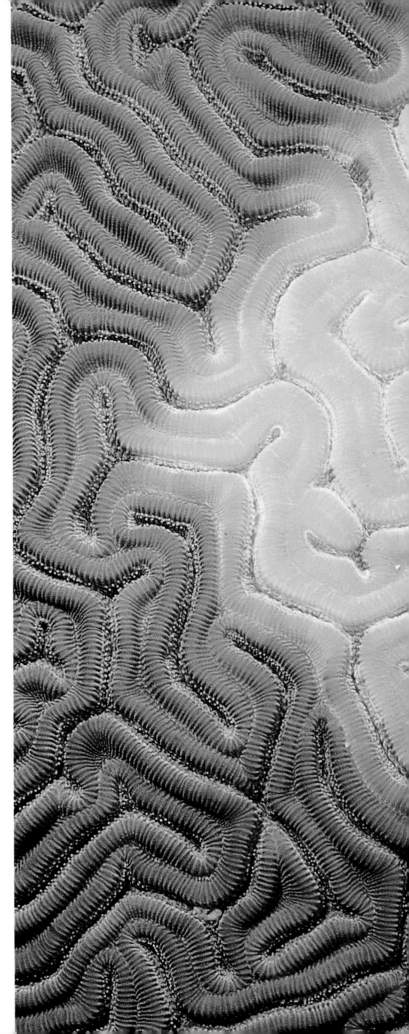

Within the past decade, marine ecologists have investigated alarming reports of coral reef die-offs around the world. In the process of trying to save these beautiful and complex ecosystems under the sea, however, researchers have reaffirmed how little science knows about them.

What Is Killing the Reefs?

by Barbie Bischof

Peering into the crystalline waters that surround Andros Island, the largest island in the Bahamas, visitors can glimpse an underwater jewel native only to the world's tropic and subtropic regions—a living coral reef. Moving shadows of barracuda, turtles, nurse sharks, tarpon, and rays attest to the vibrance of this ecosystem. Ribbons of sunlight undulate across ramparts of coral-built mounds and branches. Fish of all shapes and sizes, colors and patterns drift about, occasionally snapping at a passing meal or bolting for cover. Startled squid fade into clouds of ink, moray eels lurk in nooks, and spiny lobsters hide beneath overhangs. Dark purple and blood-red sea fans sway in the gentle currents as spiny sea urchins graze along the rocks at an almost imperceptible pace. Starfishes lie scattered in a neighboring sea-grass bed.

Despite their popularity as an angler's paradise for bonefish and tarpon, the outlying reefs around Andros appear pristine and healthy to the researchers who are studying them. Scientists from the University of Miami, Florida's Rosenstiel School of Marine and Atmospheric Science (RS-MAS), however, hesitate to give the Andros reefs a clean bill of health—there are few available data on coral reefs in the region or around the world with which to draw comparisons. The scientists are also especially cautious in light of re-

Barbie Bischof is a Miami, Florida-based science journalist specializing in marine topics.

In 1994 a new coral disease was reported in the Florida Keys. Known as yellow-blotch or yellow-band disease, the malady is characterized by yellowish-colored patches that grow on the corals' surface. As the patch enlarges, the coral tissue in the center dies and fills with sediments and algae. The cause of the disease remains unknown.

(Overleaf) Stephen Frink—WaterHouse Stock Photography; (below) Norbert Wu

Scientists are studying healthy reefs far from crowded human population centers, including remote reefs in the Caribbean (below), to help them distinguish the differences between human and natural causes of reef deterioration.

cent reports showing that even some reefs in places relatively untouched by humans are showing troubling signs of deterioration. According to Clive Wilkinson of the Global Coral Reef Monitoring Network, Townsville, Australia, about 10% of Earth's reefs are dying, 30% are in critical condition, and another 30% are being subjected to environmental stresses that could lead to their demise by the year 2050. Included in these statistics are localized reefs throughout the Caribbean and parts of the Indo-Pacific, especially around the Philippines and Micronesia. By making regular visits to study the Andros reefs, the Florida scientists plan to compile a database of their condition. "By studying reefs remote from population centers, we can get an idea of natural vs. anthropogenic effects," says Robert Ginsburg, a marine geologist and RSMAS reef expert, "and determine whether there is some regional disease, pathogen, or pollutant among our reefs."

In the future, places such as Andros Island will become even more important, since many reefs in more populated parts of the world are already too damaged for scientists to untangle the complicated factors that led to their degeneration.

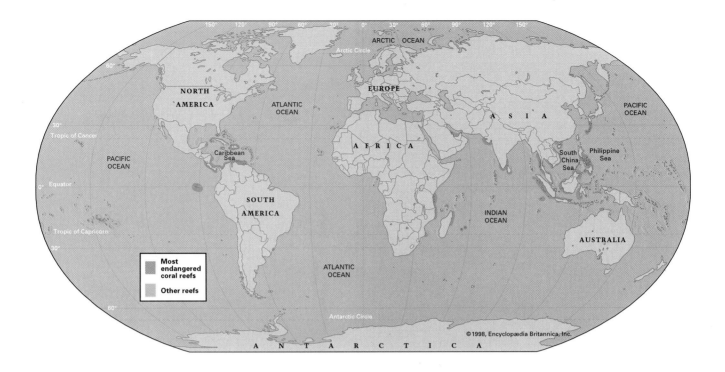

Most endangered coral reefs

Other reefs

© 1998, Encyclopædia Britannica, Inc.

Many of the world's most endangered reefs are located near populated coastal areas. In some places vibrant reefs are becoming fields of gray, algae-choked rubble at lightning speeds.

The Andros study is part of a worldwide focus on coral reefs that has gained momentum within the last 10 years. Although scientists had been voicing concern about suspected reef declines since the mid-1970s, few steps were taken to verify reef deterioration and to determine the extent and the causes of the problem. That changed in 1993 when scientists at an RSMAS colloquium on coral reefs agreed that many reefs near populated centers were in decline. Virtually nothing was known, however, about the condition of reefs in more remote locations. For the first time, several major initiatives were launched to address the problematic gap in knowledge. In 1994 a partnership was established between the U.S., Australia, Japan, the U.K., Sweden, France, Jamaica, the Philippines, and a host of nongovernmental organizations. Called the International Coral Reef Initiative (ICRI), the project has aimed to protect, restore, and encourage the sustainable use of reefs through research, education, and technical assistance in developing reef-management plans. Some of the programs sponsored by the ICRI have provided training for nonscientists, especially advanced divers, in surveying and monitoring reefs and teaching people who depend on reefs as a source of food and income about more sustainable practices.

In an effort to give greater visibility to the plight of the world's reefs, Ginsburg proposed that 1997 be declared the International Year of the Reef (IYOR). Under his leadership as chair of IYOR's organizing committee, dozens of organizations and more than 40 countries have participated in reef-related activities, many of which continued throughout 1998, the International Year of the Ocean.

Despite these focused measures, however, the future of coral reefs is uncertain. Vibrant living reefs near densely populated areas are becoming fields of gray, algae-covered rubble at lightning speeds. In most cases reef scientists are struggling just to assess the damage and determine possible causes, since even these fundamentals, for the most part, are unknown.

Their task is made all the more difficult by the sheer complexity of reef ecosystems. As Charles Birkeland, a professor of marine science at the University of Guam, has observed, the coral reef's "combination of attributes—creative power and fragility, resilience and sensitivity, productivity and vulnerability to overexploitation—makes management of coral-reef systems a special challenge to science."

NATURE'S PATIENT BUILDERS

Few living organisms have been more instrumental in shaping our planet than the colonial stony corals. Australia's Great Barrier Reef, for example, spans more than 2,000 kilometers (1,240 miles) in length. The depths of many reefs are equally astounding, especially in view of the slow rate of most coral growth. On average, coral animals deposit about 10 vertical centimeters (nearly 4 inches) of limestone every century as living organisms secrete limestone to make their protective cup-shaped homes, known as calices. Only the veneer on the surface of the colony is alive. As the colony grows upward, new calices are built on top of old ones. Cores extracted from Pacific atolls, for example, have measured reefs more than 1,500 meters (4,900 feet) in depth. Geologic processes folded some of these massive ancient constructs into

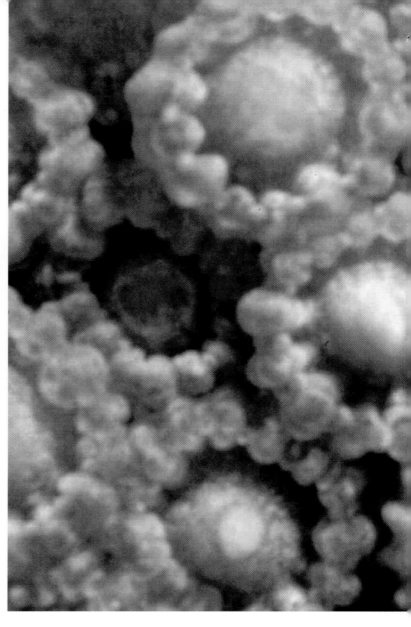

(Right) Susan B. Colley/University of Miami—AP/Wide World

Coral reefs are built by colonies of animals that are typically no bigger than the eraser on a pencil (below). Corals reproduce either by asexual budding or by the synchronized release of eggs and sperm (right) into the surrounding water. The developing larvae may settle on nearby substrates or be swept into ocean currents that carry them hundreds of kilometers from their place of origin.

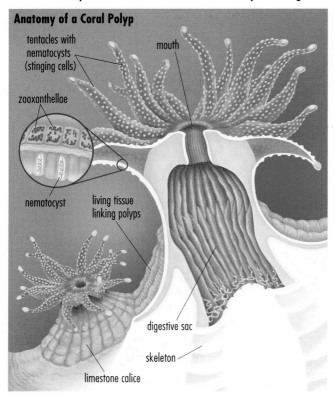

Anatomy of a Coral Polyp

- tentacles with nematocysts (stinging cells)
- mouth
- zooxanthellae
- nematocyst
- living tissue linking polyps
- digestive sac
- skeleton
- limestone calice

the mountain ranges of Europe and China and buried others deep within the Earth beneath such places as present-day Texas and the Persian Gulf, where the conglomerate of their tiny porous homes became the holding tank for oil supplies.

These massive natural structures are the products of animals typically no bigger than the eraser on a pencil. The coral polyp, as the adult coral animal is known, begins life floating in tropical sea currents as a tiny ciliated orb, the product of the fusion of egg and

sperm. In this larval stage corals can survive up to several weeks. When the coral larvae settle on a hard surface, they begin to transform into their adult shape. The base of the animal elongates into a stumpy trunklike form, and stinging tentacles, which corals use to grab food, sprout from the top. Soon the polyp begins to secrete a limestone cup to protect its soft body.

Vital to reef-building corals are single-celled photosynthesizing algae that live inside the polyps' tissues in concentrations as high as 30,000 cells

per cubic millimeter. These colorful symbionts, called zooxanthellae, give the corals their rich orange, red, purple, and yellow hues. As they convert sunlight and water into amino acids, sugars, and oxygen, the zooxanthellae provide the coral polyp with the supplemental energy it needs to build its limestone casing. As a result, reef-building corals are found only in the shallow areas of the ocean, at depths generally not much greater than 90 meters (300 feet), where sunlight is abundant and water is clear.

Once settled and attached to a stable substrate, the lone polyp forms a colony by asexual reproduction, cloning itself in a process called budding. Corals also reproduce sexually. Changes in ambient water temperatures, length of the day-night cycles, and phases of the Moon trigger synchronized releases of eggs and sperm in a variety of coral species. The gametes enter the water column, forming a dense cloud of reproductive material. Some species of corals, known as brooders, keep their eggs attached to the walls of their

12

stomach cavity, where they are fertilized by sperm carried on currents from neighboring colonies and are then expelled as larvae.

Many of the ejected offspring settle around the parental reef. Others are swept into ocean currents, where they join streams of plankton on a journey that may take them hundreds of kilometers from their place of origin. If the larvae survive the trip, they will eventually colonize downstream regions. The recent discovery that the replenishment of a reef's species, particularly cor-

als, may depend on processes that occur on distant shores has become one of the foremost concerns of marine-sanctuary managers. There is no such thing as an isolated reef, and countries sharing rich reef resources are now beginning to explore cooperative management strategies.

VETERANS OF CHANGE

According to some scientists, any conclusions about recent changes in coral-reef ecosystems must consider that coral reefs are extremely resilient,

having survived great environmental changes over the millennia. Studies of the geologic record reveal that reef builders have been present in some form since the Cambrian Period (540 million to 505 million years ago). Although coral reefs have been most abundant during millennia of high sea levels and few continental collisions, over time their extent has fluctuated anywhere from 40 times the 255,000 square kilometers (98,500 square miles) that reefs occupy today to less than a hundredth of the current figure.

Modern corals first appear in the rock record in the Middle Triassic about 230 million years ago. Many of these families of organisms thrive in today's seas. However, at the end of the Cretaceous (about 65 million years ago), the same blow that brought an end to the dominance of dinosaurs on land also greatly reduced the number of species living in shallow-water ecosystems. Because most shallow-water fossil reefs were not preserved in the geologic record from 60 million–70 million years ago, paleoecologists theorize that corals must have suffered greatly as well. Many of the coral families, however, survived, particularly those in deeper waters, and had flourished again in shallow seas by about 58 million years ago.

Coral reefs not only are survivors of change but also may actually require a constant level of disturbance in order to maintain their great biological diversity. According to the intermediate disturbance hypothesis formulated about reefs in the 1970s, too few environmental disturbances allow reef organisms that are dominant competitors and fast growers to squeeze out the slower-growing but more rugged species and colonizers. In environments that are exposed to constant stress, on the other hand, the slow-growing organisms dominate. Scientists generally concur that occasional upsets to an ecosystem will promote the highest biodiversity.

Disturbances changed the appearance of reef ecosystems many times in the geologic past. Scientists, however, are concerned that under the influence of new external pressures, the balance of reef species over the past 20 years is not merely shifting from slower-growing to more prolific species, or vice versa, but that reefs are assuming a whole new identity. In the past two decades, reefs located

Many different kinds of marine organisms feed on algae and keep their growth in check. Among the beneficiaries of algae grazers are these pillar corals (above). When algae-eating organisms are destroyed or eliminated from the reef ecosystem through overfishing, pillar corals can be overtaken by fleshy stands of macroalgae (opposite page).

near highly populated regions have experienced a decrease in the area covered by living corallites (polyp members in a growing colony) and an increase in macroalgae (large-bodied algal species like kelp) that outcompete corals and overgrow reef structures in dense, fleshy stands. Coral experts remain divided over how much of this shift can be attributed to human forces versus natural events. Most will agree, however, that the change is a combination of both.

Clouding the issue even further is the fact that scientists cannot explicitly define the characteristics of a "normal" or "pristine" reef. With the exception of a few well-studied ones in Jamaica's Discovery Bay, scientists have not monitored coral reefs—especially those untouched by humans—long enough to have amassed sufficient baseline data from which to draw any solid conclusions. Before they were toppled by Hurricane Allen in 1980, the reefs in Discovery Bay had not been visited by a hurricane in 40 years. A lush reef with some of the most abundant coral growth ever recorded by scientists, Discovery Bay's delicate structures were reduced to a rubble mound by the storm. Since then the reefs have been hit by other natural disasters and also have been adversely affected by growth in nearby coastal populations. As a result, they have not recovered their prestorm levels of coral diversity. Pointing to such examples, some scientists argue that a trend toward an overall decline in coral cover should be expected, since most well-studied reefs have been selected because of their luxuriant growth. Others contend that in naturally volatile ecosystems such as coral reefs, high coral cover is unusual; therefore, it is

not surprising to see a shift favoring algal abundance.

This controversy has led paleontologists to look for answers in reefs of the recent past, particularly the Pleistocene and Early Holocene epochs. Preliminary studies of fossil coral-reef communities have shown that at least for the past two million years, corals probably have dominated reef environments much as they now prevail in healthy reefs in the Florida Keys National Marine Sanctuary or more remote islands in the Bahamas.

Despite the ability of reefs to weather massive environmental disturbances, scientists warn that they are extremely fragile. The health of coral-reef ecosystems largely depends on the tightly entwined interactions between the species that live in them. Most other marine ecosystems have short food webs, in which the top species that humans harvest for food are only one or two steps removed from the system's primary food producers, such as plankton. The food chain is especially short for some species of whales, for example, that rely almost exclusively on plankton. Within coral ecosystems, on the other hand, the top organisms on the food chain may be separated from the system's primary producers by as many as six different levels. The loss

of organisms in only one of these levels can change the entire system. The mass die-off, for example, of herbivorous spiny sea urchins (*Diadema* species), which began in Panama in the early 1980s and spread throughout the Caribbean, resulted in major chain-reaction changes in the reefs. Without the algae-grazing echinoderms, macroalgae overgrew the reefs. Furthermore, as a result of the crash in their prey base, the numbers of urchin-eating fish also plummeted, which led to a decline in populations of commercial fish that, in turn, rely on these species for food.

DESTRUCTIVE FISHING PRACTICES

Archaeological excavations of sites such as Aboriginal middens in the Great Barrier Reef revealed that people have relied on reef ecosystems for at least 17,000 years. (This dependence most likely extends far deeper into human history, but the rise and fall of sea levels over time have destroyed much of the earlier evidence.) Today coral reefs continue to serve as an important source of human sustenance. Even though reefs occupy only about 0.2% of the world's oceans, reef systems provide an estimated 10% of all harvested fish worldwide.

More than 60,000 small-scale fishery operations depend on approximately 180 reef-related species in the Caribbean. In Jamaica alone the potential harvest of these species is about 95,000 tons per year. In the Philippines around 150 different species are taken in one local fishery in Boliano alone, and in the Tigak Islands of Papua New Guinea, an estimated 250 reef species are fished heavily.

In the 20th century, however, a steady increase in the human population of coastal regions and the development of a global market economy have intensified the exploitation of reef resources, often to the point of plunder. Indeed, this concentrated dependence has been identified as one of the biggest threats to their long-term survival, since overfishing ranks highest among the most commonly reported problems on reefs worldwide. Solving the problem is especially difficult, since it involves many complicated economic and cultural factors. After World War II, for example, people's dependence on reefs for food in many Pacific nations, such as American Samoa, decreased as Western economies became established. Canned and packaged products were in high demand and readily available, and the time-honored bonds

between local people and reefs were severed. Eventually, certain rare species, once protected by cultural taboos or used only in special ceremonies, became a boon to commercial fisheries.

Cultural mores have imperiled reef species in other ways as well. In many Asian countries today, the consumption of rare seafood is considered a sign of wealth, and almost any price will be paid for a sizable or prized catch. In 1996 the *South China Morning Post* reported that a single grouper, a fish species already commercially extinct in many areas of the world, was purchased for more than $10,000 in Hong Kong. In the same city a serving of lips from the humphead wrasse, a reef fish, goes for about $225. In Guam a small bowl of shark's fin soup, a broth that contains almost no shark's fin, costs about $80. This gainful and expanding market allows fishermen to demand outrageous prices and thereby reinforces the general disregard for the conservation laws and regulations that govern protected reef areas. Furthermore, many countries lack the staff and funds to enforce these laws. Even if perpetrators are caught, most fishing operators find that paying the fines, having their crews arrested, or even losing their vessels by sei-

zure are well worth the risk, since these losses are easily covered by their profits.

Fishing pressures also are spreading to remote areas. Because most of the large fish have been harvested from reefs around the populated Asian continent, many areas such as the South China Sea are now home only to sexually immature juvenile fish. As a result, large-scale fishing operations in search of bigger, more valuable seafood have been forced to venture greater distances, sometimes as far away as the South Pacific islands. Because of the high transportation costs and the great investment of time in these long-distance forays, commercial fleets have found it far more profitable to harvest everything in one sweep rather than engage in a sustainable practice that entails smaller hauls and repeated visits. Overfishing disrupts the system of checks and balances that is critical to the healthy functioning of complex reef ecosystems. In some places it has resulted in localized extinc-

tions of large fish species. The jewfish, a commercially important grouper once common in the Caribbean, for example, has virtually disappeared from the region's reefs.

Reefs near Egypt, Tanzania, India, and the Caribbean are also feeling the ecological effects of the economic transition from subsistence fishing to extractive fishing. In the Caribbean basin, overfishing has depleted important herbivores such as parrot fish that are critical to keeping the growth of algae on coral reefs in check. As larger fish have disappeared from reefs, fishermen have reduced the size of the mesh in their nets to trap the smaller fish that remain. The practice often eliminates juvenile fish before they have had an opportunity to reproduce.

Other fishing methods have damaged or destroyed reefs in more direct ways. Fishermen in the Indo-Pacific and along African coasts frequently toss dynamite into schools of reef fish. The force of the explosion ruptures the air bladders that the

Among the most harmful fishing practices is the use of dynamite on reefs to harvest reef species, a method frequently practiced by fishermen in the Indo-Pacific and along stretches of the African coast. Dead or injured fish, including this prized grouper (opposite page), float to the surface, where they can be easily netted. Dynamite fishing, however, indiscriminately kills or maims marine life and destroys whole sections of coral reefs (below) in a single blast.

fish use to control buoyancy, and fishermen can easily harvest the injured fish that float to the surface. Dead or mangled individuals and commercially undesirable species are left behind. The explosions also destroy much of the reef structure. Stretches of fishless reefs around the Tanzanian island of Zanzibar, for example, are riddled with holes from blast fishing, some as big as 10 meters (33 feet) in diameter.

Muro-ami fishing is another destructive fishing method commonly practiced in the Indo-Pacific. The technique originated in Japan as a way to increase fish yields without the use of expensive trawl nets, which become snagged on reefs. Using rocks tied to "scarelines" that are flagged with brightly colored streamers, boys and young men swim together over the reef and pound on its ridges. The ruckus scares the fish out of hiding, and the streamers herd them into a semicircular net known as a muro-ami.

The lucrative sushi and marine-aquarium trade in Asia has also promoted the widespread use of sodium cyanide, particularly around the Philippines. In some cases drums of the poison are poured overboard, which temporarily asphyxiates the reef fish so that they float to the surface for easy capture. Fishermen in pursuit of smaller organisms will snorkel or dive along reefs with squirt bottles of bleach or cyanide in hand. Witnesses in the Bahamas have reported seeing local fishermen pour vats of bleach on reefs to roust spiny lobsters and other crevice dwellers out of hiding.

Collecting reef species for the Asian restaurant trade has become such a profitable industry that people are even willing to risk their lives. In some reefs, for example, sought-after species have been depleted in shallow waters, which has prompted large-scale commercial fishing businesses to outfit local residents with compressed air. Motivated by the lucrative pay and lacking important scuba safety training, local residents gamble with their lives, staying underwater longer than is safe in search of lobsters or sea cucumbers. In the last several years, about 50 Pacific Island and Central American divers have died, and thousands more have experienced decompression sickness,

the result of the formation of nitrogen bubbles in the bloodstream when divers ascend too quickly. Field researchers claim that the death toll is much higher. The fear of reprisal among survivors, the absence of laws protecting divers from exploitation, and the shortage of medical personnel in many less-developed countries to determine and accurately document the cause of diving fatalities, however, have prevented the gathering of more accurate information.

THREATS FROM COASTAL DEVELOPMENT

Human activities located at considerable distances from offshore reefs have also left their mark. Clear-cutting maritime forests and filling wetlands to satisfy the increasing demands for coastal real estate have had detrimental effects on reefs. Wetlands and forests trap suspended sediment, and, like treatment plants, filter many pollutants out of ocean-bound waters before they reach the

(Opposite page) Mark Edwards—Still Pictures/Peter Arnold; (below) Lynn Funkhouser—Peter Arnold; (bottom) Darrell Jones—Allstock/PNI

Coral reefs along many of the rapidly growing coastal regions of the world are threatened by silt-laden runoff that results from such human disturbances as the clear-cutting of maritime forests (opposite page) and residential development (below right). Sediments can choke fragile corallites and sometimes bury an entire coral reef, as seen in this photograph of a reef in the Philippines (right).

reefs. Although healthy corals can live with small sporadic inputs of sediments, a constant or heavy flow of silt can choke the fragile corallites and sometimes bury an entire reef.

In many countries the facilities for treating waste from this coastal human-population boom are inadequate or nonexistent. New housing and resorts are rapidly springing up in the tropical less-developed nations of the South Pacific, Africa, Central America, and the Caribbean basin. Proper water-treatment facilities to manage wastes from the increasing throng of tourists, however, are seldom considered, and laws mandating such accommodations rarely exist or are not enforced. In many countries sewage pipes carry waste directly from houses into the nearby sea. According to a report by the Nature Conservancy, for example, Haiti does not have a single water-treatment facility. Moreover, because of poor land management, almost 99% of the island's vegetation has been denuded, which allows sewage, agricultural runoff, and sediment to flow unchecked onto nearby reefs. The steady supply of nutrients in the runoff fertilizes the water and can stimulate the growth of strangling seaweeds, fleshy algae, and microscopic unicellular algae such as dinoflagellates. The problem is already chronic in localized areas throughout the Caribbean and Pacific and may be affecting human health. Some reef experts suspect that the phosphates in urban and agricultural runoff may promote blooms of dinoflagellates, collectively known as red tides. When dinoflagellates are present in large numbers, the potent toxins they produce are concentrated. These toxins are notorious for causing fish kills and shellfish poisoning along most coastlines and have been blamed for the death of 156 endangered Florida manatees in 1996. When red tides are blown to shore, the toxic cells thrown aloft in the spray of breaking waves can cause serious respiratory problems for animals that inhale them. Each year in the U.S., about 90,000 cases of illness caused by eating toxic finfish and shellfish are reported. Symptoms range from amnesia to paralysis. More than 50% of these cases are ciguatera, a chronic nervous system disorder caused by eating reef fish that have accumulated toxins from a tropical dinoflagellate.

The migrations of people to coastal regions and increased tourist traffic have brought other localized pressures to reef systems. Coral rock is mined from living reefs for use as building materials; coral sands are extracted for cement production; and rare species are collected for jewelry, aphrodisiacs, and souvenirs. In some places reef-walking, an activity that tramples fragile corals and other marine organisms, are still common. Reef damage from anchors also is frequently reported, although the cheap and effective installation of mooring buoys is helping to alleviate this problem.

INTENSIFYING NATURE'S TOLL

Natural cycles also exert a profound influence on coral reefs. Throughout geologic time up to the present, coral reefs have been significantly altered by pests, disease, and physical forces. Infestations of crown-of-thorns sea stars (*Acanthaster planci*) have intermittently plagued Australia's reefs since the 1960s. The sea star covers the reef's surface with the stomach lining it extrudes through its mouth, and in a single feeding the animal can devour corals in an area 15–25 centimeters (6–10 inches) in diameter. Not only do the starfishes secrete a chemical as they feed, but as they absorb the corallites, they also spread the scent of food to other members of their species. *A. planci* are often found feeding in groups. Scientists have docu-

mented clusters of hundreds of individuals. It is estimated that approximately 25% of the reefs in 228 surveyed sites on the Great Barrier Reef have fallen prey to these predators.

Although hurricanes and cyclones can reduce a reef to rubble, they play a vital role in maintaining the biodiversity in reef systems. Faster-growing branching species such as elkhorn and staghorn corals, for example, are damaged more easily and extensively than slower-growing coral mounds. Periodic storms prevent the faster-growing corals from dominating coral ecosystems and thus ensure a greater species diversity. Hurricanes can also be beneficial by promoting the spread of reefs. Storm waves and currents toss coral mounds into neighboring lagoons and sea-grass beds, potentially seeding new reefs. Some of the polyps may survive and recolonize the displaced mounds or be joined by larvae from neighboring colonies.

Many scientists are concerned, however, that human activities are changing the frequency and severity of these recurring cycles and stressing corals beyond their ability to rebound. When corals undergo stress, such as extended periods of exposure to air, to water that is too salty or too fresh, to

Scientists suspect that phosphates in urban and agricultural runoff may be contributing to the increasing severity and frequency of toxic red tides, which kill marine organisms and threaten human health.

pollution, or to extreme temperatures, either they will expel the zooxanthellae residing in their tissues or the symbionts themselves may lose their pigmentation. Without the color provided by their algal tenants, the transparent coral tissues reveal their white skeletons, a condition known as bleaching. From fall 1997 to spring 1998, researchers reported extensive bleaching throughout the Caribbean and the Galápagos Islands. Prolonged exposure to temperature extremes caused by the El Niño–Southern Oscillation (ENSO)—fluctuations that ranged as high as 5° above normal sea-surface temperatures of 26° C (79° F)—are

Although reef tourism has benefited the economies of many coastal nations, it has also damaged fragile marine resources. In some places, reef walking (top) is still common. In the waters around Bali, a woman harvests coral for use in jewelry and souvenirs.

to rising sea levels. These changes are not necessarily harmful to reefs if corals can keep pace with the rising water level. If submerged too deeply, corals will be deprived of necessary sunlight and eventually drown as growth slows.

Changes in ocean chemistry are also expected as greenhouse gases increase in the Earth's atmosphere. Scientists predict that elevated levels of carbon dioxide in the air will increase the amount of dissolved carbon dioxide in surface waters and thus reduce the abundance of calcium-carbonate ions. Although the ocean is supersaturated with these limestone components, a recent report confirmed that even a slight reduction in these ions would make it more difficult for corals to manufacture their homes.

Some scientists suspect that environmental pressures, including global warming, will further reduce overall coral health and make reefs less resistant to pathogens. Already, reef scientists are reporting an increasing incidence of coral diseases and the discovery of new maladies. For the most part, their causes are unknown. Even obtaining accurate estimates of their relative abundance is nearly impossible, since many diseases are difficult to identify.

responsible for many of the coral deaths by bleaching seen in the Eastern Pacific. According to Peter Glynn, an RSMAS coral ecologist and a leading researcher on coral bleaching, it will take scientists at least a year after this El Niño event,

the strongest on record thus far, to determine which reefs will have survived the months-long fever.

Corals can recover from bleaching episodes if the stress is not prolonged. How long corals can survive under siege

depends on the species and the type, intensity, and duration of the stress. One of the most hotly debated issues among reef scientists is the prediction of the effects of global warming on shallow-water ecosystems. Many scientists expect that a warming trend will increase the rate of sea-level rise. Low-lying areas, such as Pacific atolls, are already experiencing significant land loss due

Since the 1980s, for example, reefs in the Caribbean have undergone a drastic reduction in elkhorn coral from white-band disease. First reported in St. Croix, U.S. Virgin Islands, the disease causes coral tissue to peel off from the base of the coral structure to the branches. More than 95% of elkhorn and staghorn coral stands in Tague Bay and Buck Island National Monument in St. Croix were denuded within 10 years.

In the mid-1990s, as reef scientists added two new diseases—white pox and patchy necrosis—to the list of coral afflictions, some diseases that had been first reported decades earlier were reappearing in a more deadly form. White plague, a disease that is thought to be caused by bacteria, was first recorded in 1977. In 1995 scientists discovered a more virulent form of white plague affecting 18 different species of reef-building corals in the Florida Keys and the Virgin Islands. The disease, which begins at the base of the coral and causes bleaching of the tissue, usually starts around a wounded area or a depression in the skeleton.

NEED FOR RESEARCH

According to some reef scientists, many of the stresses seen today on coral reef ecosystems

(Below) Louisa Preston—Photo Researchers; (opposite page) Nancy Sefton—Photo Researchers

The establishment of buoys on reefs for the mooring of boats has helped to prevent damage to corals like this cavity caused by a boat anchor.

are not new but were rarely seen and were almost never reported in the past. Others contend that reef systems are undergoing radical changes owing, at least in part, to a mishandling of these rich resources. In the absence of sound scientific data, however, the causes, extent, and significance of reef deterioration and death will remain a matter of intense debate. Relatively little is known about coral reefs. It is estimated, for example, that about 90% of Pacific and Caribbean reefs remain unexplored.

Through collaborative research efforts and ongoing monitoring, scientists hope to soon understand the condition of coral reefs around the world. Within the past decade, for example, reef-surveying programs have sprung up as re-

searchers strive to compile data and to establish a baseline from which to compare reef conditions in the future. Information has been collected through the use of divers, submersible watercraft, aerial photography, and sensors on satellites, ships, and boats.

To cover the vast territory involved in such endeavors, some projects have enlisted the help of volunteers. The organizing committee for the IYOR, for example, sponsored Reef Check 1997, an international effort that offered one-day training in completing simple reef surveys to volunteer recreational divers. Directed by Gregor Hodgson, a marine ecologist at the Hong Kong University of Science and Technology's Institute for Environment and Sustainable Development Research Centre,

the project was designed to provide scientists with a global snapshot of reefs. Other survey methods, such as the ReefBase Aquanaut Survey Method, developed by John McManus at the International Center for Living Aquatic Resources Management (ICLARM) in Manila and his colleagues, use a more advanced protocol than Reef Check. In a four-day course, nonscientist scuba divers are trained in methods for collecting ecological data around reef systems.

These efforts have begun to pay off. Extensive databases already are widely available, including ICLARM's *ReefBase* CD-ROM, which contains information on about 7,000 reefs worldwide. Other organizations, such as the Global Coral Reef Monitoring Network, the World Conservation Monitoring Centre, and the Coral Health and Monitoring Program, accessible internationally on the Internet, also offer shared databases and monitoring networks.

Within the past decade, the management of marine parks and sanctuaries also has undergone a philosophical shift. Until recently, for example, restricted areas within marine preserves of many less-developed nations routinely were designated without regard for the rights or historic har-

Crown-of-thorns sea stars are destructive reef pests that have plagued the Great Barrier Reef since the 1960s. Voracious communal feeders, the sea stars can consume an area 15–25 centimeters (6–10 inches) in diameter in a single feeding.

vesting practices of local inhabitants. As a result, regulations often were simply ignored. Today, however, the design of some marine parks takes a multiple-use approach that balances zones of total protection with those in which various human activities are allowed. The Great Barrier Reef Marine Park, the Virgin Islands National Park on St. John, and the Florida Keys National Marine Sanctuary, for example, reserve areas for tourism, military training, collecting, scientific research, and commercial and recreational fishing.

There also has been an increase in cooperative planning and management among marine parks. Recent research by Callum Roberts of the University of York, England, has shown that ocean currents weaving among the Caribbean islands unify and regenerate regional reef systems by serving as conduits for the transport and distribution of larvae. Many park managers and governments within these regional

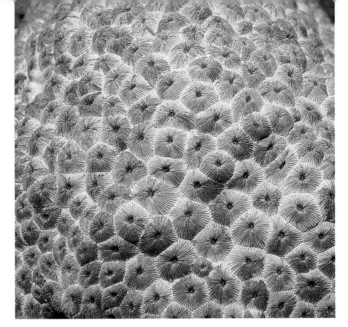

reef systems now are viewing the health of their own reefs as part of a larger regionwide network.

Increasingly, reef-preservation efforts are being led by the governments of countries that benefit from having healthy, beautiful reefs. Concerned that pot fishing (trapping marine species in underwater cages), for example, was depleting fish stocks on Bermuda reefs and threatening the country's $9 million tourist trade, the government of Bermuda solved the problem in 1990 by offering each fisherman a $75,000 buyout plus compensation for their retired nets, traps, and winches. Similarly, after learning that snorkeling and scuba diving generated $12 million for the country's coffers, the government of Palau passed the Marine Protection Act of 1994, which set limits on the less-lucrative extractive-fishing industry. The law increased reproductive success and larvae survival by prohibiting the commercial export of any fish from March to July, the spawning season for many reef species.

Marine-conservation scientists also have made significant advances in reef restoration, particularly in reefs that have been damaged by ship groundings. Between 1984 and 1989 more than 4,160 square kilo-

Environmental stresses can cause coral polyps to expel the algae in their tissue that provide them with colorful pigments. Under this condition, known as bleaching (top), corals appear white. Scientists suspect that these stresses also may weaken corals and make them susceptible to other afflictions, including black-band disease (center) and white pox (bottom).

Photographs, James M. Cervino

meters (1,600 square miles) of reefs in the Florida Keys National Marine Sanctuary were ruined in ship groundings. Fortunately, reef-restoration efforts following grounding accidents have become more common and so far seem to be successful. In June 1997, for example, a freighter loaded with frozen fish en route to Puerto Rico ran aground near a marine protected area. Instead of battling the prolonged and expensive legal maneuvering that has delayed rehabilitation efforts in the past, reef scientists were able to quickly mobilize insurance money to begin emergency transplanting. After clearing the debris left by the wreckage, contractors were able to wire between 500 and 1,000 broken limbs of the fast-growing elkhorn coral back onto the reef. The success of this restoration effort is as yet uncertain, but a similar project that was mounted following the

January 1996 grounding of the *Maasdam* in the vicinity of the Grand Cayman Islands has shown high coral regrowth.

THE FUTURE

Without widespread data, many reef experts are reluctant to make comparisons about the state of coral reefs. They are especially hesitant to claim with any certainty that reefs are in decline worldwide. Stan-dardized data-collecting techniques are being developed to help make quantitative regional and global comparisons possible. The RSMAS scientists studying the Andros Island reefs, for example, are testing a rapid-screening technique designed to scientifically measure the condition of a reef. Known as the Rapid Assessment Protocol (RAP), the technique is based on three principal indicators: corals, fish, and algae. In the future, scientists will be able to use the results gathered by this standardized method to make comparisons between regional systems.

In June 1998 Robert Ginsburg and colleague Phil Kramer, an RSMAS coral reef expert and scientific leader of the Andros project, met with more than 50 other reef experts to refine RAP methodology. "Reef scientists must do more homework," Kramer says.

Research is yielding important insights into the science of reef restoration. After this freighter ran aground near Puerto Rico in 1997, divers rewired between 500 and 1,000 pieces of elkhorn coral back onto the damaged reef.

Ricardo Figueroa—AP/Wide World

FOR ADDITIONAL READING

- *Collaborative and Community-Based Management of Coral Reefs: Lessons from Experience,* Alan T. White, Lynne Zeitlin Hale, Yves Renard, and Lafcadio Cortesi, eds. (Kumarian Press, 1994).
- *Corals in Space and Time: The Biogeography and Evolution of the Scleractinia,* J.E.N. Veron (Cornell University Press, 1995).
- *The Greenpeace Book of Coral Reefs,* Sue Wells and Nick Hanna (Sterling Publications Co., 1992).
- *Indo-Pacific Coral Reef Field Guide,* Gerald R. Allen and Roger Steene (Tropical Reef Research, 1994).
- *Life and Death of Coral Reefs,* Charles Birkleland, ed. (Chapman & Hall, 1997).
- *Palaces Under the Sea: A Guide to Understanding the Coral Reef Environment,* Joe Strykowski and Rena M. Bonem (Star Thrower Foundation, 1993).
- *The Reef Set,* Paul Humann (New World Publications, 1989).
- *The Structure and Distribution of Coral Reefs,* Charles Darwin (University of California Press, 1962).

INTERNET RESOURCES

- Atlantic and Gulf Reef Assessment
  http://coral.aoml.noaa.gov/agra/
- Coral Health and Monitoring Program
  http://coral.aoml.noaa.gov/
- Coral Reef Research Foundation
  http://underwatercolours.com/crrf.html
- Earthwatch
  http://www.earthwatch.org/
- Fisheye View Cam
  http://web.FisheyeView.com/FVCAM/
- Great Barrier Reef Marine Park Authority
  http://www.gbrmpa.gov.au/
- International Coral Reef Initiative
  http://www.mbnet.mb.ca/vps/icri/csd-intro.html
- The International Year of the Reef
  http://coral.cea.edu/IYOR/index.html
- National Oceanic and Atmospheric Administration
  http://coral.aoml.noaa.gov/bulls/52final.html
- Reef Check
  http://www.ust.hk/~webrc/ReefCheck/reef.html
- Reef Resource Page
  http://www.indiana.edu/~reefpage/
- Sea World: Corals and Coral Reefs
  http://www.seaworld.org/coral_reefs/introcr.html
- Smithsonian Tropical Research Institute
  http://www.si.edu:80/organiza/centers/stri/start.htm
- World Conservation Monitoring Centre Marine Programme
  http://www.wcmc.org.uk/marine/

Attitudes toward the building of new megadams and the operation of existing structures have changed dramatically. In 1996, for example, scientists opened the floodgates of Arizona's Glen Canyon Dam in a heavily publicized experiment to restore the ecology of the Colorado River's downstream reaches.

Nicholas Devore III—Photographers/Aspen/PNI

Going with the Flow

Societies once considered megadams the ultimate triumph of humankind over nature. After weighing their benefits against some of the enormous social, environmental, and economic costs, however, many countries now are considering the unthinkable—letting some rivers run free.

by Stephen M. Born

In December 1995 NASA geophysicist Benjamin Fong Chao made a startling announcement: dams constructed in the Earth's temperate zones had impounded great enough volumes of water—10 trillion tons—to slightly, but measurably, tilt the planet's axis, alter its gravitational field, and speed up its rotation.

Although these changes are too small to have any substantive effect, they are an astonishing measure of the extent to which humans have altered natural river systems. According to estimates by the International Commission on Large Dams, the world's rivers are obstructed by more than 40,000 large dams (defined as structures measuring more than 15 meters [49 feet] in height). In 1994 two Swedish scientists, for example, reported that the flows of more than three-quarters of the largest rivers in the U.S., Canada, Europe, and the former Soviet Union were strongly or moderately regulated. Dams obstruct virtually all the large rivers in Africa, and comparable levels of development exist in Latin America, South America, and Asia. In addition, hundreds of thousands of smaller dams have been constructed on the planet's waterways so that most of the world's river basins now are regulated to variable degrees.

Built primarily in the past 40 years, these dams have transformed the economies—and the imaginations—of societies around the world. On the one hand, they have served functional ends, harnessing the flow of rivers for water storage, supply, and irrigation; flood control; navigation; power generation; and, more recently, recreation. At the same time, for many nations and their po-

Stephen M. Born is Professor of Planning and Environmental Studies at the University of Wisconsin, Madison.

By late October 1997 Chinese earth-movers had nearly closed the Chang Jiang (Yangzte River) in preparation for construction of the Three Gorges Dam. When completed in 2009, it will be the largest dam on Earth.

AFP Photo

litical leaders, these monuments of engineering achievement also have epitomized economic and scientific progress and served as icons of political power. Controlling the flows of the world's most powerful river systems represents the ultimate expression of the ideology of the technological age—the taming of nature to serve humankind. As Chinese Pres. Jiang Zemin declared at an official ceremony for the Three Gorges Dam in November 1997, a megastructure that will contain the Chang Jiang (Yangtze River): "Blocking the Yangtze is a great moment in the modernization of our country. It vividly proves once again that socialism is superior in organizing people to do big jobs."

Today, however, the future of dam construction faces great uncertainty and controversy. Although huge dams are still being planned and built throughout the world, the rate of dam building has declined sharply from the mid-20th-century high, in which some 1,000 large dams were constructed annually. As the era of big dam building wanes, many countries are weighing the benefits of megadam projects against their social, economic, and environmental costs. In the U.S., Canada, and Western Europe, where only a few potential sites for large dams remain, calls for protecting the complexities of river environments are growing in the wake of mounting research that has revealed the extensive ecological damage re-

sulting from dams and dam-related structures. Dramatic national policy changes are leading to greater emphases on water conservation, the restoration of degraded aquatic environments, and the maintenance of healthy ecosystems, including changed operating regimes for existing dam-reservoir complexes. In some cases officials have removed smaller dams and are investigating the removal of even larger ones in an effort to restore functioning ecosystems and provide more effective and less-costly flood control.

In countries such as China, India, Pakistan, and the less-developed nations of Latin America, where dams are regarded as solutions to water-management problems and a

key component of regional development, large dam projects continue to be planned and built. These projects, however, have met with unprecedented controversy, stirring protests that will only intensify in the future.

5,000 YEARS OF DAMS

People have built structures across waterways to exert control over natural river flows for nearly 5,000 years. Although remnants of ancient irrigation canals have been found on the eastern edge of Mesopotamia and along the lower Tigris and Euphrates rivers, the earliest-documented dam was built across the Nile River upstream of present-day Cairo around 2900 BC. By the late 1st millennium BC, dams had been erected on rivers around the Mediterranean, the Middle East, China, South Asia, and Central America. These early dams most likely were built to supply water for irrigation, flood control, and consumption.

By the late Middle Ages, people in the great industrial centers of Western Europe had harnessed the energy of rivers to power waterwheels for crushing ores, grinding grain, pulping rags for paper, and other tasks. Dams increased little in size and technological complexity, however, until the Industrial Revolution in the 18th and 19th centuries, when a demand for water power stimulated many engineering innovations. The development of an effective water turbine by the French engineer Benoît Fourneyron in 1827 was followed by electrical engineering advances, including hydroelectric plants and transmission lines, as well as new dam-construction technologies.

Together they ushered in a new era of river development. In 1882 the first hydroelectric plant in the U.S. was built in Appleton, Wisconsin. Lacking provisions for water storage, the facility obtained its power from the natural flow of the river and produced a mere 12.5 kilowatts of power, a minuscule amount compared with the enormous generating capacity of modern behemoth hydroelectric installations and their storage reservoirs, such as the Grand Coulee Dam (more than 6.2 million kilowatts) in eastern Washington and the Itaipú Dam (12.6 million kilowatts) on the border of Brazil and Paraguay. Engineers discovered that more power could be generated if rivers were impounded behind dams in reservoirs. This scheme also had one great advantage over other means of generating electricity—water could be stored in

reservoirs during times of low demand and then quickly harnessed to produce power during peak hours of electricity usage. Once engineers had amassed greater knowledge about the strength of materials, loads and stresses within structures, the geologic conditions of a dam site, and the design of dam foundations, they were able to increase the heights of dams and enlarge reservoir capacities.

In the U.S., the world's pioneer in megadam engineering, the era of big dam building was launched with passage of the National Reclamation Act in 1902, which established the agency that later became the Federal Bureau of Reclamation. The agency's mandate was to bring irrigated agriculture to the arid West by means of government-financed water projects. The numerous dam, reservoir, and water-distribution projects that currently exist across the landscape testify to the success of this mission.

Aided by the growing knowledge of dam engineering, the pace of large dam construction accelerated from 1935 to 1965, with the U.S. Army Corps of Engineers joining the Bureau of Reclamation and other agencies as a leader in dam-building initiatives. One of the era's most influential governmental bodies was the

Tennessee Valley Authority (TVA), a powerful federal corporation established in 1933. The TVA pioneered the concept of unified river-basin development, building an integrated multipurpose system of 29 dams and reservoirs throughout the Tennessee River basin. This idea of a relatively autonomous governmental entity's overseeing basinwide river development to advance a region's economy and social well-being had an enormous influence on the subsequent damming of the world's river systems. In 1957, for example, the U.S. Army Corps of Engineers proposed a cascade of seven large-scale dam projects in Southeast Asia's Mekong River basin designed to create more than 23,000 megawatts of power and to curb perceived flooding problems.

Although the Vietnam War halted implementation of the project, the TVA-style model of comprehensive river-basin development had seized the imagination of the world's nations, and government-sponsored development schemes were launched around the world from Canada to Africa and Asia. After World War II, for example, the Soviet Union accelerated its river development. Today extensive systems of dams regulate entire rivers, especially in Russia and

Ukraine. Other countries also were swept away by similar dam-building binges. In the three decades after China's 1949 revolution, more than 600 large dams were built every year in China. Today with some 19,000 large dams, China leads the world, followed by the U.S., the former Soviet republics, Japan, and India. Even countries with relatively modest construction agendas still have a vast infrastructure of dams. Mexico, for example, has about 4,000 water-storage and flood-control structures, 640 of which are ranked as large dams. With aid from the

The Industrial Revolution's demand for hydropower stimulated many engineering innovations, including this water turbine invented by Benoît Fourneyron in 1827.

Jean-Loup Charmet

In the U.S. the heyday of megadam construction lasted from 1935 to 1965. Among the many projects completed during this period was the Grand Coulee Dam on the Columbia River in Washington, shown here in mid construction.

industrialized countries and an assortment of donor and lending institutions, numerous river-development schemes were undertaken in the Southern Hemisphere, including such giant dams as the Aswan High Dam in Egypt, the Kariba Dam in Zimbabwe and Zambia, the Cabora Bassa Dam in Mozambique, and the Guri Dam in Venezuela.

In the U.S. the era of megadam construction drew to a close in the mid-1960s. Water needs had been largely satisfied by existing projects. Furthermore, dams already occupied the most buildable sites. The remaining sites were economi-cally marginal or environmentally sensitive. In the wake of the country's growing environmental movement, most big water projects were defeated by stiff opposition.

ENVIRONMENTAL COSTS

The benefits of dams are widely recognized, largely because of their great economic value. By storing water, dams regulate the natural variability of a river's flow due to seasonal cycles and storm events. The impounded water then can be released as needed for a host of human needs. In some cases the construction of dams has catalyzed whole industries. Cheap hydropower supplied by dams on the Columbia River, for example, is the lifeblood of the aluminum industry in the Pacific Northwest. Recently, however, the benefit-cost analyses that have been used to justify the construction, maintenance, and renovation of most dams have come under increasing scrutiny and criticism. In the early 1990s, for example, the U.S. Army Corps of Engineers conducted a $44.2 million study to examine the feasibility of expanding navigation on the upper Mississippi River, the 2,164-kilometer (1,345-mile) stretch of water between the river's headwaters in north-central Minnesota and Cairo, Illinois. Included in the study was a look at rehabilitating the upper Mississippi's aging infrastructure of 29 locks and dams. One of these dams at Alton, Illinois, was rebuilt at a price tag of $1.2 billion, which fueled fears that the reconstruction of the remaining dams in the upper Mississippi system could be one of the most expensive public-works projects in the nation's history.

Dam opponents have been especially vocal about the environmental downsides of big water projects, even though dams have offered some environmental benefits. For example, dams have enabled aquatic life dependent on uniform water levels to flourish in downstream river reaches, especially in arid, drought-prone environments where seasonal flows tend to be extreme. Water flows released from impoundments also dilute the agricultural and urban pollutants that contaminate rivers along their reaches. Although dam projects provide some ecological benefits, the losses far outweigh gains on the environmental side of the ledger. In the past two decades, researchers have demonstrated that the damming of a river is a cataclysmic event in the life of a river ecosystem. In 1997 researchers at Umeå (Sweden) University released the results of a study showing that following the damming of a river, the number of plant species around large reservoirs declined by about 50%.

Until recently, scientists assumed that the biggest ecological changes on dammed rivers were caused by the formation of giant upstream reservoirs. New hypotheses, however, about the physical and biological dynamics of rivers have challenged this old paradigm. According to recent, more holistic scientific models, healthy

The Tennessee Valley Authority promoted river development throughout the Tennessee River basin for the purposes of social and economic development. Alabama's Wilson Dam is one of 29 dams built under the agency's jurisdiction.

31

rivers depend on unobstructed physical and biological exchanges between their upper and lower reaches (known as the river continuum) as well as interactions with their flanking floodplains in seasonal inundations called the river's flood pulse.

Dams, scientists have discovered, disrupt the upstream-downstream continuity of the river channel. The sluggish impoundments, for example, change the makeup of aquatic communities by favoring animals adapted to low water velocities and warm, deep water. These basins also trap sediments above the dam, depriving the river of the material it needs to sculpt the contours of its downstream channels and backwater areas.

As new studies have demonstrated, dams can wreak ecological havoc far from their place of origin. In March 1997 scientists at the Romanian Institute for Marine Research, Constanta, and the University of Hamburg and the Baltic Sea Research Institute, Rostock, Germany, released the results of combined data showing that the Iron Gates Dam located on the Danube River between Romania and Yugoslavia has adversely affected marine life in the Black Sea approximately

Phototake/PNI

The Iron Gates Dam on the Danube River has blocked the transport of minute grains of river sand that feed Black Sea diatoms (left), a critical component of the region's marine food chain.

(Left) Jorn Stjerneklar—Impact; (bottom) Art Wolfe—Allstock/PNI

Dams can wreak ecological havoc far from their place of origin. Mozambique's Cabora Bassa Dam (left) has disrupted downstream flood cycles in the Zambezi River delta, threatening the delta's mangrove forest and population of wattled cranes (bottom).

that have been responsible for widespread die-offs of fish and other marine organisms.

The introduction of barriers in river ecosystems, in spite of varied mitigation measures, also has had major effects on migratory river organisms, most notably spawning fish. Dams built along the Columbia River in the U.S. Pacific Northwest and along other rivers of the Pacific seaboard, for example, have led to marked population declines in anadromous salmonid species—migratory ocean fish that return to natal rivers to spawn. Prior to the 20th century, the Columbia supported some 200 distinct stocks of salmonids. Today 69 stocks have disappeared, and 75 others are at risk of extinction, and fish stocks have been reduced to 10–30% of their original distribution. In Finland, where nearly all of the country's major salmon rivers flowing into the Baltic Sea have been harnessed for hydroelectric power, migratory wild fish stocks have been seriously damaged. Atlantic salmon have completely disappeared from all the large rivers on the European Atlantic coast, including the Rhine, Thames, Elbe, and Seine. Dams on rivers on the North American side of the Atlantic Ocean have decimated popula-

tions of migratory Atlantic salmon as well.

Obstructions that prevent the lateral flooding of floodplain areas also have had a major effect on the ecological diversity of river plants and animals. Many species have come to depend on seasonal floods that spill over the banks of the river's main channel into adjoining areas. These events return nutrients and sediments to the river's floodplain meadows, wetlands, and lakes. Research has shown that the overwhelming proportion of animal biomass in a river is produced within these areas.

In some cases disruption of the river's seasonal pulse has led to the near collapse of whole ecosystems. Completed in 1974, Mozambique's huge Cabora Bassa Dam, for example, has flattened the natural

1,000 kilometers (620 miles) downriver. Researchers found that before the dam was built in 1972, tiny grains of river sand were washed into the sea, where they contributed an important component to the diets of minute algae called diatoms. Each spring profuse blooms of the diatoms provided a critical link in a larger marine food chain. Today the balance of species has shifted in favor of algae that are able to grow in the absence of the river's silicates. Unlike the diatoms, however, these ascendant algae species form great toxic blooms

flood cycle in the Zambezi River delta, degrading this highly productive wetland and threatening the wattled crane, a globally endangered bird that depends on the rise and fall of flood cycles for its nesting success. For millennia the Zambezi River's annual floodwaters and their nutrient-rich river sediments also have sustained impenetrable stands of coastal mangroves. Today, as dams capture these replenishing resources, the mangrove forest is being lost to erosion, and the coast is being left vulnerable to destructive ocean storms.

A more drastic fate has befallen the mangrove forests of the Indus River delta. Sediment-containing dams in India and Pakistan have contributed to the demise of much of the delta's 250,000-hectare (620,000-acre) forest. With it has gone a critical nursery for fish. According to some scientists, Egypt's Aswan High Dam, which was finished in 1970, has disrupted

33

the ecology of the eastern Mediterranean Sea. Among other effects, elimination of the annual nutrient-rich flood flows has resulted in dramatically reduced sardine harvests in the Mediterranean off the Nile Delta. Without the river's natural cycle of sediment renewal, the delta itself is eroding. In an ironic reversal of fortune, agriculture in the Nile Valley is suffering as well. Once naturally fertilized by the deposition of 40 million tons of rich silt during flood periods, the valley's farm fields now require one million tons of human-made fertilizers.

EFFECTS ON PEOPLE

The plans for flooding the Chang Jiang's Three Gorges—spectacular river canyons as famous in China as the Grand Canyon is in the U.S.—recently drew attention to the threats that dams pose to the world's significant cultural and scenic resources. In the U.S. there is renewed controversy over Arizona's Glen Canyon Dam in the wake of calls by some environmental groups for its dismantling. The dam's gates closed in 1963, creating a massive impoundment of the Colorado River, Lake Powell, that stretched nearly 300 kilometers (186 miles) and extended into Utah. In a recent

New York Times article, David Brower, former longtime leader of the Sierra Club who fought the construction of the dam, lamented the lost beauty of Glen Canyon: "That dam destroyed one of the most magnificent places on earth, in order to have flatwater recreation." Some believe that the single greatest loss of the planet's scenic heritage was the inundation of the world's biggest and most impressive waterfall at Salto del Guairá on the Brazil-Paraguay border. The falls featured 18 deafening cataracts that dropped a spectacular 114 meters (375 feet) and created a perpetual rainbow. So loud was the sound of its turbulent waters that it could be heard 32 kilometers (20 miles) away. With the completion of the Itaipú Dam in 1982, one of the world's largest hydroelectric plants, the roaring cataracts were silenced by the waters of the dam's reservoir.

Because dams inundate extensive areas of occupied land with impounded waters, they have dramatically changed human communities as well. Around the world millions of people have been removed from their homes, some forcibly, to make room for dam and reservoir complexes. When completed, China's Three Gorges Dam, for example, will

swamp 13 major cities and force the relocation of more than one million people. Ghana's Volta reservoir, the world's largest impoundment (as measured by surface area) to date, covers approximately 8,500 square kilometers (3,300 square miles)—nearly 4% of the country's land area. As Patrick McCully, campaigns director for International Rivers Network, Berkeley, California, points out in his 1996 book *Silenced Rivers: The Ecology and Politics of Large Dams,* a significant proportion of these displaced people have been poor or indigenous people or other ethnic minorities who experience economic, cultural, and emotional devastation in resettlement programs. In many countries violence and conflict have resulted as local residents resisted evacuation and subsequent relocation. For many others the new dams and reservoirs have led to profound changes in their customary subsistence and way of life. The loss of salmon populations in the U.S., for example, radically changed the lives and livelihoods of numerous Native American tribes whose cultures and economies were dependent on salmon. Over the past three decades in Africa, dam construction has destroyed not only floodplain ecosystems downstream of dams but also a

whole way of life for the hundreds of thousands of people who depended on the fisheries they nurtured.

Concerns about dam safety also have fueled controversy. Even the most technologically advanced dams are not completely safe from the vagaries of Earth's climate and geology. Furthermore, the risk of catastrophic failure has increased as the world's dam infrastructure has aged. The average age of dams in the U.S. is about 40 years. Around the world some 5,000 large dams now are more than 50 years old. Not surprisingly, dam safety has become a major and costly issue worldwide, particularly in the wake of such dam disasters as the one that occurred in central China in 1975, where more than 200,000 people are suspected to have died in a dam-reservoir failure on a tributary of the lower Chang Jiang.

Dams, reservoirs, and associated irrigation systems also create habitats that serve as vectors for disease. For instance, the spread of the debilitating disease schistosomiasis, caused by parasitic blood flukes that are propagated through a snail host, is directly related to dam and irrigation projects. The disease has infected people in more than 70 countries, with especially severe effects in Africa.

The construction of dams also has the potential to exacerbate political and social unrest. Historically, the division of waters, particularly in arid regions, has led to heightened international tensions and conflict. Plans for Turkey's Southeastern Anatolia Project (known by the Turkish acronym GAP), for example, will include 22 dams and will cost about $32 billion. When completed, this massive river-development scheme will give Turkey the ability to regulate the headwaters of the Euphrates and Tigris rivers and control much of the water supply for water-deficient Syria and Iraq—a volatile situation that will require the utmost in "hydrodiplomacy" if international conflicts are to be avoided.

THE FUTURE OF DAMS

As the ecological devastation of dams is more fully understood and the controversy about their socioeconomic costs heightens, will megadam projects continue to be built? Moreover, what is the future of existing dams?

Although new dam construction is slowing down worldwide, particularly in industrialized countries, in less-developed nations hundreds of new dams remain under construction and numerous dam projects are in the planning stage. Countries such as India and China, where the majority of people still live without running water or electricity, find it difficult to abandon development projects that will enhance human well-being, even if they are likely to adversely affect river ecosystems.

The reservoir created by the completion of the Itaipú Dam in 1982 submerged the world's largest and most spectacular waterfall, including 18 deafening cataracts that dropped 114 meters (375 feet).

The level of conflict and opposition to many projects, however, is expected to increase dramatically. Within the past decade a loosely organized antidam movement has emerged around the world. Originally spurred on by environmental concerns, dam opponents have built alliances with indigenous peoples organizations, human rights advocates, and others to create an uncertain future for many planned and proposed large dam projects. Fifty years ago such a gigantic initiative as the Three Gorges Dam (which, if completed, will be the largest dam on the planet) would have received unqualified praise for its technological achievements. In today's dam-building era, however, the project has been condemned not only by critics within China but by opponents around the world.

With the protests against constructing new projects has come a fundamental rethinking of existing infrastructure. Following the disastrous weather-related flooding that occurred in the U.S., Western Europe, and Bangladesh in the mid-1990s, hard questions were asked about the effectiveness and cost of traditional structure-oriented flood-control and flood-management policies. Out of the disasters grew a citizen antidam movement that forced the postponement or cancellation of several dam projects around the world and promoted an awareness about the potential for reducing future flood damage by preserving and restoring floodplain ecosystems.

In the U.S. and Western Europe in particular, this new movement has reshaped national water policies. The major U.S. dam-building agencies—the Army Corps of Engineers and the Bureau of Reclamation—for example, are radically changing their missions from water-resource development to management. New project initiatives will be extremely limited, with construction largely confined to replacement and rehabilitation of existing infrastructure. U.S. federal agencies are assuming new roles aimed at better management of existing water projects and water supplies, including the establishment of more water-conserving and market-oriented institutional arrangements to govern water usage. Furthermore, restoration or rehabilitation of degraded river systems has become a high priority, as evidenced by bold efforts to restore the immense delta of the Danube River in Europe and to recover endangered salmon populations in North America.

The environmental and social controversy surrounding dams also has prompted lending agencies to reexamine their own willingness to finance megadam projects. Huge cost overruns, unrealized benefits, environmental degradation, and other undesirable consequences, along with the social unrest and political uncertainty that have accompanied many dam projects in the past, have caused some multilateral banks and other funding entities to back away from new construc-

Critics of China's Three Gorges Dam have protested the dam's destruction of ecological, cultural, and scenic resources. River waters will rise to the height of the bridge shown in the photo below, submerging such cultural treasures as Fengdu Ghost City (seen in the background) and displacing the region's more than one million people.

tion, including the Three Gorges Dam. The U.S. Export-Import Bank and the World Bank, for example, have both adopted environmental guidelines since 1990 and are financing fewer dam projects as a result.

What will become of the world's vast water-management infrastructure—more than 40,000 large dams and hundreds of thousands of smaller water projects and related works? The demolition of all existing dams and the complete restoration of rivers, particularly large rivers, to a pristine state are neither compatible with existing population levels nor practical. There is great potential, however, for partial restoration of river habitats and ecosystems, with the goal of recovering some of their ecological functions and values. Knowledge about river rehabilitation, especially on a large scale, is still in its infancy. Nonetheless, several countries already are conducting substantial experimentation followed by changes in dam-reservoir operations in order to manage rivers in more environmentally sustainable and less socially disruptive ways.

One of the most dramatic illustrations of this movement toward more sustainable management of dammed rivers is the experimental flooding of

In the 1990s extensive flooding in the U.S., Bangladesh, and Europe, including rural France (below), fueled an antidam movement and prompted many countries to rethink the effectiveness of conventional methods of flood control.

the Colorado River in 1996. Extensive national media coverage of this pioneer attempt to use intentional flooding to benefit the canyon's biological diversity and recreational use captured the public's attention. Flows in the Colorado below the Glen Canyon Dam first declined when the dam began operations in the 1960s. Without the great surge of annual spring floods, the river's ecology downstream of the dam changed dramatically. In 1992, following a decade of scientific studies, the U.S. Congress passed the Grand Canyon Protection Act, authorizing a dual objective for the operation of the Glen Canyon Dam: meeting environmental goals as well

as serving the more traditional functions of water storage and power generation.

On March 26, 1996, researchers began a $3 million weeklong experiment designed to mimic predam hydrology in an effort to restore and sustain the river's natural function. A total of 900 million cubic meters (32 billion cubic feet) of water—which flowed at a peak rate of 1,275 cubic meters (45,000 cubic feet) per second, only about half the flow of an average natural flood—surged through the canyon. Even though preliminary scientific assessments suggest that the experimental flood significantly flushed the main river channel of debris, redeposited

sediments that improved the size and number of beaches along the river, and reestablished backwater habitats for spawning fish, it is premature to gauge the flood's long-term effects. Results were successful enough, however, to support plans for additional controlled flooding in coming years and to institute new regulations that will restrict power officials from releasing water in short-term bursts to accommodate peaks in power demand.

In some cases government agencies are taking even more radical steps—selectively removing existing dams. Until recently, dams have been viewed as more or less permanent fixtures on rivers that re-

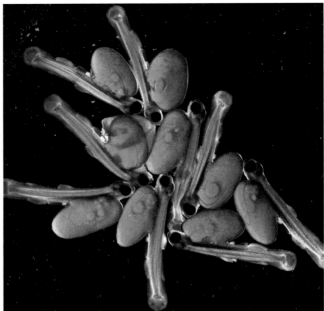

The experimental flooding of the Colorado River in 1996 was intended to mimic the scouring action of natural floodwaters. Before the flood, fan-shaped debris, seen on the left bank in the photo below, had narrowed one section of the river's course. Powerful floodwaters cleared and widened the river channel (bottom photo).

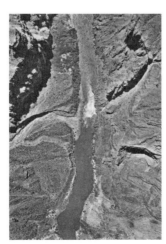

quire only periodic maintenance. The aging of the world's dams, however, along with safety concerns, the costs of dam repair, the filling of reservoirs with sediment, and the potential for aquatic ecosystem rehabilitation are all driving serious consideration of dam dismantling. In the U.S., for example, hundreds of small dams, most only a few meters in height, have been taken down, many for reasons of public safety and to avoid the high costs of structural rehabilitation.

Increasingly, plans are calling for dismantling dams with the aim of restoring the ecological function and recreational values of natural river ecosystems. One of the largest dams removed in the U.S. was the 19-meter (62-foot) Grangeville Dam on the Clearwater River in Idaho, which was dynamited in 1963 in an effort to restore salmon runs. Similar measures are under consideration in the Pacific Northwest. In spite of fish ladders and other mitigation measures, dams have

greatly impeded the migration of adult salmon and the downstream migration of juveniles. The most notable dam-removal effort to help restore the region's once enormously productive fisheries is a plan drafted by federal officials to decommission two dams on the Elwha River in Washington's Olympic Peninsula. Built in the early 1900s for electrical generation, the dams incorporate no provisions for fish passage. Together they are largely responsible for the near destruction of the large runs of anadromous fish, including coho, pink, chum, sockeye, and chinook salmon, as well as other fish species. Federal legislation directed at restoring the Elwha's fish stocks was enacted in 1992. The process of removing the 31-meter (102-foot) and 70-meter (230-foot) dams, however, slowed down in 1996–97 amid controversy over dismantling costs, which range between $60 million and $200 million, depending on the methods used for redistributing the accumulated sediment and

the level and source of compensation to private power users for power losses.

Because some $3 billion has been expended on salmon recovery in the Pacific Northwest's Columbia-Snake river system in recent years and the fishery is still in serious decline, additional dam removals are being carefully examined. A study is under way to evaluate the removal of four dams built in the 1960s by the U.S. Army Corps of Engineers on the lower Snake River, and other dams are undergoing similar scrutiny in an effort to mimic natural flow conditions and aid the migration of young fish. The Federal Energy Regulatory Commission recently asserted its authority to order the decommissioning and removal of dams. Under this authority a dam was dismantled on the Clyde River in Vermont, removing a barrier to Atlantic salmon migration. In late November 1997 the agency issued a landmark decision, denying a license-renewal request for Edwards Dam, a 160-year-old hydroelectric dam on Maine's Kennebec River. The commission went one step farther, ordering the dam's owner to demolish the structure to help restore spawning habitat and protect nine species of migratory fish. Because some 550 dams will face the relicensing

In a landmark 1997 decision, the Federal Energy Regulatory Commission ordered the removal of the 160-year-old Edwards Dam in Maine. The demolition is part of an effort to restore nine species of migratory fish, including Atlantic salmon.

process by the year 2015, the Edwards Dam recommendation is regarded as an important precedent with regard to dam removal and ecological restoration.

Similar moves have been made in France's Loire River basin, where the government has altered proposed dam projects to save an endangered Atlantic salmon population. Plans call for the removal of two smaller dams in the upper part of the river system to help restore the fish's habitat. Such societal changes in the Western Hemisphere have emboldened antidam forces and environmentalists, who in 1997 advanced a contentious (some would say unthinkable) proposal for the removal of Glen Canyon Dam and the restoration of a free-flowing Colorado River.

The 1990s, with hindsight, are likely to be seen as the start of a change in direction in the ways in which humans perceive, develop, and utilize the Earth's water resources. The era of river-basin development and dam building appears to be coming to an end, first in the industrialized Western countries and, in time, worldwide.

In the meantime, more dams will be dismantled while scientific and engineering research will increasingly turn to helping humankind find options for

the sustainable use and management of existing structures on the world's river ecosystems.

FOR ADDITIONAL READING

- *Cadillac Desert: The American West and Its Disappearing Water,* rev. ed., Marc P. Reisner (Viking Penguin, 1993).
- "Dambusting," Pratap Chatterjee, *New Scientist* (May 17, 1997, pp. 34–37).
- *Dams and Rivers: A Primer on the Downstream Effects of Dams,* Michael P. Collier, Robert H. Webb, and John C. Schmidt, U.S. Geological Survey Circular 1126 (1996).
- "Experimental Flooding in Grand Canyon," Michael P. Collier, Robert H. Webb, and Edmund D. Andrews, *Scientific American* (January 1997, pp. 82–89).
- "Last Look at the Long River," Ann Zwinger, *Audubon* (May–June 1997, pp. 78–86).
- "The Long River's Journey Ends," Erling Hoh, *Natural History* (July 1996, pp. 29–39).
- "Need for Ecosystem Management of Large Rivers and Their Floodplains," Richard E. Sparks, *BioScience* (March 1995, pp. 168–182).
- *Restoration of Aquatic Ecosystems: Science, Technology, and Public Policy,* National Research Council (National Academy Press, 1992).
- *The Rivers Handbook: Hydrological and Ecological Principles,* Peter Calow and Geoffrey E. Petts, eds. (Blackwell Scientific, 1992).
- *Silenced Rivers: The Ecology and Politics of Large Dams,* Patrick McCully (Zed Books, 1996).
- "The Trouble with Dams," Robert S. Devine, *The Atlantic Monthly* (August 1995, pp. 64–74).

INTERNET RESOURCES

- International Rivers Network home page http://www.irn.org
- International Commission on Large Dams home page http://genepi.louis-jean.com/cigb/index.html

Jean-François Allaux

40

Warming Up to the Outer Solar System

The solar system may be centered on a ball of fire, but it appears to fade away in bits of ice. As astronomers explore the brink of interstellar space, they are finding vast numbers of cometlike chunks of matter that have been drifting in cold storage for eons.

by Dale P. Cruikshank

Where does the solar system end?

This straightforward question seemed to have a clear answer in 1543 when Nicolaus Copernicus showed that the planets circle the Sun rather than Earth. Although he and his contemporaries did not perceive the actual size of the system of the six planets known to them, they realized that Saturn was the most distant from its center.

Today the answer to this same question is far less precise although much more fascinating. In the intervening four and a half centuries, the discovery of three planets beyond Saturn encouraged astronomers to wonder about what else exists in the coldest, outermost parts of the solar system. Two decades after the detection of Pluto, they began to realize that a large cloud of icy objects resides far beyond that planet's

Dale P. Cruikshank *is a research scientist in the Astrophysics Branch, NASA Ames Research Center, Moffett Field, California.*

orbit. Then, beginning in the early 1990s, dozens of telescopic observations confirmed the presence of a second, much closer population of such objects near and beyond the orbits of Neptune and Pluto. This recent find, coupled with new studies of Pluto, suggests that Pluto may not even be a planet in the conventional sense but may be just the dominant member among a kingdom of smaller, but otherwise quite similar, objects in its vicinity.

The discovery of tiny, remote Pluto in 1930 by Clyde Tombaugh broke the pattern of small, rocky inner planets and giant, gaseous outer planets that scientists had come to expect for the arrangement of the solar system.

The universe of Copernicus—with the Sun at the center and the six known planets, from Mercury to Saturn, circling around it—is depicted in an illustration from a 17th-century atlas of the heavens.

One reason that astronomers are interested in these remote objects is that they are thought to be well-preserved remnants of the original solar nebula that condensed to form the Sun and the planets. They thus promise insight into events that happened in our region of space more than four and a half billion years ago and that likely have happened, or are happening now, elsewhere as well. Just as intriguing, however, is the fact that they are the source of the comets that sweep into the inner solar system. Knowledge of their distribution and of the mechanisms that occasionally send them hurtling inward in our direction are helping scientists understand the forces that shaped the Earth's geologic history and the evolution of life itself.

EXTENDING THE FRONTIER

The first evidence that the solar system extends beyond Saturn had to await the invention of the telescope and its application to astronomy. In 1781 the English astronomer William Herschel discovered Uranus with a homemade telescope from his backyard in Bath. The planet was found orbiting the Sun at 20 times the average Earth–Sun distance—*i.e.,* 20 AU (astronomical units; 1 AU is 150 million kilometers)—which is twice the distance of Saturn. (A kilometer is about 0.62 mile.) The discovery of Uranus had doubled the size of the known solar system.

Astronomers now realized that additional unseen planets might exist at even greater distances from the Sun. Not long after Herschel's discovery, precise measurements of Uranus's position suggested that a planet was perturbing its motion through gravitational interaction. Mathematical studies aimed at predicting its location eventually resulted in the discovery of Neptune in 1846, when the German astronomer Johann Galle pointed his telescope at the place in the sky where his French colleague Urbain-Jean-Joseph Le Verrier had calculated that the new planet should lie. The discovery of Neptune at 30 AU from the Sun further increased the size of the known planetary system.

Continued speculation on the presence of additional planets ultimately led to the discovery of Pluto, at a mean distance of nearly 40 AU, by the American astronomer Clyde Tombaugh in 1930 during a photographic search of large areas of the sky. The initial excitement of the find, however, was quickly tempered by the fact that Pluto is clearly not a giant planet in the sense of Jupiter, Saturn, Uranus, and Neptune. That realization broke an apparent pattern for the arrangement of the solar system, namely, a group of rocky Earth-sized planets close to the Sun and a group of giant gaseous planets at greater distances. Astronomers now wondered not only what other bodies might lie beyond Pluto but also what kind they might be.

MOTHS AROUND A STREETLIGHT

Photographic searches following Pluto's discovery could have revealed Neptune-sized objects even at 200 AU from the Sun, but none were found. Nevertheless, the idea that Neptune and tiny Pluto marked the edge of the solar system was unsettling for astronomers, who expected that a number of small planets might exist beyond Neptune. In fact, it had been clear for many years that comets making their brief passes through the inner solar system must come from distances vastly greater than Pluto.

From the nature of their orbits, comets on their first visit to our part of the solar system appear to arrive from two dis-

A cutaway view of the solar system as seen from the center of our galaxy shows two reservoirs for the sources of comets. The Kuiper disk lies in the plane of the planets and extends from the orbits of Neptune and Pluto. Beyond it is the spherical Oort cloud. Whether the outer edge of the Kuiper disk blends into the Oort cloud, as suggested here, is not known.

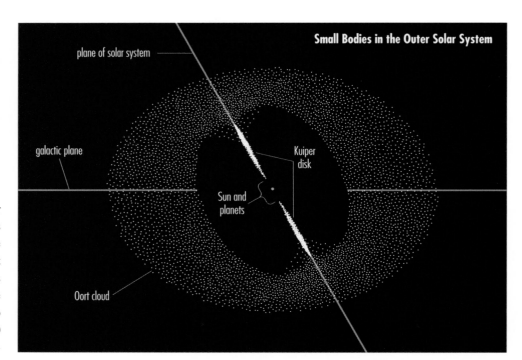

plane of solar system

galactic plane

Oort cloud

Kuiper disk

Sun and planets

tinctly different groupings or reservoirs. Some have orbits that lie roughly in the same plane as the orbits of the most of the planets; these comets tend to have periods—the time it takes to make a complete trip around the Sun—of about 200 years or less. Other new comets travel in much larger orbits that are inclined steeply to the planets' orbital plane, and their periods are usually much longer than 200 years. In 1950 the Dutch astronomer Jan Oort showed from his study of the orbits of the long-period comets that the solar system must be surrounded by a large cloud of small objects, each in orbit around the Sun.

This reservoir, now called the Oort cloud, is thought to begin at about 20,000 AU and to extend as far as 100,000 AU, or 1.5 light-years, which is about a third of the distance to the nearest star. It is estimated to contain as many as two trillion little bodies—bodies less than 100 kilometers in diameter—each a potential comet. Because they orbit so far from the Sun, the gravitational effects of nearby stars and the mass of the Milky Way Galaxy itself have jumbled their orbits such that a snapshot view at any moment in time would show them as a spherical cloud of tiny specks, like moths around a streetlight.

The Oort cloud is the source of about half the comets that enter the inner solar system, including the spectacular Comet Hale-Bopp (right), which appeared in the Earth's sky in early 1997.

Although comet-sized bodies in the Oort cloud are invisible at their usual distances, the cloud is the source of about half of the comets that come to the inner solar system. Their near approach gives astronomers the opportunity to study their individual behavior as they warm up and their ices begin to evaporate, carrying a fine dust of silicate minerals and solid clumps of organic molecules into the surrounding space. Recent examples of Oort cloud comets are Comet Hyakutake, which made a spectacular appearance in Earth's sky in early 1996, and Comet Hale-Bopp, which was one of the great comets of the 20th century and was brightly visible to the naked eye for months in early 1997. Both comets approached the Sun along very

Wally Pacholka

large orbits that were highly inclined to the orbital plane of the planets. Even Halley's Comet, which last approached the Sun in 1985–86, was originally an Oort cloud comet; this is made clear by the fact that it orbits the Sun in the reverse direction to the planets. Halley now has a relatively short period of 76 years because of a gravitational encounter with Jupiter sometime in the past.

Apart from studies of the occasional visiting Oort cloud comet, most of what is known about their distant source comes from computer simula-

tions of the dynamical—i.e., gravitational—interactions between them. From such simulations, and from studies of the statistics of comet orbits, Paul Weissman of NASA's Jet Propulsion Laboratory, Pasadena, California, and his colleagues have arrived at the figure of 100,000 AU for the outward extent of the cloud. This distance represents the farthest points of Oort cloud bodies in their elliptical orbits and is about as far from the Sun that such a body can be without escaping the weak gravitational field and falling into interstellar space. As the

H.U. Keller, Max-Planck-Institut fur Aeronomie, Lindau, Germany, 1986

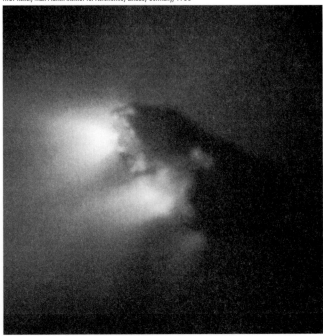

Close-up images of the nucleus of Halley's Comet, such as that made by the Giotto spacecraft in 1986 (left), changed the "dirty snowball" concept of comets. Halley turned out to be very black, with most of its ice hidden beneath a dusty crust. The finding suggested that comet nuclei are probably larger than had been thought.

solar system revolves around the center of our galaxy, it dips below and rises above the galactic plane in our local spiral arm every 30 million to 35 million years. Owing to this motion, the mass of the galaxy exerts gravitational effects that can slightly disrupt the orbits of bodies in the Oort cloud. These tiny perturbations, called disk tides, are sufficient to send Oort cloud bodies either inward toward the Sun or outward and away from the Sun's pull. Even the mass of the central region of the galaxy may jostle some bodies free of the Oort cloud. Yet another source of disruption to distant orbits is the occasional passage of another star near the solar system—Oort's original idea in 1950. Each century a few stars approach closely enough to affect the orbits of objects in the cloud, although the galactic disk tides appear to have the greatest influence.

The periodicity of the solar system's passage through the galactic plane has inspired speculation that swarms of comets are nudged from the Oort cloud with the same rhythm. If true, a connection may exist between mass extinctions of life on Earth, which appear to be periodic in occurrence, and catastrophic impacts on Earth of icy bodies perturbed from the distant reservoir identified by Oort.

BEYOND NEPTUNE AND PLUTO

About the same time that Oort was studying the long-period comets, the Dutch-American astronomer Gerard P. Kuiper proposed that the short-period comets—those with periods of less than 200 years—that travel near the plane of the planets originated in another, nearer reservoir. This reservoir would take the form of a disk extending beyond Neptune and Pluto. Kuiper suggested that millions of small, kilometer-sized chunks of matter might populate this disk, an accumulation of leftovers from the formation of the Sun and major planets, held in cold storage since the origin of the solar system some 4.6 billion years ago. A suggestion along these lines had been made just two years earlier by a less-prominent astronomer, Kenneth Essex Edgeworth, but the reservoir of short-period, low-inclination comets is now generally called the Kuiper disk, or Kuiper belt.

While Oort and Kuiper were proposing solutions to the dynamical nature of comets—that they appear to originate in two separate reservoirs—the American astronomer Fred Whipple was attempting to describe their physical nature. In 1950 he published his now well-known "dirty snowball" concept, the view that comets are made mostly of frozen water, with some dust and other materials mixed in. In addition, most comets must be quite small, just a few kilometers across. The brilliant coma and tail seen during their occasional dramatic passages through the inner solar system result from the illumination of gas and dust released from the icy nucleus by the warmth of the Sun.

Thus, in the space of a year or two, astronomers' conceptual understanding of comets made important advances, although the technology of the time was not sufficiently advanced to allow the new ideas to be tested by direct observation. Whereas an icy mix of frozen water and other volatile substances was finally identified in comets by Earth-based spectroscopy almost 40 years after Whipple's prediction, direct views of the nucleus of Halley's Comet from spacecraft flying nearby in 1986 showed that, unlike a snowball, it was very black, with most of the ice hidden beneath a dusty crust. This observation suggested that comet nuclei are probably significantly larger on average than had been previously thought. Astronomers' current view is that most objects in the Oort cloud and the Kuiper disk are similarly black or have a very dark reddish color resulting from the solid organic particles thought to make up much of their dust component.

Although the Oort cloud remained a bit beyond visual reach even near the end of the 1990s, advances in technology enabled astronomers to probe the solar system beyond Neptune for bodies in the Kuiper disk. The search with large telescopes and sensitive electronic light detectors at Hawaii's Mauna Kea Observatory began to net results in 1992 when David Jewitt and Jane Luu reported an object about 200 kilometers in diameter in

David Jewitt

The first small body to be detected beyond Neptune was discovered by David Jewitt and Jane Luu (left) at Hawaii's Mauna Kea Observatory in 1992. Provisionally designated 1992 QB1 (below, center), this Kuiper disk object is about 200 kilometers in diameter and takes 295 years to orbit the Sun, almost 50 years longer than Pluto.

an orbit just beyond Pluto. This body, provisionally designated 1992 QB1, was the ideal first discovery in the Kuiper disk. (Astronomers assign provisional names to newly discovered small bodies, using a rather arcane alphanumeric code relating to the year, half month, and order of discovery.) It lies in a nearly circular orbit in the same plane as the major planets, has an orbital period of 295 years (Pluto's is 248 years), and lies about 44 AU from the Sun. At the time of its discovery, it was unlike any other body in the solar system, and it caught the attention of planetary astronomers worldwide.

GATEWAY TO THE OUTER REACHES

Jewitt and Luu's detection of 1992 QB1 opened an entirely new vista on the solar system beyond Neptune and Pluto. Their discovery was quickly followed by additional sightings by the Hawaii team and by colleagues using a large telescope in the Canary Islands. After a few objects were discovered through surveys of small patches of sky in the plane of the planetary orbits as seen from Earth, Jewitt and Luu calculated that in the region between 30 and 50 AU from the Sun, the Kuiper disk

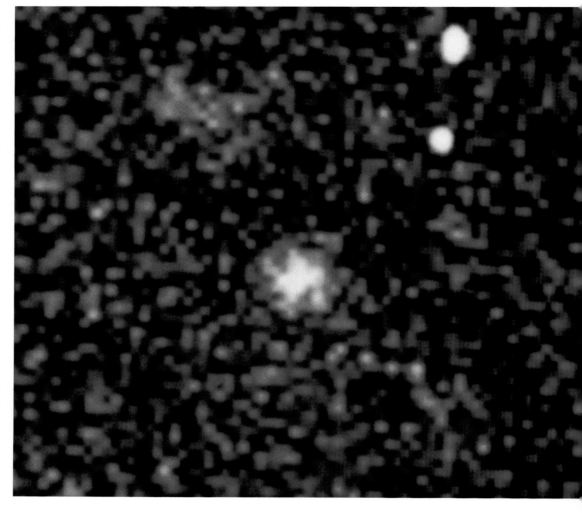

should contain upwards of 70,000 objects larger than 100 kilometers in diameter. This is about 1,000 times the number of similar-sized bodies that lie in the more familiar asteroid belt between Mars and Jupiter.

By early 1998 some 60 objects ranging from about 100 to 700 kilometers in diameter had been discovered near and beyond the orbits of Neptune and

Pluto. Their diameters were not measured directly but instead were calculated from the observed brightness of the object, its distance, and the assumption that its surface reflects only a small fraction (about 4%) of the sunlight that falls on it. These objects are much larger than the traditional comets that come our way from the outer solar system. If there are

70,000 large ones, there should be an even greater number of objects a few kilometers in size. Searches with the Earth-orbiting Hubble Space Telescope (HST) have given preliminary indication of a huge population of 10-kilometer-sized objects in just a very small part of the Kuiper disk. If confirmed, the work indicates the presence of a hundred

(Below) David Jewitt, University of Hawaii, and Jane Luu,
Harvard University; (bottom) Michael Carroll

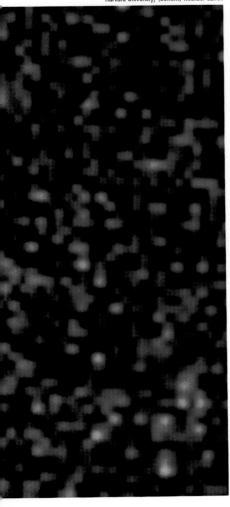

million or more of these smaller bodies out to about 50 AU.

Because of their great distance from the Sun, the orbital periods of Kuiper disk objects are typically 200 years or more. Observations over the short time interval since their discovery have been insufficient to define their orbital characteristics with the desired

precision. Nevertheless, their orbits clearly fall into distinct categories that are helping astronomers understand their origin and evolution.

Just like the planets, Kuiper disk objects revolve in elliptical orbits having the Sun at one focus of the ellipse. The shape of the orbit—how elongated it is compared with a perfect circle—is described by a number called the eccentricity. The size of the orbit is given by a number representing half of its length measured in the longest dimension—in geometric terms, by the length of the semimajor axis of the ellipse. Astronomers also often characterize the orbit of a planet by its perihelion and aphelion distances, the closest and farthest points from the Sun. Finally, the orientation of the orbit in space is described by its inclination to the Earth's orbit and two other parameters.

The gravitational fields of the many bodies in the solar system have interacted over time to arrange some of the orbits of the planets and the smaller bodies into patterns called resonances. This means that small bodies are often in orbits that have periods related by certain ratios to the orbital period of a nearby large planet. For example, Pluto makes two trips around its orbit for every three trips that Neptune makes;

it is therefore in a 2:3 resonance with Neptune. Jupiter's large satellites are in resonant orbits with one another, and many other examples exist throughout the solar system.

Bodies in the outer solar system, lying so far from the gravitational influence of the Sun, are particularly susceptible to organization in resonant orbits. Just as Pluto is in a 2:3 resonance with Neptune, so are many of the Kuiper disk objects. Jewitt has dubbed these bodies Plutinos, meaning "little Plutos." Other disk objects lie in a 3:4 resonance—they make three revolutions for every four

of Neptune—and at least one body is a 3:5 resonance with Neptune. Roughly a third of the known Kuiper disk objects are Plutinos in 2:3 resonance orbits.

The first Kuiper disk object found, 1992 QB1, is a good representative of those bodies that have an orbital semimajor axis between about 42 and 47 AU and that are not in resonance with Neptune. About two-thirds of the newfound objects are in this category.

Some objects do not fit into these broad classifications. For example, the object 1996 TL66 has a highly elliptical orbit that

A Kuiper disk object orbits far from the Sun in an artist's conception. Results from the Hubble Space Telescope suggest that a hundred million or more of these icy bodies, each a few kilometers across, may populate the disk.

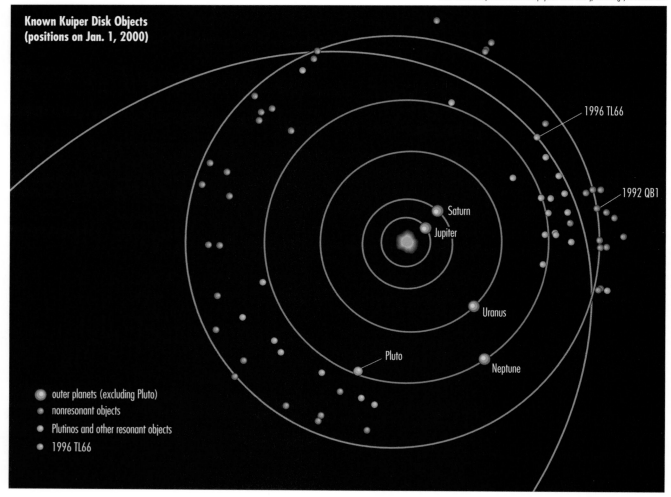

Known Kuiper Disk Objects (positions on Jan. 1, 2000)

1996 TL66

1992 QB1

Saturn

Jupiter

Uranus

Pluto

Neptune

- outer planets (excluding Pluto)
- nonresonant objects
- Plutinos and other resonant objects
- 1996 TL66

comes as close to the Sun as 35 AU—inside the orbit of Pluto—and reaches as far as 134 AU, which may be well beyond the orbits of the main concentration of Kuiper disk objects; it is also somewhat inclined to the plane of the solar system. It takes nearly 800 years to trace a complete orbit around the Sun. Its estimated diameter of 700 kilometers also makes it among the largest of the known Kuiper belt objects.

Yet another important category of bodies is the Centaurs. These objects, as large as a few hundred kilometers in diameter, are thought to have originated in the Kuiper disk but now follow orbits that cross the paths of the giant planets. The present orbits of the Centaurs

are unstable because of the strong gravitational interaction that they experience when they pass near a large planet. The usual effect of such close passages is that the small object is thrown outward into a new orbit far from the Sun. Occasionally the object collides with the planet or is flung inward to the region of the inner planets (Earth and Mars) or even on a collision path with the Sun. All this dynamical interaction occurs on a very short time scale in astronomical terms, usually less than a million years.

The first and best-known Centaur was discovered in 1977. Named Chiron, it measures about 200–300 kilometers in diameter and travels in a highly elliptical orbit having

a perihelion of 8.4 AU, which lies between the orbits of Jupiter and Saturn, and an aphelion of 18.8 AU, which nearly reaches the orbit of Uranus. At the time it was found, Chiron was thought to be an asteroid that had strayed outward from the asteroid belt. Later, after astronomers detected a dusty cloud around it, they concluded that Chiron was likely an icy, cometlike object that had come in from the Kuiper disk. The fact that Chiron and the other half dozen known Centaur objects are on planet-crossing orbits at the present time, together with their very short lifetimes, indicates that new Centaurs are being introduced continuously to the planetary region of the solar system.

Positions for Jan. 1, 2000, of all known Kuiper disk objects are located with respect to the giant outer planets. The orbits of 1992 QB1 and 1996 TL66 are included. Pluto is treated as a disk object.

ORIGIN AND EVOLUTION

Astronomers think that the Kuiper disk objects accumulated from tiny particles as the Sun and planets formed from the rotating, collapsing solar nebula. The solar nebula was a huge structure made of gas and dust derived from a large cloud of interstellar matter in the Milky Way Galaxy. Once the Sun began its production of nuclear energy, the remaining dust and gas were blown by radiation pressure back into the

(Below) Brian G. Marsden, Smithsonian Astrophysical Observatory, Cambridge, Massachusetts; (bottom) Jane Luu, Harvard University, and David Jewitt, University of Hawaii

(Right) The orbits and positions for Jan. 1, 2000, of the seven known Centaur objects are plotted among the orbits of the giant outer planets. Chiron, the first Centaur discovered, was originally thought to be an asteroid. Subsequent detection of a dusty cloud around Chiron (below) led astronomers to conclude that it was a cometlike object from the Kuiper disk.

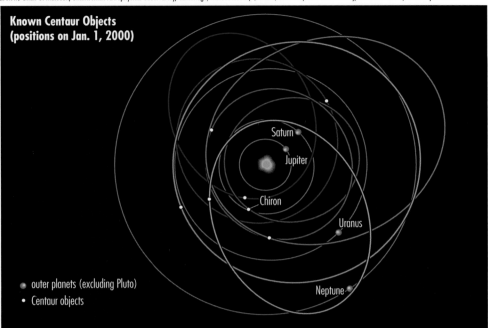

Known Centaur Objects
(positions on Jan. 1, 2000)

Saturn
Jupiter
Chiron
Uranus
Neptune

• outer planets (excluding Pluto)
• Centaur objects

interstellar medium. Small bodies collided with larger planets and satellites, and the solar system settled into its present structure relatively quickly, perhaps in just a few hundred thousand years.

Solid bodies and gas-rich planets accreted from material in the solar nebula at various distances from the new Sun, depending on the materials available in those places where the planets ultimately would form. The solar nebula ranged greatly in temperature, from well above 750° C (1,380° F) in the innermost regions to a very cold −230° C (−382° F) or so in the outer regions. Thus, the materials available for the formation of the planets and smaller bodies depended critically on the temperature of the region where formation occurred. In the inner regions, where the planets Mercury through Mars formed, the first materials to condense and accrete were metals and silicates, but the temperature was never sufficiently low to allow much volatile material, such as water, nitrogen, and carbon dioxide, to condense. About five astronomical units from the new Sun, Jupiter formed in a cooler region, first as a mass of rocky and metallic material, after which it acquired its enormous mantle of the most volatile elements, hydrogen and helium

gas. Its moons formed from rock and ice.

Beyond the last large planet, Neptune, the very low temperature in the solar nebula favored the freezing of water, carbon dioxide, carbon monoxide, methane, nitrogen, and such other volatile materials that had been a part of the original molecular cloud or had been blown away from the inner regions by the young Sun. It seems clear that a great amount of original interstellar dust and ice remained little changed in the outer solar nebula, where it accumulated into larger and larger particles, eventually being incorporated into the bodies now recognized as the Kuiper disk objects.

Thus, the Kuiper disk family formed essentially in its present location.

Gravitational interactions with the planets and other solar system bodies, particularly Neptune, have altered the arrangement of the inner part of the Kuiper disk since its formation. To study such effects, Harold Levison of the Southwest Research Institute, Boulder, Colorado, Martin Duncan of Queen's University at Kingston, Ontario, and colleagues have used computer programs designed to simulate the orbital motion of thousands of bodies simultaneously over the age of the solar system. Starting with a Kuiper disk model having small bodies with orbits between 30 and 50 AU, they find that Neptune quickly perturbs some of the orbits. Objects with perihelion distances less than 35 AU are sent into orbits that cross over Neptune's orbit, similar to the presently observed Centaurs. Objects with perihelion distances between 35 and about 42 AU are un-

stable over long periods of time, unless they lie in resonances with Neptune. Objects beyond about 42 AU appear to be stable for as long as four billion years, but even then an orbit can change, sending the object inward toward the planets or outward toward the edge of the disk. The object 1996 TL66, at an aphelion distance at the outer edge of or beyond the disk, is probably representative of a predicted class of Kuiper disk bodies that were gravitationally scattered by Neptune out of the original disk into highly elliptical, highly inclined orbits sometime in the past.

Just how far outward the main Kuiper disk actually extends is not known; it may reach 100 or 200 AU or more. The computer simulations show that beyond about 50 AU, however, the inclinations and eccentricities of the orbits of the combined population of main disk and gravitationally scattered objects begin to increase. This scattered popula-

49

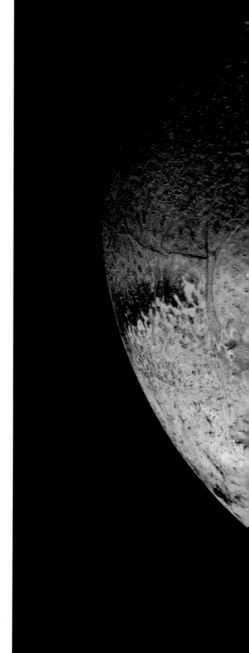

This Voyager 2 image of Neptune's moon Triton shows a south polar cap of frozen gases marked with impact craters and geyser plume deposits. Although Triton's surface has been altered by internal and external forces over billions of years, astronomers have good reason to suspect that the moon originated as a very large member of the Kuiper disk.

JPL/NASA

tion may reach beyond 1,000 AU, although whether it blends into the innermost edge of the Oort cloud is entirely speculative.

The comets that steadily come in from the Kuiper disk, the replenishment of the supply of Centaur objects, and the computer simulations just described show that the Kuiper disk has been dynamically active and even now continues to evolve. Just how uniform over time this evolution has been is not clear, but it is likely that even as the small bodies in the disk and nearby Neptune were accreting in the solar nebula, the initial sorting out had begun. An intense episode of crater formation on the moons of the outer planets about 4.1 billion to 4.3 billion years ago probably resulted from impacts by objects perturbed out of the disk. A storm of such bodies also must have struck Earth, Mars, and Venus, making huge craters and leaving behind some of the molecular material contributing to the early atmospheres and oceans of those planets.

At the time of planet formation, there was probably insufficient material in the solar nebula beyond the Kuiper disk for comet-sized objects to accrete there. The Oort cloud is therefore thought to have been generated by bodies thrown out

of the Kuiper disk and from a zone near Uranus and Saturn. The latter region was originally populated with a vast number of small icy objects that failed to be incorporated into the giant planets as they formed and were instead hurled outward by the gravitational action of the newly formed planets.

RUMMAGING THROUGH THE DEEP FREEZE

Planetary astronomers are interested in the compositions of the planets and other objects in the solar system, as well as their dynamics. In trying to reconstruct the events that led to the formation of the solar system, they seek to understand the original starting mix of gases, ices, and particles of dust. This most primitive material, which accumulated from the giant molecular cloud that spawned the Sun and its planets, reacted chemically as well as through the force due to gravity. Knowledge of the chemistry of the earliest solar nebula, which is now lost in the mist blown away on the solar wind, is a kind of holy grail long sought by astronomers who are inquisitive about the formation of all the bodies of the solar system and of all kinds of stars and the orbiting objects that some of these stars may possess.

Comets carry some of this information, but when they approach the vicinity of Earth, they are in such a vigorous state of chemical change that they do not directly reveal the original recipe for the Sun and the planets. For their part, the planets and most of their moons have been so greatly modified by their own geologic activity and atmospheres and the ravages of space that the original materials from which they formed are well disguised. These forces, plus the Sun's heat, have evaporated all the original interstellar ices in which the organic chemicals of our galaxy were forged.

To find some of the original materials, particularly the volatile ices and organic chemicals that reveal so much, scientists have turned toward the edge of the solar system. These outer reaches are very cold; for example, the noontime temperature on the little gray world Umbriel, a moon of Uranus, is −198° C (−324° F), and a midsummer day on Pluto or Neptune's largest moon, Triton, barely reaches −233° C (−387° F). Perhaps these worlds in the dimly lit deep freeze nearly five billion kilometers from the Sun have preserved some trace of the volatile ices present in the early solar nebula.

From observations with Earth- and space-based tele-scopes and far-ranging spacecraft, the chemistries of Pluto and Triton have been explored over the last decade. The emerging picture is that the surfaces of these two bodies are covered with a mixture of ices, of which frozen nitrogen appears to be the most abundant. Common to both Triton and Pluto, and frozen in the nitrogen as a chemical mixture, are methane and carbon monoxide. Expanses of ordinary frozen water are also found,

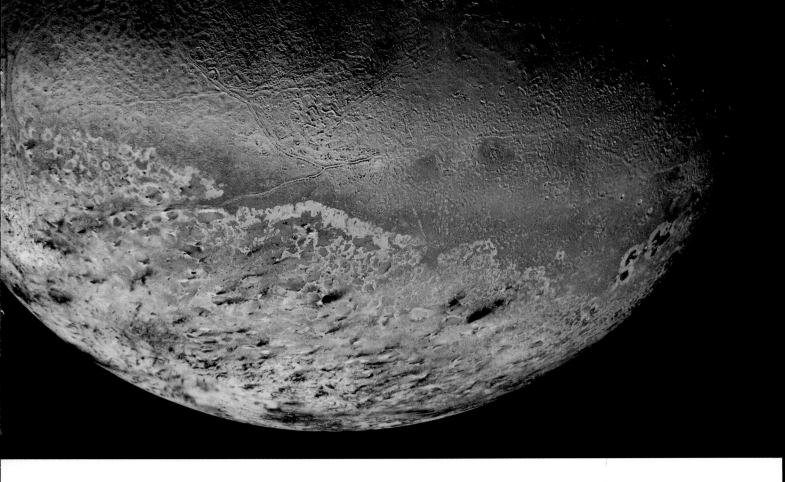

and in the case of Triton, there are regions that incorporate solid carbon dioxide. These are all frozen forms of simple molecules that probably were present in the outer solar nebula at the time of planet formation. But do these ices on Pluto and Triton reflect surfaces that have remained unchanged for billions of years?

The answer must surely be no, because both Triton and Pluto show various lines of evidence for change that has af-

fected their surfaces in major ways. In the case of Triton, images from the Voyager 2 spacecraft that flew by in 1989 show not only an atmosphere but recent geologic activity. Even today, active geyserlike plumes emanating from spots on the surface loft huge pillars of dust or ice particles into the thin atmosphere. Furthermore, chemistry high in Triton's atmosphere, where ultraviolet light from the Sun and electrons trapped by nearby Nep-

tune's magnetic field impinge on molecules of carbon monoxide, nitrogen, and methane, is constantly producing new and more complex molecules. These molecules are thought to be slowly settling out of the atmosphere, forming thick layers on the surface.

Because Triton moves in its orbit around Neptune in the opposite direction from Neptune's rotation, it could not have formed with the planet from the solar nebula. Instead,

it must have formed elsewhere and later been gravitationally captured by Neptune. Perhaps it is the heat energy retained from that capture that drives the geologic activity of the crust and surface via a process that has been termed ice volcanism. Triton also experiences a cycle of seasons in which the elevation of the Sun seen from the surface varies widely over a period of 680 years. The more volatile ices (nitrogen, carbon monoxide, and methane) evaporate from the surface in sunny regions and freeze back on the surface in dark, cold zones.

Pluto's surface is also basically icy, although HST images made in 1996 showed it to be littered with dark material, probably organic solid matter formed from the thin atmosphere or directly in the ices by the long-term chemical action of the Sun's ultraviolet light. The planet's surface of mixed ices and its thin atmosphere of nitrogen, methane, and carbon monoxide make for a chemically rich environment where complex organic molecules are being made from simple ingredients even now. Telescopic observations showed in 1978 that Pluto has a satellite, called Charon, that is fully half the size of Pluto itself. Because scientists have yet to send a spacecraft to view the surface of Pluto, the degree to which it might be currently geologically active can only be surmised.

The compositional similarities of Triton and Pluto are more than skin deep. The mass and density of Triton have been determined from the measurements by Voyager, and the same quantities for Pluto have been measured from Earth-based telescopes and the HST. Both bodies have about the same density, which suggests that their internal compositions

are nearly identical. They are also twins in terms of size and surface temperature. Although Triton is now a moon of Neptune and Pluto has a moon of its own, there are compelling reasons to believe that they originated under similar circumstances as very large members of the Kuiper disk family of objects. The fact that a number of Plutinos have been found with the same orbital characteristics as Pluto sug-

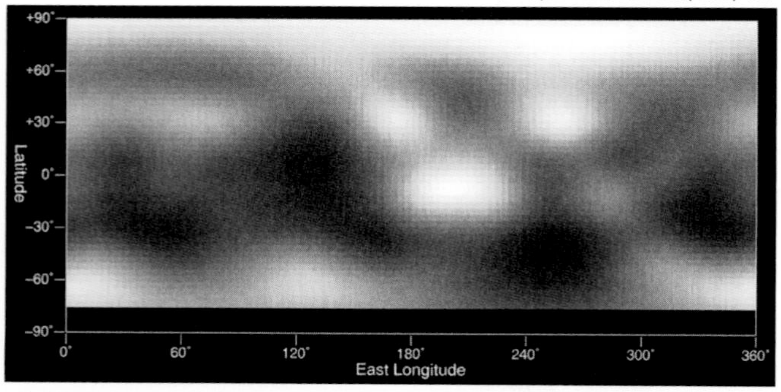

The first glimpse of Pluto's surface came in 1996, when the Hubble Space Telescope showed it to have extensive dark patches. Like Triton, Pluto appears to have formed as a Kuiper disk object.

gests that rather than being a full-fledged planet, Pluto might be considered just the largest known member of the group. By analogy, Triton probably had a similar origin.

Are the compositions of Triton and Pluto reliable clues to the materials comprising the smaller bodies residing in the Kuiper disk? When the first disk objects were discovered at the limit of the sensitivity of

modern telescopes and their electronic cameras, it seemed utterly hopeless that something about the compositions of these faint, distant bodies would be learned anytime soon. Nevertheless, technology applied to astronomy moves at a rapid pace, and with the recent availability of the tremendous light-gathering power of the twin Keck 10-meter (400-inch) telescopes on Mauna Kea, it became possible to consider infrared spectroscopy of these small bodies.

Early spectroscopic results on the compositions of the brightest of the Kuiper disk objects from Robert H. Brown of the University of Arizona and his colleagues show them to be highly diverse. Some give evidence of hydrocarbons (as yet unidentified), water ice, and possibly frozen methane and nitrogen. Some have a distinct

red color that is characteristic of solid organic polymers, and others are as black as coal. All are thought to contain large quantities of frozen water and the other volatile materials found in comets. The Centaurs are also quite varied. Some show clear evidence of the red organic material mixed with frozen water and frozen methanol (as is found in comets); others reveal only frozen water. Chiron, although it exhibits episodic behavior as a comet, has a completely featureless spectrum. Continuing work on the compositions of Kuiper disk objects and the Centaurs is expected to reveal a range of materials representing the inventory of minerals and volatile and organic substances present in the early solar nebula.

PROFOUND IMPLICATIONS

The exploration of the outer fringes of the solar system, where the remains of the formation of the Sun and planets have lain hidden from view for nearly five billion years, is a bit like a piece-by-piece examination of the contents of an ancient cold-storage locker. Scientists are not even fully aware of the entire contents of the locker, but as they uncover individual objects and entire classes of new objects, they are

Bombardment of the early Earth by comets is thought to have provided many or most of the materials needed for life—and perhaps even a trace of complex organic compounds that helped life get started.

gaining insight into the origin of the solar system and all that it contains.

Astronomers' view of the outer solar system is being changed not only by new discoveries in the Oort cloud and the Kuiper disk but also by breakthroughs in the study of individual comets that come from those great storage reservoirs beyond the planets. In the past several years, comet studies have focused on the origin of cometary material in the solar system's nascent molecular cloud, on organic matter preserved from interstellar dust grains, and on issues of the origin of life on Earth and possibly Mars. This new view of comets began to emerge as scientists worldwide prepared for the approach of Halley's Comet in 1985, and it continues as they carry the quest for our origins to the most fundamental level.

Comets are central to major new concepts in both geology and biology. Impacts on Earth by comets (and asteroids) are now viewed as having given rise to the origin of the Earth's Moon and having been a significant factor in shaping our planet's crust. In biology, likewise on a grand scale, comets are seen as the givers and takers of life. After the newly formed Earth began to cool, comets provided many or most of the volatile materials—water, carbon dioxide, nitrogen, and even carbon—essential to life, as well as a sprinkling of complex organic molecular matter that may have helped life get started. Subsequent impacts shattered Earth's crust, perhaps extinguishing the earliest life entirely. As the debris of planet formation cleared and the frequency of catastrophic impacts declined, life finally took hold about four billion years ago and has survived ever since. Nevertheless, impacts of comets and asteroids every few million years have continued to have globally significant ecological effects, causing mass extinctions of species and redirecting biological evolution planetwide.

With each new bright comet that passes near the Earth and each new discovery about those denizens of the outermost reaches beyond the planets, we gain not only more information about the origin of the solar system but also insight into our own origins.

FOR ADDITIONAL READING

- "The Kuiper Belt," Jane X. Luu and David C. Jewitt, *Scientific American* (May 1996, pp. 46–52).
- *Pluto and Charon*, Alan Stern and Jacqueline Mitton (John Wiley and Sons, 1998).

INTERNET RESOURCES

- International Astronomical Union Minor Planet Center home page http://cfa-www.harvard.edu/cfa/ps/mpc.html
- Kuiper Belt home page http://www.ifa.hawaii.edu/faculty/jewitt/kb.html
- The Nine Planets home page http://seds.lpl.arizona.edu/nineplanets/nineplanets/nineplanets.html
- Views of the Solar System home page http://www.hawastsoc.org/solar/homepage.htm

Star Maps of the Ancient Orient

by F. Richard Stephenson

Pictorial representations and descriptive accounts of the night sky preserved from bygone centuries in China, Korea, and Japan are providing astronomers with valuable information about the past visitations of Halley's Comet and its kin and the catastrophic death of stars.

W hen we look up into the sky on a clear moonless night, well away from artificial light, we can see perhaps 3,000 stars, which appear as scattered points of light that range widely in brightness. Certain stars seem to form natural groupings—for example, the Big Dipper, or Plough, and the brighter stars of Orion. Nevertheless, it is evident that the division of most stars into groups is a fairly arbitrary matter. It is thus remarkable that throughout history only two separate schemes of mapping the stars have enjoyed widespread usage. One, of Babylonian-Greek origin, forms the basis of our modern system of star identification. The other scheme is of ancient Chinese origin; it was in widespread use throughout China, Korea, and Japan until early in the 20th century, when it was supplanted by the occidental system.

F. Richard Stephenson is a professor and a professorial fellow in the Department of Physics, University of Durham, England.

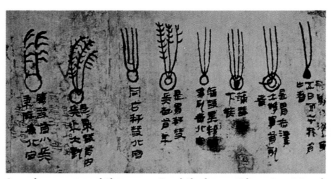

Several comets, termed "broom stars" and "bushy stars" by ancient Oriental astronomers, are portrayed on a silk manuscript found in a Chinese tomb and dating from about 250 BC. In the early histories of China, Korea, and Japan, many hundreds of observations of comets are recorded.

Today there remain preserved a wide range of charts of the night sky as it looked in past centuries to people of the Orient. This astronomical treasury has historical significance in that throughout East Asia star groupings were pictured quite differently from those in the Western world. Furthermore, some of the charts are of considerable importance to modern science because the Oriental astronomers consistently recorded the positions, relative to individual star groups, of transitory "broom stars," "guest stars," and other objects, which are recognized today as comets, novas, and supernovas. These early records enable modern astronomers to obtain valuable information about cometary orbits. They also allow ancient supernova outbursts to be linked with the present-day remnants that have been detected with radio telescopes and X-ray instruments.

GREEK AND CHINESE SYSTEMS

A major difference between occidental and Oriental star maps is in the sizes and shapes of the star patterns. The extensive star catalog in the *Almagest,* an astronomical and mathematical encyclopedia compiled by Ptolemy around AD 140, lists 1,022 stars grouped in 48 constellations— roughly one-quarter of the stars visible from the Mediterranean region during the course of a year. The reason for Ptolemy's choice of these specific numbers of constellations and stars is obscure, but he is known to have included many star groups of Babylonian origin in his catalog.

Ptolemy gives approximate positional measurements for each star (to the nearest one-sixth of a degree, at best) and a description of where the star lies in relation to its appropriate constellation. For example, the bright star Pollux, in the constellation Gemini, is described as "the reddish star on the head of the rear twin," and Aldebaran, in Taurus, is designated "the bright star of the Hyades, the reddish one on the southern eye [of the Bull]." Ptolemy's star catalog formed the basis of star mapping in Europe and the Islamic world throughout medieval times. Only since the 17th century has his list of constellations been extended, mainly to allow for newly discovered stars in the south circumpolar regions, which are invisible from northern latitudes.

By comparison, early Chinese star maps and catalogs typically include about 1,450 stars divided into as many as 280 asterisms, or small star groups. Only a few clearly defined patterns are shared between Oriental and occidental star maps. They include *Beidou* ("Northern Dipper"), identical to the Big Dipper; *Shen* ("Triad"), equivalent to the central part of Orion; and *Wei* ("Tail"), the tail of the Dragon in Oriental astronomy and of the Scorpion in the West.

Ptolemy grouped the stars that he cataloged into six classes of magnitude, denoting brightness. This division forms the basis of our modern system. Most Western star maps represent stars of different magnitude by symbols of different sizes. By contrast, early Oriental star maps make little, if any, attempt to display relative brightness. Although they do systematically depict all the known brighter stars, they overlook many fainter stars. Medieval European and Arab star maps, which were patterned after the brief descrip-

tions of the constellations in the 3rd century BC by the Greek poet Aratus in his *Phaenomena* and the more accurate ones by Ptolemy, lavished much attention on representing the figures of Babylonian and Greek mythology after which the constellations are named. This decorative practice remained in vogue well into the 19th century. On the other hand, East Asian star maps almost always portrayed only the star patterns themselves, although these were sometimes depicted in an idealized form.

In China, asterisms were regarded as representing the Chinese empire. Individual star groups denoted, for example, the emperor and members of the imperial family, ministers, generals, domestic animals, and buildings from palaces to prisons. To illustrate, in the 7th-century *Jinshu* ("History of the Jin Dynasty")—as translated in the 1960s by Ho Peng Yoke—the asterism *Fang* ("Chamber") in Scorpio is described as follows:

The four stars of *Fang* form the "Hall of Light" where the emperor sits and rules. They are also the "Four Assistants"—

This 17th-century European star map lavishes attention on the figures of mythology associated with the constellations. Oriental star maps, by contrast, almost always show only the star patterns themselves.

the lowest star denoting the Commanding General, the second the Lieutenant General, the third the Minister of State and the last star at the top the Prime Minister.

In particular, when the Moon or a planet—or more especially a strange object, a guest star or broom star—was seen to enter an asterism, the event was regarded as portentous for the as-

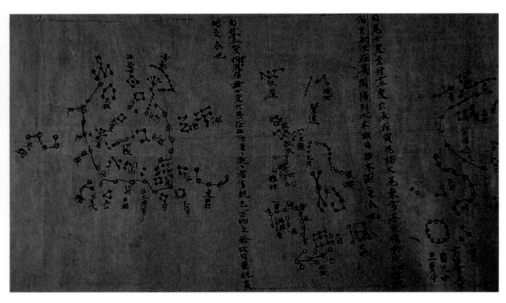

A detail from a painting in a Han dynasty tomb (above) shows star patterns of some of the lunar lodges. Dating from about 25 BC, the painting is the earliest Chinese star chart.

sociated person or thing. This is the main reason why Chinese astronomers were concerned to record unusual celestial phenomena. Thus, in AD 369 when a new star appeared in the polar region, it was regarded as a portent of ill for the emperor. Again, quoting from *Jinshu:*

> During the 2nd month of the 4th year of the Taihe reign period a guest star appeared at the western wall of the Purple Palace [the asterism *Ziwei*] and went out of sight only at the 7th month. According to the standard prognostication one may expect the emperor to be assassinated by his subordinates whenever a guest star guards the Purple Palace. During the 6th year Huan Wen dethroned the emperor and gave him the title "Duke of Hai Xi."

Later, in Korea and Japan, much the same astrological system was developed, with the same kinds of links to persons and things. In both nations, however, portents were regarded as directly affecting the country of observation—*i.e.,* Korea or Japan—rather than China.

CHINESE STAR MAPS

The very earliest star maps in East Asia originated in China. Charting the stars was a much later development in Korea and Japan and contributed little that was innovative. Although the names of a few asterisms can be found on the Shang dynasty oracle bones, which date from perhaps 1200–1300 BC, the earliest Chinese star chart dates from around 25 BC. It exists as a painting on the ceiling of a tomb that was excavated at the city of Xi'an in 1987 and rather sketchily displays the star patterns of the 28 lunar lodges. This special group of asterisms, which had a number of parallels with the 12 constellations of the Western zodiac, were very important in Chinese astrology and often were used to measure the positions of other stars.

Possibly as early as the 3rd century BC, Chinese astronomers mapped the stars into 283 asterisms. Traditionally these groups contained a total of 1,464 stars, roughly one-third of those visible to the unaided eye from the latitudes of China. The origin of both numbers—asterisms and constituent stars—cannot be traced satisfactorily. Nevertheless, their choice profoundly influenced later celestial mapmaking throughout East Asia.

No star chart or detailed list of star positions is known to survive from before the 1st century BC. A star catalog copied in an 8th-century work has lately been identified as originating from the 1st century BC. This catalog contains measurements of 120 star positions, many of which are quoted to the nearest quarter of a degree. Although there is evidence for the production of detailed star charts and celestial globes from the 1st century AD onward in China, all of the earliest artifacts have long since disappeared. In fact, the oldest extensive star chart that survives today dates from about AD 700. This crude but colorful map, on paper, was discovered early in

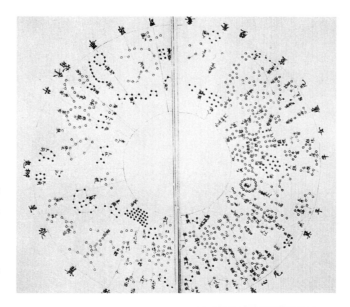

Crude but colorful renderings of asterisms on paper (opposite page, right) are part of the Dunhuang star map, dating from about AD 700. A polar projection of the southern hemisphere (right) from the 1094 star map compiled by the astronomer Su Song is preserved in an 18th-century copy. The void surrounding the south pole represents that part of the sky invisible from central China. A rubbing (below) depicts the stone Suzhou star map. Engraved in 1247, the Suzhou map is the oldest original star chart that accurately shows all of the night sky visible from China.

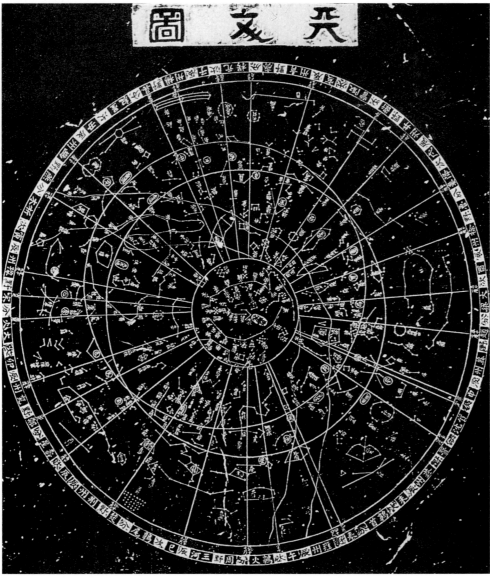

the 20th century in a grotto at Dunhuang in western China and is now in the British Library in London.

Two of the best-known medieval Chinese star maps were produced during the Song dynasty (AD 960–1279). One, first printed in 1094, exists only in the form of late copies. The other, however, engraved on stone in 1247, is still in an excellent state of preservation and can be seen at Suzhou in eastern China. It is the oldest original star chart that accurately depicts the whole of the night sky visible from China. This circular star map, or planisphere, is 83 centimeters (33 inches) in diameter and displays the stars on a polar projection. On the chart are marked the circumpolar circle (within which the stars never set), the celestial equator, and the ecliptic (the apparent path of the Sun across the celestial sphere). The circular border of the chart represents the edge of the visible sky as seen from central China. The boundaries of the sky zones associated with the 28 lunar lodges are shown by radial lines. As on other Oriental star maps, these zones are of unequal width, ranging from 1° to 33°. A satisfactory explanation for this variation has yet to found.

In all, some 1,440 stars are represented on the Suzhou

(Above) Star positions are marked with raised nodules on a section of a bronze celestial globe produced in China in 1673 by the Jesuit astronomer Ferdinand Verbiest (opposite page). In 17th-century China, Verbiest and fellow Jesuit Adam Schall von Bell (left) prepared detailed star maps incorporating accurate European measurements.

(Above) F. Richard Stephenson; (left) The Granger Collection, New York; (opposite page) Culver Pictures

chart. Modern measurements indicate that the accuracy of most star positions on it is tolerably good—typically about 2°. In 1995 it was shown that a colorful star map at the Adler Planetarium in Chicago is an early copy of the Suzhou chart and is at least two centuries old—apparently the oldest copy of this impressive planisphere in existence.

The star map printed in 1094 was produced by the great astronomer Su Song, who two years earlier had constructed for the imperial observatory at Kaifeng a revolving celestial globe driven by a water clock. This globe was said to display 1,464 stars in 283 asterisms—the traditional figures. Regrettably the globe, along with the rest of the observatory equipment, was captured by invading armies from the north in 1126 and soon afterward disappeared. It is on record, however, that a series of charts printed in 1781 and now in the National Library in Beijing is

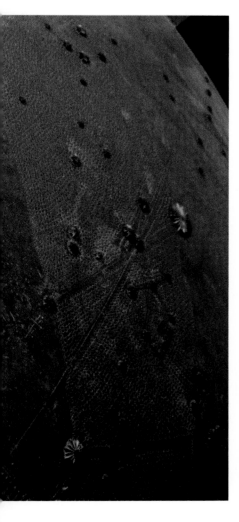

based on an accurate copy of the original printing. The northern and southern skies are depicted on two circular maps, each on a polar projection, whereas the equatorial asterisms are shown on two rectangular charts. In all, 1,455 stars are displayed in 283 groups—more or less the numbers depicted on the celestial globe. The map of the southern sky is particularly interesting because it has a central void surrounding the south polar region. This void represents the region of sky that is invisible from central China; it was never adequately mapped until the 17th century when Jesuit missionaries brought information about the far southern star patterns.

After 1276 no other Chinese star maps are preserved until the Ming dynasty in the 15th century. Some of these latter maps show close parallels with the Suzhou chart, but in general the positioning of the stars is less precise. When Jesuit astronomers arrived in China in the 17th century, several of them, notably Adam Schall von Bell and Ferdinand Verbiest, prepared detailed maps of the stars, incorporating accurate European measurements. From 1644 to 1826, Roman Catholic missionaries held the position of astronomer royal in China almost without interruption. Despite their use of Western techniques for mapping the night sky, the Jesuits were careful to follow the traditional Chinese style of representing asterisms. Several of their charts, which were printed on paper, are preserved today in both Chinese and European libraries. Moreover, a bronze celestial globe produced by Verbiest in 1673 and still in almost pristine condition can be seen at the Beijing Ancient Observatory.

KOREAN AND JAPANESE MAPS

Early star maps made in Korea and Japan clearly show Chinese influence. In general, the asterism names and star patterns are the same as those envisaged in China. The earliest Korean chart of the night sky dates from 1395. This planisphere, about 90 centimeters (35 inches) in diameter and engraved on a huge stela, or stone slab, depicts 1,460 stars. The stela is on view at Doksu Palace in Seoul. Somewhat damaged during the Japanese invasion of Korea in 1592, it has a surface that is about 90% intact, although the rest is badly worn. Quite recently it was discovered that the stone slab, which had lain in a horizontal position for many years, has an almost identical star map on the opposite face. The surface, however, is in relatively poor condition. A suggested date for this chart is 1433, nearly 40 years after the first surface was engraved.

The Korean planisphere has an interesting history. It is recorded that many centuries ago the emperor of China presented a stone star chart to the king of Koguryo, the northernmost of the three ancient kingdoms of Korea. Around AD 670, when Koguryo was overrun by the armies of the southeastern kingdom of Silla, the stone was lost in a river and never recovered. Centuries later—in 1392—when the Yi dynasty was founded, a man presented to the first king a rubbing of the original star map, which formed the basis of the engraving of 1395. Measurements of the star positions as engraved on the planisphere indicate an original date sometime in the 1st century BC. Hence, the Korean star chart may portray a Chinese representation of Oriental star groups created earlier than anything on such an extensive scale preserved in China itself.

Many careful copies of this planisphere, from the 17th century onward, exist. The largest, engraved on stone in 1687 and in an excellent state of preservation, is on display in Seoul, and smaller bronze copies are in museums in Edinburgh and Saga, Japan.

Several Korean star maps from the 18th and early 19th centuries are copied from Jesuit artifacts. For instance, a large, colorful silk screen, now in Cambridge, England, depicts both the 1395 Korean planisphere and charts of the northern and southern sky produced in China in 1723 by the Jesuit astronomer Ignatius Kögler. Similar screens have recently

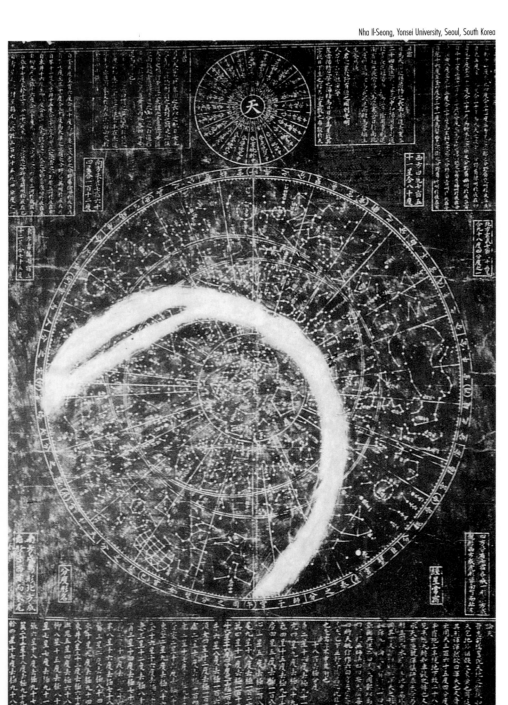

The earliest-known Korean star chart, engraved on a stone slab, dates from 1395. This block print is based on a rubbing from a 17th-century copy of the chart. The original was damaged during the Japanese invasion of Korea in 1592.

come to light in both Korea and Japan. Although no Jesuit missionaries reached Korea until the 20th century, Korean ambassadors to China encountered Jesuits in Beijing and returned with star maps and other artifacts of Western origin.

A poorly preserved star map on the ceiling of a tomb near Nara, Japan, is the earliest-known example of Japanese celestial cartography. The painting dates from approximately AD 700; in addition to a few polar asterisms, it shows the characteristic Chinese 28 lunar lodges. Other surviving Japanese maps of the night sky are much more recent. As a result of the unfortunate loss of a 14th-century star map in an air raid on Japan in 1945, the oldest extensive Japanese charts of the night sky now date from the 16th century. These and later star maps, most of which are on paper, portray the traditional Chinese asterisms, sometimes in considerable detail. Several copies of Jesuit star charts are also preserved in Japan, although the missionary work of the Jesuits—and indeed the introduction of Western knowledge—was long opposed by the Japanese.

COMET TALES

The investigation of early star maps has considerably assisted present-day investigations of comets, those small bodies composed of ices and dust that revolve around the Sun in extremely elongated orbits. (For information on the origin and orbital characteristics of comets, *see* Feature Article: WARMING UP TO THE OUTER SOLAR SYSTEM.) In the histories of China, Korea, and Japan, many hundreds of observations of comets are recorded, and their movements among the Oriental asterisms are often described in detail. Comets are usually called *huixing* ("broom stars") or *boxing* ("bushy stars"), a reference to their diffuse appearance and luminous tails, which set them apart in the sky from the pointlike stars and planets.

Most of the Oriental sightings relate to long-period comets, which after leaving the inner solar system and Earth's vicinity do not return for many hundreds or thousands of years. Halley's Comet is unique in being the only known bright comet that has an extensive history of repeated visitation. Reports of 30 apparitions of this comet—at intervals of 70–80 years—exist from AD 1986 back to 240 BC. Most of these records are to be found in Far Eastern history.

In recent years the technique of numerical integration—the use of computers to systemati-

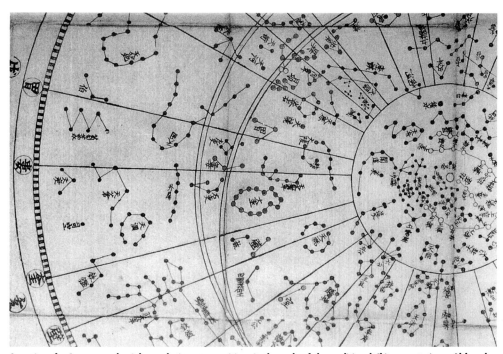

A section of a Japanese celestial map depicts star positions in the style of the traditional Chinese asterisms. Although not precisely dated, the map is thought to be the work of Nakakubo Sekisui in the 18th century. As a result of the loss of a 14th-century map during World War II, the oldest extensive Japanese star charts now date from the 16th century.

cally calculate the gravitational effects of the various planets on an orbiting body's motion—has allowed astronomers to model and study the past orbit of Halley's Comet. The power of this computational method notwithstanding, some of the modern calculations have benefited from corrections provided by early observations. Notable among these observations are the unusually careful Chinese measurements made in AD 837, when the comet made a remarkably close approach to Earth—only about 12 times as far away as the Moon.

At its apparition in 1378, Halley's Comet was carefully observed in both China and Korea and was also noted briefly in Japan. This was the last occasion when Oriental observations of the comet were superior to those made in the West. Following are translations of the Chinese and Korean records of Halley's Comet in 1378. In each case the original source is identified, and the Oriental date is given in its original form (year of reign, lunar month, and day of the 60-day cycle) and converted to the Julian calendar.

China (from *Ming Shilu* ["Annals of the Ming Dynasty"]):

In the 11th year of the Hungwu reign period, 9th month, day *jichou* [Oct. 11, 1378], a guest star swept *Tianbian*, moved southwest and entered *Wei* [lunar lodge]. Before this, on day *jiaxu* [September 26] it was seen to the northwest of *Wuche*. On day *dingchou* [September 29] it entered *Ziwei*. On day *wuyin* [September 30] it emitted rays more than 10° in length; it swept *Neijie*. On day *gengchen* [October 2] it entered *Ziwei* palace and swept the five stars of *Beiji*. On day *renwu* [October 4] it trespassed against [the star] *Shaozai* at the eastern wall [of *Ziwei*]. On day *jiashen* [October

天紀十一月甲申月食乙酉暈戊子亦如之

孛于紫薇西藩犯四輔北極出東藩犯天梧

八月丙午歲星犯房及鉤鈐九月己卯有星

In the text above, from the Korean *Koryo-sa,* the highlighted passage carries an account of the visit of Halley's Comet in 1378. The charts show the computed motion of the comet during September and October 1378 with respect to the asterisms and the star *Shaozai* mentioned in the Chinese and Korean records. The lower chart also shows the zone covered by the lunar lodge *Wei.*

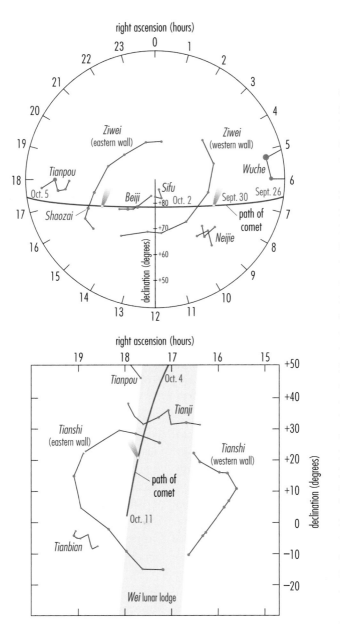

6] it entered the wall of *Tianshi* and on day *dinghai* [October 9] it entered *Tianshi* itself. From now on [*i.e.,* after October 11] until the 10th month, day *jiwei* [November 10], it was cloudy and [the guest star] was not seen [again].

Korea (from *Koryo-sa* ["History of Koryo"]):

In the 4th year of King Sinu, 9th month, day *jimao* [Oct. 1, 1378], there was a bushy star at the western fence of *Ziwei.* It trespassed against *Sifu* at the North

Pole and emerged at the eastern fence [of *Ziwei*]. It trespassed against *Tianpou* and *Tianji.*

In Japan the comet was described as a broom star. It was first sighted on October 1, as in Korea, but there are no reports of its movement among the asterisms.

Both the Chinese and Korean observations allow the motion of the comet to be followed closely. In particular, the roughly elliptical asterism *Ziwei,* mentioned in both Chinese and Korean accounts, acts as a marker for the circumpolar circle. Computation using the carefully dated Chinese observations, especially the close approach of the comet to the star *Shaozai* (*i.e.,* η Draconis), enable the date and approximate time of closest approach of the comet to the Sun—that is, its perihelion—to be deduced. The perihelion date is a standard orbital element for a comet. The result, within five hours of noon (universal time) on November 10, is in very close accord with that derived from numerical integration; the discrepancy is only five hours.

Oriental observations of Halley's Comet for each of the four apparitions between 989 and 1145 have led astronomers to correct the computed date of its perihelion by as much as three days. The most likely explanation for the discrepancy between computation and observation is an unusual degree of evaporation of volatile materials from the nucleus, causing a rocket effect that opposed and slowed its orbital motion.

Investigation of early records of comets is by no means confined to Halley's Comet. In 1994 a team from NASA's Jet Propulsion Laboratory in California showed that Comet Swift-Tuttle, which returns to the inner solar system every 130 years or so, was noted in ancient Chinese records. The researchers made a long-term numerical investigation of the comet's orbit and, by comparing computation with observation, showed that the comet was recorded in China in both 69 BC and AD 188. For more recent centuries the history of this comet is far less complete than that of Halley's Comet, largely because Comet Swift-Tuttle seldom approaches Earth sufficiently close to attract the attention of the unaided eye.

BLASTS FROM THE PAST

Several times during a typical century, a "new star" shines out among the brightest stars in the sky for a few weeks or so and then gradually fades into insignificance. These are celestial explosions and come in two main categories: novas, which shine as brightly as 100,000

Suns, and supernovas, which may be 1,000 times as bright as novas.

Novas occur in old double-star, or binary, systems in which a swollen red giant and a dense white dwarf are orbiting each other in close proximity. Gradual transfer of matter under gravity from the outer layers of the giant star to the white dwarf causes hydrogen-rich material to build up on the surface of the smaller star. The accreted material eventually triggers a thermonuclear explosion, which consumes much of the hydrogen and blows off some of the material into space.

One type of supernova is produced in binary systems by a process similar to that of novas but with much more violent results. The transfer of matter to the surface of the white dwarf may cause this star to reach a certain critical mass, resulting in its total disruption. A second type, the better-known "classic" variety of supernova, signals the end of the active life of a massive star, which has built up a core of heavy elements by nuclear fusion. When the dense core collapses, the action sends a shock wave through the star that throws off the outer layers, which creates an expanding nebula of hot gas and dust and leaves behind a highly con-

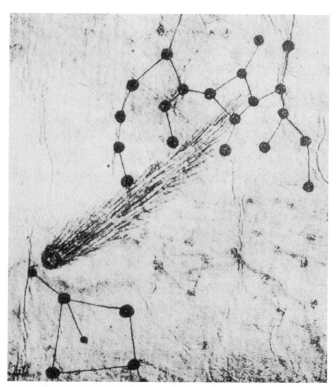

A comet that appeared in 1664 is depicted among the asterisms in this Korean sketch. Another comet mentioned in early East Asian records is Comet Swift-Tuttle, which was shown recently by NASA scientists to have been seen in China in 69 BC and AD 188.

densed neutron star—or perhaps in extreme cases a black hole. Unlike the aftermath of a nova, the remnant left by a supernova is a source of intense electromagnetic radiation in wavelengths ranging from radio waves to X-rays. This radiation can be detected many thousands of years after the original outburst.

To date, more than 200 sources of radio waves in our Milky Way Galaxy have been identified as products of super-

novas. Several of them are known to contain pulsars—neutron stars that emit extremely regular pulses of radio waves. In most cases, however, there is no record of the original explosion. In the past millennium five supernovas have been observed and recorded in our galaxy. These events, which occurred in the years 1006, 1054, 1181, 1572, and 1604, were reported as brilliant stars and were seen for many months if not years. All were discerned by the astronomers of East Asia, but the supernovas of 1006, 1572, and 1604 were also extensively observed in the West. No supernova has been definitely sighted in our galaxy since 1604, although in 1987 a supernova was detected in the Large Magellanic Cloud, a satellite galaxy of the Milky Way. Although never brilliant because of its great distance from the solar system, this explosion was distinctly visible to the unaided eye for several weeks.

Historical records of supernovas have the value of telling astronomers exactly how long the hot gaseous remnant of the explosion has been expanding since the initial outburst. By comparison, studies of remnant nebulas alone provide only very rough age estimates. Precise ages, as revealed by investigation of historical supernovas, provide important information for astronomers who aim to model the supernova mechanism.

The supernova of 1181 offers a good example by which to illustrate this process of investigation. In August of that year, a new star appeared in the vicinity of the constellation Cassiopeia; it remained visible for about six months. The star attracted much interest in both South and North China, which were then two independent empires, and also in Japan, but there is no surviving record from Korea. Because there are no known European or Arabic records, the East Asian reports provide the sole source of information on the initial outburst. From the various Chinese and Japanese descriptions, it is possible to obtain a good fix on the position of the star. Following are translations of four of the key records:

South China (from *Wenxian Toungkao* ["Comprehensive History of Civilization"] by Ma Duanlin; a summary can be found in *Songshu* ["History of the Song Dynasty"]):

In the 8th year [of the Chunxi reign period], 6th month, day *jisi* [Aug. 6, 1181], a guest star appeared in *Kui* lunar lodge. It was trespassing against *Chuanshe*. According to divination, the guest star was a star of ill omen… [astrological commentary]. The guest star appeared at the edge of *Ziwei* among the stars of *Chuanshe*… [further astrological commentary]. On day *jiaxu* [August 11] the guest star guarded the fifth star of *Chuanshe*. In the 9th year, 1st month, day *guiyou* [Feb. 6, 1182], the guest star disappeared. From the previous year, 6th month, day *jisi* until the present was a total of 185 days.

North China (from *Jinshu*):
In the 21st year of the Ta-ting reign period, 6th month, day *jiawu* (Aug. 11, 1181), a guest star was seen at *Huagai* altogether for 156 days; then it was extinguished.

Japan (from *Meigetsuki* ["Diary of the Full Moon"] by Fujiwara Sadaie):

In the first year of the Yowa reign period, 6th month, 25th day [Aug. 7, 1181], a guest star appeared at the north near *Wangliang* and guarding *Chuanshe*.

Japan (from *Azuma Kagami*, a history of the Kamakura shogunate):

In the first year of the Yowa reign period, 6th month, 25th day, at the hour *xu* [7–9 PM], a guest star was seen at the northeast. It was like Saturn and its color was purple; it had rays. There had been no other example since that appearing in the

Star patterns of several of the lunar lodges are illustrated on a Japanese carriage from the 15th century. These 28 asterisms had a special significance in ancient Oriental astrology and often were used to measure the positions of other stars. Like the constellations of the Western zodiac, they are associated with certain regions of the sky.

時虜使久在館至是乃去

不見自去年六月己巳至是凡一百八十五日乃消伏

儀甲戌客星守傳舍第五星　九年正月癸酉客星始

奎宿爲兵姦臣僞惑天子於是金虜遣使來爭執進書

客星出紫微外座傳舍星宜備姦使邊夷侵境又云出

舍以示休咎星大者事大而禍深色白其分有兵喪今

傳舍占客星亦妖星天之使者見於天而無常所入列

八年六月己巳客星出奎宿犯

In each instance the new star is described as *kexing* ("guest star"), the usual Oriental term for a starlike object, although in 1378 the expression was applied to Halley's Comet. Although the Japanese records do not indicate the period of visibility of the star, the two independent records from South and North China affirm a lengthy duration. The *Azuma Kagami* passage seems to imply that the star was about as bright as the planet Saturn—*i.e.,* among the brightest stars in the sky but by no means a really brilliant object—which may account for its lack of mention in Korea. (Although Korean astronomical records around this time are fairly detailed, they all relate to meteors and lunar and planetary movements.) The supernova of 1006, to which the guest star was compared in Japan, was a brilliant object, but it had occurred nearly two centuries earlier, so no direct comparison could be made.

In the record from South China, the phrase "in *Kui* lunar lodge" reveals the approximate range of right ascension within which the star appeared. This is a zone about 15° in width, extending north and south from Andromeda and Pisces. As mentioned above, the asterism *Ziwei* is near the edge of the circumpolar circle, the circle of perpetual visibility. Other star groups near which the guest star appeared are *Chuanshe, Wangliang,* and *Huagai.* These are neighboring asterisms in Cassiopeia and lie in the Milky Way region, the faint, luminous band of stars and dust along the galactic equator that represents the disk of our galaxy seen edge-on from Earth. Comparison between early Oriental star maps and detailed modern charts shows that *Wangliang,* a group of five stars named after a famed charioteer, includes some of the brightest stars of Cassiopeia. Although much fainter, the seven stars of *Hua-gai* ("Gilded Canopy") form a well-defined cluster shaped like a parasol and are fairly readily identified. *Chuanshe* ("Inns," "Guest Houses") is an extended asterism consisting of nine dim stars barely visible to the unaided eye and extending more or less along an east–west direction. It lies roughly midway between *Wangliang* and *Huagai.*

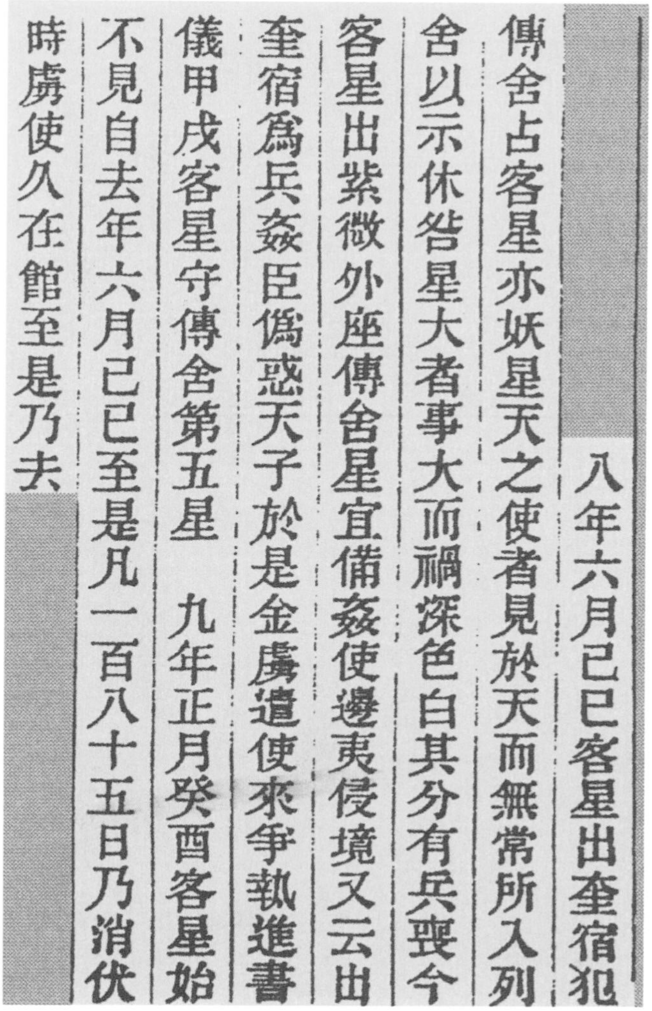

(Below) F. Richard Stephenson

Text (left) from the *Wenxian Toungkao* contains a detailed report of the supernova of 1181 as observed from the Song capital of Linan (now Hangzhou) in the ancient empire of South China. (Below) A simplified armillary, or torquetum, originally made about 1280 in China, is represented in a copy dating from the Ming dynasty. Oriental astronomers employed such instruments for measuring star positions.

A chart locates the positions of the supernova remnants 3C 10 and 3C 58 among the sky features mentioned in the Chinese and Japanese records of the supernova of 1181. Greek letters identify stars in the Western constellation of Cassiopeia. The position of 3C 58 fits the ancient descriptions remarkably well.

(Bottom) Anglo-Australian Observatory/Royal Observatory, Edinburgh

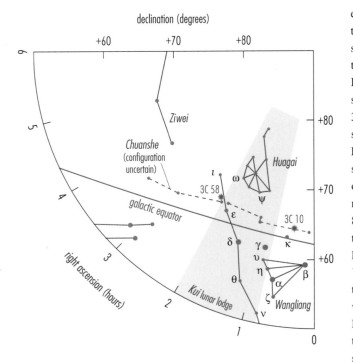

declination (degrees)

+60   +70   +80

Ziwei

Chuanshe
(configuration
uncertain)

Huagai

3C 58

galactic equator

+80

+70

ι   ω
ε   ζ   3C 10
δ   γ   κ
υ
θ   η   β
α
ζ   Wangliang
ν

+60

right ascension (hours)

Kui lunar lodge

6   5   4   3   2   1   0

The record with the most detailed position information is that from South China, which asserts that the guest star "guarded the fifth star of *Chuanshe*." The Japanese account in *Meigetsuki* also notes that the guest star was "guarding" this same asterism; the term implies a stationary position. According to the extensive historical researches of the Beijing astronomer Yi Shitong, the fifth constituent of *Chuanshe* is a faint star quite close to the star ε Cassiopeia.

A long period of visibility and proximity to the galactic equator, where the stars of our galaxy are mainly concentrated, are both characteristic of supernovas. Of the known remnant nebulas of supernovas that today are detectable by radio telescopes and X-ray satellites, only two relatively young ones lie in this part of the sky. One is 3C 10, but it is well established as the remnant of the supernova of 1572 that was seen and accurately located by the Danish astronomer Tycho Brahe and other European observers. The other remnant is 3C 58. Allowing for precession—a cyclic wobbling in the Earth's axis of rotation that shifts observed star positions over time—a star at this remnant's present location would, 800 years ago, have been close to the eastern edge of *Kui* lunar lodge and roughly between *Wangliang* and *Huagai*. Furthermore, it would have been very near to ε Cassiopeia. Hence, the recorded position of the guest star and that of the supernova remnant 3C 58 are in remarkable accord.

The supernova remnant 3C 58 is estimated to be about 10,000 light-years from the solar system, relatively close in galactic terms, and is now

In carrying out observations of Halley's Comet (below) and the supernova remnant 3C 58 (opposite page, in a radio telescope image), modern astronomers are much indebted to their Oriental stargazing predecessors, who left behind a rich treasure of celestial recorded history.

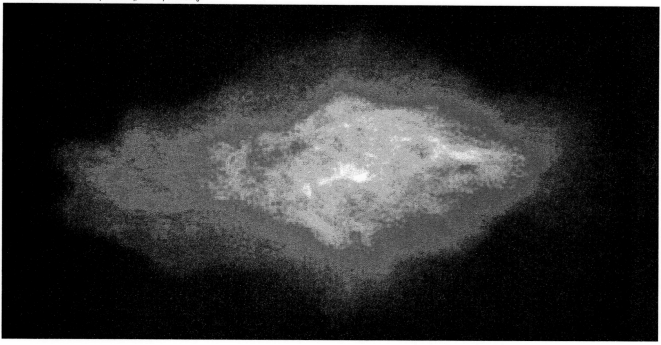

about 30 light-years across. (A light-year is about 9.5 trillion kilometers, or 5.9 trillion miles.) Astrophysicists generally agree that the remnant could well have taken about 1,000 years to reach its present size, so an actual age of about 800 years is considered quite acceptable. There is thus a consensus that the new star of 1181 is a member of the select group of historically recorded supernovas.

A VALUABLE RESOURCE

The study of early records of comets and supernovas is only one aspect of a much wider field known as applied histori-

cal astronomy. Research in this field, which is concerned with the application of all kinds of early observations to problems in present-day science, has expanded considerably in recent years.

An important advantage of applied historical astronomy is that it allows the investigation of long-term trends that cannot be determined from modern observations alone. For example, solar and lunar eclipse observations—some dating as far back as 700 BC—recently have been used to study changes in the Earth's rate of rotation—largely caused by tides—on a time scale of millennia. Naked-eye sunspot sightings, nearly

all reported in Chinese and Korean records, have been systematically analyzed to investigate major changes in solar activity, which may well be associated with long-term climatic variations on Earth.

Future studies of early astronomical records likely have much more to tell us. Present-day scientists have good reason to be grateful to the stargazers of a bygone age.

FOR ADDITIONAL READING

- *Comets: A Chronological History of Observation, Science, Myth, and Folklore,* Donald K. Yeomans (John Wiley & Sons, 1991).

- "Eclipses," "Lunar Mansions in Chinese Astronomy," and "Celestial East Asian Maps," F. Richard Stephenson, *Encyclopaedia of the History of Science, Technology, and Medicine in Non-Western Cultures,* Helaine Selin, ed. (Kluwer Academic, 1997).

- *The History of Cartography: Cartography in the Traditional East and Southeast Asian Societies,* vol. 2, book 2, J.B. Darley and David Woodward, eds. (University of Chicago Press, 1994).

- *Supernovae,* Paul Murdin and Lesley Murdin (Cambridge University Press, 1985).

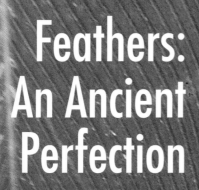

Feathers: An Ancient Perfection

*Feathers achieved an
extraordinary complexity early in
their evolutionary development.
For some 150 million years they
have remained essentially
unchanged and are among the
most varied, beautiful, and
multifunctional of all animal
features.*

by Alan Feduccia

**Feather detail from the wing of a
white-fronted Amazon parrot.**
Bill Beatty

I n 1860 a fossilized feather was discovered in a quarry near Munich, Germany. One year later a fossilized skeleton with feathered wings and tail was unearthed. The finds created an overnight sensation. Scientists determined that they had fallen into a tropical saltwater lagoon some 150 million years ago. It was a shocking revelation, since birds were thought not to have existed during the Jurassic Period.

Alan Feduccia is S.K. Heninger Professor of Biology at the University of North Carolina at Chapel Hill.

Equally astounding was how much the design and proportions of the ancient feather resembled those of its modern counterparts. With the vane on one side of the quill measuring half as wide as the vane on the

other, for example, the asymmetrical fossilized feather was identical to the secondary flight feathers of living birds, which demonstrated that the complexity and perfection of feathers were achieved rapidly in early bird development. Remarkably, feathers have remained virtually unchanged—even in their microscopic structure—throughout more than 150 million years of evolution.

Indeed, feathers are the most complex appendages ever produced by the skin of a back-

Humans have been intrigued by feathers for millennia, celebrating their colors and patterns in ceremonial garb (top) or studying their engineering for clues to the mysteries of flight (left).

boned animal, distinguishing birds from all other classes of vertebrates. Rarely do animals possess a single physical feature that serves such widely different functions. Feathers allow birds to fly across continents and oceans, survive temperatures in places like the Antarctic that are too frigid for any land mammal, and evade predators by blending into their environments. The colors and patterns in their plumage enable individuals to communicate with others of their own species in ways that continue to astound and perplex biologists.

It is small wonder that for millennia humans have closely studied feathers, celebrating their beauty and ingenious de-

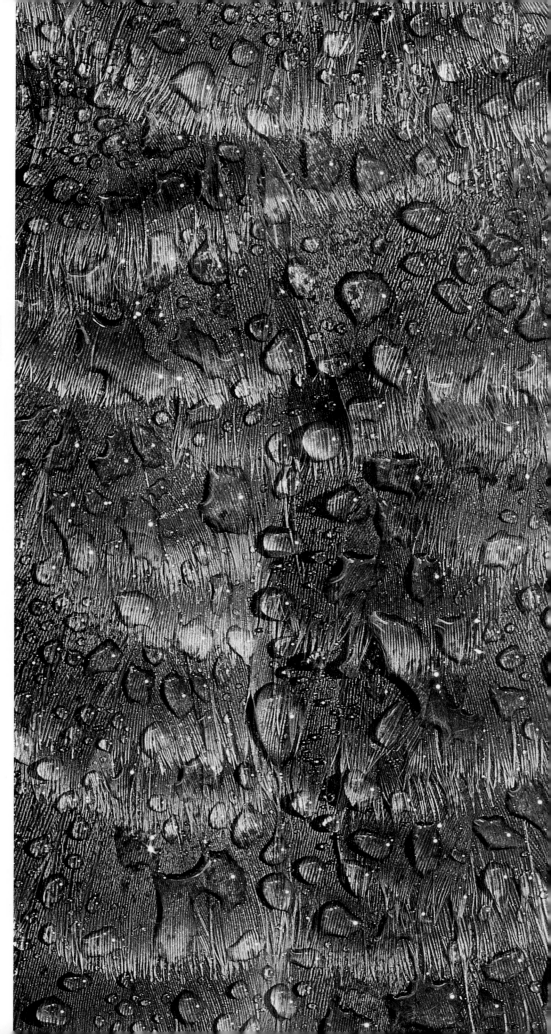

sign in poetry, art, and human adornment while probing their intricate engineering for answers to the mysteries of flight.

FORM FOLLOWS FUNCTION

"Airy and flexible, yet nearly indestructible," says writer Doug Stewart in a 1997 *National Wildlife* article, feathers "are masterpieces of engineering." In order to understand the complex nature of this unique animal feature, it is first necessary to take a look at the details of feather structure.

Strong, lightweight, and waterproof, feathers primarily serve two functions: flight and insulation. Animals with backbones and two pairs of limbs, or tetrapods, regulate their body temperature via two distinct pathways. Because they obtain their body heat from the ambient environment, amphibians and reptiles, known as cold-blooded vertebrates, or ectotherms, tend to be sluggish until the sun warms their bodies. Birds and mammals, on the other hand, are warm-blooded, or endothermic; most of their

S. Nielson—Bruce Coleman Inc.

Feathers perform an astounding variety of functions, including weather protection. Here the well-conditioned feathers of a Canadian goose easily shed the rain droplets that collect on their surface.

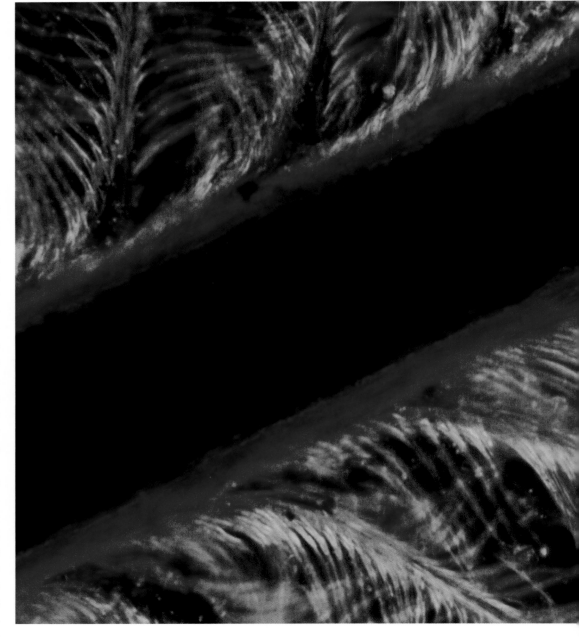

body heat is produced from within. Because they tend to be very active and maintain high metabolic rates around the clock, they rely on a much greater intake of food to fuel their metabolic machinery. To conserve body heat, endothermic tetrapods have an insulatory coat. In mammals the insulatory coat—hair—is a rather simple derivative of the skin. Birds, on the other hand, have a much more complex system for preventing heat loss. They possess several different kinds of feathers.

The most visible feathers are the stiff-vaned contour feathers, which include the larger ones on the wings and the tail that are used for flight and the body feathers that cover the animal and help it to conserve and release heat. Although the design of flight and body feathers differs in some details, both share several basic characteristics. All feathers, for example, are composed of an inert protein known as keratin, the same tough, pliable, and lightweight substance that constitutes claws, nails, and hair in mammals and scales in reptiles.

The structural backbone of stiff-vaned feathers consists of a central shaft, or rachis. Branching from both sides of the shaft are filaments called barbs. The barbs form the body of the broad, flat vanes on ei-

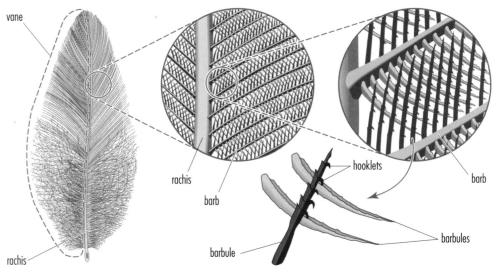

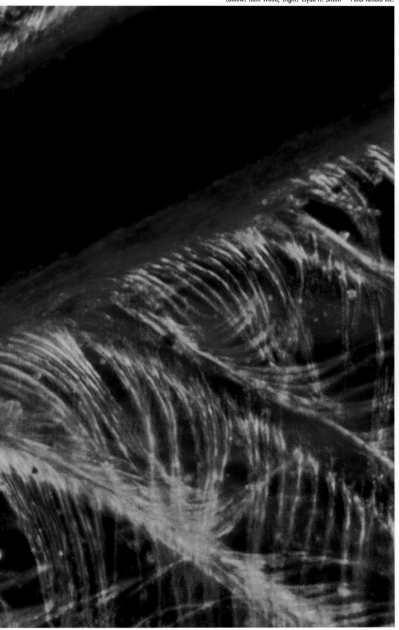

A photomicrograph (left) reveals the interlocking structure found in contour feathers, which include flight feathers (bottom) and body feathers (opposite page, bottom). Small hooklets located on the feather's barbules create the structural stability in the feather vane that makes flight possible. The feathers of flightless birds, such as the brown kiwi (below), lack these hooklets. As a result, their feathers have a loose, almost hairy appearance.

ther side of the rachis. The barbs, in turn, produce their own tiny branching filaments known as barbules. In flight and body feathers, these barbules bear small hooklets that grab on to the shafts of nearby barbules, almost like the hook-and-loop mechanism of Velcro. This system creates a tight interlocking but flexible structure that can resist even a strong airstream.

This detail is critical to a flying animal. Simplified, hair-like feathers known as filoplumes, which are scattered around the bases of flight and body feathers and are connected to sensory receptors in the skin, alert the bird when its feathers are disturbed. Using

its beak to rearrange the ruffled feather, the bird is able to "comb" the barbules back into place. The hooklets help the vanes to quickly regain and hold their original shape. In the feathers of flightless birds, on the other hand, which have lost this complex adaptation over evolutionary time, the hooklets are undeveloped or missing. As a result, the feathers of flightless birds, such as the brown kiwi, have a loose, almost hairy appearance.

A bird's wings are fashioned out of flight feathers. The outer set of flight feathers, the primaries, vary in number among bird groups but typically include 10 feathers per wing. In flying birds these feathers are asymmetrical, the narrower vane serving as the leading edge to reduce air resistance and increase maneuverability during flight.

Birds also use their primary feathers to generate forward thrust. During the downstroke of a bird's wings, the tips are kept at right angles to the rest of the wings' surface, propelling the body forward. The long shafts of the primaries, which attach to the bones of the hand, can be neatly folded against the body when the bird is at rest. The inner flight feathers of the wing, known as

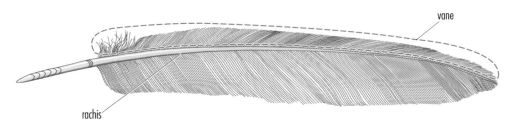

vane

rachis

secondaries, attach to the ulna (the equivalent in birds of the human forearm) and are used to provide lift in flight.

Birds also have long tail feathers, called rectrices, that resemble the flight feathers of the wings. Avian tail feathers are attached to a plowshare-shaped bone of fused vertebrae known as the pygostyle. In flying birds the tail is particularly important, since it produces additional wing surface for lift and steering. When the tail feathers are spread and depressed at low speeds, particularly during takeoffs and landings, they provide increased lift as well as a mechanism for braking. Tail feathers also provide birds with additional control during low-speed flights.

Like the flight feathers, the body feathers also are stiffly vaned. These feathers, however, can be distinguished from flight feathers by their symmetry. Unlike flight feathers, they serve both aerodynamic and insulatory functions. The barbules at the base of the feather, the part closest to the bird's body, for example, lack hooklets, which results in loose fil-

aments that can be fluffed up to trap warm air. In warm weather the body feathers can be flattened against the body to

allow heat to escape. The sleeker and stiffer-vaned portion of the body feathers covers this downy base in an overlapping pattern much like scales, streamlining the bird's body and increasing its aerodynamic performance.

Not all feathers, however, have stiff vanes. The plush down feathers that cover newly hatched birds until they have attained their adult feathers, for example, do not have a stiffened central shaft. Instead, their long, loosely entangled barbules form a soft, insulating layer next to the skin. Many birds

also have body feathers that produce a downylike secondary feather, known as an aftershaft, that grows from the base of the main feather. In many birds that live in high northern latitudes, such as the grouse, aftershaft feathers provide an insulatory coat. Other birds such as sea ducks have developed an impervious barrier to severe cold with an underlayer of dense down feathers up to 1.25 centimeters (one-half inch) thick. So effective are the insulatory properties of down that for centuries humans have used the down feathers of ducks and swans to line clothing and blankets. Despite the availability of today's synthetic

Photographs, Tom Vezo

Contour feathers, which include flight and body feathers, keep birds warm and enable them to fly. (Clockwise from top) The body feathers found on the head of this northern flicker streamline the bird's exterior in an overlapping pattern much like scales, improving its aerodynamic performance. The asymmetrical vanes of the flight feathers help to reduce air resistance and increase maneuverability. For insulation against the cold, body feathers, like these breast feathers, can be fluffed up to trap air next to the skin.

Not all feathers have the familiar shaft-and-vane structure. The down feathers that cover chicks, such as this day-old screech owl (below), lack a stiffened central shaft. The downy woodpecker (right) possesses hairlike feathers known as bristles around its nostrils.

products for insulation, there still is no substitute for a coat of goose down.

Some feathers bear little resemblance to the more familiar shaft-and-vane structure. Rictal bristles are hairlike feathers found around the mouth of such aerial insect eaters as whippoorwills or chuck-will's-widows. Composed of little more than a tapered rachis with a few wispy barbs, these tactile filaments aid in capturing flying insects. Bristles also provide birds with a measure of protection. Some birds, for example, have small bristles located on their eyelids. Bristles located around the nostrils of woodpeckers may help keep out tiny wood chips. Since bristles, like filoplumes, are attached to special sensors in the skin, some researchers suspect that they also may help to collect sensory information simi-

lar to the way whiskers function on a cat.

Another unusual feather produces powder down. Serving as a kind of talcum powder for use in feather grooming, this substance is formed when the barbs of mature powder down feathers disintegrate into a fine dust. In the course of preening, birds distribute the powder to their feathers, which helps to condition and waterproof them. Powder down feathers are most abundant in birds that lack preening glands, the powder down serving as a substitute for the oils that are otherwise provided by the gland.

LIGHT AS A FEATHER?

Feathers in the plumage of most birds number in the thousands. Feather counts by the American ornithologist Alexander Wetmore showed that songbirds typically have 2,000 to 4,000 body feathers, but large birds such as swans can have up to 25,000 feathers. The tiny ruby-throated hummingbird had a count of 940 feathers. As a rule, large birds tend to have more feathers than small birds, and seabirds, such as ducks and penguins, have more feathers than land birds, primarily ow-

(Above) Bill Beatty; (right) Tom Vezo

(continued on page 81)

Contested Origins: The Evolution of Birds and Feathers

About 150 million years ago, when tropical palmlike vegetation covered the land and dinosaurs dominated the Earth, an animal that looked like a cross between a reptile and a bird sank to the bottom of an ancient saltwater lagoon in present-day Bavaria. Preserved in the lagoon's oxygen-starved silts, the animal's remains slowly fossilized as the enveloping muck became compacted into fine-grained limestone. In 1861 the bird once again saw the light of day when its fossilized skeleton was unearthed from what had become a limestone quarry. The German naturalist Hermann von Meyer called it *Archaeopteryx lithographica* (*archaios,* "ancient"; *pteryx,* "wing"; and *lithographica,* for the lithographic stone in which the fossil was found).

The discovery of *Archaeopteryx,* which came just two years after the publication of Charles Darwin's *On the Origin of Species,* created quite a stir in the learned halls of Europe. Supporters of the fledgling theory of evolution claimed that the find provided proof that new organisms could evolve from older life forms; in this case *Archaeopteryx* was seen as the intermediary between reptiles and birds. In fact, the fossil, along with the six other *Archaeopteryx* speci-mens that were subsequently discovered in the region, are considered by some to be a veritable Rosetta Stone of bird evolution.

Archaeopteryx exhibited many features common to reptiles of the time, including a jaw lined with sharp reptilian teeth, a long, lizardlike tail, and a hand with three fingers ending in sharp claws. By modern standards, however, *Archaeopteryx* was clearly a bird. The primary evidence was the presence of feathers that resembled those of modern birds, even in their microscopic detail. The vanes of the primary flight feathers also were strikingly asymmetrical, a telltale indication of their aerodynamic function. Even the wings were shaped like the fairly typical elliptical wings of a modern woodland bird. Additional evidence suggested that the body was covered by contour feathers.

The discovery of the first *Archaeopteryx* launched the era of inquiry into the origin of birds, fueling debates that remain unresolved to this day. Paleontologists agree that birds are derived from reptiles, specifically from a group known as archosaurs ("ruling reptiles"). This class includes the ancestral stock of all other ar-chosaurs, which is the group called thecodonts ("socket-toothed reptiles"), and all their derivatives: dinosaurs, pterosaurs (flying reptiles), and the still-existing order of crocodiles and alligators. Pinpointing the group of archosaurs that gave rise to birds, however, is a matter of scientific disagreement. According to one contingent of paleontologists, birds are the direct descendants of small theropod dinosaurs, which were agile, upright, bipedal animals. (The British biologist Thomas Huxley was the first to suggest, in the 1860s, that birds descended from dinosaurs, purportedly having reached his conclusion while eating a chicken and noting that the leg bone resembled a dinosaur's.) Others argue that birds and dinosaurs shared a common reptilian ancestor—a small tree-dwelling quadruped from the group of thecodonts—and that they evolved independently of one another.

Clouding the issue is a dearth of evidence in the fossil record. Judging from the complex structure of its feathers, *Archaeopteryx* was the product of a long avian history. Unfortunately, no fossil evidence of earlier birds exists to help scientists reconstruct this evolutionary history. Most scientists, however, believe that evidence for the bird-reptile link can be

American Museum of Natural History, New York; (opposite) AP/Wide World

found in the developmental biology of the two classes of animals. One way to determine whether animals share a common ancestry is to compare details of their embryonic development. Bird feathers have an embryonic development similar to that of reptilian scales and, like them, are composed of the substance keratin. It may be, however, that feathers were not necessarily derived from simple reptilian scales. The fossil record contains a number of early reptiles with highly modified scales, the most spectacular being the 220 million-year-old late-Triassic thecodont *Longisquama insignis* from Kazakstan.

Russian zoologist A.G. Sharov, discoverer of this thumb-sized reptile, identified *Longisquama* as a member of a thecodont group of reptiles known as the pseudosuchians ("false crocodiles," considered by some adherents of the tree-dwelling-ancestor theory to have been the precursors of both dinosaurs and birds). Sharov noted the "presence of

long, featherlike appendages along the dorsum" and observed that the "structure of the dorsal [back] appendages shows that they functioned as a kind of parachute, breaking the animal's fall as it jumped from branch to branch, or from the trees to the ground." Whether these structures played a role in the development of feathers cannot be ascertained, but some scientists believe that these appendages have all the features of a protofeather. The structures are elongated with central thickenings similar to feather shafts. They also include a series of transverse thickenings regularly arranged along this central shaft resembling feather vanes.

The lack of decisive evidence has not hindered speculation among scientists about the origin of feathers and, by extension, the evolution of birds. Most theories fall into two categories: that feathers initially evolved either for thermoregulation or for flight. Many reptile experts argue that the featherlike fraying of reptile scales increased their effectiveness as shields protecting against excessive heat during the day and providing insulation against nighttime drops in temperature. Only later, argue proponents of thermoregulation, did feathers evolve for use in flight. One idea that gained considerable popularity during the early 1970s and continues

to be argued today is that dinosaurs were warm-blooded, or endothermic, and acquired feathers for insulation. These feathered dinosaurs purportedly gave rise to birds.

Speculation about the existence of feathered dinosaurs was rekindled after scientists recently discovered fossils of several small dinosaurs in China that have a series of filaments extending from the nape of the neck to the tip of the tail and around the bottom of the tail. The investigators initially described them as feathered dinosaurs, but subsequent study has shown that these structures most likely served as internal supports for a reptilian frill (an elevated

Argentine paleontologist Fernando Novas points out the birdlike limbs on the fossilized bones of a small dinosaur that he and fellow researchers uncovered in Patagonia in January 1996. Some scientists argue that the fossil represents an intermediate stage of development between dinosaurs and *Archaeopteryx*.

ridge along the back). Analysis of recent discoveries of fossilized theropod skins in both South America and Spain also has shown no signs of feathers; instead, research concluded that these animals possessed typical reptilian scales.

Critics of the theory that birds evolved from dinosaurs—feathered or otherwise—have raised other issues as well. They argue that dinosaurs were not warm-blooded, pointing out their commonalities with living cold-blooded animals such as alligators. Among their shared characteristics are growth rings in their bones and teeth that result from certain types of seasonal growth. They also point out that dinosaurs had highly specialized inward curving, serrated teeth, whereas the teeth of early birds were simple peg-like structures, constricted at the base and devoid of serrations. Theropod dinosaurs also had a major joint in the lower jaw for holding prey, a feature missing in the early birds.

Adding to the considerable controversy are the results of new embryological studies of modern birds and reptiles, reported by me and biologist Ann Burke at the University of North Carolina at Chapel Hill, which cast doubt on the bird-dinosaur theory. The hands of theropod dinosaurs possessed

three digits, like those of early birds, but the sequence of fingers was different. The dinosaur's grasping, raking hand consisted of the human equivalent of a thumb, forefinger, and middle finger—a sequence of 1-2-3. The digit sequence on the hands of birds is 2-3-4, the equivalent of a forefinger, middle finger, and ring finger.

The theory that birds evolved from dinosaurs also poses a temporal paradox. Dromaeosaurs, the Cretaceous-era theropods thought to have possibly given rise to birds, became increasingly birdlike toward the end of the Cretaceous. The most birdlike forms of these dinosaurs emerged some 80 million years after the appearance of the first-known bird, the *Archaeopteryx*.

Finally, opponents of the dinosaur-bird theory point to what they consider physical impossibilities in the evolution of flight. Scientists who support the theory that dinosaurs gave rise to birds say that as dinosaurs began to run faster

and jump higher in pursuit of insects, they evolved longer forelimbs for greater control and heightened leaping ability. Opponents of this ground-up, or cursorial, theory of flight, however, maintain that theropod dinosaurs—bipedal, earthbound creatures the size of modern turkeys—possessed the worst possible body plan for the evolution of bird flight. They were very bottom-heavy (their balancing tails were huge in proportion to the rest of their bodies), and their foreshortened forelimbs typically measured half the length of the hind limbs. Furthermore, because feathers produce air resistance, they would have hindered the animals from catching their prey.

A second theory on the origin of flight is based on a trees-down, or arboreal, model. This theory assumes that birds were derived from small tree-dwelling reptiles that preceded dinosaurs. Jumping from branch to branch, these small creatures would have benefited from

structures such as protofeathers (evolved from scales along the back of the arm) that would have created drag to help break a fall. Therefore, incremental elongations of these advantageous structures would have developed through natural selection. Further evolutionary changes would have led to gliding—and ultimately flying. This improved means of locomotion would have resulted in energy savings and increased foraging efficiency over the practice of ascending and descending from trees. Contour feathers would have developed over the entire body as an insulatory covering as these creatures became warm-blooded.

Proponents of the arboreal theory maintain that birds were not the only animals to have evolved aerial characteristics for more efficient locomotion. Other vertebrates have developed some measure of flight, including frogs that parachute by using their foot pads, snakes that parachute with expanded rib cages, and lizards that glide on the winglike surface of their ribs. Many mammals, including bats and flying squirrels, also have developed some degree of flight. All of these "flying" vertebrates, say arboreal-theory proponents, have one thing in common: they, like birds, developed flight from the trees down.

(Below) Frans Lanting—Minden Pictures; (bottom) Art Wolf—Allstock/PNI

Feathers grow in clusters known as pterylae, seen below in the developing feather shafts of a pigeon chick. Feathers spread out from these source points to cover the body. Some scientists theorize that this economical plumage pattern may reduce a bird's weight, since, on average, its feathers are two to three times as heavy as its bones. The feathers on a bald eagle (bottom), for example, make up about 17% of the bird's body weight.

(continued from page 77) ing to their need for greater insulation.

Unlike mammalian hair, however, which evenly covers the entire body, feathers grow in distinctive clusters and spread out from these source points to cover the bird's body. These concentrations of feather attachments are called feather tracts, or pterylae. The tracts are attached to a complicated system of tiny muscles that are capable of elevating and depressing feathers for the purposes of insulation or display. Between the pterylae are areas of bare skin called apteria.

The reasons for this clustered plumage pattern remain a matter of debate. Some scientists hypothesize that this economical arrangement offers flight advantages by reducing a bird's weight. On average, a bird's plumage is two to three times as heavy as its bones. Wetmore found that a white wyandotte chicken's 9,115 feathers, for example, accounted for 6.05% of its body weight. A bald eagle's feather coat constituted about 17% of the bird's body weight, whereas its skeleton surprisingly made up only 7%. Economizing on the number of feathers also lessens a bird's investment in molting, an energy-intensive process of shedding and replacing feathers that most birds undergo at least once annually.

FEATHERY ADAPTATIONS

In some birds both flight and body feathers have been adapted to serve functions other than simply flight and insulation. In the courtship display of the male African standard-wing nightjar, for

The male club-winged manakin uses the clublike shafts of its secondary feathers to produce a loud snapping sound during courtship.

example, the rachises of the bird's second primary wing feathers become hyperextended such that the vanes trail from the wings as if connected to them by a string. In the male American woodcock, the three outer primaries of the wing become narrowed and stiffened, which enables the bird to produce a soft, insectlike twittering when it rapidly flaps its wings during its spectacular courtship flights. Also making use of feathers to produce sounds is the male Amazonian club-winged manakin. The bird uses the clublike shafts of its secondaries to produce a loud snapping noise when the wings

The male sandgrouse provides water for its young by soaking its belly feathers at watering holes located great distances from the nest. The chicks strip the water from the male's wet feathers with their bills.

(Below) Jeff Foott—Bruce Coleman Inc.;
(opposite page, top) J. Dunning—VIREO; (opposite page, bottom) Jen and Des Bartlett—Bruce Coleman Inc.

Resting birds such as this brown pelican preen their feathers as often as once each hour, obtaining replenishing secretions from the uropygial gland, located at the base of the bird's tail.

ture is seen in the sandgrouse, which occupies the dry deserts of Africa and Asia. Pigeonlike birds thought to be closely related to shorebirds, the sandgrouse make long-distance treks to the nearest water hole to drink. Here they also obtain water for their young, which may occupy nests 30 kilometers (20 miles) away. Male sandgrouse have evolved flattened and coiled barbules on the inner surfaces of their belly feathers that allow them to hold water in flight. The males soak their belly feathers and return to the nest, where the young birds drink water by squeezing the wet feathers in their bills.

FEATHER MAINTENANCE AND REPLACEMENT

Since their very survival depends on a coat of healthy feathers, it is not surprising that birds expend significant effort in keeping their plumage in top condition. Because feathers, like human hair, are inert, birds must continually groom and condition them—as often as once each hour for resting birds. The birds rub their heads

and bills against the opening of a specialized gland, the uropygial gland, located at the base of the tail, to obtain replenishing secretions. As they preen, the birds distribute the oil—a combination of waxes, fatty acids, fats, and water—to their feathers, helping to waterproof them as well as maintain their insulatory properties. (Not surprisingly, preening glands are most developed in aquatic bird species.) This lubricating oil also works to extend the life of feathers by keeping them from drying and prematurely fraying. In some birds preening oil also can protect feathers against keratin-eating fungi and bacteria. Other species have evolved preening oils with noxious odors, a development that ornithologists suspect may help to keep mammalian predators at bay.

Once they are damaged or worn out, however, feathers cannot be repaired. Instead, birds must wait for periodic molts. Adults normally shed and regrow their plumage each summer. Birds that live in harsh environments such as deserts with abrasive wind and sand, for example, molt more frequently, as do birds that migrate long distances or live in brushy habitats, where feathers can catch and tear.

In most birds the feather tracts follow a sequential molt

are clapped together. In some birds the secondary flight feathers become not only highly modified in structure but also brightly colored for species recognition or courtship display, as in the golden, flaglike secondary feather that figures prominently in courtship rituals of the mandarin duck.

Birds have developed feather adaptations that also serve more ordinary functions. In the

flightless cassowary the bird's primary feathers have lost their vanes and evolved into strong, spikelike structures that protect its sides as it moves through the forest. Interestingly, these structures—modified flight feathers—reveal that the cassowary, like all flightless birds, is a descendant of flying ancestors long since extinct.

One of the most unusual modifications of feather struc-

pattern to ensure that important functions are not significantly interrupted. Woodpeckers that rely on long tail feathers to help hoist and steady themselves as they climb trees, for example, will wait to shed their inner tail feathers until their outer tail feathers have molted and regrown.

Some aquatic birds, however, lose all their flight feathers at the same time, remaining earthbound for up to a month until the feathers have been replaced. Often they will take refuge on isolated lakes to es-

cape the dangers of terrestrial predators.

FEATHERS AND COLOR

Although humans have long been intrigued by the structural complexity of feathers, the beauty of their varied colors and designs has been their primary appeal. In addition to songs, birds communicate with each other by means of visual displays, using the hues and patterns of their plumage for recognition of species and individuals, attraction and court-

ship, territorial maintenance and defense, and flocking behavior. Perhaps the most spectacular example is the plumage of the male common peafowl, or peacock, which struts a great fan of brilliantly colored tail feathers to attract the attention of females.

Certain birds also use their feathered coats to avoid predators. Some exhibit bold colored patterns to break up the contrast between their silhouettes and the background environment. Others cleverly employ cryptic coloration to blend in

Male peafowl, or peacocks, use their spectacular spray of tail feathers to capture the attention of female birds.

with the environment. Forest birds, such as whippoorwills and woodcocks, for example, sport plumage that blends so perfectly with dead leaves that they become almost invisible on the forest floor. Other birds are even more finely tuned to the seasonal changes in their environment. The plumage of the ptarmigan, a species of northern grouse, for example, is nearly pure white in the win-

(Below left) Wayne Lankinen—Bruce Coleman Inc.; (below right)
Mickey Gibson—Animals Animals; (bottom) Bob and Clara Calhoun—Bruce Coleman Inc.; (opposite page) Bill Beatty

Feather color is determined by the wavelengths of light that are absorbed or reflected by a feather's pigmentation. Ravens appear black because light is absorbed by their feather pigments.

The plumage of the rock ptarmigan undergoes seasonal variations. In winter the feathers become white to blend in with the bird's ice-bound environment. As the snows begin to melt in spring, the bird's mottled coloration matches its snow-patched alpine habitat.

ter when snow covers the mountains. In the spring, however, the bird's feathers molt into a mottled white-and-brown pattern to match the snow-patched alpine meadows in which they live. (Interestingly, in the spring the male ptarmigan keeps his winter coat longer than the female, a mechanism that biologists say diverts attention from the well-camouflaged female incubating eggs in her nest.) In the summer the ptarmigan's plumage makes yet another seasonal adjustment, changing to fine bars of black and brown hues that blend seamlessly with the summer meadows and lichen-covered rocks.

Feather colors, like the hues of butterfly and moth wings, are produced by two distinct chemical and physical mechanisms—pigmentation and feather structure. The more common is the deposition of biochrome pigments (pigments produced by the body) in the microstructure of the feather or skin. A bird's color is determined by the wavelengths of light that are absorbed or re-flected by the feather's pigments. Ravens, for example, appear black to the human eye because the light is absorbed by their feather pigments. On the other hand, the winter coat of the ptarmigan appears white because the light is reflected. There are three major varieties of biochrome pigments. The most common are the melanins, which produce browns, grays, and blacks. Pigments known as carotenoids are responsible for bright yellows, oranges, reds and some blues and greens. The porphyrins produce certain browns and greens.

Many of the brightest, most complex colors, however, including the spectacular iridescent collars of hummingbirds, are structural in origin, the re-sult of the physical alteration of incident light on the feather itself. The brilliant blue of the blue jay, for example, results from melanin particles on the feather barbs that scatter (reflect in every direction) only the shorter wavelengths, which appear blue, whereas the longer wavelengths are absorbed. One way, therefore, to distinguish structural from biochromatic colors is to place a feather under a microscope with a light source under the feather. Only biochromatic feathers will appear colored.

Iridescent colors are created when the melanin particles in the shape of flat "platelets" are stacked in layers on the barbules (up to 15 layers in the most shimmering hummingbirds). The lively play of colors depends on the angle of illumination on these complex layers and the wavelengths of light that are either disrupted or reflected by their structure.

SOUNDING THE CALL FOR CONSERVATION

Ironically, the beauty of feathers historically has contributed

Many of the brightest and most complex feather colors, including those of the mountain bluebird (detail opposite page) and iridescent hummingbirds such as this purple-throated mountain-gem (below), are caused by minute structures that scatter light in myriad ways.

(Below) Michael Fogden—Animals Animals; (opposite page) Bill Beatty

to the decline of the birds that produced them. While strolling through the streets of Manhattan in 1886, for example, Frank Chapman, ornithologist for New York City's American Museum of Natural History, counted no fewer than 40 different native bird species. He found them not in the branches of trees but fixed—sometimes whole or only in the form of a few select feathers—to the exterior of women's hats. Some species in particular caught the attention of the millinery trade.

Highly prized, for example, were the showy breeding plumes of great and snowy egrets. So coveted were these ornamental feathers in the early 20th century that at one point they sold for $80 per ounce, five times their weight in gold. The result—the slaughter of millions of birds—pushed egrets to the brink of extinction.

Fortunately, concerned citizens put an end to this carnage by forming conservation organizations to publicize the bird's

cause. To this day the Audubon Society uses the egret as its emblem. Elegant but fragile, it serves as a reminder of both the human passion for feathers and the care that must be exercised on behalf of their preservation.

FOR ADDITIONAL READING

- *Bird Flight: An Illustrated Study of Birds' Aerial Mastery,* Robert Burton (Facts on File, 1990).
- "A Bird Is Not a Plane," Doug Stewart, *National Wildlife* (February–March 1996, pp. 32–40).
- "Finding Beautiful Facts in Feathers," Cynthia Berger, *National Wildlife* (August–September 1997, pp. 14–23).
- *Manual of Ornithology: Avian Structure and Function,* Noble S. Proctor and Patrick J. Lynch (Yale University Press, 1993).
- *The Origin and Evolution of Birds,* Alan Feduccia (Yale University Press, 1996).
- *Ornithology,* Frank B. Gill (W.H. Freeman and Co., 1995).
- *Taking Wing: Archaeopteryx and the Evolution of Bird Flight,* Pat Shipman (Simon & Schuster, 1998).

"I just want to say one word to you. Just one word.

Yes, sir.

Are you listening?

Yes, sir, I am.

Plastics."

—The Graduate

Embassy Pictures/ Kobal Collection

If you have in the end a couple hundred serious uses for plastics you are an observant man. Among those uses you may list your fountain pen, your false-teeth plate, light switches, lamp shades, shoe heels, and spectacle frames.... Plastics are not even potentially a universal material, and a Plastic Age, in the sense that we have had a Steel Age, is more or less a myth. Given a little time, however, the semblance of it may come about.

—*Fortune* magazine,
March 1936

Celluloid Dreams

Chemists first began to experiment with making plastics in the mid-19th century. Today these synthetic materials have so thoroughly penetrated every arena of human activity that it is difficult to imagine the world without them.

by John Kenly Smith, Jr.

Throughout history, humans have used materials as a symbolic means for critically assessing the times in which they lived. Mired in what they considered to be a decadent Iron Age, for example, the ancient Greek historians harkened to the idealized harmony of mythical Golden and Silver ages. The Victorians, on the other hand, proudly declared their own era as a heroic Iron Age and trumpeted the superiority of their achievements over those of earlier Stone and Bronze ages.

Perhaps reflecting the speed of technological innovation, 20th-century civilization has acquired a whole series of labels that attempt to characterize its cultural achievements and engineering prowess, including the steel age, the

John Kenly Smith, Jr., is Associate Professor of History at Lehigh University, Bethlehem, Pennsylvania.

machine age, the atomic age, and the information age. Arguably, the most emblematic material of modern times, however, has been plastics.

Plastics have been used to praise the progressiveness of the modern era and to condemn its decadence. On the one hand, plastics have been viewed as shoddy, cheap, and polluting; at the same time, they have been regarded as elegant, modern, and high tech. Plastics serve a range of purposes from the sublime to the mundane. They are used in products that save and enhance human lives (bulletproof vests, heart catheters, and artificial limbs), in objects of entertainment (Silly Putty, CDs, and in-line skates), and in the most ordinary of functional items (toilet seats, nonstick skillets, and outdoor clothing). They have made space exploration possible, and by lessening the weight of automobiles, they have made terrestrial travel more fuel-efficient. Products made of plastic materials have saved lives; according to critics, by contaminating the environment they have endangered countless others.

Despite the ambivalence about their contradictory nature, over the past century plastics have become incorporated into countless products and virtually every technology. This versatility results from their chemical makeup. Plastics are human-made polymers (from the Greek, meaning "having many parts"). Their structures—large chainlike molecules that are composed of repeating chemical units—lend themselves to tremendous variation. Today's design engineers can choose from a mind-boggling array of materials that encompass an incredible range of properties. As the history of plastics demonstrates, plastics have redefined everyday life—and shaped its possibilities.

PLASTICS FROM NATURE

On Jan. 23, 1914, leaders of the American chemical industry gathered in New York City for a gala dinner to honor the father of modern plastics, John Wesley Hyatt. In his address the 77-year-old Hyatt recounted the events that led to the patenting of celluloid in 1870. Hyatt recalled that in his youth the game of billiards became wildly popular in the U.S. There was only one problem—the overharvesting of elephants in northern Ceylon (now Sri Lanka) threatened the supply of the finest source of billiard-ball ivory. So desperate was the situation that the largest U.S. supplier of billiard products, Phelan & Collender, posted ads in newspapers offering a $10,000 reward to the person who could invent an alternative material to ivory. This strategy—to replace exotic materials with cheaper, more available substitutes—was not new. Craftspeople commonly gilded ordinary materials to simulate solid gold and used precious wood veneers over common woods to make furniture appear more valuable. The 19th century witnessed the proliferation of silver plate, a layer of silver bonded to more common metals such as copper.

Hoping to find a substitute for ivory, Hyatt discovered that mixing camphor and nitrocellulose with an alcohol solvent produced a moldable and durable plastic. In his experiment Hyatt drew on research conducted by chemists earlier in the century. Although natural polymers—wood, cotton, wool, silk, rubber, and amber, for example—had been an important part of human material culture for thousands of years, their chemical structures remained a mystery until chemists began to study them after 1800. At first they simply treated materials with acids and bases to see what would happen. In 1846 the German chemist Christian Friedrich Schönbein discovered that a mixture of nitric and sulfuric acids reacted with the cellulose in cotton fibers to produce a new substance, nitrocellulose. When dissolved in various organic solvents, nitrocellulose could be molded into shapes, which made it the object of considerable experimentation by chemists and inventors in the 1850s and '60s.

Unfortunately for Hyatt, the camphor-nitrocellulose plastic he called celluloid (meaning "cellulose-like") did not make good billiard balls. Hyatt realized, however, that if his plastic could be made to resemble ivory, it also could mimic other, less-attractive materials such as wood and horn, which

The Du Pont Co. was one of the earliest pioneers in the development of new plastic materials and products. One of the company's inventions in the 1920s was a durable automobile finish, known as Duco (right), that allowed cars to be painted in colors other than black. Around the same time, the company launched a packaging revolution with its invention of cellophane, celebrated here in a 1930s ad (below right).

"Looks like new, doesn't it?"

Of course, it looks like new. It has been refinished in Duco

were used in toilet articles and a variety of novelty items. Hyatt also turned his attention to another pressing need—a replacement for wood or hard rubber in denture plates—but without success. Not only did the celluloid have the dismaying tendency to warp when warm, but it also left a lingering camphor taste in the mouths of wearers. Nonetheless, by the 1890s celluloid had found a unique application. Its flexibility and transparency made it a suitable material for photographic film, especially motion picture film, an application that was so successful that the word *celluloid* became a synonym for *cinema*.

The success of celluloid in replacing exotic materials encouraged chemists to seek a synthetic substitute for silk, a material whose popularity began growing in the late 19th century and skyrocketed in the early decades of the 20th century. Most of the silk supplies came from Asia, where countless numbers of silk-spinning caterpillars were farmed. In the 1880s chemists created nitrocellulose fibers that resembled silk filaments but were far inferior to the real thing. In 1891 a more successful artificial silk, viscose (later called rayon), was developed in Great Britain by the chemical firm Cross & Bevan. In this new process cel-

lulose was chemically treated until it became a syrup. The fluid was extruded through small holes into an acid bath, where it solidified into filaments. Although rayon could not match the durability or comfort of silk, it became an affordable alternative to silk and replaced mundane cotton in socks, underwear, and dresses. After World War I the market for attractive and inexpensive rayon expanded dramatically worldwide, so much so that the production of rayon became the largest new chemical industry created between the two world wars.

Scientists continued to explore other methods for transforming cellulose into plastic. One of the most influential companies in the development of plastics and synthetic fibers was the Du Pont Co., located in Wilmington, Delaware. In the late 1920s, for example, Du Pont chemist William Hale Charch developed a nitrocellulose-coated rayon film called cellophane. This transparent, moisture-proof film soon was dubbed the "silent salesman" because of its success in selling food that was wrapped in it. Cellophane launched a veritable revolution in food packaging and merchandising in the new self-service supermarkets that proliferated during the 1930s.

Around the same time, other Du Pont chemists stumbled on a revolutionary new nitrocellulose automotive finish that they named Duco. During experiments designed to improve motion picture film, chemists discovered how to produce significantly less-viscous nitrocellulose solutions. It occurred to one of them that these solutions might make an economical and durable automobile paint that could be easily applied with spray guns. Not only did this turn out to be true, but the new Duco lacquers also made it possible to paint cars in a wide variety of colors instead of the standard black prescribed by the older paint and varnish technology. It would not be long, however, before the cellulose-based Duco was challenged by new types of finishes made synthetically from common organic chemicals.

FROM NATURE TO NYLON

In their early experiments with plastics, chemists relied on the natural polymer cellulose as the basic ingredient. That changed with the introduction of Bakelite, a completely synthetic polymer that resulted from the reaction of two common chemicals, phenol and formaldehyde. Bakelite was

While searching for a synthetic substitute for lac, a resin derived from the secretions of insects, inventor Leo Hendrik Baekeland created Bakelite, a hard and durable plastic that was used in items ranging from billiard balls (left) to toys and household items (below). Initially the enthusiasm for such plastic materials was slow to build. In time, however, these synthetics became celebrated symbols of progress and modernity, as evidenced by an early French ad for men's underwear (opposite) that depicts the progressive evolution of human clothing from animal skins to nylon.

developed in 1907 by the inventor Leo Hendrik Baekeland. After he had made a fortune in 1899 by selling the camera and film manufacturer George Eastman the rights to Velox, a photographic paper that he invented, Baekeland set out to find a synthetic substitute for lac, a resin derived from secretions of a Southeast Asian scale insect that formed the basis for shellac finishes and molding compositions. In the traditional method of making shellac, tens of thousands of insects were needed to produce one-half kilogram (one pound) of the resin. Carrying out his experiments at elevated temperatures and pressure in a "Bakelizer," a copper chamber that he invented for the procedure, Baekeland produced resins that, when mixed with fillers and molded under heat and pressure, produced hard and extremely

durable plastic objects. Because of its excellent insulating properties, Bakelite was used in numerous electrical applications. It also made an excellent billiard ball material. During the 1920s and '30s Bakelite inspired other chemists to develop related synthetic resins from formaldehyde mixed with urea (a fertilizer) or casein (a milk protein).

Despite the fact that plastic materials such as Bakelite were relatively cheap and performed some unique functions, their applications were limited in comparison with natural materials. The enthusiasm of plastics promoters, however, was not easily dampened. They predicted that plastics would soon replace glass, wood, porcelain, and even metal. As the writer of a 1930 article in *Fortune* magazine noted: "Plastic prophets believe that their industry will be as important as steel in two decades. Already its products are indispensable to such major contrivances in this machine age as radios, airplanes, telephones, automobiles and electric power lines." The plastics revolution, however, was slow

to take off. Nonetheless, in the 1930s chemists were making significant strides. New plastic materials were being developed that would find industrial and consumer applications in the decades to come. They included polyethylene, polyvinyl chloride (PVC), polystyrene, silicones, several synthetic rubbers, lightweight and transparent acrylic plastics, Teflon, and nylon.

Some of the delays in finding more widespread applications for plastics were due to the lack of scientific understanding of polymers. To remedy this situation, in 1927 Du Pont's executives gave Charles M.A. Stine, head of the company's central research laboratory, generous financial support and a new building for his fundamental research program. One of the young organic chemists hired for his new program—Wallace H. Carothers, a 31-year-old professor from Harvard University—had an interest in polymers and was

strongly encouraged to do research in this field.

Carothers proposed using an approach that had been developed by the German chemist and Nobel laureate Emil Fischer in the early 1900s: to build long chains of molecules in stepwise fashion, using standard organic chemical reactions. One such reaction involved combining an alcohol and an acid to form single-ester molecules. By choosing alcohol and acid molecules that had reactive groups on both ends (rather than on just one end), Carothers was able to link the ester molecules together, as they formed, into a long chain known as a polyester. In his first two years at Du Pont, Carothers and his research group succeeded in making many kinds of polyesters but could not get beyond the molecular size barrier—namely, molecules with a molecular weight above 5,000—that Fischer believed represented some natural limit. Carothers hypothesized that the buildup of a by-product—in this case, water—was halting the chain-

In 1937 students from Vassar College burned their silk clothing to protest an attack on an American vessel by Japan, the primary exporter of silk to the U.S. Under the direction of Wallace H. Carothers (right), Du Pont capitalized on the vulnerability of Japanese silk by inventing a silk substitute known as nylon. Having overcome numerous manufacturing obstacles, Du Pont launched the first national sale of nylon stockings to enthusiastic crowds (opposite) in May 1940.

building reaction. Using a specially designed vacuum-distillation apparatus, Carothers's associate Julian W. Hill was able to remove these trace quantities of water during the reaction process and make polymers with molecular weights of more than 10,000.

After one of Hill's experiments in April 1930 unexpectedly yielded a strong fiber, 3-16 aliphatic polyester, Du Pont chemists began to search for a commercially successful fiber. Particularly important properties were strength, elasticity, heat resistance, and insolubility in water. This proved to be an especially

challenging task, since the preparation and testing of polymer samples were far from a rigorous science. In May 1934, however, a breakthrough occurred when Carothers's associate Donald D. Coffman successfully synthesized an exotic organic compound, polymerized it, and drew a fiber with outstanding characteristics. It took another six years of intensive development to turn this laboratory finding into a successful new product—nylon.

The difficulties of commercializing nylon probably would have discouraged most other corporations. Du Pont, however, identified a potential mar-

ket that could offer lucrative returns on its research investment—a replacement for silk in women's stockings. In 1938 *The Atlantic Monthly* noted that in that era of shortened skirts, "the silk stocking has become for virtually everyone, rich or poor, young or old, the symbol of liberty, democracy, and undisputed self-respect." Virtually all the silk used in women's stockings was imported from Japanese silk farms. In the 1930s, as Japa-

nese aggression in Manchuria and China strained relations with the U.S., silk took on political overtones. After the Japanese attacked the American gunboat *Panay* in China in 1937, the students of then all-female Vassar College, Poughkeepsie, New York, for example, responded by burning their silk garments in a huge bonfire.

The monopoly on silk was vulnerable, and Du Pont executives knew it. In virtually every step of the nylon-produc-

tion process, however, Du Pont faced unprecedented problems. The choice of which structural variant of nylon to manufacture, for example, depended on what cheap and plentiful raw materials were available. Before petrochemical technology dramatically increased the supply and variety of basic chemicals in the post-World War II era, these options were limited. Du Pont had no choice but to use benzene, a chemical recovered from coal processing. This

use, however, created numerous complications. The conversion of benzene into the two chemicals used to make nylon—hexamethylenediamine and adipic acid—required considerable virtuosity in chemical engineering. The next step—hooking up the two molecules into long chains—also posed numerous challenges. Because the length of the chain determined the properties of the fiber, for example, chemists were forced to invent methods

to control chain length. Finally, the polymer had to be melted, spun into a filament, and knitted into stockings.

By 1938 great strides had been made, and Du Pont decided it was time to inform the public of its discovery. Instead of announcing its new product at a gathering of scientists and engineers, however, company officials decided to go straight to the prospective customer—the American woman. On Oct. 27, 1938, Stine dramatically

95

launched Du Pont's new product at a meeting of 3,000 women's club members at the Eighth Annual *Herald Tribune* Forum on Current Problems, held in New York City.

To this audience...I am making the first announcement of a brand new chemical textile fiber. This textile fiber is the first man-made organic textile fiber prepared wholly from new materials from the mineral kingdom. I refer to the fiber produced from nylon....Though wholly fabricated from such common raw materials as coal, water, and air, nylon can be fashioned into filaments as strong as steel, as fine as a spider's web, yet more elastic than any of the common natural fibers.

Mistakenly assuming that nylon materials would create indestructible stockings (on average, the American working woman wore out 36 pairs of silk stockings each year), the women at the forum burst into applause. The *New York Times* reported enthusiastically about the modern alchemists who could turn base materials into silk but wondered whether women would be happy with stockings that lasted forever. Cartoonists had a field day depicting modern sewing baskets containing coal, air, and water. Public anticipation grew steadily over the next year and a half until nylons went on national public sale in May 1940. In their first two years, nylon stockings captured about one-third of the U.S. market even though they were priced 10% higher than silk stockings and were far less comfortable.

PLASTICS: WORLD WAR II AND BEYOND

World War II had a profound effect not only on the pace of plastics manufacturing but also on the kinds of plastics that were produced. To accommodate wartime needs, chemical companies switched the focus of plastics production to military purposes. Materials such as nylon, for example, were diverted from such consumer products as women's stockings into parachutes and airplane tire cords. This global conflict also interrupted world trade in exotic materials such as rubber, put enormous demands on supplies of more ordinary materials, and created new technolo-

The needs of the U.S. military during World War II profoundly shaped the direction of the fledgling polymer industry. Women's discarded stockings were recycled (opposite top) for use in parachutes and airplane tire cords. Japanese control of natural sources of Southeast Asian rubber led chemists to develop a rubberlike polymer (bottom) from butadiene and styrene. Clear acrylic polymers formed lightweight, shatterproof windows for military aircraft (left).

gies that required materials with unprecedented properties. As a result, the U.S. government encouraged manufacturers to substitute plastics for brass, aluminum, and other strategic materials.

U.S. government intervention led to the rapid expansion of markets for plastics. Among the most dramatic and strategically important polymer developments during World War II was the creation of an American synthetic rubber industry. This $670 million program was sponsored by the U.S. government after the Japanese conquest of Southeast Asia in 1942 had cut off the major source of natural rubber on which the U.S. military depended. Because U.S. chemists lacked the technical know-how to reproduce the rubber polymer, they developed a rubberlike polymer made from butadiene and styrene, using a process that had been pioneered in Germany in the 1930s. A large-scale cooperative effort between the oil, chemical, and rubber companies was launched to produce large quantities of the raw chemical materials, polymerize them, and process them into tires and other goods. The project was so successful that the production of synthetic rubber went from virtually nothing in 1942 to 630 million kilo-

grams (1.4 billion pounds) in 1945. This multi-industry model later became the prototype for the postwar expansion of petrochemical and polymer technologies.

Other polymers also found unique applications in military high technology. Clear acrylic polymers were used extensively in the construction of airplanes for lightweight, shatterproof windows, nose cones, and machine-gun turrets. Polyethylene plastic provided a critical component in the electrical insulation of radar equipment. Du Pont's exotic plastic Teflon, which remained stable at very high temperatures and resisted solvents, found uses as electrical insulation in proximity fuses (the small radar sets in the nose of antiaircraft shells that could detect a nearby plane and detonate an explosive) and as corrosion-resistant seals in equipment used to isolate the uranium isotope employed in the atomic bomb.

After the war ended, the plastics industry was poised to continue its dramatic wartime growth. Advances in petrochemical processing ensured the ample and cheap supply of a wide variety of chemicals that could be polymerized into plastics. In addition, manufacturers of consumer and industrial goods had learned how to

(continued on page 99)

The Development of Polymer Science

Polymer science—the study of long-chain molecules—began after 1850, when scientists started to investigate the chemical composition of natural materials such as rubber, starches, sugars, cellulose, and proteins.

The pioneer in this new research was Friedrich August Kekulé, a German chemist who is credited with having established modern structural theory in organic chemistry—the way that carbon atoms are arranged in organic molecules. In 1858 Kekulé demonstrated that carbon atoms possess four bonds that can be linked to other carbon atoms to form long chains.

In 1877 Kekulé hypothesized that natural organic molecules might have a backbone of very long chains of carbon atoms. Some indirect measurements suggested that these molecules could consist of chains thousands of carbon atoms long. Given the limited analytic techniques at the time, confirmation of this hypothesis proved to be difficult.

Emil Fischer, a student of Kekulé who performed groundbreaking research into the structure of sugars, took a novel approach to the problem. Fischer took small molecules whose size already was known and linked them to create larger chains. In 1913 he succeeded in making a starch derivative with a carbon chain more than 200 atoms long and a molecular weight of 4,000. Unable to produce substantially larger molecules, Fischer declared a molecular weight of 5,000 to be the natural limit. His challenge to chemists to exceed this limit went unheeded for nearly two decades.

Progress in understanding polymers was slow, in part because an influential group of physical chemists in Germany, the leading center of chemical research, argued that large molecules were actually aggregates of much smaller molecules held together by relatively weak "colloidal" forces. They believed that these colloidal forces were a fundamental aspect of matter and that an entirely new science analogous to physics and chemistry would be based on its principles. (The chemists maintained that physics was the science of the structure of the atom; chemistry was the science of the structure of molecules; and colloids, they believed, would become the science of the structure of molecule aggregates.)

In 1920 a bitter academic dispute broke out in Germany when an organic chemist, Hermann Staudinger, challenged the proponents of the colloidal theory. He asserted that long-chain molecules (polymers) were formed not by colloidal forces but by chemical bonding. At the time, his dissent was largely ignored.

In the end Staudinger was vindicated. In 1953 his work on the molecular structure of polymers was awarded the Nobel Prize for Chemistry. Today he is widely credited as having laid the theoretical foundation for the expansion of the modern plastics industry.

Structure of Bakelite (phenol formaldehyde)

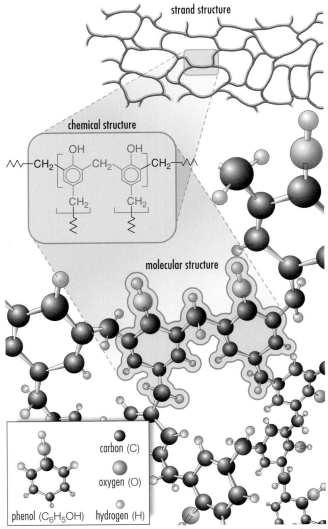

strand structure

chemical structure

molecular structure

carbon (C)

oxygen (O)

phenol (C_6H_5OH)   hydrogen (H)

In the mid-19th century, chemists theorized that carbon atoms possess four bonds that can be linked to other carbon atoms to form long chains. This discovery allowed scientists to create many different kinds of plastics, including phenol-formaldehyde resin, popularly known as Bakelite.

(*continued from page 97*)
use plastics in their products. Perhaps most important, scientists and engineers in academia joined their colleagues in industry to focus on polymers, unraveling some of the immense complexity of these materials. In 1953 James Watson and Francis Crick of the Cavendish Laboratory at the University of Cambridge determined the structure of the most important biological polymer—DNA—and offered explanations of how it codified heredity and masterminded the production of chemicals within living cells. That same year the scientific community recognized the importance of polymer science when chemist Hermann Staudinger at the Albert Ludwig University of Freiburg in Breisgau, Germany, was awarded the Nobel Prize for Chemistry for his research into the molecular structure of polymers, which laid the foundation for the expansion of the modern plastics industry.

Plastics became one of the glamour industries of the postwar decades. The World War II generation of plastics—polyethylene, PVC, polystyrene, and nylon—expanded rapidly and was joined by new polymers. In 1953 German chemist (and later winner of the Nobel Prize for Chemistry) Karl Ziegler discovered a new type of

In the decades following World War II, plastics found a wide range of applications, from panels used to construct this 1959 radome (top) for detecting enemy missiles to the material for a 1966 minidress (right).

catalyst that hooked up molecules in unique ways, a breakthrough that paved the way for the creation of a truly synthetic rubber.

New generations of polymers soon emerged from laboratories around the world. Polyesters, for example, replaced cellulose-based photographic and movie film. Polyurethanes supplanted foam rubber and rubberized-cotton elastic threads. Polycarbonates were used to make shatterproof windows. Polypropylene became the stuff of packaging films. By the late 1950s entrepreneurs were using plastics to create popular products that became icons of consumer culture, including Barbie dolls, Silly Putty, Tupperware, Velcro, Frisbees, hula hoops, Teflon cookware, and pink flamingo lawn ornaments.

Plastics were most revolutionary in the textile and packaging industries. Before the era of synthetic fibers, cotton commanded 80% of the U.S. textile market, and wool claimed most of the remainder. By the early 1950s the production of rayon had far surpassed that of wool

99

and was equal to half the cotton market. During that time additional synthetic fibers such as polyester and polyacrylic (acrylic) were introduced and quickly began to make significant inroads into the textile market.

Furthermore, nylon, which heretofore had been largely diverted into military uses during World War II, became available once again for consumer products, such as lingerie. Acrylic fibers substituted for wool in sweaters and other knit goods, and polyester, when blended with cotton, created wrinkle-resistant shirts.

These new synthetic fibers appealed to consumers for a variety of reasons, including their easy care, versatility of styles, and low cost. Although cotton retained a significant market share against these new synthetics, the consumption of wool plummeted by 75% in the U.S. from its peak in the late 1940s.

Synthetic materials commandeered more than just the

clothing market. During the 1960s a new nylon-processing technology created a bulky fiber that could be woven into relatively cheap and durable carpets, an innovation that spurred a trend in wall-to-wall carpeting. Today more than one-third of all synthetic fiber in the U.S. goes into the making of carpets.

Another major growth area for plastics was packaging. Packaging held out the promise of time savings just when the

pace of life seemed to accelerate, particularly in the aftermath of the great American invention of the 1930s—the supermarket. While shoppers briskly cruised aisles stocked with a cornucopia of neatly packaged and efficiently arranged goods, a traffic jam occurred at meat counters, where butchers continued to cut and wrap meat to order. Studies showed that consumers who wasted precious time standing in lines bought less than those who kept moving. To solve this problem, sophisticated packaging films were developed to

preserve the fresh appearance of precut red meat.

Plastics soon found a wider range of applications than simply preserving food on supermarket shelves. Disposable plastic plates, trays, and utensils were ideal for facilitating "mass feeding" in airplanes, schools, industry, and the emerging fast-food business. The use of plastic materials in the food industry skyrocketed. By 1970 packaging annually consumed two million tons of plastic and accounted for one-quarter of all resin production in the U.S.

(Opposite page, bottom) Archive Photos; (below) David Nunuk—Science Photo Library/Photo Researchers; (right)
James King-Holmes—Science Photo Library/Photo Researchers; (bottom right) Art Wolfe—Tony Stone Images

By 1970 plastics were widely used—for example, in dishware for the emerging fast-food business (opposite page, bottom). Opposition to plastics, however, grew as environmental problems surfaced. Nonbiodegradable materials began to endanger wildlife, such as this cape fur seal entangled in a plastic fishing net in Namibia. The choking of landfills by plastic garbage (left) and concerns about polluting chemicals and oil resources used in plastics production prompted scientists to develop methods for their recycling. An engineer (top) holds a beaker of oil feedstock reclaimed from shredded plastic wastes.

ENVIRONMENTAL CONCERNS

Although widely praised for their numerous benefits, plastics began to attract criticism from activists in the emerging environmental movement of the late 1960s. In his widely influential 1971 book, *The Closing Circle: Nature, Man, and Technology,* biologist Barry Commoner, whom the *New York Post* dubbed the Paul Revere of ecology, linked hazardous pollution to the increased production of synthetic chemicals, many of which were used to make plastics. These human-made materials, Commoner asserted, had no counterpart in nature, and their proliferation threatened to disrupt the Earth's ecological balance. Because they were not part of the natural environment, Commoner warned, synthetic chemicals could lead to major malfunctions in cells, the basis of all life. A dramatic example of this risk was discovered in 1974 when vinyl chloride monomer, the building block of PVC plastic, was linked to several cases of fatal liver cancer among workers in PVC-manufacturing plants. This led to stricter standards for workers' exposure to vinyl chloride and better methods for removing unreacted monomer from the plastic.

Critics charged that plastics created environmental havoc throughout their life cycle. During the energy crises of the 1970s, plastics were criticized as being wasteful of precious energy resources even though only about 1.5% of a barrel of oil was used in their manufacture. They also became associated with pollution created by the chemical industry in general.

Not only did the manufacture of plastics create pollution, but their disposal also became problematic. As Commoner pointed out, because synthetic polymers were not biodegradable—nothing in nature had evolved to eat them—they persisted in the environment indefinitely, scarring the landscape, clogging rivers and streams, and piling up in landfills. Problems with plastics disposal were heightened during the U.S. landfill crisis of the 1980s, when political opposition to their economic and environmental costs prevented the siting of many new garbage dumps. Because of their inertness, plastics are not considered a major contributor to the landfill leachate that has pol-

luted groundwater around landfills, but they constitute about 20% of the volume of trash.

MATERIALS OF THE FUTURE

Despite these environmental concerns, the use of plastics and the creation of new engineering resins and specialty fibers show no sign of slowing. In 1996 in the U.S. alone, 720,000 kilograms (1.6 million pounds) of plastic per year were used in household appliances. That number is expected to jump to almost 900 million kilograms (2 billion pounds) by the year 2000. According to the American Plastics Council, in the early 1960s plastics made up only 1% of the weight of materials used in home appliances. By 1997 the number had climbed to 25%. In appliances, as well as in many other applications, engineering plastics—those used for structural purposes—have replaced metal gears, valves, and zippers.

Also widely used, especially in such large-scale applications as automobile bodies, are composite materials—high-strength fibers bound together with a plastic resin. In 1996 composites sales in the U.S. reached nearly 1.4 billion kilograms (3 billion pounds) per year; nearly one-third of these materials are used in transportation equipment.

Future applications for composite materials are likely to increase. In 1997, for example, the Chrysler Corp. unveiled a prototype for a plastic car that the company hopes to market in the emerging economies of such countries as China and India. (In 1998 Chrysler unveiled two additional models geared to the American market.) Known as the Composite Concept Vehicle (CCV), the car features a steel frame and a body made of polyethylene terephthalate (PET), the thermoplastic used in making soft-drink bottles. Affordability guided the choice of materials as well as the car's design and engineering. Made of injection-molded plastic components, the CCV would cut manufacturing costs by eliminating the number of automobile parts (the CCV has 1,100 parts, compared with approximately 4,000 parts in the company's Neon car model). Colors can be mixed into the plastic, which eliminates the need for spraying paints and rustproofing compounds to the car's surface. The composite-plastic body also results in a more lightweight car—540 kilograms (1,200 pounds)—and thereby makes the CCV more fuel-efficient while cutting its emissions. Furthermore, the CCV's body can be made from recycled plastic—the prototype was manufactured from 2,132 discarded soda bottles. According to the automaker, the CCV's plastic components can be recycled at the end of the car's life cycle and used to manufacture other cars or consumer products.

Other developments in new plastics technology address health and safety issues as well as environmental concerns. In 1997 researchers at the University of Utah announced a new drug-delivery system based on biodegradable polymers. Instead of being administered intravenously or through surgical implants, a drug can be mixed with the polymer and water and injected under the skin, where it forms a time-release gel capsule.

Researchers also are investigating the synthesis of new polymers in environmental applications. Because food packaging, for example, makes a

Scientists have found a wide range of innovative new applications for recycled plastics such as polyethylene terephthalate (PET), the thermoplastic used in making soda bottles. PET was used as a fabric for sportswear (opposite bottom) and by Chrysler to form the body of the car company's new Composite Concept Vehicle (left). Researchers also have continued to synthesize new polymers. Du Pont's bullet-resistant Kevlar lines a leather vest (below) created by New Centurion Body Armor, a Florida store that specializes in stylish protective clothing for celebrities.

significant contribution to the solid-waste stream, packaging manufacturers are researching the development of edible or biodegradable polymer films that perform as well as traditional plastic wraps in retaining the moisture and flavor of foods without adding to waste-disposal problems. In the future, lighter and more environmentally benign plastics may even replace conventional batteries, a major source of the heavy metals that contaminate soil and water. In 1997 research engineers at Johns Hopkins University, Baltimore, Maryland, announced the creation of an all-plastic battery. The new batteries, which produce 45 watt-hours of electricity per kilogram and can be recharged hundreds of times, initially will be used to power U.S. Air Force satellites. Although this new technology holds great promise for use in a variety of consumer products, its first commercial application will be a three-volt battery.

Inventing new plastic materials, however, remains an expensive, time-consuming process. Du Pont's experience in developing its revolutionary fiber Kevlar is instructive. Using new polymerization techniques, Du Pont researchers in 1964 created Kevlar, a new type of nylon (an aromatic nylon or aramid) that yielded fibers five times as strong as steel. It took years to develop large-scale manufacturing processes and to find applications for the material. Even though it performs many important functions, such as dramatically improving the life-saving capabilities of military helmets and bulletproof vests and the limb-protecting qualities of gloves and chaps, Kevlar has not been a major financial success. It also has been substituted for hazardous asbestos in automobile brake lining.

Where Kevlar's strength and lightness have proved especially useful is in the manufacture of sporting goods, an important market for new high-technology materials. Even amateur athletes are willing to pay significant premiums to gain the incremental performance improvements promised by lighter and stronger materials. The experience with new materials gained from the manufacture of sporting goods—bicycle tires, surfboards, canoes, and hockey sticks, for example—has helped provide performance data needed for larger-scale applications. In one such application engineers are designing and testing experimental bridges made of composite materials.

Today, as in the past, the complexity of polymer materials has slowed their development and product possibilities. On the other hand, this complexity, despite its drawbacks, gives plastics its greatest advantage as a material. By altering the composition and structure of polymer molecules, the properties of materials can be tailored for specific applications. For most of human history, people worked with combinations of properties that were available in natural substances. The properties of these materials limited the kinds of things humans could build and the forces they could command. To a large extent, plastics have liberated people from these constraints and allowed them to imagine technical possibilities and then design the materials needed to do the job.

FOR ADDITIONAL READING

- *American Plastic: A Cultural History,* Jeffrey L. Meikle (Rutgers University Press, 1995).
  - *Pioneer Plastic: The Making and Selling of Celluloid,* Robert D. Friedel (University of Wisconsin Press, 1983).
  - *Plastic: The Making of a Synthetic Century,* Stephen Fenichell (HarperBusiness, 1996).

The Great Consciousness Debate

For centuries philosophers have argued about the nature of human consciousness. Propelled by the substantial progress that scientists have recently made in researching the working of the brain, the mind-body problem is once again at the center of vigorous disagreement.

by James Trefil

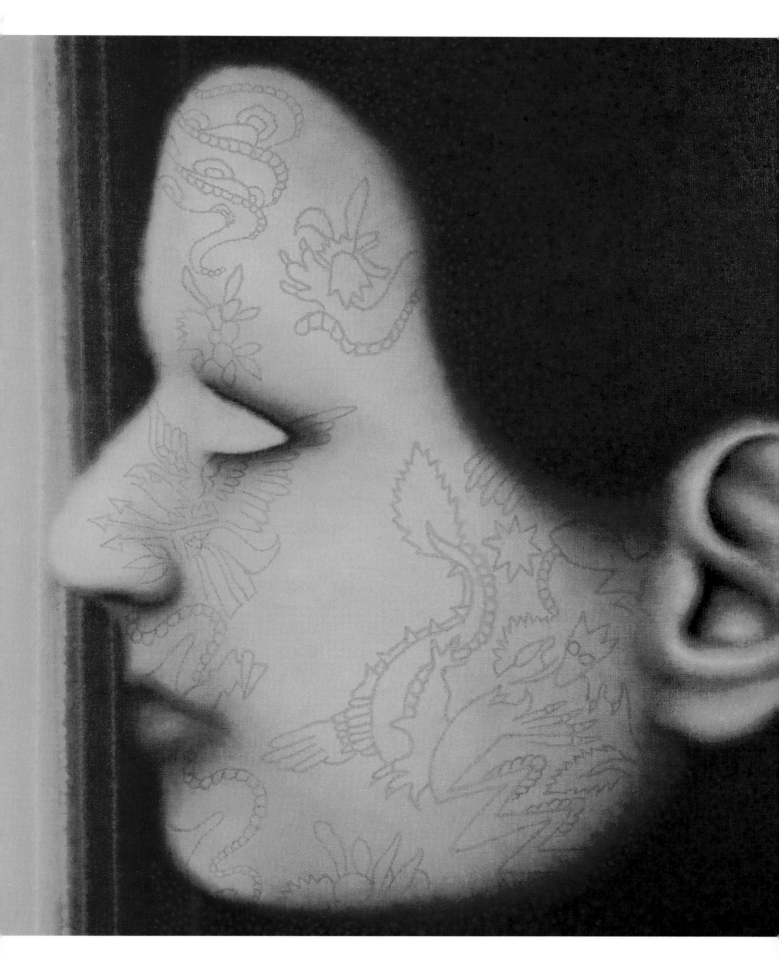

W hen Charles Darwin published his monumental work *On the Origin of Species by Means of Natural Selection* in 1859, he inaugurated a unique period in the history of science. The work began a long debate on the na-

ture of humanity and the place of human beings in the universe. What was unusual about this debate was that it was largely carried out in books expressly written for a general audience. Even today anyone reading Darwin is struck by the elegance of his writing and the fact that his ideas are entirely understandable to the average educated person.

James Trefil is Clarence J. Robinson Professor of Physics at George Mason University, Fairfax, Virginia. His latest book is Are We Unique?: A Scientist Explores the Unparalleled Intelligence of the Human Mind.

Like the first edition of Charles Darwin's *On the Origin of Species by Means of Natural Selection,* which sold out immediately upon its publication in 1859, recent books that wrestle with the problem of the nature of consciousness have proved to be immensely popular with scientists and general readers alike.

Since Darwin's time, scientific debates have moved to a much more rarefied atmosphere. Those wishing to keep up with the latest research in a particular field of science have only two choices. One is to read the very difficult and technical professional literature; the other is to rely on secondhand accounts in scientific publications intended for a popular audience. A widening gulf exists between the degree of specialization demanded of contemporary scientists and the kind of scientific background that most laypersons can be expected to have.

It is therefore with much pleasure that I have watched the beginnings of what I believe will become the great scientific debate of the 21st century—the debate on the nature of consciousness—and have noted that like the quarrel over Darwin's theory of evolution, it is being conducted largely in works aimed at the general reader. Recent years have seen the publication of a number of stimulating books that wrestle with the problem of the nature of consciousness, among them Francis Crick's *The Astonishing Hypothesis: The Scientific Search for the Soul* (1994), David Chalmers's *The Conscious Mind: In Search of a Fundamental Theory* (1996), Steven Pinker's *How the Mind*

Works (1997), and Daniel C. Dennett's *Consciousness Explained* (1991) and *Kinds of Minds: Toward an Understanding of Consciousness* (1996). One striking aspect of the consciousness debate is the interdisciplinary approach taken by most of the participants. Many of the thinkers now contemplating this issue are conversant in a wide range of fields, including philosophy, physics, neuroscience, artificial intelligence, and cognitive psychology.

ASKING THE QUESTION

The problem of consciousness is easy to state, if difficult to think about. It is this: Why do human beings, who are, after all, collections of cells and molecules like every other living thing, have the mental property that we refer to as consciousness?

It may be helpful to look at the problem this way. Like all human beings, you are equipped with a brain. This brain consists of about one and a half kilograms (three pounds) of material, and its main working components are cells known as neurons. You have about 10 billion neurons in your brain. Each neuron is a cell governed by known (or at least knowable) laws of physics and chemistry. Anything your

Because of the availability of sophisticated computer-based technologies, the ability of researchers to examine complex systems like the brain has grown enormously in recent years.

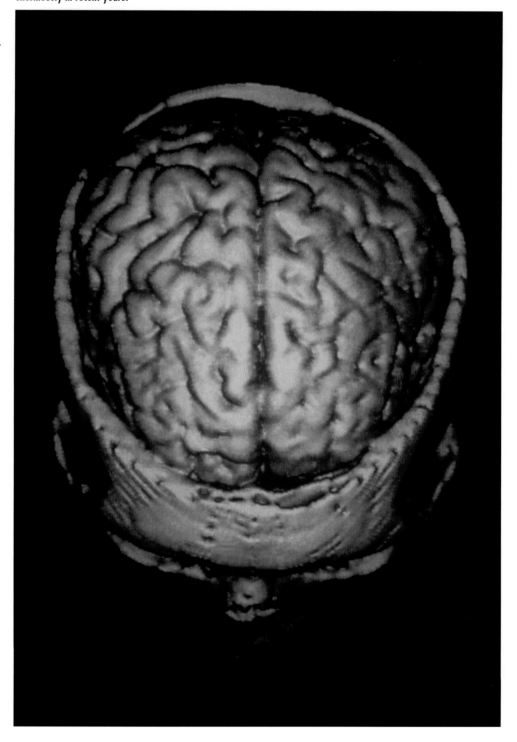

Samburu tribesmen in Kenya huddle to exchange words. In an attempt to gain insight into how the brain functions, some researchers have begun to focus their studies on language and linguistic behavior.

brain does, anything you experience, must eventually involve the activities of those neurons in some way.

Consider this: it is an indisputable fact that you are reading this page. It is also an indisputable fact, now that your attention has been drawn to it, that you are aware that you are reading this page. One way of stating the problem of consciousness is to ask how one goes from the activities of ordinary cells like neurons to the state of self-awareness.

For many decades scientists who studied the brain had to be content with simply mapping out the location of different sorts of cells and, in some cases, working out which parts of the brain are involved in various mental functions. The discovery that speech is controlled by areas in the brain's left hemisphere and that spatial perceptions are governed by areas in its right hemisphere is one example of the fruits of such work. Detailed knowledge of this kind is extremely important, particularly in the treatment of neurological disorders. Until recently, however, the deeper question of how it is possible for the brain to produce consciousness was simply beyond the grasp of science. In fact, as Dennett, an American philosopher and cognitive researcher, has pointed out, this field of inquiry is so new that we are not even sure what questions we should be asking.

The problem is exacerbated by the fact that consciousness is one of those terms whose meaning everyone knows but for which no two people will give the same definition. Hearing people arguing about the nature of consciousness is reminiscent of what the early Christian thinker St. Augustine had to say about another term that is hard to define—time: "What is time? If no one asks me, I know what it is. If I wish to explain to him who asks me, I do not know."

The harder one tries, the more difficult it becomes to define consciousness. An example from my own experience will illustrate this point. In 1993 the Krasnow Institute for Advanced Study was established at George Mason University, Fairfax, Virginia. It is an institute devoted to the study of complex adaptive systems like the brain, and early discussion groups included physical scientists like myself, a large number of computer people, biologists, psychologists, educators, philosophers, and even one very brave political scientist. After the first few rounds of discussion, it became clear that we were getting bogged down repeatedly in semantics. We would begin a meeting with a substantive issue, such as artificial intelligence, and wind up arguing about what we meant by the term *intelligence*. Hoping to move things forward, I put together a list of disputed terms, which started with *brain* and ended with more abstruse words like *consciousness*. We set aside a couple of hours one rainy fall afternoon to see if we could come to a consensus about the meaning of those terms. I thought—naively, as it turned out—that we would have no trouble with the first

In several engaging books, American philosopher Daniel C. Dennett has advocated a materialist approach to consciousness, arguing that the mind can be described solely in terms of the workings of the brain.

few terms at least. As it happened, however, this group of scholars argued heatedly for more than two hours without agreeing on what we meant by the term *brain*. To have a field so new that even the most basic terms are undefined is unusual, to say the least.

Although not everyone can agree on a definition of consciousness, a number of thinkers have already staked out intellectual territory and fought skirmishes over how consciousness originates in the human brain. Some of the impetus for the current boom in consciousness studies comes from new experimental techniques, but it may have more to do with the availability of high-speed digital computers. Because of these machines, the ability of researchers to examine complex systems like the brain has grown enormously. Even though investigators are nowhere near to arriving at a definitive explanation of the brain itself, they are beginning to explore the kinds of behavior that complex systems exhibit. These explorations promise to shed light on how thoughts and feelings are to be reconciled with the nerve cells and molecules that make up the brain.

As already mentioned, a large part of the scientific debate on consciousness is being carried out in books intended for the general public. Not surprisingly, given the many scientists and philosophers who have joined the debate on the mind-body problem, a wide variety of opinion is represented in these books. A survey of the major points of view may thus be useful.

There are two ways to categorize the current thinkers on the problem of consciousness. One way involves the methods by which they work; the other way involves their philosophical views about what consciousness is. In terms of work method, most thinkers have approached consciousness either by first considering the neuron and gradually working their

Dusan Petricic

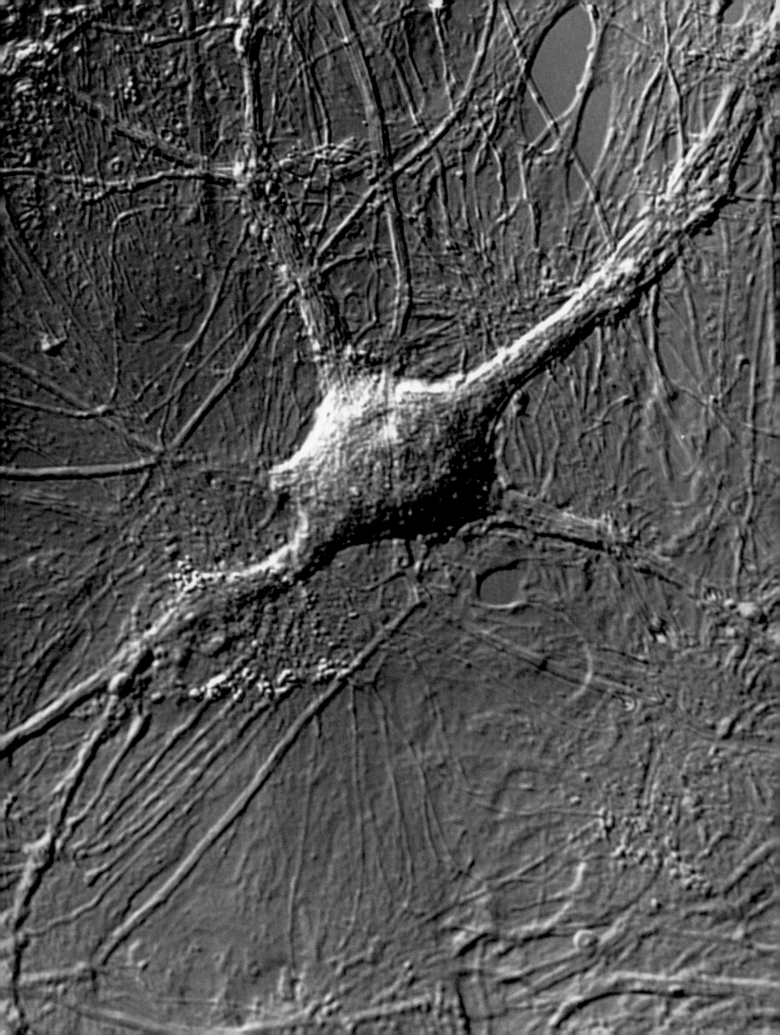

A microscopic image of a neuron reveals a weblike pattern of fibers. Are neurons the key to understanding consciousness? That question is at the heart of the current debate among philosophers and scientists.

(Opposite page and below) Dan McCoy—Rainbow/PNI

way up to the brain or by looking first at how the brain functions as a whole and then considering how its wiring operates. These methods may be called, respectively, the "bottom-up" and "top-down" approaches. In general, people who study how neurons connect to one another, such as neurophysiologists, are likely to choose the bottom-up approach, whereas those who rely on tests to see how people perform mental functions, such as behavioral physiologists, are more likely to take a top-down approach. Currently there are many people in both camps, and it is a measure of how much remains to be learned that almost no common ground exists between these two groups.

As for philosophical views about the nature of consciousness, the positions are rather more diverse. It is possible, however, to divide the debaters into three general categories: materialists, mysterians, and deniers.

MATERIALISTS

The idea that the mind can be described solely in terms of the workings of the brain is fundamental to the materialist point of view. To materialists the notion that there is anything about human consciousness that is

not definable by the standard laws of physics and chemistry is anathema. Although materialists do not believe that they now know enough of these laws to understand consciousness, they do believe that these laws are knowable by methods of science and that given enough effort on the part of scientists and sufficient funding for their research, these laws will someday be known.

Perhaps the most visible proponent of the materialist viewpoint is Crick, the British biophysicist who shared the 1962 Nobel Prize for Physiology or Medicine for having determined the molecular structure of DNA. In Crick's *The Astonishing Hypothesis*, he states his position most emphatically:

"You," your joys and your sorrows, your memories and your ambitions, your

sense of personal liberty and free will, are in fact no more than the behavior of a vast assembly of nerve cells…. "You're nothing but a pack of neurons."

Crick is also decidedly in the bottom-up camp of researchers. In fact, a good deal of *The Astonishing Hypothesis* is devoted to a detailed discussion of the process of vision. How the human brain takes a flood of incoming light and produces a mental image of the environment is one of the great unsolved mysteries about the working of the brain. It has been established that when incoming photons (particle-like units of light energy) trigger the light-sensitive cells in the eye, the processing of visual data starts immediately. The wiring of the cells in the back of the retina is such that the signals that travel the optic

nerve to the brain depend on the patterns of light and dark seen by each site on the retina. Some signals, for example, will be sent only if a certain group of cells sees a dark spot with a white surround, whereas other signals will be sent only if a group of cells sees a white spot with a dark surround. In the retina itself the incoming light is thus broken down into a set of nerve signals. What remains to be answered is how the brain reconstructs those signals to make the image that we experience.

Since it is now possible to detect the firing of individual neurons, investigators can actually trace this process of reconstruction some little distance into the brain. The optic nerve connects to cells in the visual cortex, the part of the brain that lies immediately under the lump at the back of the skull. There, signals from different parts of the retina are put together by sets of specialized cells. Some of these cells will fire only if there is a vertical line in the visual field, whereas others will fire if there are lines slanted at some specific angle. The signals from these cells are

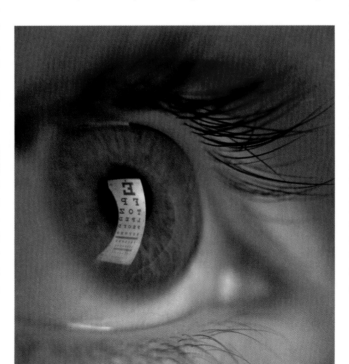

How the human brain reconstructs signals from light-sensitive cells in the eye to produce a mental image of the environment is one of the great unsolved mysteries of science and the subject of intense ongoing research.

then sent forward to other parts of the brain and, in some way that is not understood, are bound together to produce an image in our minds. Unraveling the details of how this reconstruction works is called the binding problem, in the jargon of brain scientists. It marks one experimental frontier of researchers who take the bottom-up materialist approach to the problem of consciousness.

tral direction. In *How the Mind Works,* Pinker, an experimental psychologist well known for his studies of the nature of language and linguistic behavior, gives a detailed account of this feature of the brain and discusses how such a brain might have developed. Using a process he calls reverse engineering, by which human behavior is analyzed in an attempt to gain insight into how the brain

plained, Dennett describes the color phi phenomenon, a standard psychology experiment involving vision. In this experiment subjects who look at a screen on which two separate lights of different color flash quickly in alternation—with a brief interval of darkness between the flashes—believe that they see a single moving light that changes color in the middle of its illusory path between two locations. The fact that the subjects believe that the color of the illusory moving light changes *before* the second light flashes on shows that the order in which we perceive things is not necessarily the order in which sensory data arrive in the brain. Obviously, there is more to vision than simply the eye recording the arrival of photons.

From an experiment of this kind, Dennett concludes that the brain does not produce pictures in the manner of a computer or a television screen but employs "multiple drafts." His idea is that the brain forms an image by first taking the sensory data and doing a very rough outline—perhaps just to see if there is something dangerous about the perceived object that it should be concerned about—and then continuing to produce increasingly better versions of that first draft until it has the final product—all in

a fraction of a second. As Dennett writes in *Consciousness Explained:*

According to the Multiple Drafts model, all varieties of perception—indeed, all varieties of thought or mental activity—are accomplished in the brain by parallel, multitrack processes of interpretation and elaboration of sensory inputs. Information entering the nervous system is under continuous "editorial revision."

From the point of view of evolutionary biology, there would appear to be a definite advantage for an organism to grasp quickly what the main features of its environment are and get the detail somewhat later. I suspect that when we arrive at a definitive theory of vision, something like the Multiple Drafts model will be a part of it.

Nevertheless, what does a detailed description of the brain's function, whether from a bottom-up or top-down perspective, have to do with consciousness? Despite all the data the materialists may gather, in the end it will still be difficult to say exactly how the organization and activity of cells can give rise to something like consciousness. In *Are We Unique?: A Scientist Explores the Unparalleled Intelligence of the Human Mind* (1997), I suggest that the resolution of this problem will likely come from something known as an emergent phenomenon.

According to a theory of consciousness known as the Multiple Drafts model, the brain forms a mental image by first creating a quick outline from sensory data and then continuing to produce increasingly better versions of that rough draft.

However the binding problem is solved, what investigators know about vision so far illustrates a very important feature of the human brain. The brain is not like some giant computer; rather, it is like a set of small, specialized pocket calculators, each of which contributes its own little bit to the final product without any cen-

evolved through natural selection, Pinker applies a Darwinian perspective to such mental capacities as three-dimensional vision and logical thought.

It is, of course, possible to be a top-down materialist as well as a bottom-up one. One philosopher who could be categorized this way is Dennett. In his book *Consciousness Ex-*

A good way to think of emergent phenomena is to imagine piling grains of sand on a table. For a while each time a new grain of sand is added, the pile simply gets bigger, but there comes a point when adding one more grain produces a new phenomenon— an avalanche. It is the realization that there are such phenomena, which appear suddenly and unexpectedly, that gives rise to sayings like "It was the straw that broke the camel's back." In systems having many agents that interact with one another, changes in behavior can occur once the system has reached certain levels of complexity. In these systems a point is achieved at which "more" suddenly becomes "different." Thus, one possible way of thinking about consciousness is that it is what happens when an "avalanche" occurs at some critical size and arrangement of neurons.

This approach has the value of allowing one to understand how human beings can be fundamentally different from our nearest genetic neighbors, the chimpanzees, even though humans and chimpanzees have so much DNA in common. It is not how much DNA we share that matters but whether the difference is enough to push us to a new avalanche. I would argue that this avalanche process happened several million years ago in the course of primate evolution. (For more information on the concepts of complex systems and emergence, see *1997 Yearbook of Science and the Future* Feature Article: COMPLEXITY: IN SEARCH OF NATURE'S PATTERNS.)

MYSTERIANS

Many people are dismayed by the notion that all of the great achievements of the human race are reducible to the impersonal workings of the laws of science, just as many people in Darwin's time were dismayed by the thought that human beings came to be as a result of the blind operation of the evolutionary process. Traditionally, people who feel this way have talked about the existence of the soul as being the thing that differentiates humans from other animals. Since the existence of the soul is not something that can be proved or disproved scientifically, I will leave that particular aspect of the debate for others.

There are people within the mainstream scientific community who claim that for one reason or another, the phenomenon of consciousness will remain outside the grasp of human knowledge or at least that it lies outside the knowledge that science now possesses. This belief is known as mysterianism, a term coined by

American philosopher Owen Flanagan. One notable exposition of the mysterian viewpoint has been put forward by Chalmers, an Australian philosopher, in his book *The Conscious Mind: In Search of a Fundamental Theory*. His argument is based not on religious thinking or mysticism but on a hard analysis of the way that scientific theories work.

In seeking to reestablish the traditional dualist position that mind and body are distinct kinds of substances or natures, Chalmers firmly rejects the materialist approach and maintains that consciousness is inexplicable simply in terms of neurons in the brain. A venerated theory in philosophy, mind-body dualism stems from

Australian philosopher David Chalmers rejects the materialist approach to consciousness, arguing instead that mind is an immaterial substance that cannot be defined within the framework of science.

the thought of the 17th-century French philosopher and mathematician René Descartes, who developed a theory of mind as an immaterial substance that, unlike matter, does not conform to the laws of physics. Chalmers likewise believes that consciousness cannot be defined within the framework of what scientists know. His basic point is that there is a fundamental difference between the firing of neurons in the brain when, for example, one sees the color red and the actual experience of seeing red. That experience, he argues, is not reducible to the action of neurons. As Chalmers states in *The Conscious Mind,* consciousness "escapes the net of reductive explanation," the attempt by scientists to explain the whole in terms of its parts.

Thinkers addressing the problem of consciousness today from the mysterian point of view are in somewhat the same position as the scientists who began the first serious studies of electricity in the 18th century. Those scientists had to deal with a new reality in nature—electrical charge—that could not be explained in terms of Newtonian matter and motion. They treated electrical charge as a fundamental new quantity that had to be studied in its own right and not as something that was dependent on other aspects of nature. In just the same way, Chalmers contends, consciousness will turn out to be a fundamentally new property of complex systems and will require a new kind of science for its explication.

The mysterian position is a perfectly valid hypothesis about the nature of consciousness and, like all scientific hypotheses, will be proved true or false by future experiments.

Edward L. Miller—Stock, Boston/PNI

Is the experience of seeing red, whether in an image of a steam cloud rising from a nuclear plant (above) or in a bed of tulips, reducible to the action of neurons? Not according to a school of thought known as mysterianism.

There are, however, points of view among the mysterians that are farther from the scientific mainstream. Some people argue, for example, that the human brain will never be able to understand its own consciousness. These sort of arguments are often couched—incorrectly, I think—in scientific terms when, in fact, they have a more profoundly spiritual or mystical flavor. Given the present state of scientists' knowledge of brain function, it will be a long time before anyone will be able to put them to the test.

DENIERS

One of the strangest phenomena associated with consciousness studies is the appearance of a rather large group of people, primarily neuroscientists, who address consciousness by denying that it exists. When I bring up the question of consciousness with my colleagues, for example, the response I sometimes get is, "Oh, consciousness—that's just an illusion. Now let me get back to my work." It is almost as if they are so involved in trying to understand such details as the visual pathways in the brain that they block out the more difficult questions related to consciousness.

Although most people familiar with the consciousness debate place Dennett among the materialists, an argument could be made for including him in the category of deniers. Dennett himself might not accept the designation, but many who read *Consciousness Explained* come to the opposite conclusion. Dennett's provocative assertion that consciousness is nothing more than a kind of "virtual machine" running in the brain is no doubt partly responsible for this perception. Reading his discussion of the Multiple Drafts model of consciousness gave me the sense of studying a tremendously de-

Although scientists are far from arriving at a definitive explanation of brain function, their research promises to shed light on how thoughts and feelings are to be reconciled with the nerve cells and molecules that make up the brain.

tailed description of the operation of an internal combustion engine only to be told that a car is "just an illusion."

There are many ways of dealing with unsolved problems in science. One technique is to ignore them until you have the means of arriving at a solution. This, in essence, is what many neuroscientists are doing. Saying that a phenomenon cannot be explained at the present time, however, is quite different from saying that the phenomenon in question does not exist. In the words of Chalmers, those who deny the existence of consciousness "are not taking science seriously."

ONLY THE BEGINNING

Because it is possible now to think about the behavior of complex systems like the brain, and because experimental techniques are beginning to allow scientists to trace the activity of individual brain cells, we are starting to entertain such important questions as how it is that the brain functions and how human beings came to be what we are. The debate on the nature of consciousness promises to help us achieve an understanding of the identity of the human species and of what separates us from the rest of the animal kingdom. Although answers to these questions may not come soon, we may take comfort from the fact that the debate is out in the open, where we can travel along with scientists and philosophers as they proceed on their great quest to unravel the mysteries of consciousness.

Who were the ancient forebears of the modern people of Japan? Long debated and suffering from no lack of theories, the question finally appears to be yielding to the efforts of archaeologists, anthropologists, linguists, and, most recently, genetic researchers.

Izanagi's Inheritors: The Search for Japanese Origins

by Brian Chisholm

A very long time ago, Izanagi and Izanami, the eighth pair of brother and sister spirits to appear after heaven and earth separated out of chaos, were ordered by their superiors to descend from heaven by way of the bridge Ukibashi. As Izanagi approached the bridge, he dipped his spear in the muddy liquid that formed the earth. When he removed the spear, some drops of mud fell from its tip and solidified, forming an island. The two heavenly spirits landed on that island and built a house, married, and produced offspring, the greater and lesser islands of Japan.

Later the couple gave birth to the gods of water, wind, trees, mountains, rivers, roads, thunder, rain, and finally the god of fire. Unfortunately, the birth of the god of fire caused the death of Izanami, his mother. In his grief Izanagi cut off the head of the child and then retreated to the region of the shadows to be with his wife. Failing at this, Izanagi returned to the surface of the earth, where he purified himself after his contact with the dead. As he removed his clothing and washed parts of his body, 26 new gods were born, including such notables as Amaterasu, the goddess of the sun, Tsukiyomi, the god of the moon, and Susanoo, the storm god. Thereafter Izanagi retired, and his realm was divided

Brian Chisholm *is a sessional lecturer in the Department of Anthropology and Sociology, University of British Columbia.*

among the gods. Over time the gods had children, who themselves had children, and eventually a grandson of Amaterasu became the ruler of Japan. His grandson, Jimmu Tenno, became the first emperor of Japan and thus established the connection between the gods and that nation's imperial rulers.

The above tale recounts the central creation myth and the beginnings of the imperial dynasty as recorded in early Japanese literature. For the modern people of Japan seeking insight into their own beginnings, however, it reveals little, other than taking for granted the presence of their forebears as subservient beings. The task of solving the puzzle regarding when and where the human subjects of those mythical early emperors actually originated has fallen to archaeologists, linguists, anthropologists, and, most recently, geneticists, who have found much more to say on the question, although their stories have been far less fanciful and certainly more convoluted and contentious. Never-

In this 19th-century Japanese silk scroll painting, Izanagi and Izanami stir the muddy liquid of primeval earth to form an island. According to the Japanese creation myth, their activities gave rise to numerous deities, one of whose descendants became the first emperor of Japan.

The clay vessel at right and *dogu* figure below are products of the Jomon culture, which existed in Japan from about 12,000 to 2,300 years ago. Jomon potters often pressed cord patterns (*jomon* in Japanese) into their works, a practice that gave the culture its name.

(Below) The Avery Brundage Collection, Asian Art Museum of San Francisco; (right) Musée des Arts Asiatiques-Guimet, Paris; photograph, P. Playnet—RMN

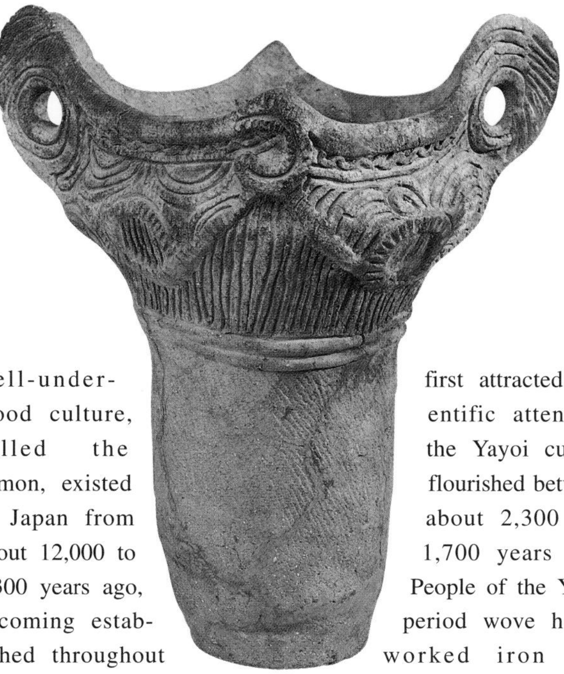

theless, research carried out in the past 10–15 years, including new DNA investigations reported in 1997, are finally allowing investigators to come to some agreement about the ancient peoples whose genes are carried in most living Japanese.

EARLIEST SETTLERS

Experts have been at odds over the origins of the Japanese for at least the past century. They have debated the times that various human populations arrived in Japan, the routes that they followed, the

affiliations of those early arrivals with possible parent groups in other lands, and the degree of their ancestral relationship to the modern Japanese. They have also differed over the relationship of the modern Japanese people and the Ainu people who live on Hokkaido, the northernmost Japanese island, and on adjacent Sakhalin Island and the Kuril Islands, which belong to Russia.

Scholars generally accept that the earliest

well-understood culture, called the Jomon, existed in Japan from about 12,000 to 2,300 years ago, becoming established throughout the archipelago. The name *Jomon* comes from a Japanese word for "cord marks," a description of the patterns found pressed in the clay pottery vessels that are characteristic of the period. Archaeological evidence indicates that the people of the Jomon culture lived in small communities near inland rivers or along the seacoast and subsisted primarily by hunting, fishing, and gathering. Scholars also generally agree that a new culture, which has been termed the Yayoi, appeared on Kyushu near the end of the Jomon period and eventually supplanted the Jomon culture in most of Japan. Named for the district in Tokyo where discovery of its distinct pottery

first attracted scientific attention, the Yayoi culture flourished between about 2,300 and 1,700 years ago. People of the Yayoi period wove hemp, worked iron and bronze, and practiced the wet rice cultivation that had originated in China.

Prior to the Jomon culture, however, evidence of the human occupation of Japan is more uncertain and disputatious. Before the end of World War II, archaeologists knew of no sites that could be considered Pre-Ceramic, a term used for Japan's Paleolithic Period, before the advent of the Jomon. In 1949 the Iwajuku site in central Honshu's Gumma prefecture was excavated, initially by archaeologist Tadao Aizawa and later by a team from Meiji University, Tokyo. That site contained stone tools that preceded those of the Jomon culture. Other Paleolithic sites subsequently were found, although none of them seemed to be older than 30,000 years.

Beginning in 1981, a number of sites were excavated in Miyagi prefecture of northern Honshu. Yielding what appeared to be Paleolithic tools such as hand axes and cleavers, they were dated as being between 200,000 and 600,000

119

Before the end of the last ice age 10,000 years ago, sea levels at times were low enough to have allowed land connections between the Japanese islands and between Japan and the Asian mainland (right). During those periods the Paleolithic first settlers of Japan may have entered the islands by any of several routes. (Opposite page) A reconstruction at a Japanese archaeological site shows one possible appearance of a Jomon-period dwelling.

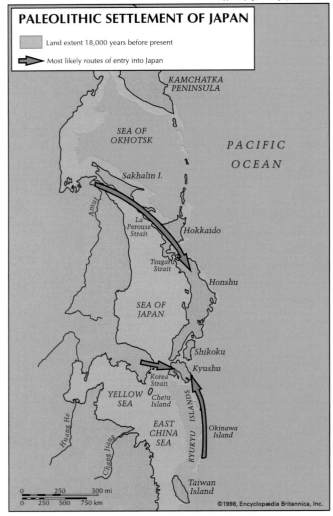

PALEOLITHIC SETTLEMENT OF JAPAN

Land extent 18,000 years before present

Most likely routes of entry into Japan

KAMCHATKA PENINSULA

SEA OF OKHOTSK

PACIFIC OCEAN

Sakhalin I.

Amur

La Perouse Strait

Hokkaido

Tsugaru Strait

Honshu

SEA OF JAPAN

Shikoku

Kyushu

Korea Strait

YELLOW SEA

Cheju Island

Huang He

Chang Jiang

EAST CHINA SEA

RYUKYU ISLANDS

Okinawa Island

Taiwan Island

0   250   500 mi
0   250   500   750 km

©1998, Encyclopædia Britannica, Inc.

years old. Many researchers, however, contested these early dates, partly because the dating techniques employed were not considered as reliable as those commonly used to date such early deposits and partly because there was evidence to suspect that the layering of the deposits had been disturbed. In addition, some researchers questioned whether the rocks that had been identified as tools were even human artifacts. Today some of these disputes seem to have been settled such that most researchers accept the early Paleolithic sites as genuine, although the exact dates of most deposits have still not been clearly resolved.

Because no human remains exist at any of these early sites, the identity of the toolmakers is completely unknown. China possesses sites containing remains of the early human *Homo erectus* that are older than 600,000 years, which makes it at least conceivable that people could have entered Japan early enough to leave behind artifacts that are hundreds of thousands of years old. Nevertheless, the earliest human remains known in Japan are all younger than 30,000 years and are of anatomically modern *H. sapiens.*

For Paleolithic humans the most likely routes of entry into Japan were from the Asian mainland through Sakhalin Island into Hokkaido in the north and from the Korean peninsula into Kyushu in the south. Another possibility is that people island-hopped along the Ryukyu Islands from the south. Two narrow straits of water, the Korea Strait between Korea and Kyushu and the Tsugaru Strait between Hokkaido and the largest Japanese Island of Honshu, are no more than 140 meters (460 feet) deep, whereas the La Perouse (Soya) Strait between Sakhalin Island and Hokkaido is only about 60 meters (200 feet) deep. At times during the last ice age (which ended about 10,000 years ago) when glaciers were at their maximum size, the lowered sea levels would have turned the La Perouse Strait and possibly the deeper straits into land bridges. If the deeper straits did not completely dry up, they would have been so narrow that crossing them, even without boats, would have been quite simple.

In addition to the obviousness of the Asian mainland as a source for early migrants to Japan, there is also some archaeological evidence to support that association: certain Chinese stone-blade forms that resemble stone knives found in Japan; a Paleolithic knife-shaped tool, the Suyanggai knife, that is found in both Korea and Kyushu; and the distribution of characteristic wedge-shaped microblade cores (stones from which flakes have been removed to create small blades) and chisel-like burins, or gravers, unique to the eastern Asian sphere. Such correla-

tions likely indicate contact and possible migration between the Asian mainland and Japan.

RICE FARMING AND NEW ARRIVALS

Just as most experts do not dispute the Paleolithic migration of humans into Japan, they also accept the existence of some kind of traffic—cultural, if not human—between the Asian mainland and Japan by the middle stages of the Jomon period, beginning about 5,000–6,000 years ago. This is supported by the common appearance of distinctive types of fishing gear on the Korean peninsula and Kyushu and of Jomon-style pottery in Korean and maritime Russian sites. Moreover, by the start of the Yayoi period about 2,300 years ago, Chinese-style rice agriculture had appeared in Japan.

What experts have strongly disputed, however, is the nature and extent of the contact between the Asian mainland and Japan and the implications for understanding the relationship of the Jomon and Yayoi peoples. What, they have asked, is signified by the association of the introduction of rice farming to Japan with the rise of the Yayoi culture? Was it only the concept of rice agriculture, perhaps with some rice seeds, that traveled to Japan, or was its introduction part of a long-term

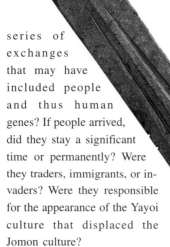

The clay jar at right is indicative of the distinct pottery made in the Yayoi period, named for a district in Tokyo where the discovery of such pottery first came to scientific attention. Flourishing between 2,300 and 1,700 years ago, the people of the Yayoi culture practiced wet rice cultivation and worked bronze and iron.

If rice farmers began encroaching on, and altering, the territories of the Jomon hunter-gatherer-fisher people, conflict might well have been a consequence. Moreover, if the rice farmers were new immigrants with a different physical appearance and perhaps a different language, the situation could have been further aggravated.

Were the rice farmers indigenous or immigrant people? Doigahama, a large Yayoi-period cemetery

series of exchanges that may have included people and thus human genes? If people arrived, did they stay a significant time or permanently? Were they traders, immigrants, or invaders? Were they responsible for the appearance of the Yayoi culture that displaced the Jomon culture?

Archaeological evidence from many hilltop sites that functioned as defensive positions attests to conflict during the early days of the Yayoi period. In addition, early Yayoi-period burial sites contain significant numbers of skeletal remains showing evidence of physical trauma and often including spear or arrow points, some still embedded in the bone. Occurrence of strife in this period, during the introduction of rice agriculture, may have parallels with the American West when "invading" farmers and sheepherders clashed, sometimes violently, with the "indigenous" ranchers.

site in western Honshu, has yielded important skeletal evidence for the existence of two different human populations in the region. One population, which had rounder heads, seems to represent the Jomon inhabitants of Japan. The other population, which had longer heads, suggests a different people—newcomers who arrived in Japan from the Asian mainland near the end of the Jomon period or the beginning of the Yayoi period.

LINGUISTIC INSIGHTS

Linguistics, the scientific study of language, is concerned in part with determining the affinities of different languages and tracing their common origins. By constructing family trees of languages, researchers often find clues about the relatedness and ancestry of their speakers, past population movements, and the influences that different cultures have

exerted on each other. One controversial line of evidence bearing on Japanese origins is that of the linguistic associations between the Japanese and other people. Among the world's major languages, Japanese and Korean are unique in being the only ones whose family relationships are still undetermined; even the extent of the relationship between Japanese and Korean continues to be debated. In the past, scholars have made attempts to show linguistic connections between Japanese and such languages as Mongolian, Finnish, or Hungarian. Some of these have produced more useful results than others.

While some linguists believe that the Japanese language is related to language groups of southern Asia, others discern links with either Austronesian languages—as are spoken in Indonesia, the Philippines, and Hawaii—or northeastern Asian Altaic languages—as are spoken in Mongolia and Siberia—or perhaps both. There are those who have argued that the Jomon people spoke a language of southern Asian origin, whereas in the Yayoi period a new language, Altaic in character, entered Japan from the Asian continent, likely by way of Korea. Some scholars associate the introduction of this new language with that of rice farming and metalworking and with the skeletal evidence for the appearance of a second human population around the beginning of the Yayoi period. They conclude that all are the result of the influx of a distinct new people from the Asian mainland at that time.

The somewhat unusual idea of links between Japanese and Austronesian languages dates to at least the early 1900s, but it is still quite controversial

The Avery Brundage Collection, Asian Art Museum of San Francisco

Yayoi-period metal objects, such as the bronze *dotaku* bell shown at right and the bronze lance on the opposite page, represent a significant departure from the artistry and technology of the Jomon period.

(Left) The Doigahama Site Anthropological Museum, Yamaguchi, Japan; (below) Judy Bellah—Photo 20 20/ PNI; (bottom) George Holton—Photo Researchers

Scholars have long argued over the reason for the differences in physical features between the modern Japanese (top) and the Ainu (above), whose round eyes and abundant body hair have been interpreted by some as being more Caucasoid than Mongoloid.

Skeletal evidence argues for the presence of two different human populations in Japan around the beginning of the Yayoi period. One population, with rounder skulls (above), seems to represent the Jomon inhabitants. The other, with longer skulls (right), appears to comprise newcomers who arrived from the Asian mainland near the time of the Jomon-Yayoi transition. The skulls come from Doigahama, a Yayoi-period cemetery site (opposite page).

among linguists. One explanation of the purported association holds that Austronesian people moved from west to east along the north coast of New Guinea about 5,000 years ago, and as they expanded into Oceania, a northern branch of the migration extended to Taiwan, then to the Ryukyu Is-lands, and finally to the Japanese main islands. The Japanese linguists who support this interpretation also acknowledge that an amalgamation of the earlier Jomon language—whatever it may have been—and one or more newly arrived Altaic languages took place in the Yayoi period.

Among those currently contesting the Austronesian input to Japanese is archaeologist Mark Hudson of Okayama University. Operating from the perspective that language relates to culture and that shifts in language have cultural counterparts, Hudson has looked for archaeological evidence in Japan and the Ryukyus that necessarily should have accompanied such linguistic shifts. He has found no evidence in Japan of any of the characteristics that usually are associated with early Austronesian culture. Furthermore, absent from the Ryukyus are pigs, a common species in Austronesian cultures, and the characteristic Austronesian Lapita red-slipped pottery. Other possible routes of entry for Austronesian languages into Japan likewise appear to show no trail of corroborating cultural evidence.

Linguists have also weighed in on the question of the ancestry of the Ainu, who are physically unlike the main Japanese population, having features that have been interpreted as more Caucasoid than Mongoloid. Until the Japanese attempted to settle the Hokkaido-dwelling Ainu into agriculture and other occupations, they hunted, fished, and trapped for their subsistence, maintaining a language and culture distinct from those of the Japanese. Linguists have been divided over the origin of the Ainu language, some contending that it is the remaining form of the Jomon language and thus points to an ancestral link between the Jomon and the Ainu.

They have also continued to debate whether and how much Ainu was influenced by the newer languages introduced in the Yayoi period.

All told, it seems most plausible that the Japanese language has its roots in whatever language was spoken by the original Paleolithic settlers of Japan, which may be largely retained in the Ainu language. That language was later modified by the linguistic input of the new arrivals associated with the Yayoi culture. Thus, modern Japanese appears to be a composite language, but one that does not have an Austronesian component.

COMPETING THEORIES

In the first half of the 20th century, during the strongly militarist period in Japan, a commonly expressed view among the country's physical anthropologists and archaeologists was that the Japanese had been in Japan for a very long time, that in no way could they be related to the people of Korea, and that a close relationship to modern Chinese people was unlikely. Whereas anthropologists outside Japan tended to be more cosmopolitan in their theorizing, their counterparts within the country were dedicated to establishing a purely Japanese origin for the

The Doigahama Site Anthropological Museum, Yamaguchi, Japan

125

Most anthropological theories of Japanese origins fall into one of three broad categories. In substitution theories (right) an initial Paleolithic population settled Japan and was then driven northward—and replaced almost completely—by one or more later migrations from the south. These theories exclude the Jomon from the ancestry of most modern Japanese populations. Hybridization theories (opposite page, left) envision a significant genetic intermixing of earlier and later arrivals. In transformation theories (opposite page, right) Japan was settled by an eastern Asian population already possessing a fair amount of variation in physical traits. Groups of this population then evolved locally in relative isolation to create most of the differences observed in Japanese populations today. Transformation theories recognize only a limited genetic intermixing of later migrants.

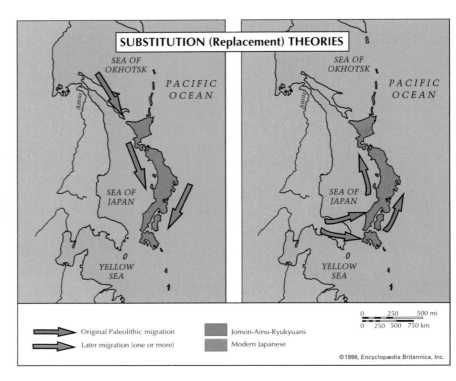

SUBSTITUTION (Replacement) THEORIES

Original Paleolithic migration
Later migration (one or more)
Jomon-Ainu-Ryukyuans
Modern Japanese

0   250   500 mi
0 250 500 750 km

©1998, Encyclopædia Britannica, Inc.

Japanese people. After the end of World War II, although its focus on Japanese origins remained, Japan's anthropological research no longer excluded the Korean peninsula or the eastern Asian mainland from consideration as source areas for the modern Japanese people. Nevertheless, the questions of routes, timing, numbers, and settlement areas have remained contentious for both Japanese and non-Japanese scholars.

Most of the anthropological theories attempting to detail the origin of the Japanese are based on skeletal studies that concentrate on what are commonly known as metric traits,

or measurements of the different bones of the body, in particular the skull. This type of research developed in the 18th and 19th centuries in Europe and the U.S. and found followers in Japan. Metric traits were used to identify the so-called racial affiliations of various groups of people. From these studies have emerged three broad categories of theories.

Substitution, or replacement, theories generally comprise variants of the idea that an original Jomon population was gradually driven northward by an invasion from the south by ancestors of the modern Japanese. Some of the theories

make the Jomon either the ancestors of the Ainu or so directly related that they essentially are the Ainu, whereas others interpret the Jomon as "pre-Ainu," meaning that neither the Japanese nor the Ainu were original to the Japanese islands. One model proposes that two successive invasions by two separate peoples forced an original Jomon-Ainu population northward. The first people, with Chinese and Korean physical traits, entered southwestern Honshu by way of Korea at some unknown period and spread northward throughout the island. The second people, a Mongoloid race resem-

bling Malayans, entered the west coast of Kyushu and then Honshu by way of Korea after the first invaders had been there for a time. The common element in substitution theories is that the invading populations replaced the Jomon with little or no amalgamation of genetic material. The theories say that although the Jomon may be the Ainu or their ancestors, they are not the ancestors of the modern Japanese.

In contrast to substitution theories, hybridization theories envision a significant genetic intermixing of populations. An early, 19th-century version suggested that the Japanese

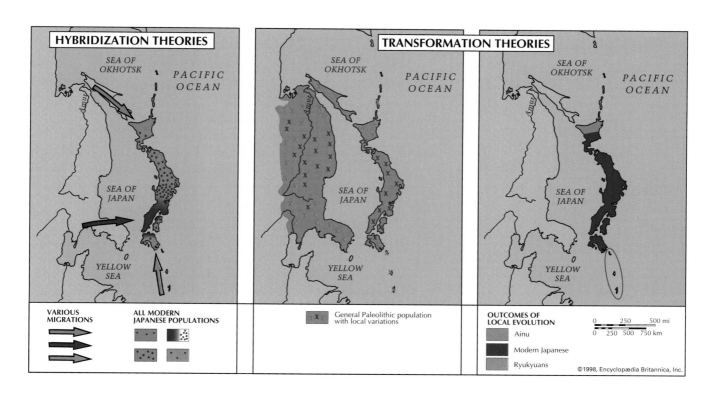

HYBRIDIZATION THEORIES

TRANSFORMATION THEORIES

SEA OF OKHOTSK
PACIFIC OCEAN
SEA OF JAPAN
YELLOW SEA

VARIOUS MIGRATIONS

ALL MODERN JAPANESE POPULATIONS

General Paleolithic population with local variations

OUTCOMES OF LOCAL EVOLUTION

Ainu

Modern Japanese

Ryukyuans

0   250   500 mi
0 250 500 750 km

©1998, Encyclopædia Britannica, Inc.

were a mixed tribe of Malayan and Mongoloid origin and that the Ainu were descended from Mongolian tribes. One of the best-known hybridization theories, from World War II-era Japan, concluded that the first populations of Japan were not Jomon, Ainu, or Korean but a proto-Japanese people who had originally lived in the Japanese islands. The modern Japanese developed gradually from the proto-Japanese as they mixed with populations from the Asian continent or the South Sea islands, whereas the modern Ainu originated from a mixture of northern Asian populations. Some hybridization

theories center on the introduction of rice agriculture, varying in such details as the numbers of migrant farmers that entered Japan, the frequency of their migrations, the extent to which they absorbed the locals, and the question of whether a lag in the development of agriculture in northern Japan retarded intermixing there and thus preserved the distinct Ainu population.

In the early 1990s Kazuro Hanihara of the University of Tokyo and the International Research Center for Japanese Studies proposed a hybridization theory for the origins of the modern Japanese and Ainu

that he termed the dual-structure model. It suggests that the Jomon people were of southeastern Asian origin, and the later arrivals were of northeastern Asian origin. Modern Japanese are a genetic mix of both of these populations, whereas modern Ainu are essentially the original Jomon.

Theories in the third category, called transformation theories, emphasize the isolation of populations and their local evolution as causes for the differences in the modern peoples of Japan. For example, a theory from the late 1940s proposed the existence in eastern Asia of a general Paleolithic population

that already contained a fair amount of variation in physical traits. As this population spread throughout most of eastern Asia, it separated into more or less disconnected groups, which went on to evolve locally. In Japan this "seed" population, the original inhabitants, then "transformed" through the various periods and forms to become the modern Japanese and the Ainu. The variation in Japanese populations today, rather than being caused by influxes of new people and intermixing, reflects the variation present in the original ancestral population and the differences in living

127

conditions across Japan that drove local evolution. Work in the past decade or two has produced transformation models that incorporate some hybridization—they recognize a limited intermixing of migrants during certain periods—but still identify significant time spans wherein most of the change took place through local evolution. Transformation theories allow for the introduction of new cultures and their effect on the evolution of the indigenous people, such as the assimilation of rice farming and metalworking that occurred in the Yayoi period, but they restrict the introduction of new genes. A number of prominent researchers, including Hanihara before he arrived at his dual-structure model, have supported such theories.

The above theories, being based primarily on measurements of morphological characteristics of the skull and other bones, suffer from an unfortunate problem: metric traits can be influenced by environmental factors. For example, an individual who engages in heavy chewing or uses the teeth as tools can develop heavy chewing muscles. This change can affect the shape of the jaw and cheekbones and possibly alter the overall shape of the face and skull. Consequently, metric traits are not

completely reliable in defining different populations. A better method is to use characteristics that are strongly influenced by the genetic makeup of the people but not by environmental factors. These are usually not quantifiable by simple measurement and are thus called nonmetric, or discontinuous, traits. Examples would be the shapes, numbers, and locations of cusps and other features on the teeth or of the various apertures in the skull through which the nerves and blood vessels pass.

From studies of nonmetric traits, Yukio Dodo of Tohoku University, Sendai, Japan, has concluded that modern Japanese and continental Asian populations fit in with classic Asian Mongoloid groups, whereas the Jomon and Ainu people belong to a less-Mongoloid population, most likely proto- or pre-Mongoloid, and that the Ainu on Hokkaido must be the direct descendants of the Jomon people. Other nonmetric studies, such as those of Nancy Ossenberg of Queen's University at Kingston, Ontario, although finding the Jomon and Ainu to be less similar than suggested by Dodo, have discerned an influx of new genetic material in southwestern Japan beginning in the Yayoi period. This new material gradually flowed

northeast, decreasing in influence as it traveled, such that the Ainu on Hokkaido retain the largest genetic inheritance from the Jomon people.

Recently Michael Pietrusewsky of the University of Hawaii, working with metric and nonmetric traits from a number of Japanese and eastern Asian populations, has likewise found a Jomon-Ainu connection. His conclusions, however, do not support an association, such as that suggested by Hanihara, between any modern people of Japan and any southeastern Asian populations. Rather, they support a northeastern Asian origin for all living populations of Japan and the concept that the modern Japanese are most closely related to the ancient Jomon and modern Ainu, with some gene flow from the mainland being responsible for the differences among them.

GENETIC STUDIES

Thus, after more than a century, lines of research by archaeologists, linguists, and physical anthropologists finally appear to be converging on the same broad picture of Japanese origins: an original peopling of Japan by migrants from Asia, followed by a second Asian influx, with the two populations mixing to varying degrees to

give rise to virtually all the modern people of Japan. Most recently, newer approaches based on genetic, or molecular, analysis have begun to address the question, helping to confirm some of the earlier work and adding new details about the degree to which various Japanese populations are related.

Like linguistics, which dissects and analyzes various details of languages to establish their relatedness, genetic analysis looks at variations in the makeup and frequency of proteins and the genes that control their production from different populations of organisms. By revealing differences in the protein forms and in the DNA that constitutes their genes, the technique can help identify and quantify similarities between, and variations among, those populations.

Some studies have focused on variations in the DNA of mitochondria, cellular structures that possess their own genetic material that is distinct from the chromosomes of the cell nucleus. Since mitochondria are transmitted only by the mother's egg cells, not the father's sperm cells, mitochondrial DNA traces only the maternal line of descent, which simplifies charting the relatedness and evolutionary history of populations. Other studies have concentrated on the DNA of that portion of the Y chromosome that does not recombine, or randomly regroup, with parts of other chromosomes during the formation of sperm cells. Studying the part of the Y chromosome that carries male-only traits and is not represented in females allows researchers to trace descent and population affiliations from the perspective of the male, as mitochondrial DNA does for females.

In 1994 L. Luca Cavalli-Sforza of the Human Population Genetics Laboratory at Stanford University and his co-workers published a summary of the genetic relationships between various populations of the world. Based on studies of differences in the frequency of occurrence of various genes in populations, their compendium includes 39 Asian populations (*see* Figure), with the genetic documentation covering an average of nearly 70 genes per population sampled. The researchers identify a major northern Mongoloid group in which modern Japanese and Ainu populations are linked in an eastern Asian subgroup with north Chinese, Koreans, Bhutanese, and Tibetans. Within the eastern Asian subgroup, the Ainu are the least-closely associated population, which suggests that they have been iso-

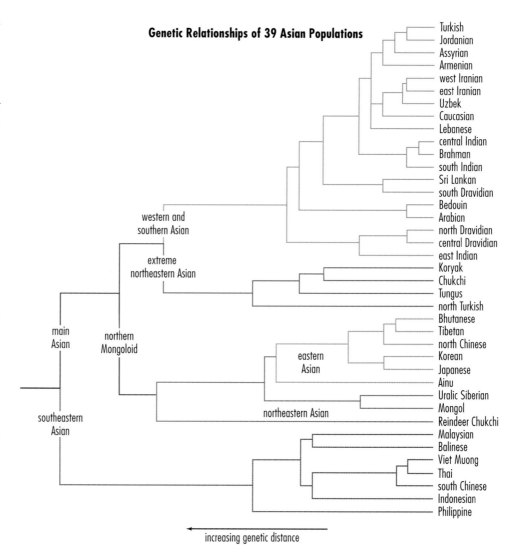

Genetic Relationships of 39 Asian Populations

increasing genetic distance

lated for a longer time than the others in the subgroup. The northern Mongoloid group in turn is subsumed in a larger main Asian group with 4 populations from the extreme northeast of Asia and 19 populations from western and southern Asia. A more distant southeastern Asian group comprises

7 populations, including south Chinese, Thai, and Indonesian. On the basis of this breakdown, it seems safe to conclude that the Japanese and Ainu populations originated in northern China or thereabouts—certainly in north-to-northeast Asia—and definitely are not derived from, or closely related

to, any populations from southeastern Asia or Oceania.

The Ainu have been the subject of numerous theories about their purported affinities with non-Japanese populations. Early European anthropologists thought that the Ainu had Caucasoid ties, suggested in part by their tendency to have more body hair than modern Mongoloid people, including the modern Japanese, and by hair characteristics supposedly more Caucasoid. This association was maintained despite the lack of supporting linguistic evidence. There have also been suggestions that the Ainu are related to the Australian Aboriginal people or that they are an independent "race" whose genetic similarity to modern Japanese is due to extensive genetic mixing.

According to Cavalli-Sforza and co-workers, the Ainu's Jomon ancestors most probably lived throughout Japan in the past until the influx of immigrants from the Korean peninsula in the 1st millennium BC. Although outliers on the northern Mongoloid group, the Ainu are in most respects northern Mongoloids and fairly closely related to populations from northeastern Asia. Their closest genetic relatives are the Japanese who live on Hokkaido, followed by the Ryukyu islanders.

The proposed scenario is that before the beginning of the Yayoi period about 2,300 years ago, the population of Japan, including the Ryukyuans, was genetically mostly similar to the modern Ainu. With the entry of the Yayoi-period immigrants and over perhaps the next 700 years—which includes a cultural period subsequent to the Yayoi called the Kofun ("burial mound"), or Tomb, period—the entry of new Mongoloid immigrants from the mainland by way of Korea to Kyushu and central Japan separated the existing population into northern and southern branches, the Ainu to the north and the Ryukyuans to the south. The modern Japanese are the descendants of those who lived between these extremes and are a blending of indigenous Jomon people and new immigrants.

In 1997 Michael F. Hammer of the University of Arizona and Satoshi Horai of the National Institute of Genetics, Mishima, Japan, reported the results of their studies of a short inheritable but nonessential stretch of DNA in the Y chromosome called the Y *Alu* polymorphic (YAP) element. Because the YAP element is not present in all men, its addition seems to have been a relatively recent event in human evolution. The two researchers found it in about 42% of Japanese men but not in Taiwanese, Chinese, or Korean men, which implies that it must have been present in Japan before the immigration in the Yayoi period. They also found that YAP appears more frequently in the Ainu and especially in the Ryukyuans than in the main Japanese population. YAP thus appears to be a marker of Jomon male lineages, and its presence in about two out of five modern Japanese men indicates genetic continuity from the Jomon population. If the absence of YAP in modern Korean and Chinese populations is assumed representative of the Yayoi-period immigrants of 2,300 years ago, then the results argue against replacement theories and their concept of a virtually complete genetic substitution of the original population.

Hammer and Horai identified another nonrecombining Y-chromosome marker, called the DSYS5 Y2 allele, of use in clarifying the relationships of the Ainu and Japanese. This piece of DNA was traced to Japan and Korea and ultimately to Henan province in northern China. Although it is present in both modern Japanese and Okinawans (who are at the extreme southwestern end of the Ryukyus), it is more common in Honshu than in Okinawa. If one accepts that Okinawans and Ainu people are descendants of the Jomon, then the distribution of DSYS5 Y2 suggests that there was indeed an influx into central Japan of new genetic material that carried the marker—material that mixed with that of the indigenous Japanese population but did not replace it.

Finally, on the assumption that the frequencies of the YAP element in today's Okinawan and Korean-Chinese populations are similar, respectively, to those of the Jomon and Yayoi-period immigrants, Hammer and Horai calculated the relative contribution of Y chromosomes by the indigenous people and the new immigrants. They determined that 39% of modern Japanese Y chromosomes are descended from immigrants during the Yayoi and subsequent Kofun periods, whereas 61% are from the indigenous Jomon population—definite support for hybridization theories.

THE FUTURE

With the examination of additional genetic material, which is expected to include samples of ancient DNA from Jomon, Yayoi, and Kofun burials, researchers should be able to clarify matters further. Although much more such work clearly needs to be done and its results reconciled with traditional evidence, it seems that the best explanatory theory for now is hybridization. The scenario is one in which the first inhabitants of Japan entered the country from northern Asia during the Paleolithic Period.

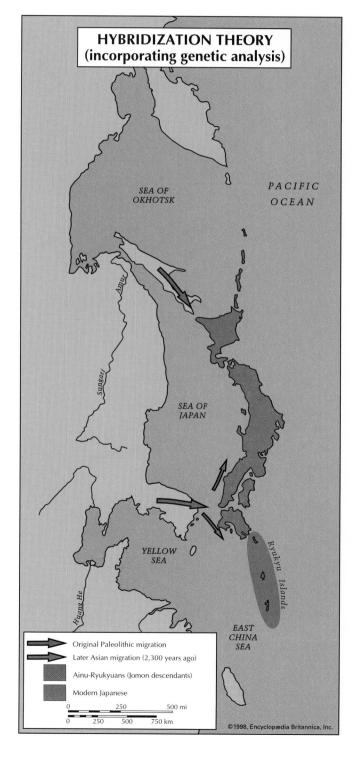

HYBRIDIZATION THEORY
(incorporating genetic analysis)

SEA OF OKHOTSK

PACIFIC OCEAN

Amur

Sungari

SEA OF JAPAN

Huang He

YELLOW SEA

Ryukyu Islands

EAST CHINA SEA

➡ Original Paleolithic migration
➡ Later Asian migration (2,300 years ago)
▓ Ainu-Ryukyuans (Jomon descendants)
▓ Modern Japanese

0   250   500 mi
0   250   500   750 km

©1998, Encyclopædia Britannica, Inc.

The emerging picture of Japanese origins, augmented by genetic studies, appears to be one of hybridization: an original peopling from northern Asia followed, 2,300 years ago, by an influx of migrants from the south. Over time the modern Japanese population developed as a hybrid of the two peoples, with gradations of intermixing extending north and south.

About 2,300 years ago new immigrants, bearing recent Mongoloid characteristics, entered the southwestern part of the main islands by way of the Korean peninsula and began to interact culturally and genetically with the indigenous people. Over time the modern Japanese population developed as a hybrid of the two peoples, forming gradations of intermixing that extended from southwestern and central Japan outward toward the northern and southern extremes of the archipelago. The Ainu and the Okinawans, who were least affected by this hybridization, retain many—perhaps most—of the characteristics of the original indigenous population of Japan.

Lest the ancient creation myths be neglected, it should be noted that any beings with the power to beget gods, islands, and the imperial lineage of Japan would be prime candidates for research. Unfortunately, scientists still have no idea whatsoever—nor any clue on how to begin the study—of the genetic makeup of Izanagi and Izanami.

FOR ADDITIONAL READING

• *The History and Geography of Human Genes,* L. Luca Cavalli-Sforza, Paolo Menozzi, and Alberto Piazza (Princeton University Press, 1994).
• "The Linguistic Prehistory of Japan: Some Archaeological Speculations," Mark Hudson, *Anthropological Science* (vol. 102, no. 3, 1994, pp. 231–255).
• *Prehistoric Japan: New Perspectives on Insular East Asia,* Keiji Imamura (University of Hawaii Press, 1996).
• *Prehistory of Japan,* C. Melvin Aikens and Takayasu Higuchi (Academic Press, 1982).
• "Y Chromosomal DNA Variation and the Peopling of Japan," Michael F. Hammer and Satoshi Horai, *American Journal of Human Genetics* (vol. 56, 1995, pp. 951–962).

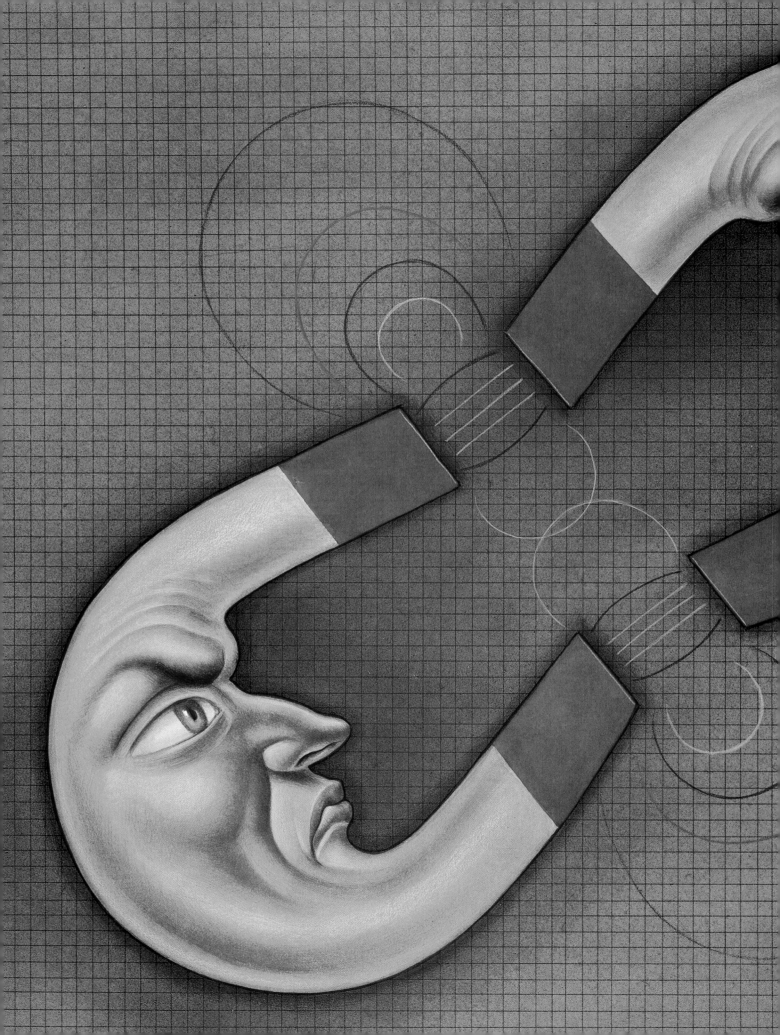

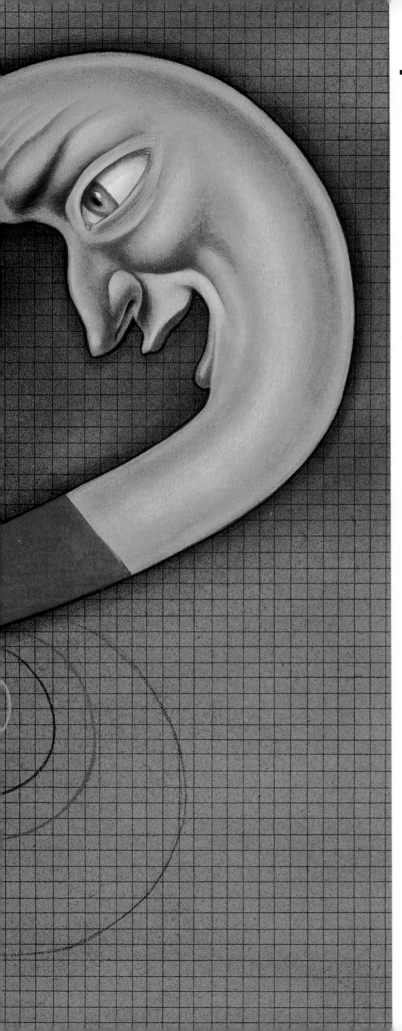

Anita Kunz

The Force Is with Us

by James D. Livingston

Lodestones and compasses first guided Columbus and others in the age of exploration. A century ago iron and steel magnets in motors, transformers, and telephones helped usher in the age of electricity. Today far more powerful, often unseen "neo" magnets are drawing us ever farther into the information age.

They hold our family photos and shopping lists to the refrigerator. They entertain us, children and adults alike, with their ability to attract and repel—the mystery of force without touch. Few of us, however, know of the multitude of hidden magnets in our homes, cars, and workplaces that enhance our daily lives—in the

James D. Livingston teaches in the department of materials science and engineering at the Massachusetts Institute of Technology. He is the author of Driving Force: The Natural Magic of Magnets.

food mixers in our kitchens and the cordless drills in our toolboxes, in the antiskid sensors that protect us from automobile accidents, or in the data strips on our credit cards and the hard disks in our computers. Fewer still are aware of the widespread technological effect of recent advances in the strength of magnets.

Despite their importance in modern technology, magnets lack the high-tech image of lasers, microchips, and superconductors, perhaps because the wonders of magnets have been known for thousands of years. In his dialogue *Ion,* written about 400 BC, Plato has Socrates say this about "the stone which Euripides calls a magnet":

This stone not only attracts iron rings, but also imparts to them a similar power of attracting other rings; and sometimes you may see a number of pieces of iron and

A compasslike device developed in China more than 2,000 years ago is depicted in a modern model (left). The bowl of the spoon, made of carved lodestone, rotated on the bronze base until its handle pointed south.

rings suspended from one another so as to form quite a long chain: and all of them derive their power of suspension from the original stone.

Plato was already aware of the two broad categories of magnetic materials. Permanent magnets, like refrigerator magnets and "the stone which Euripides calls a magnet," employ a "hard" magnetic material that provides a steady magnetic field. Temporary magnets, like refrigerator doors and Plato's iron rings, employ "soft" magnetic materials that produce no field of their own until acted upon by the field from

a permanent magnet (or by the field produced by the current-carrying wire coil of an electromagnet). Although a great variety of hard and soft magnetic materials are in use today, Plato knew of only magnetic stones and iron.

Magnetic stones, today called lodestones, are found throughout the world wherever iron ores are found. They consist primarily of a mineral called magnetite, an iron oxide with the chemical formula Fe_3O_4. The magnetic forces between lodestones must have been noticed, and wondered

16.

ORBIS LONGITVDINE

Magnete paulum vtrinque sæpe

INES REPERTÆ E MAGNETIS À POLO DECLINATIONE.

e deuia   Dat inuenire portum vbique Plancius.

about, by prehistoric people. Once the smelting of iron was developed (about 1200 BC) and the use of metallic iron became widespread, the ability of lodestones to attract iron probably also became widely known. Until about 300 years ago, lodestones and iron were the dominant hard and soft magnetic materials.

"LEADING" STONES

The magnetic compass is a common object that is usually taken for granted. Nevertheless, when Albert Einstein, at the age of four or five, received one from his father, it created an impact that he recalled in his autobiography: "I can still remember...that this experience made a deep and lasting impression upon me. Something deeply hidden had to be behind things." Today scientists know that the magnetic field that turns the compass needle results from electric

Beginning in the 16th century, mariners on long sea voyages used armed lodestones to remagnetize their compass needles. The brass-capped armed lodestone on the opposite page is fitted with pieces of iron at its north and south poles to make it a more powerful magnet.

Magnet Magic

The mysterious response of a magnetized iron needle to the "invisible hand" of the Earth's magnetic field has inspired many fancies. What has become known as the "sympathetic telegraph" was first described in the Italian natural philosopher Giambattista della Porta's *Magia Naturalis* ("Natural Magic"), published in Naples in 1558. This imaginary device consisted of two compasses with their dials, rather than showing directions, labeled with the letters of the alphabet. If the two compasses were magnetized by the same lodestone, della Porta claimed, the movement of one needle would cause the identical movement of the other and thereby allow messages to be sent, letter by letter, from afar—a concept that predated Samuel Morse and Western Union by 300 years.

Unfortunately for 16th-century Europe, the "natural magic" of magnets was not powerful enough to allow construction of such a device. Nevertheless, three centuries later magnets permitted long-distance communication via telegraphs and telephones, whose systems today incorporate the cellular phones, fax machines, and E-mail on which people depend to reach one another around the world. Whereas our modern magnetic means of communication indeed are real, in some ways they seem as magical as della Porta's imaginary invention did to Famianus Strada, a 17th-century Italian poet:

> Thus, if at Rome thy hand the steel
>   applies
> Tho' seas may roll between, or
>   mountains rise,
> To this some sister needle will incline,
> Such nature's mystic pow'r, and dark
>   design!

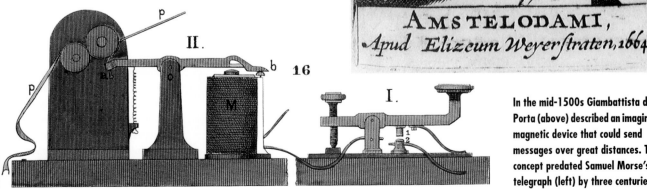

IOH. BAPTISTÆ PORTÆ
Neapolitani
MAGIÆ NATVRALIS
Libri Viginti.

AMSTELODAMI,
Apud Elizeum Weyerstraten, 1664

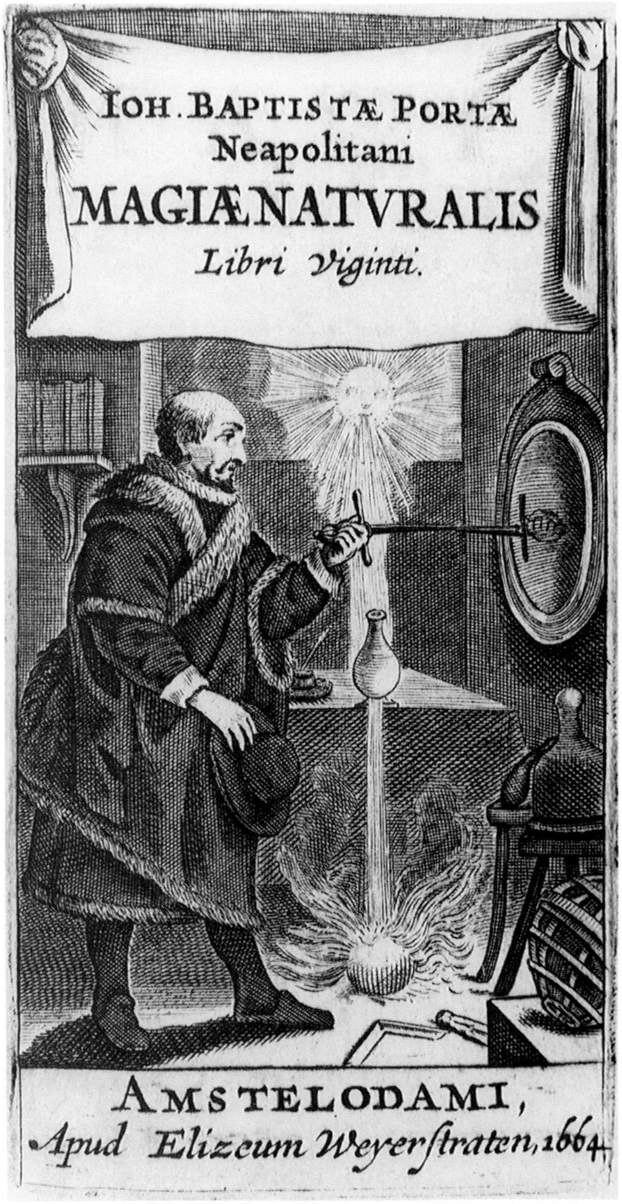

In the mid-1500s Giambattista della Porta (above) described an imaginary magnetic device that could send messages over great distances. The concept predated Samuel Morse's telegraph (left) by three centuries.

136

currents in the molten core of the Earth, 2,900 kilometers (1,800 miles) beneath our feet—"something deeply hidden" indeed.

Western literature carries no mention of the north-south orienting of magnets until nearly AD 1200. The term *lodestone,* referring to the use of the mineral for navigation (*lode* being a Middle English word for "leading" or "guiding"), did not appear until about 1500. There is convincing evidence, however, that the Chinese had developed a compasslike device, held as a secret of magicians of the emperor's court, as early as 200 BC.

The Chinese device was a spoon carved from a lodestone and placed on a polished bronze plate, where it was free to rotate in response to the Earth's field. The spoon shape is believed to have represented the constellation Ursa Major, or the Big Dipper, which is still used today to locate north in the night sky. There is no evidence that the Chinese actually used the lodestone spoon for navigation. It was probably put to more magical ends in the ancient practice of geomancy, in which good fortune could be encouraged by accurate alignment of houses, beds, and other objects with the heavens.

By at least the 6th century AD, the Chinese had learned

Electric generators, such as this early Gramme dynamo, set electrons flowing by the motion of a wire coil turning in a magnetic field. The first electric generators relied both on hard magnetic materials for the permanent magnets used to generate the field and on soft magnetic materials for the armature core.

how to use the lodestone to magnetize iron. The first use of magnetized iron needles for navigation probably occurred in China about AD 900, two or three centuries before they became known in Europe. Early iron compass needles, however, did not retain their magnetization well. Columbus relied heavily on his mariner's compass, and his needles had to be remagnetized frequently with a lodestone that he "guarded with his life," according to the American historian Samuel Eliot Morison in his account of Columbus's voyages.

Although lodestones excelled in retaining their magnetization, iron, once magnetized, was actually a stronger magnet. By the 16th century the two materials, hard and soft, had been combined to produce a permanent magnet that was more powerful than either material separately could be. Lodestones with iron attachments, called armed lodestones, became the strongest magnets available.

A quantitative comparison of lodestones and iron requires recourse to two quantities used to describe magnetic properties. One, the saturation magnetization, represents the ultimate magnetic field that the magnet, temporary or permanent, can produce. Roughly speaking, the saturation magnetization is a measure of the magnet's strength once fully magnetized, and rated by this property, iron wins hands down. The saturation magnetization of iron is more than 20,000 gauss, whereas that of a lodestone is typically less than 4,000 gauss. (Many different units are used to describe magnetic properties, but the gauss remains the most familiar. The Earth's magnetic field is about half a gauss.) Iron is a great temporary magnet.

Another important property measures how permanent the magnet is—that is, how much field in the opposite direction is needed to demagnetize it. This property is called the coercivity and can also be ex-

pressed in gauss. In this case, lodestones are the winners. Their coercivities are typically about 200 gauss, whereas those of pure iron are usually one gauss or less. Lodestones are clearly better permanent magnets than iron. In the case of the armed lodestone, the high coercivity of lodestone keeps it—and the iron in contact with it—magnetized, and the high saturation magnetization of the iron provides an enhanced magnetic field.

HORSESHOES AND WAR HEROES

Lodestones reigned supreme as the hard magnetic material until the early 18th century, when strong magnets made from carbon steels (iron containing about 1% carbon) were first produced in England. Advances in steelmaking in the 19th and early 20th centuries led to alloy steels (containing tungsten, molybdenum, cobalt, chromium, or some combination) that yielded still stronger magnets. Although their coercivities remained inferior to those of lodestones, their saturation magnetizations were much higher. Engineers then developed a single measure of magnet quality that depended on both saturation magnetization and coercivity: energy product. In most cases the volume of magnet required for a given application was found to be inversely proportional to its energy product. Put another way, the higher the energy product, the smaller the magnet needed. The cobalt-chromium steels of the 1920s had energy products 4 times those of carbon steels and almost 10 times those of lodestones.

Despite the higher energy products of alloy steels, their softness (coercivities of less than 100 gauss) required the magnets to be long, to minimize the demagnetizing effects of the magnetic poles at each end. Long steel magnets were often bent into the familiar horseshoe shape, which allowed both poles to contact the object to be acted upon. Until the development of harder magnets in the 1930s, the telephone's earpiece, which housed the receiver, was separate from the transmitter in the mouthpiece because it contained a long steel horseshoe magnet. Modern magnets are seldom horseshoe-shaped, but this stereotyped image persists even though the steel magnets

(Top) Archive Photos/PNI; (below) Leonard Lessin—Peter Arnold

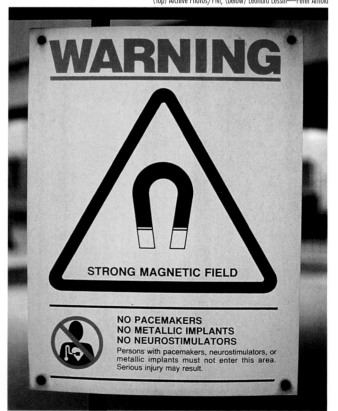

STRONG MAGNETIC FIELD

**NO PACEMAKERS
NO METALLIC IMPLANTS
NO NEUROSTIMULATORS**
Persons with pacemakers, neurostimulators, or metallic implants must not enter this area. Serious injury may result.

The earpiece of actress Dorothy Lamour's telephone contains a long steel horseshoe magnet. Until harder magnets were developed in the 1930s, the bulky earpiece had to be separate from the mouthpiece.

suited to that shape have long been obsolete.

Steel magnets were surpassed in the 1930s by iron-based magnets containing aluminum, nickel, and cobalt that had energy products and coercivities substantially higher than those of steels. These "alnico" magnets reduced the size of telephone receivers and many other devices and arrived just in time to play an important role in World War II, providing the magnetic field in the specialized vacuum tubes called magnetrons that generated high-power microwaves for Allied radar systems. The Germans first became aware of

The horseshoe remains a familiar, widely recognizable symbol for magnets and magnetic fields, even though the steel magnets that require that shape have not been used for decades.

microwave radar when in February 1943 they downed a British plane carrying a magnetron. The Axis, however, had very limited supplies of cobalt and nickel, essential components of alnico magnets, and were unable to capitalize on the discovery. Fleet Adm. Karl Dönitz, commander of Germany's U-boat fleet, cited microwave radar as "the one single weapon that defeated the submarine and the Third Reich." One German author called alnico magnets "the magnets that won the war." While the magnetron remains a key component in modern radar systems, it is also the source of power for microwave ovens.

THE BEST MAGNETS AROUND

Alnico magnets remain in use but are steadily losing market share to two newer classes of permanent magnets: ferrites and rare-earths. Ferrite magnets, which are made of iron oxides containing barium or strontium, were introduced in the 1950s by the Dutch electronics company Philips and surpassed alnicos in annual tonnage within about 10 years. Close chemically to lodestones, ferrites have low saturation magnetizations; thus, their energy products are less than many of the alnico magnets.

Despite this weakness, ferrites in the late 1990s accounted for more than 90% of the permanent-magnet market by weight. Their two advantages are hardness (coercivities of several thousand gauss, compared with several hundred gauss for most alnicos) and low cost. Their high resistance to demagnetization allows them to be thin in the direction of magnetization, a great advantage for engineers designing motors, speakers, and other electromagnetic devices. Their low cost allows them to have, among all hard magnetic materials, the highest values of a quality measure that is more important in many applications than energy product alone: energy product per dollar. In that category ferrites win easily.

For applications in which price is secondary to magnetic properties, the winners are the newest class of permanent magnets, the rare-earth magnets. Whereas the energy products of alnicos are limited by low coercivities, and those of ferrites by low saturation magnetizations, rare-earth magnets have superior values of both,

and this leads to record-breaking energy products.

The rare-earth metals comprise the elements scandium, yttrium, and lanthanum through lutetium on the periodic table. Although most are actually not very rare (some are more abundant than lead or tin), they commonly occur in ores as mixed oxides. Being chemically very similar, the individual rare-earth metals were at first difficult to separate and were not available in high purity or large quantities prior to World War II, when work on the atomic bomb led to a practical means of separation. By the 1960s several research groups were studying the properties of compounds of the recently available rare-earth metals with various other elements, including cobalt and iron.

The first commercial rare-earth magnets, introduced by the General Electric Co. in 1970, were based on a compound of cobalt and samarium. Energy products were several times greater than the alnicos, and coercivities exceeded 10,000 gauss. Their high cost, however, initially limited their use largely to military applications, such as traveling-wave tubes for airborne radar, and to commercial products, like wristwatches, in which the amount of material needed is so minute that it represents a

British radar of the 1930s (above) employed radio waves, but by the start of World War II, the advantages of microwaves had become recognized. For generating high-power microwaves, researchers developed specialized vacuum tubes called magnetrons, which depended on alnico magnets for their operation.

small fraction of manufacturing costs. A typical quartz watch, for example, contains a rare-earth magnet only two to three millimeters (roughly a 10th of an inch) in diameter.

In the late 1970s political upheavals in Zaire (now the

Democratic Republic of the Congo), the dominant world producer of cobalt ore, led to severe cost and supply problems with cobalt, and development of cobalt-free magnets became a high priority. The resulting research activity led to

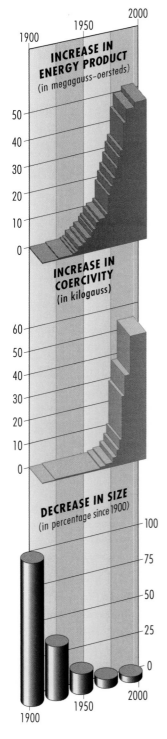

INCREASE IN ENERGY PRODUCT
(in megagauss-oersteds)

INCREASE IN COERCIVITY
(in kilogauss)

DECREASE IN SIZE
(in percentage since 1900)

Increases in the energy product and coercivity of permanent-magnet materials since 1900 have been striking, as has the reduction in the size of a magnet required for a specific task.

the announcement in 1983 of a new generation of rare-earth magnets based on a compound of iron, neodymium, and boron. Independently developed by Sumitomo Metals in Japan and the General Motors Corp. in the U.S., these "neo" magnets had even higher saturation magnetizations and energy products than samarium-cobalt magnets, and the raw materials were less costly. Neodymium is much more abundant than samarium, and iron is much more abundant and less expensive than cobalt. Neo magnets rapidly began to replace samarium-cobalt in many applications and accelerated the replacement of alnicos.

Currently the world's most powerful magnets, neo magnets have energy products 10 times higher than those of ferrites and more than 100 times higher than the steel magnets of the 19th century. Although the low-cost ferrites remain the choice for many applications, the higher energy products of neos allow the use of much smaller magnets and permit very compact designs. Because size, weight, and overall cost of a device are often more important than the cost of the magnet alone, neos can compete successfully with ferrites in many cases. The production and use of neo magnets have grown rapidly and are expected to account for half of the permanent-magnet market (in monetary value) by the year 2000.

ON THE ATOMIC SCALE

Physicists know that, strictly speaking, all matter is magnetic. With sufficiently sensi-

Inside this small quartz watch, shown magnified about nine times, the tiny rare-earth magnet that serves as the rotor of its electric motor lies within the circle below the copper coil of the electromagnet.

(Left) Adapted from information obtained from *Driving Force: The Natural Magic of Magnets,* ©1996 James D. Livingston, p. 56, Harvard University Press, Cambridge, Massachusetts; (above) Leonard Lessin—Peter Arnold; (opposite page) A.K. Geim—High Field Magnet Laboratory, University of Nijmegen, The Netherlands

tive equipment, they can measure the magnetic properties of copper, glass, plastic, water, and even living things. Moreover, in magnetic fields far stronger than those normally encountered, magnetic forces on seemingly nonmagnetic materials can become substantial. In a dramatic example, scientists in The Netherlands in 1997 used a powerful electromagnet to produce an upward force strong enough to overcome gravity and levitate a live frog, a feat that attracted worldwide media attention.

While most animate and inanimate matter is only very weakly magnetic, some matter is quite different. The force between lodestone and iron was obvious to Plato without the need for sensitive equipment or powerful electromagnets. This selectivity is one of the most fascinating and often useful aspects of magnetic forces. Notwithstanding the usual meaning of the phrase "to find a needle in a haystack," the task is easy with a magnet, provided that the needle is made of steel. Understanding what distinguishes iron and steel from most other materials requires thinking on the scale of atoms and their electrons.

All magnetism results from the motion of electric charge.

All matter is magnetic, as is dramatically demonstrated by a living frog levitated within the hollow core of an electromagnet capable of producing a force strong enough to oppose gravity. The researchers who did the experiment also levitated a variety of other objects, from strawberries to plastic.

An electromagnet generates a magnetic field from a coil of wire carrying an electric current, which is the motion of negatively charged electrons over long distances. Electrons, however, also can produce magnetism without ever leaving their home atoms. Both the orbital motion of electrons around the atomic nucleus and their spinning motion about their own axes create magnetism, although in most solids the major source of magnetism is electron spin.

Most electrons in most atoms are paired with electrons of opposite spin, which makes the net magnetism nearly zero. In some materials the atoms possess a few electrons having unopposed spins. The net spin makes each such atom a tiny magnet, but because these atomic magnets point in random directions, the material as a whole shows no net magnetism. For a few special materials, however, called ferromagnetic materials, the net spins of neighboring atoms are aligned in parallel via a force called the exchange interaction. Because of the alignment, all the individual atomic magnets act in

unison and create the special macroscopic effects shown by ferromagnetic materials. Ferromagnetism is a phenomenon of large-scale interatomic cooperation, and among the few elements that are ferromagnetic at room temperature is the one known to Plato: iron.

Among the elements, iron is quite special for a number of reasons. Lying at the end of a sequence of nuclear reactions by which most of the lighter elements are created in stars, iron has the most stable nucleus of all the elements. As a result, it is the most common metal in the universe and in the Earth as a whole. Iron ores are also easily mined, and they easily yield the metal when reacted with carbon. These characteristics make iron very inexpensive to produce compared with the only other elements that are ferromagnetic at room temperature: nickel and cobalt. Had iron not been ferromagnetic and easy to obtain, modern technology would be very different.

SOFT AND HARD

In the absence of a magnetic field from an external magnet, the atoms in a soft magnetic material like iron—say, the

(Below) Alfred Pasieka—Science Photo Library/Photo Researchers; (opposite page, top) General Electric Corporate Research and Development; (bottom) adapted from information obtained from *Driving Force: The Natural Magic of Magnets,* © 1996 James D. Livingston, pp. 92–93, Harvard University Press, Cambridge, Mass.

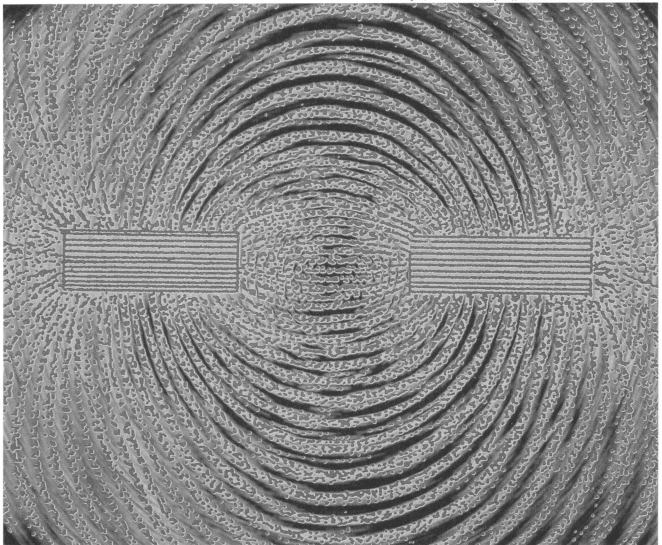

iron of a refrigerator door—are divided into small local regions of magnetization, called magnetic domains. Each domain is fully magnetized, with all of its atomic magnets aligned in parallel, but the magnetization direction varies from one domain to another. Macroscopically the domains cancel each other out, and the door remains unmagnetized. In some materials the domains may be large, on the scale of millimeters, but even when much smaller, each domain contains many billions of atomic magnets aligned in one direction.

When someone places a magnet on a refrigerator door, conditions change locally inside the door. Each atomic magnet, like a tiny compass needle, tries to align with the applied field of the magnet; as a result, some domains grow and others shrink. If the south pole of the magnet faces the door, the domains that grow will be those with north poles at the surface. As domains grow and shrink, most of the change takes place within the moving walls between the domains, where the atomic magnets are flipping from one direction to another as the wall moves.

In a soft magnetic material, it is important that domain walls move easily and thereby enable the macroscopic magnetization to change easily. This is particularly important for applications that use alternating current (AC), in which the flow of electric charge and thus the magnetic field periodically reverse. Within the iron core of a power-line transformer, for example, the magnetic domain structure must reverse as often as 120 times each second in response to the alternating magnetic fields from the primary windings. Similarly, the domain structure in the magnetic recording head of an audio or video recorder or a computer disk drive must change thousands of times each second.

The ideal behavior for a hard magnetic material, on the other hand, is just the opposite. To retain its magnetization, its domain walls should form and move only with much difficulty. Once it has been magnetized in one direction, the material should require a large

The net magnetization of an ideal soft magnet varies with the direction and strength of an applied magnetic field. Within the material, domains (insets) grow and shrink as atoms gradually realign with the applied field.

field in the opposite direction for moving domain walls and demagnetizing it; *i.e.,* it should have a large coercivity.

Given the foregoing, it becomes clearer that for materials scientists trying to develop better magnets, the fundamental properties of saturation magnetization and coercivity each require a rather different focus. Saturation magnetization is the net magnetization obtained when all the atomic magnets are aligned; it therefore depends on the individual strengths of the atomic magnets and the degree to which

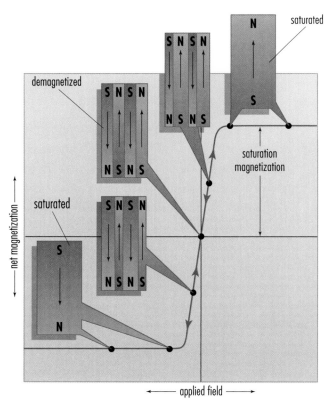

In this magnified view of a cluster of iron-neodymium-boron crystals, domains of opposite magnetization are visible as light and dark ripples in each crystal.

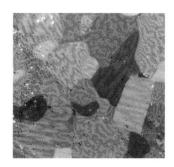

the exchange interactions line up the atomic magnets in parallel. This, in turn, depends primarily on the chemical composition of the material and the crystalline structure. For instance, the saturation magnetization of ferrite magnets is low in part because, being oxides, ferrites contain oxygen atoms, which are nonmagnetic and so do not contribute as atomic

magnets. It is also low because the exchange interactions in the ferrites' particular crystalline structure result in an antiparallel arrangement of some of the iron atoms, an arrangement that reduces the net magnetization.

On the other hand, coercivity depends on the ease with which atomic magnets can change their direction in the presence of a reverse applied field and therefore on how easily magnetic domain walls can move. Coercivity is very sensitive to the homogeneity of the material's microstructure, including the size of the individual crystals, the uniformity of the chemical constitution, and the presence of particles of other compounds. For example, 20th-century electron microscopy finally revealed the reason for the high coercivity of lodestones: the presence in the material of tiny particles of iron oxides other than magnetite, which block the motion of magnetic domain walls. (Samples of pure laboratory-made magnetite, which lack these particles, are not permanent magnets; they have little or no coercivity.) Thus, the creation of microscopic barriers to the formation and motion of domain walls has become a major strategy of scientists working to improve coercivity in modern magnets.

Coercivity is also influenced by a factor at the atomic level called magnetocrystalline anisotropy. In rare-earth atoms like samarium and neodymium, the distribution of electrons around the nucleus is very non-spherical, which leads to a strong preference for the atomic magnets to align in a particular crystalline direction. (A coin is more resistant to being turned over than a ball.) The strong magnetocrystalline anisotropy of rare-earth atoms makes the domain walls in samarium-cobalt and neo magnets easy to immobilize with structural and chemical inhomogeneities. In rare-earth magnets the iron and cobalt atoms are the major source of magnetization, but the rare-earth atoms are the major source of coercivity.

Scientists interested in soft magnetic materials are in search of low coercivities. They seek materials with homogeneous microstructures and low magnetocrystalline anisotropies, aiming at easy

domain-wall motion and easy magnetization change. One result of that search has been the commercial development in the past decade of amorphous, or noncrystalline, soft magnetic alloys, which have found numerous AC applications, including transformers and recording heads. Because amorphous materials entirely lack crystalline boundaries, they greatly facilitate domain-wall movement.

MOVERS AND SHAKERS

The dramatic improvements in hard magnetic materials since the 1930s have greatly increased the technological importance of permanent magnets. By providing the steady magnetic fields that make motors whir and loudspeakers blare, they are literally the "movers and shakers" of modern technology. Today, increasingly it is a neo magnet that is doing the moving and shaking.

The technology on which neo magnets probably have had the greatest impact is electric motors. A motor consists, basically, of one magnet—the rotor—turning inside another—the stator—by virtue of the magnetic forces between them.

Formerly, both magnets in most motors were iron-core electromagnets, but the successive development of alnicos, ferrites, and rare-earth magnets has greatly increased the proportion of motors that use permanent magnets for either the rotor or the stator. For a given power rating, a permanent-magnet motor can be smaller and lighter than one that uses only electromagnets, and it can be more energy-efficient because it avoids the waste associated with the losses to resistance in the windings of an electromagnet.

Increasing energy products have allowed the use of smaller and smaller magnets, and increasing coercivities have removed design constraints that

(Top) Yoav Levy—Phototake; (below) Peter Morgan—Reuter/Corbis-Bettmann

once were necessary to avoid demagnetization. The trend started with motors of low power ratings, but neo magnets now allow the construction of efficient 1,000-horsepower motors that are a fifth the weight and size of traditional motors of the same power.

At any power level, the engineer now has more flexibility of motor design. Early permanent-magnet motors used the permanent magnet as the stator and an electromagnet as the rotor. Today the virtues of neo magnets make feasible "inside-out" designs with permanent-magnet rotors. Such motors are more amenable to control because it is simpler to feed electronic signals into a stator than into a rapidly spinning rotor. One application of inside-out motors, commonly called brushless DC or electronically commutated motors, is in cassette tape drives. Another design option facilitated by modern magnets is that of disk motors, which find use, for example, in the hard-disk, floppy-disk, and compact-disc drives of laptop computers, in which space limitations require extremely thin motors. In disk motors the main magnetic field is directed along the axis of rotation rather than radially. Such designs require hard magnetic materials with high coercivity.

A similar development has occurred in loudspeakers, which can now be more compact than ever before. In most speakers a permanent magnet produces vibratory forces on a coil of wire, the voice coil, that is carrying rapidly changing electric current corresponding to the sound being reproduced. The vibration of the voice coil is transferred to a diaphragm attached to the coil and thereby generates sound in the adjoining air. When alnico and ferrite magnets displaced steel horseshoe magnets, telephones appeared with receiver and transmitter in a single handset. More recently, rare-earth magnets have enabled high-quality, high-volume sound to be generated in the tiny earphones that made possible personal stereo systems and led to improved hearing aids.

Dozens of components of the typical modern automobile rely on the ability of modern magnets to provide adequate magnetic fields in tiny, space-saving packages. In addition to speakers and a multitude of

North News and Pictures

electric motors, magnets are the basis for numerous sensors that measure, for example, the rotation speeds of various shafts and axles in cruise-control and antilock brake systems. In such sensors a tiny magnet attached to a rotating part triggers an electrical pulse each time it passes a stationary coil or other device. Magnets also are the crucial element in most airbag sensors—the rapid deceleration experienced in a crash moves a magnet through a coil and triggers deployment. Likewise, in computers and printers, industrial control systems and home-security systems, and hundreds of other applications, small hidden magnets provide the forces that drive much of modern technology.

At the opposite end of the size scale is a growing application that requires tons of permanent magnets—magnetic resonance imaging (MRI). This noninvasive medical diagnostic technique uses strong magnetic fields acting on hydrogen nuclei in the body to create images of the body's internal structures. In general, the stronger the field, the sharper the image. Although most MRI systems use superconducting electromagnets, permanent-magnet systems are attractive in that they avoid the cumbersome, expensive cooling needed to keep the magnetic coils chilled to their superconducting state. Moreover, they allow designs that better limit extraneous magnetic fields. Currently the best permanent magnets for MRI are neo magnets. An MRI system designed to use a field of 2,000 gauss requires 21 tons of ferrite

145

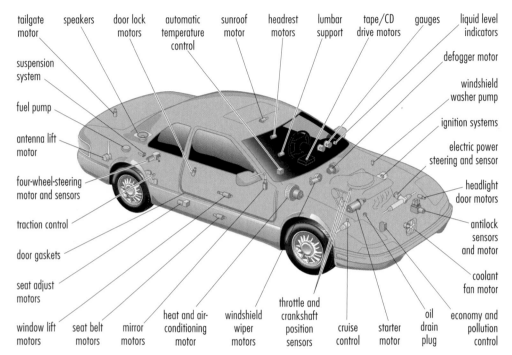

tailgate motor · speakers · door lock motors · automatic temperature control · sunroof motor · headrest motors · lumbar support · tape/CD drive motors · gauges · liquid level indicators

suspension system

fuel pump

antenna lift motor

four-wheel-steering motor and sensors

traction control

door gaskets

seat adjust motors

window lift motors · seat belt motors · mirror motors · heat and air-conditioning motor · windshield wiper motors · throttle and crankshaft position sensors · cruise control · starter motor · oil drain plug · economy and pollution control

defogger motor

windshield washer pump

ignition systems

electric power steering and sensor

headlight door motors

antilock sensors and motor

coolant fan motor

Dozens of motors and sensors in the modern automobile make use of today's most powerful permanent magnets to provide adequate magnetic fields in tiny, space-saving packages.

magnets but only 2.6 tons of neo magnets. Although cost considerations alone favor ferrites, the importance of overall size and weight makes neos the magnet of choice for permanent-magnet MRI systems using fields of 2,000 gauss and higher.

Modern technology is also indebted to advances in soft magnetic materials, which have greatly reduced energy losses in transformers and other AC devices. Especially dramatic have been the improvements in magnetic recording materials, allowing the data-storage densities of computer disks to increase by a factor of 100,000 in less than 40 years. Despite

growing competition from optical storage, by the end of the 1990s magnetic recording media still stored most of the world's data.

BEYOND NEOS

Even the best of today's magnets, the neos, have their shortcomings, including low resistance to corrosion, a rapid decrease in performance with rising temperature, and relatively high cost. As some scientists and engineers seek to alleviate these problems, others search for new and better materials. Current understanding of the physics of magnetic materials suggests that energy

products two or three times higher than those of neo magnets are achievable. Just as important, however, could be the development of hard magnetic materials that have properties superior to ferrites but are less expensive than rare-earth magnets. Both avenues of future development—materials that outperform neos and materials that are less-costly alternatives to neos—are wide open because so many compounds exist whose magnetic properties are incompletely known.

Researchers have already measured the basic properties of most two-element (binary) compounds and have followed

The use of permanent magnets to provide the strong fields needed in this magnetic resonance imaging (MRI) system offers several advantages, including elimination of coolants and refrigeration, reduced electric power consumption, and a design that offers improved control of extraneous magnetic fields.

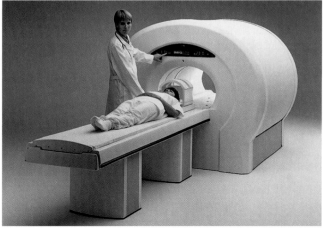

Field Effects division of Intermagnetics General Corporation

A neo magnet floats above a disk of high-temperature superconductor. In a sense, room-temperature superconducting electromagnets already exist in the form of permanent magnets.

up on the success of alnicos with investigations of most simple alloys. Nevertheless, those accomplishments still leave thousands to millions of three-element (ternary) and four-element (quaternary) compounds to be studied. As a case in point, it was only when scientists focused on certain ternary compounds that the iron-neodymium-boron neo magnets were found.

Recent research has concentrated largely on compounds combining a rare-earth element with iron or cobalt and a third element, often a metalloid like nitrogen, carbon, or boron. (Metalloids are nonmetal elements that can form alloys with metals.) For example, a compound of iron, samarium, and nitrogen reported at Trinity College, Dublin, in 1990 shows promise of yielding magnetic properties similar to neo magnets but capable of operating at higher temperatures. Some scientists also regard compounds of iron or cobalt with two or more metalloids as a good place to look for magnets to fill the gap between cheap ferrites and expensive neos.

For years researchers around the world have been laboring to find the holy grail of materials science—a room-temperature superconductor capable of carrying a large current without suffering energy losses to electrical resistance. An electromagnet made of such a material, once energized with a circulating current of electrons, would sustain its magnetic field in a shirt-sleeve environment with negligible additional input of energy. On the other hand, it should be encouraging to note that, in a sense, technology already has such a device—the permanent magnet—whose persistent field results from the resistance-free motion of electrons, albeit on the atomic level. Moreover, the history of permanent magnets, which has been one of steady improvement, intimates that even better materials are out there, waiting to be found by those willing to make the effort.

FOR ADDITIONAL READING

- *Advances in Permanent Magnetism,* Roland J. Parker (Wiley, 1990).
- *Driving Force: The Natural Magic of Magnets,* James D. Livingston (Harvard University Press, 1996).
- *Hidden Attraction: The Mystery and History of Magnetism,* Gerrit L. Verschuur (Oxford University Press, 1993).
- *Rare-Earth Iron Permanent Magnets,* J.M.D. Coey, ed. (Oxford University Press, 1996).

The Birds and the Bees, the Flowers and the Trees

by May Berenbaum

S ome metaphors based on biological interactions are so ubiquitous that they almost border on cliché. The interaction between flowers and their pollinators, for example, is so familiar that for centuries writers have appro-

A soldier beetle (family Cantharidae) pollinates the blossom of a primrose willow.

priated the exchange to express romantic attraction. The American poet Emily Dickinson was one of many who immortalized the relationship in verse:

Auto-da-fé and judgment
Are nothing to the bee;
His separation from his rose
To him seems misery.

All too often in literature, however, scientific understanding lags behind poetic appreciation. As any entomologist knows, Dickinson had her genders wrong. Male bees, or drones, leave the hive only to mate with the queen or when they are forcibly ejected by their fellow bees during lean times. Visiting flowers to col-

lect nectar and pollen is the sole responsibility of the female workers.

Biologists, however, are on precarious ground criticizing the limited understanding of pollination biology manifested in poetry. The deceptively simple interaction between flowers and their animal pollinators has "bee-deviled" (as it were) biologists for centuries. Despite stepped-up research in the past several decades, the complexities of pollination still are not very well understood. Increasingly, scientists realize that working out the details of these exchanges is more than simply an esoteric intellectual exer-

cise, says Stephen L. Buchmann, research entomologist at the Carl Hayden Bee Research Center, Tucson, Arizona. In *The Forgotten Pollinators* (1996), a book by Buchmann and Gary Paul Nabhan, director of science at the Arizona–Sonora Desert Museum, Tucson, the authors state, "Precise

May Berenbaum is Professor of Insect Ecology at the University of Illinois at Urbana-Champaign. She is the author of numerous magazine articles and three books about insects for the general public, including, most recently, Bugs in the System: Insects and Their Impact on Human Affairs.

More than 75% of the world's crop plants and countless species in the wild depend on the services of pollinating insects and other animals. With a decline in pollinators, however, many scientists warn that both our farm fields and wild areas may be facing a reproductive crisis.

(Opposite) John Shaw—Bruce Coleman

knowledge of pollination ecology remains the weakest link in our efforts to keep endangered plants from suffering further declines. It is also a weak link in efforts to sustain agricultural productivity to feed the world's burgeoning human population."

Recently many biologists have joined Buchmann and Nabhan in sounding an alarm about this knowledge gap, in large part because pollination is the linchpin in the most fundamental processes of life— and because many pollinators may be dangerously in decline. Approximately one-third of all

The magnifying lens of a microscope reveals that the structure of pollen grains is as varied as the forms of the flowers that produce them. Pollen grains of (clockwise from below) a sunflower (foreground) and mallow; dandelions; and forsythia.

Photographs, Oliver Meckes—Photo Researchers

food items consumed in a Western diet are the direct result of pollination activities. In fact, the benefits that wild and domestic honeybees provide through pollination are 40–50 times more valuable than the profits reaped by harvesting their honey. These benefits, however, may be in jeopardy. In the U.S., for example, populations of honeybees on which agricultural producers depend—both feral (wild) and domesticated, or managed, honeybees—have crashed under the combined stress of pests, disease, and bad weather. According to some estimates, American beekeepers have lost approximately 20% of their colonies since 1990. Regional declines have been even more dramatic. Pennsylvania beekeepers lost more than half of their colonies between 1995 and 1996. In feral colonies, where mortality is more difficult to track, losses may be greater still. In a study of one feral colony in California, researchers documented a 75% decline in honeybee numbers between 1990 and 1993. It all adds up to what the U.S. Department of Agriculture calls an "impending pollination crisis."

Unfortunately, biologists know very little about the distribution, habits, and potential for domestication of the 3,500-

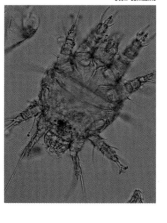

The Western honeybee (*Apis mellifera*), shown here visiting an apple blossom, pollinates crops worth more than $10 billion annually in the U.S. alone. This valuable service is jeopardized by the tracheal mite (top right), a microscopic parasite of the insect's respiratory system that weakens the colony's ability to withstand a variety of stresses.

have plowed up, fragmented, or flooded through irrigation their critical habitats.

According to Buchmann and Nabhan, pollination is "one of the world's most vital processes linking plants and animals—a process that not only keeps us fed and clothed but feeds our domesticated animals and their wild cousins as well." Without it, as Buchmann and Nabhan put it, the planet would be a place of "silent springs and fruitless falls."

PUTTING FOOD ON THE TABLE

The call to place a higher scientific priority on understanding pollinator-plant interactions has been sounded most urgently following the recent crash in honeybee populations in North America. In economic terms the Western honeybee (*Apis mellifera*) is perhaps the single most important pollinating species on the entire continent. In the U.S., for example, this insect is responsible for the pollination of hundreds of plant species every year, providing close to 80% of the pollination services required by cultivated crops. Bee-pollinated crops in the U.S. alone are worth more than $10 billion annually and include such high-value dietary staples as citrus fruits, apples, pumpkins, squashes, strawber-

ries, and blueberries. An even greater proportion of food is produced indirectly through pollination. Many crop plants rely on pollination not for setting fruit but for generating seed (as is the case for onions and carrots). Furthermore, despite the fact that some species of plants are capable of self-pollination, fruit set is improved by pollinator visitation, and seed quality and quantity are higher as well. Researchers have found that bee visitation to pear flowers, for example, significantly increases the fruits' diameter, which results in increased yields. In comparisons of self-pollinated and honeybee-pollinated soybean flowers, biologists discovered that bee pollination increased soybean yields more than 15%.

The honeybee has become central to agriculture in part because of its capacity for domestication. Colonies can be maintained year-round, manip-

plus species of native North American pollinators that in some cases might have helped to fill the breach. Moreover, preliminary research suggests that many species of native bees, and possibly even pollinating bats, reptiles, birds, and other insects, may themselves

be part of a larger pattern of decline. The numbers of some species of wild pollinators have plummeted owing to a combination of factors that includes competition with domesticated bees, the indiscriminate use of insecticides, and urban and agricultural developments that

The accidental release of the African bee (*Apis mellifera scutellata*) has wreaked havoc on commercial beekeeping operations throughout South and Central America. Known for its aggressiveness, the African bee has interbred with European bees and passed its combative traits on to domesticated colonies, which has forced many beekeepers to abandon their operations.

ulated with comparative safety, and even transported to areas where pollination services are required. Although it is now found in every U.S. state and in Canada, the honeybee is not native to North America. *A. mellifera mellifera,* a subspecies known as the "dark bee" of Northern Europe, was introduced in the 17th century and became established in the U.S. Through a series of introductions in the late 19th century, this disease-prone and irritable race was commercially supplanted by the better-tempered *A. mellifera ligustica,* the Italian bee and the pollinator of choice in today's beekeeping industry.

The extraordinary dependence of U.S. agriculture upon a single commercial pollinator, however, has the potential for creating considerable vulnerability and instability in the food supply. Particularly alarming has been the recent series of pests and diseases afflicting honeybee colonies. In 1984 entomologists discovered the tracheal mite in U.S. bees, a microscopic parasite of the honeybee's respiratory system that was introduced from Latin America. These mites reduce the ability of a colony to withstand disease, harsh winter conditions, and other stresses. Shortly thereafter, another more devastating parasite, the varroa mite, was detected in American colonies. Left unchecked, the varroa mite, which consumes the blood of bee larvae and pupae, can cause the collapse of an entire colony. These two mites have had a catastrophic impact on feral colonies of honeybees, virtually eliminating them in some parts of the U.S. More than 20% of the country's commercial honeybees have succumbed to the combined invasion of tracheal and varroa mites.

Also undermining the general viability of the honeybee are a host of microbial diseases, not the least of which is *Nosema apis,* a protozoan pathogen that affects more than half of American colonies. Last but not least, the accidental release of *A. mellifera scutellata,* an African race originally imported into Brazil for the purpose of breeding bees resistant to tropical heat, has created unprecedented havoc in the beekeeping industry of the Western Hemisphere. Noted for

The varroa mite, shown here infecting honeybee pupae (left) and an adult insect, feeds on the blood of honeybees. The invasions of the varroa mite and tracheal mite have in combination wiped out more than 20% of the commercial honeybee population in the U.S.

(Left) Nigel Cattlin—Holt Studios International/Photo Researchers; (right and top) Scott Camazine

153

their extreme aggressiveness, the African bees have spread throughout South and Central America, interbreeding with European honeybees and passing their combative traits on to domesticated colonies. As a result, many beekeepers have abandoned their businesses. In 1990 Africanized bees crossed the border from Mexico into Texas, and some analysts predict that the establishment of the Africanized bee will have similar devastating effects, at least initially, on the American beekeeping industry.

POLLINATION IN THE WILD

Entomologists point out that some of the pollination services formerly provided by commercial honeybees could be filled by wild bees and other native pollinators domesticated for that purpose. In many cases, however, scientists must first bridge enormous gaps in the knowledge of pollination biology, even with respect to economically important plants. Virtually nothing, for example, is known of the pollination needs of at least one-third of European crop plants. Even less is known about pollination in the wild. Buchmann and Nabhan point out that in one region of the U.S., researchers had identified the pollinators

for only one in every 15 federally protected species of native plants. Not even the number and diversity of pollinators have been accurately inventoried. It is entirely likely that more than two-thirds of all bee species have yet to be discovered and named. How many tiny flies and other obscure insects are involved in the pollination process, unrecognized and undescribed, is anyone's guess.

At the same time, a variety of human-induced changes on the landscape may be destroying the relationship between pollinators and plants before scientists have an opportunity to assess them. Humans have profoundly—and in some cases irreversibly—altered the ways in which plants and pollinators,

particularly insect pollinators, interact. Some of the earliest and most obvious disruptions were caused by the application of synthetic organic insecticides that began in the 1940s with the discovery of the broad-spectrum insecticide DDT. The fact that synthetic organic insecticides were cheap to produce, long-lasting once applied, and apparently relatively nontoxic to mammals led to their widespread use.

Their deadly efficacy against a wide range of insects and arachnids was initially viewed as a benefit; however, soon after these compounds were released into the environment, it became apparent that they generally did not discriminate between detrimental and beneficial insects. Examples are

Many human activities have altered or destroyed the relationship between native plants and their pollinators. The aerial spraying of insecticides against grasshoppers in the western U.S. (below), which coincides with the flowering period of many native plants, kills numerous beneficial insects on which these plants depend. The conversion of native landscapes to farmland (opposite) has fragmented and often eliminated habitat for native plants and insects.

legion. In the early 1980s widespread aerial spraying of the agrochemical aminocarb in New Brunswick to control spruce budworm (*Choristoneura fumiferana*) profoundly affected populations of native

154

bees in at least three families as well as several species of pollinating flies. Researchers suggest that subsequent declines in the reproductive success of native understory plants may have been attributable to reductions in the availability of effective pollinators. In the western United States, the annual large-scale spraying of rangeland with carbamates and other synthetic organic insecticides for grasshopper control coincides with the flowering period of many native plants, a time when many insects are most active. Researchers suspect that this spraying can kill native bees and may reduce the populations of other endemic insect species, many of which are already regarded as endangered.

Paradoxically, efforts to make insecticides more environmentally benign in some (continued on page 160)

Plants and Pollinators:
An Ancient Reciprocity

Like many other successful terrestrial organisms, most plants engage in biparental sexual reproduction; that is, male and female sex cells, or gametes, each containing half of a full genetic complement, must fuse to form a viable embryo. The male sex cells, produced in structures called anthers, are the pollen grains; in females the sex cells, known as ovules, are housed in a structure called the pistil.

When it comes to reproduction, however, plants suffer from a disadvantage that sets them apart from animals. In all but the most extraordinary circumstances, plants are firmly rooted to the ground for most of their lives, unable to move about in order to carry pollen to receptive stigmas. Some plants rely on abiotic forces—wind and water, for example—for pollen transport. Air and water currents, however, are notoriously unpredictable, and their movement of pollen is so generalized that they can not ensure its delivery to a specific address. To compensate, plants that rely on wind or water pollination produce enormous amounts of pollen, much of which never arrives at its intended destination.

As transporters of pollen, animal intermediaries have proved to be far more accurate and efficient. Surprisingly, the idea that plants rely on animal partners to reproduce, known today to every child schooled in the "birds and the bees," is fairly modern in origin. In 1682 Nehemiah Grew, one of the founders of the science of plant anatomy, was among the first to recognize that the stamen (a flower's pollen-producing male organ) and the pistil

The 17th-century botanist Nehemiah Grew was among the first in modern science to identify the anatomy of plant sexual reproduction (opposite).

Hulton Getty/Tony Stone Images

were necessary for seed production. This relatively simple observation was neither quickly nor widely accepted. Nearly 80 years passed before another scientist, Josef Kölreuter, was able to demonstrate that pollen produced by the anthers must be deposited on the stigma in order for seeds to be formed. In 1793 the German botanist Christian Konrad Sprengel first suggested that flowers, which serve no physiological function in the life of the plant, existed solely for the purpose of attracting and rewarding pollinators.

One reason why this seemingly simple concept was so slow to be recognized has to do with the fact that most plants are not built according to the same body plan as more familiar animals. Most higher animals are dioecious—a single individual possesses only one kind of sex organ. Many plants, on the other hand, are hermaphrodites; that is, a single individual can possess both male and female sex organs. The necessity for cross-fertilization—for bringing together male and female reproductive products from different individuals—thus was not readily apparent in plants. The idea of self-incompatibility—that some hermaphroditic organisms are incapable of fertilizing themselves—was even less intuitive. Only in the past 200 years have scientists realized that organisms that can produce genetically varied offspring (via cross-fertilization) enjoy an advantage over those that can produce only identical copies of their own genetic material through self-fertilization.

Pollination by animals is not only a relatively recent discovery in the history of science but also a relatively recent innovation in the evolutionary history of green plants. It is effectively restricted to the higher plants—angiosperms (flowering plants) and a few gymnosperms—plants that produce seeds rather than spores. Angiosperms produce their seeds within a ripened ovary, or fruit; gymnosperms produce "naked" seeds, which are not enclosed by an ovary. If species diversity is an indication of success, then animal-pollinated plants have been fantastically successful, representing at least two-thirds of the 250,000-plus species of known angiosperms.

The edge that pollination has given flowering plants is evident in the fossil record. Following the appearance of the major taxa of pollinators (including bees and butterflies) 80 million years ago, plant diversity increased with unprecedented speed and numbers, as did a striking differentiation of floral morphology.

Flowering plants have evolved a variety of enticements to attract potential pollinators. The most direct reward is pollen, probably the first attractant used by flowering plants. Pollen grains first appear in the geologic record about 125 million years ago. Pollen is high in protein, a nutritional component often in short supply in animal diets and thus potentially very attractive to animal visitors. Animals capable of consuming

Parts of a Flower

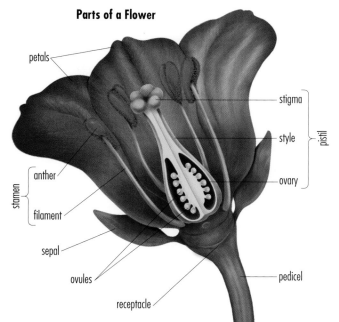

petals — stigma — style — pistil — ovary — pedicel — anther — stamen — filament — sepal — ovules — receptacle

pollen, however, must come equipped with the strength and mouthparts to handle the exine, the largely indigestible coat that helps to keep the pollen viable in dry environments. Because plants would receive no benefit if all their pollen was consumed, many plants that use pollen to attract pollinators produce relatively large quantities of it.

Flowering plants also lure pollinators by other means, including nectar, a relatively new plant development that is unique to flowering plants. Unlike pollen grains, which serve as both gametes and pollinator rewards, nectar is pure reward; it plays no known role in the reproductive life of the plant. Nectar is primarily a sugar solution in water composed of variable amounts of amino acids, lipids, water-soluble vitamins, organic acids, some proteins, and complex carbohydrates. Of all floral rewards, nectar probably holds the greatest appeal among both vertebrates and invertebrates. It is also prone to removal by thieves—visitors that take nectar but do not transfer pollen to the stigma in the process. To discourage this pilfering, some plants mix toxic substances with their nectar to which the plants' pollinators are resistant.

In the course of visiting flowers, pollinators may re-

ceive additional rewards. The surface of many flowers, for example, is covered with elaiophors, or hairs containing fatty acids. Anthophorid bees collect the oil onto absorbent brushes on their bodies and then squeeze it out and mix it with pollen for provisioning brood cells. Euglossine bees collect odoriferous substances from some orchids and transfer them to a specialized collector organ. These substances are later used in sexual display and courtship. Not all plants, however, deliver on their promises of material rewards. Some species attract pollinators by deceit, luring visitors by mimicking fragrances of flowers that offer abundant nectar or pollen. Others imitate desirable objects in the environment such as female wasps or bees, a ploy that effects pollination by eliciting copulatory movements from visiting males.

On the whole, however, the interaction between pollinator and plant is mutually beneficial; most pollinators derive

nutritional benefit for themselves or their offspring while plants achieve reproduction. It has been suggested, therefore, that pollinators and plants act as reciprocal selective agents, each modifying the evolution of the other in order to refine the partnership. For plants this alternating selection pressure brings about modifications in the pollinator-signaling system: petal color, flower shape, arrangements of flowers within a blossom, and pollen and nectar placement. For pollinators, whose fitness depends on the efficiency with which they can obtain food, selection brings about changes in sensitivity to visual and chemical signals, modification of body structure for pollen transport or nectar gathering, and alteration in behaviors associated with foraging and flower handling.

Plants and animals that have evolved a collection of traits in response to one another can be classified by categories known as pollination syndromes. One of the most generalized syn-

dromes is cantharophily, or beetle pollination. Most flower-associated beetles are pollen chewers. To compensate, beetle-pollinated flowers produce an overabundance of pollen. Some flowers even produce two different kinds of anthers, one for reproduction and one for feeding the beetles. Since beetles in general are not highly specialized morphologically or behaviorally for pollen collecting and transport, beetle-pollinated flowers tend to be rather unspecialized in structure. Blossoms are large, open, and dish- or bowl-shaped, a structure that allows easy access to pollen and nectar.

Myophily—fly pollination—represents a greater range of specific adaptations. Flies, for example, present significant limitations. The shortness of the insect's proboscis prevents access to concealed nectar, and its small body limits the number of pollen grains that can be transported. On the other hand, some flies have less-stringent seasonal requirements than other insect pollinators and are available to pollinate plants that flower in "off-peak" times of the year, including late winter, long before most plants have even poked their leaves out of the ground. The syndrome known as sapromyophily, for example, includes flies that are attracted

Flowers pollinated by beetles, such as the wild geranium visited here by a long-horned woodborer beetle, tend to be large, open, and dish- or bowl-shaped.

by the odor of carrion and dung. Plants in the families Aristolochiaceae, Sterculiaceae, Rafflesiaceae, and Araceae (*e.g.,* skunk cabbage), among others, often develop blooms before the snow has melted. To attract sapromyophilic flies, they produce scents that mimic those of dung or carrion, a deception that frequently traps insects inside blossoms where sexual organs are hidden. Besides exuding a stench, sapromyophilous flowers are generally a dark, purplish green color, their dull hues reminiscent of carrion.

Pollinating moths (phalaenophily) and butterflies (psychophily) also have certain features in common, including a long thin proboscis that helps the insects extract nectar concealed in floral tubes or spurs. Differences in moth and butter-

fly ecology, however, have given rise to differences in floral characteristics. Whereas butterfly-pollinated flowers tend to open during the day, most moth-pollinated flowers open at night, when moths are active. For the same reason, butterfly-pollinated flowers tend to display vivid colors, whereas moth-pollinated blossoms are mostly white.

Even more specialized and restrictive is the relationship between bees and bee blossoms, or melittophily. Morphologically, bees are well adapted for pollen transfer—hairy bumblebees, for example, can carry as many as 15,000 pollen grains. Correspondingly, because many ovules can benefit from this great pollen load, seed numbers are high in bee-pollinated plants. In addition, the advanced learning capacity of certain bees leads to increased frequency of visitation of flowers of the same species and results in a greater probability of pollination. They can form search images, memorize

landmarks, or communicate information to nest mates so that revisitation is far more likely. The melittophily syndrome includes flowers with strong landing surfaces, vivid colors, ultraviolet reflectance patterns, odors subtle enough to escape the attention of nonpollinating visitors, concealed nectar that only insects with the appropriately shaped tongues can access, and sexual organs that are hidden in order to protect pollen from interlopers.

Some pollination syndromes include plants that are adapted to an extremely narrow range of pollinators. Among the most notable examples is the reciprocal selection between agaonid wasps and figs. Worldwide, there are nearly 800 species of figs, classified in the genus *Ficus.* The overwhelming majority are pollinated by only one (or at most two or three) species of fig wasp. For their part, the majority of fig wasps are dependent upon a single species of fig plant. In hermaphroditic figs (those pos-

sessing both male and female sexual organs on the same plant), for example, both female and male flowers are produced within a distinctive enclosed structure called a syconium. Pollen-laden female wasps enter the syconium and lay eggs in some of the female flowers (one egg per flower). In the process, they pollinate the remaining female flowers. The grubs hatching from the eggs develop in the ovary of the flower, which forms gall-like structures in response to the grubs' presence. When development is complete, male wasps emerge from their galls and travel within the syconium in search of female wasps; when they are located, males mate with them and then assist them in escaping from their galls. Leaving the males behind, the mated females then collect pollen from uninfested flowers within the syconium, abandon the structure, and fly to another fig tree in search of flowers in which to lay their eggs.

Despite these compelling examples, biologists have not reached any consensus on the extent to which specialization affects the relationship between pollinators and the flowers they visit. Recent analyses suggest that pollination syndromes may be due for revision—that the majority of plants receive visits from a wide range of animals. In one study 91% of plant species were visited by more than a single species of pollinator, and some species received visits from more than 300 different insect species.

Not all visitors, however, are equally effective pollinators. Studies consistently demonstrate that the most conspicuous visitors are not necessarily the most effective pollinators; only a small percentage of visitors may actually bring about pollination. In a study of the pollination of (*Calathea ovandensis*), for example, bees and other hymenopterans were responsible for 99% of the fruit set, even though the flowers were visited by many different kinds of insects. Furthermore, for long-lived perennials the variety of available pollinators changes over time. On the other hand, with some conspicuous exceptions (such as yucca moths and fig wasps), it is also abundantly clear that most pollinators are by no means loyal to particular species of plants. Over the course of a single season, long-lived pollinators necessarily visit a range of species that flower sequentially. The seasonal variation in the availability of particular species also means that many species of pollinators visit a wide range of flowers.

That scientists have reached no consensus about the degree of exclusivity in most pollinator-plant relationships indicates the fragmentary state of the information available on this important mechanism in nature. New research, however, is slowly bridging this gap and leading us not only to appreciate the aesthetics of plants but also to recognize the critical role of pollination in the structure, function, and future of terrestrial ecosystems.

In the course of evolution, plants and their pollinators have developed traits in tandem. Bee-pollinated flowers, for example, produce many seeds in response to the great pollen loads carried by bees. This bumblebee, visiting a hibiscus flower, can transport as many as 15,000 pollen grains.

Richard Shiell—Animals Animals

(*continued from page 155*)
cases have inadvertently resulted in the increased mortality of beneficial pollinators. In the 1970s scientists reformulated methyl parathion, a highly toxic organophosphate insecticide used on cotton crops, from a powder into microcapsules in order to reduce the effects of spraying on nontargeted organisms. Unfortunately, because the methyl parathion particles were approximately the same size as pollen grains, the bees collected them from flower heads. The electrically charged capsules stuck firmly to the insects' hairs and were assiduously groomed off and deposited into the bees' pollen stores. When consumed by bee grubs, the toxic imposters caused substantial mortality.

Industrialization and urbanization have disrupted plant-pollinator interactions just as profoundly as have agronomic practices. One of the most damaging consequences of human settlement has been the division of formerly continuous landscapes into compartments or parcels. This habitat fragmentation threatens to destroy

Chris R. Sharp—Oxford Scientific Films

A 1996 study of purple loosestrife in Sweden showed that plants in small, isolated, and fragmented parcels attracted fewer pollinators. The researchers found that insects preferred large floral tracts to smaller ones.

fragile relationships between plants and their pollinators. In the past two centuries, the vast prairies of the Midwestern U.S., for example, were cut into isolated patches by farms and cities. This fragmentation reduced the habitat available for many species of native plants. Plants in small, isolated populations are at a disadvantage in attracting and maintaining populations of pollinators because for many pollinators the attractiveness of a floral display depends upon its size. In a 1996 study of purple loosestrife (*Lythrum salicaria*) in northern Sweden, for example, researchers found that plants in small populations set fewer seeds than plants in large populations because they were visited by fewer pollinators. Furthermore, plants growing in small populations also may be more likely to receive pollen from close relatives, which thereby increases the probability of inbreeding. Over time an inbred population loses its genetic diversity and is thus less able to weather environmental changes.

The accidental or intentional importation of both nonnative plants and insects due to the globalization of trade also has led to the breakdown of special relationships between plants and pollinators that have developed over thousands of years.

Introduced species of weeds, for example, can drive into extinction native flowers upon which specialized pollinators may depend. Even outwardly beneficial introductions, such as the honeybee to the Americas, have had costs associated with their arrival. With its enormous colonies of 30,000 or more workers, its generalized foraging habits, and its sophisticated system for communicating information to foragers about the location of flowers, the European bee is well equipped to compete with native pollinators for floral nectar and pollen resources. In the U.S. and elsewhere, the ascendancy of the honeybee has been associated with the decline of many native bees. This decline has been particularly well documented in Panama. In the early 1980s scientists reported that honeybees had begun to overwhelm social stingless bees. According to the recent results of ongoing research, this competition has contributed to localized extinctions of native bees.

Some researchers suspect that these declines may result in a decrease in the abundance of certain plant species formerly pollinated by native species. Although honeybees visit a staggeringly diverse array of plants, they are not necessarily efficient pollinators of all the

Some scientists fear that domesticated honeybees may be outcompeting native pollinators in some regions of the U.S. Called "ugly" pollinators by some biologists, honeybees hoard great quantities of pollen in "baskets" located on their hind legs and thereby deprive other pollinators of food.

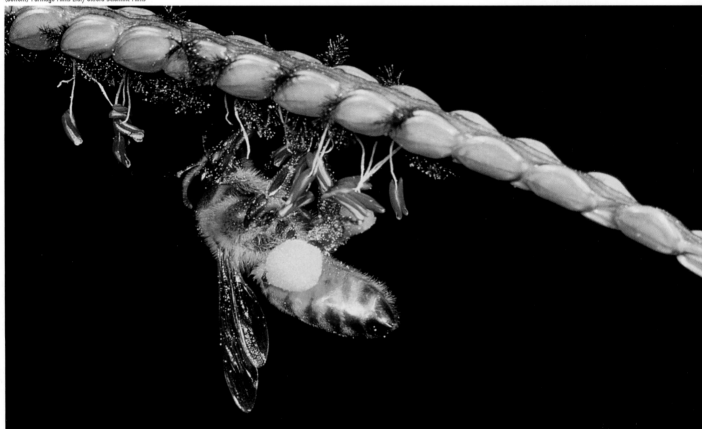

species they call on. Their tendency to intermingle nectar and saliva with the pollen that they pack into "baskets" located on their hind legs can reduce pollen viability in transport. They also deprive other pollinators by collecting large quantities of pollen, a practice for which they are sometimes called "ugly" pollinators by pollination biologists. Furthermore, while honeybees may load up on pollen, they do not necessarily deposit it on the appropriate stigma (the receptive sur-

face of a flower's pistil on which pollen is deposited) largely because they efficiently groom the accumulated pollen from their bodies into their pollen baskets. Nabhan and Buchmann have observed that whereas honeybees must make on average 3.3 visits to pollinate some native Sonoran Desert wild gourds effectively, native carpenter bees and specialized squash bees require only 1.1–1.3 visits.

In some places the loss of native pollinators could result

Fig trees, which depend on tiny wasps for pollination, are a keystone species of tropical communities. Figs provide an essential food source for a wide variety of vertebrates, including birds, monkeys, and bats (below).

in the collapse of entire communities. Many of the plants pollinated by animals are so-called keystone species; that is, their presence or absence can determine the structure of an entire assemblage of plants and animals. In tropical communities fig trees (species in the genus *Ficus*) are entirely dependent on tiny agaonid wasps for pollination and fruit production. Fig fruits, in turn, are critical components of the diet of a wide variety of tropical vertebrates, including many

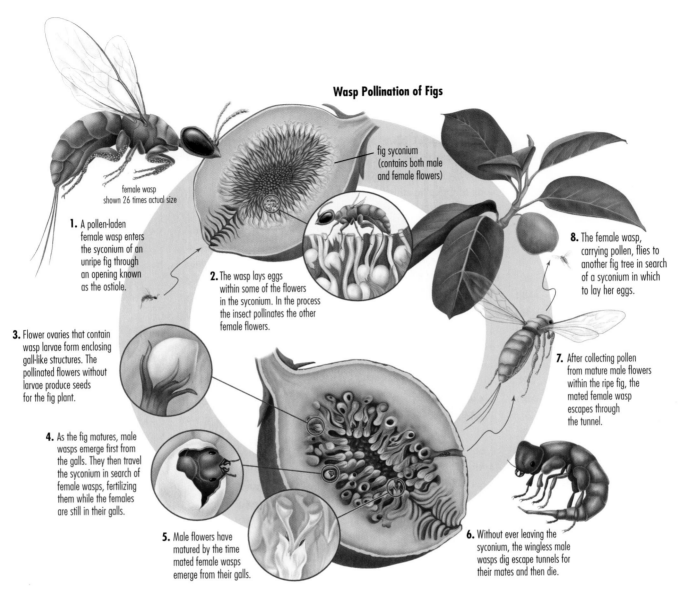

Wasp Pollination of Figs

female wasp
shown 26 times actual size

fig syconium
(contains both male
and female flowers)

1. A pollen-laden female wasp enters the syconium of an unripe fig through an opening known as the ostiole.

2. The wasp lays eggs within some of the flowers in the syconium. In the process the insect pollinates the other female flowers.

3. Flower ovaries that contain wasp larvae form enclosing gall-like structures. The pollinated flowers without larvae produce seeds for the fig plant.

4. As the fig matures, male wasps emerge first from the galls. They then travel the syconium in search of female wasps, fertilizing them while the females are still in their galls.

5. Male flowers have matured by the time mated female wasps emerge from their galls.

6. Without ever leaving the syconium, the wingless male wasps dig escape tunnels for their mates and then die.

7. After collecting pollen from mature male flowers within the ripe fig, the mated female wasp escapes through the tunnel.

8. The female wasp, carrying pollen, flies to another fig tree in search of a syconium in which to lay her eggs.

species of birds, bats, and monkeys. Figs play such an important role in the structure of tropical communities in part because they are capable of continuous fruiting; such fruiting may, in fact, be necessary for the trees to maintain viable populations of pollinating wasps. Fig fruits, in turn, become a particularly important source of food for many vertebrate species when other food resources are scarce. Any disruption in the fig-wasp inter-

action has the potential to undermine the health of entire communities of organisms.

AVOIDING A POLLINATION CRISIS

Whether the problems facing pollinators develop into an ecological disaster depends in part on the interests and actions of the scientific community. A considerable research effort has been launched to restore the health and vigor of *A. mellifera*

largely because of the honeybee's economic role in agriculture in the U.S. and throughout the world. Finding solutions, however, will not be easy. Ridding bees of mite infestations, for example, presents a tricky scientific challenge. Although they are not technically considered insects (belonging instead to the same class as spiders and ticks), mites share many physiological and biochemical similarities with bees. Most chemicals that kill mites also have

negative effects on insects. Moreover, the use of synthetic chemical pesticides in honeybee colonies could contaminate human food resources, including honey, bee pollen that is consumed as a health-food supplement, and even beeswax, which is used as a coating in many candies and confections.

Despite these difficulties, some chemical agents have been shown to be effective and relatively safe. Fluvalinate, a pyrethroid pesticide, was successfully used in Austria against varroa mites and now is widely applied throughout the world. Researchers developed a system in which honeybees serve as their own mite exterminators. Fluvalinate is affixed to "pest strips" that are suspended in the hive. As bees brush against the strips, they accumulate the chemical on their body hairs, distributing it as they move through the colony. Unfortunately, the heavy use of fluvalinate has resulted in a resistance to the insecticide in some mite populations, limiting its long-term efficacy.

Researchers also have used the antibiotic oxytetracycline to help bees cope with the stresses caused by tracheal and varroa mites. The drug is administered in the hive in oil patties or blocks of shortening sweetened with sugar. Although the antibiotic does not eliminate the mites, it appears to aid the bees in overcoming secondary infections associated with mite infestations. The oils in the patty also alter the composition of the waxy outer coating of the bee's exoskeleton that mites use to "sniff out" their hosts, which makes it dif-

More than half of the bee colonies in the U.S. are afflicted by the protozoan parasite Nosema apis, shown here infecting a bee's stomach.

ficult for mites to find new hosts. Bees also have found a measure of relief from the use of menthol crystals (the same odoriferous compound used in some cough drops). This preparation can easily volatilize, or vaporize, and penetrate the respiratory tract, where it kills tracheal mites.

Researchers also are investigating selective breeding as a way to protect honeybees from their enemies. Honeybees are a cosmopolitan species that exhibits considerable genetic variation across its range. Efforts are under way to identify populations of bees with natu-

ral resistance to such enemies as mites or *Nosema*. The history of tracheal mites in Europe offers researchers hope that these strategies could be effective. Shortly after they were first reported in 1921, the

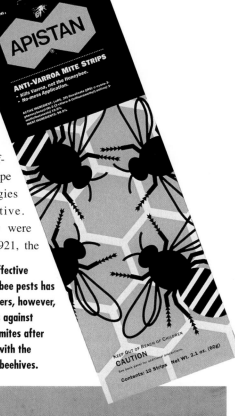

Developing safe and effective controls against honeybee pests has been difficult. Beekeepers, however, have had some success against infestations of varroa mites after hanging strips coated with the chemical fluvalinate in beehives.

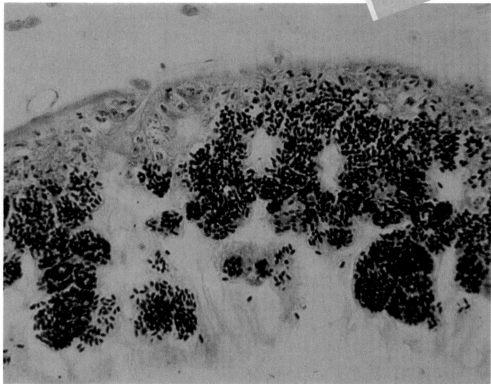

The native alkali bee (top) nests in the saline soils of the American West (below). Farmers rely on the wild bee for pollination of several crops, including alfalfa, a principal forage for beef and dairy cattle.

mites devastated Europe's beekeeping industry. In time, however, the bees apparently developed a resistance to the mites on their own. Today tracheal mites are no longer considered a problem in Europe.

To some extent the decline in numbers of the Western honeybee may be ameliorated by the augmentation and conservation of native pollinators. Only a tiny fraction of the world's 20,000 known species of bees currently are managed for pollination purposes.

In some parts of the U.S., native pollinators have long overshadowed *A. mellifera*. In the saline soils of the Great Basin in the American West, for example, the ground-nesting alkali bee (*Nomia melanderi*) has been the principal pollinator of alfalfa, clover, and mint. These native bees are particularly important in the pollination of alfalfa, a major forage plant for beef and dairy cattle, because they are far more efficient than honeybees at manipulating the complex morphology of the alfalfa blossom. For almost half a century, farmers in this area have constructed nesting beds for these bees in order to manage their populations more effectively. In recent years, however, plowing practices, pesticide residues, and a run of wet, rainy weather have placed the continued use of these bees in jeopardy.

In addition to the alkali bee, the alfalfa leaf-cutter bee (*Megachile rotundata*) has been used extensively throughout the western states for alfalfa pollination. Several species of bumblebees also are managed for pollination purposes; some species are even sold commercially for release year-round into greenhouses for pollination of hydroponic crops. A handful of species of mason bees have found gainful employment as well, including the hornfaced bee (*Osmia cornifrons*), which has been used for more than half a century to pollinate apple trees in

Pollination is one of the least-understood interactions in nature. Citing recent downturns in commercial bee operations as well as the disappearance of native pollinators in the wild, scientists have called for further research.

Japan. Other potential candidates for managed pollination are colletid bees, also known as polyester bees because of their habit of lining underground brood cells with a transparent, water-repellent membranous material. Some 100 native American species in this family are important pollinators of such crops as blueberries. Their ground-nesting habit may be conducive to management.

Scott Camazine

(Opposite page) Photographs, David Thompson—Oxford Scientific Films

In one of her poems about nature, Dickinson wrote:

> To make a prairie it takes
> a clover and one bee,—
> One clover, and a bee,
> And revery.
> The revery alone will do
> If bees are few.

Although the sentiment is lovely, the poem misses the scientific mark. Revery alone will not restore populations of pollinators that have been decimated by environmental change. More concerted biological investigation will be needed to understand the complexities of one of the most important—and possibly among the most delicate—interactions that occur in nature.

FOR ADDITIONAL READING

- "Conserving Europe's Bees: Why All the Buzz?" Christopher S. Williams, *Trends in Ecology & Evolution* (August 1995, pp. 309–310).
- *The Forgotten Pollinators,* Stephen L. Buchmann and Gary Paul Nabhan (Island Press, 1996).
- "Generalization in Pollination Systems, and Why It Matters," Nickolas M. Waser, Lars Chittka, Mary V. Price, Neal M. Williams, and Jeff Ollerton, *Ecology* (June 1996, pp. 1043–60).
- "Pollination Worries Rise as Honeybees Decline," Myrna E. Watanabe, *Science* (Aug. 26, 1994, p. 1170).
- "Pollinators, Flowering Plants, and Conservation Biology," Carol Ann Kearns and David W. Inouye, *BioScience* (May 1997, pp. 297–307).
- "Reconciling Ecological Processes with Phylogenetic Patterns: The Apparent Paradox of Plant-Pollinator Systems," Jeff Ollerton, *Journal of Ecology* (vol. 84, no. 5, 1996, pp. 767–769).
- "Role of Pollinators in Species Preservation, Conservation, Ecosystem Stability, and Genetic Diversity," Sarah A. Corbet, *Acta Horticulturae* (vol. 437, 1997, pp. 219–228).
- "Trouble with Honeybees," Sue Hubbell, *Natural History* (May 1997, pp. 32–43).

Science for the Soldier: The U.S. Army's Natick Labs

by Philip Brandler

In conducting state-of-the-art research in the basic and applied sciences, the U.S. Army Natick Research, Development and Engineering Center is taking its mandate of protecting and sustaining the individual soldier into the new millennium.

U.S. Army SSCOM Photo

Throughout its nearly 50-year history, the U.S. Army Natick Research, Development and Engineering Center has followed a simple mandate: to ensure that American soldiers are the best fed, best protected, and most highly mobile in the world. From its World War II roots as a facility of the Quartermaster Corps to its present-day status as a premier research and development organization, the Natick center has consistently embraced the principle that sustaining and protecting the individual soldier with ever more sophisticated technology will lead to a stronger national defense and a safer nation. Today, as a recognized leader in the food, textile, aerodynamics, and engineering sciences, Natick is home to ideas, technologies, and products that have been shaping both the U.S. military forces and the broader world for decades and that will continue to do so well into the 21st century.

In conducting both basic and applied research, Natick's scientists, engineers, and equipment designers provide the army and other branches of the U.S. military with a wide range of field-feeding and life-support systems, clothing, precision airdrop equipment, and protective gear against ballistic, chemical, and laser weapons. Basic research into textile materials, for example, has led to the creation of new fabrics that are lighter in weight, more du-

rable, and more weather-resistant than anything soldiers have ever worn. Research into polymeric composites has resulted in helmets that are stronger, lighter, and more protective than the steel "pots" used in World War II and the Korean and Vietnam wars. Investigation of the nutritional requirements of the human body has led to a new understanding of how to sustain a soldier's peak performance under stress with rations that contain the optimum mix of ingredients and are easy to prepare in remote locations.

In addition to its role in crafting the soldier of the future, Natick has pioneered ways of reaching out to the

Philip Brandler is Director of the U.S. Army Natick (Massachusetts) Research, Development and Engineering Center.

The extreme environmental conditions encountered in World War II sent the U.S. Army a sobering message that the equipment it had designed for its soldiers was clearly inadequate and that changes were imperative.

nonmilitary community. Through cooperative agreements with other government agencies and private industry, it has developed much of the food eaten by space shuttle astronauts during their missions; outfitted police forces with special ballistic protection against bullets, shrapnel, and other flying objects; and developed shelf-stable sandwich foods that promise to combine convenience and nutrition for a consumer market.

EARLY YEARS

Ground was broken in 1952 on a 32-hectare (78-acre) site in Natick, Massachusetts, for what was then called the Quartermaster Research Laboratory. In actuality, however, the facility can trace its origins back another decade, to the early years of World War II. That war delivered a stark message to the U.S. Army that the equipment it had designed following World War I was decidedly inadequate for the extreme climatic conditions that American forces were encountering in such places as the jungles of the southwest Pacific and the sands of northern Africa. As reports came in of tents falling

168

victim to mildew in the Pacific, of troops being immobilized by trench foot in the Aleutians, and of food being pitched into the sea after commercial packaging techniques had failed to keep it wholesome, it became apparent to army leaders that changes needed to be made.

The office of the Quartermaster General established a Research and Development Branch in 1942 to augment existing army material with equipment that would serve the soldier in any environment in the world. The new branch was headed by Col. Georges Doriot, a French-born American who would later rise to the rank of brigadier general. Doriot envisioned an "Institute of Man," a scientific laboratory that would measure the effects of the battlefield environment upon soldiers. The belief driving his vision was that the limitations placed upon human capabilities by the battlefield had to be determined if the most efficient food, clothing, and equipment were to be designed. By understanding the stresses that soldiers faced, scientists would be able to develop strategies to counteract them.

With this philosophy serving as a beacon, improvements came rapidly. Climatic chambers in Lawrence, Massachusetts, were put to wartime use for studying and testing cloth-ing and equipment in hot and cold environments. These studies, complemented by others conducted at the Quartermaster Center at Ft. Lee, Virginia, generated basic fabric-performance criteria for the design of new and improved material. Similarly, work done at the Climatic Research Laboratory in Jeffersonville, Indiana, resulted in advances in mildew-resistant finishes for tent fabrics. Meanwhile, at the Subsistence Research Laboratory in Chicago, scientists developed field-feeding systems that enabled a variety of new foods to be quickly produced and shipped to troops around the world.

The strides that had been made in research and development during World War II convinced the army of the need for a continuing program devoted to protecting and sustaining soldiers. Just as clear, however, was the need for consolidating the scattered elements of the Quartermaster Research and Development Branch. A campaign was launched to establish a single modern laboratory dedicated to the study of human beings and their environment—the realization of Doriot's Institute of Man.

In 1947 legislation was introduced in Congress to create such a facility in the Boston area. New England was the favored location from the beginning, boasting not only some of the most renowned educational centers in the country but also the wide climatic variation that would aid in the kind of experiments that the laboratory would be conducting. Other parts of the country did not view the issue as plainly, however, and waged a pitched battle in congressional hearings for the privilege of being the host of the new facility. Eventually Congress agreed to turn the matter of site selection over to the Department of Defense, which after reviewing some 278 proposals from 40 states, finally announced its choice of Natick in 1951. Three years later the facility was dedicated as the Quartermaster Research and Development Center.

The name of the facility has changed several times over the years, as has the army command under which it serves.

Today the Natick Research, Development and Engineering Center serves as a subordinate activity of the U.S. Army Soldier Systems Command (SSCOM), which is also headquartered in Natick. Together these agencies pursue a concept of the 21st-century military that sees the soldier as a system and that integrates all the elements that support the soldier into a single package to enhance performance and improve the quality of life.

ORGANIZATION AND FACILITIES

Known locally by its most enduring name, the Natick Labs, the center is situated on a peninsula overlooking Lake Cochituate, a fertile body of water divided into three basins stretched across almost 250 hectares (more than 600 acres) and connected by navigable culverts. Much of the shoreline has been preserved as a state park, which gives the area around the Natick Labs a pristine, natural feeling. Although the lake originally provided the center with water for cooling purposes, today it serves only as a picturesque backdrop for visitors, employees, and military families.

The town of Natick is a residential community located 24 kilometers (15 miles) south-

U.S. Army SSCOM Photo

Col. Georges Doriot established the philosophy of the Natick Labs with his vision of a scientific institute that would study the effects of the battlefield environment on soldiers.

west of Boston, mixing an older downtown area with modern suburban architecture and Victorian-era mansions hidden on quiet, leafy streets. The Natick Labs participates in the life of the community in a number of ways. For example, school groups and interested citizens are regularly invited to the post to tour the facilities, and Natick researchers travel to local schools to perform classroom demonstrations aimed at increasing students' interest in science.

With its colorful foliage and 1950s-era design, SSCOM's campus has the look of a small college. The post comprises 36 buildings, although much of the work of the Natick Labs is done in the two most prominent, the appropriately named Research and Development buildings. Another large building, affectionately dubbed the Blue Palace, houses the kitchen facilities used for research into ration design.

Natick employs about 500 people, mostly civilians, and is divided into four research groups. The Mobility Directorate is charged with developing airdrop systems, including personnel and cargo parachutes. The Science and Technology Directorate investigates human behavior and performance and explores new materials and textiles. The task of developing rations, shelters, field kitchens, and other equipment for use in the field, including showers and latrines, falls to the Sustainability Directorate. Finally, the Survivability Directorate develops protective clothing, helmets, boots, and other personal equipment for soldiers.

Natick has several exceptional design and testing facilities that support the directorates in their research. In the Camouflage Evaluation Facility, scientists and engineers test and evaluate new camouflage patterns in four environmental settings: woodland, desert, urban, and arctic. Because the lighting in the facility can be adjusted to simulate various day and night conditions, including different levels of moonlit and moonless night skies, evaluators have a realistic and reliable tool for measuring the performance of new and non-U.S. camouflage materials under a variety of conditions. The facility is complemented by a digital Terrain Analysis System, which breaks down videotaped footage of real environments into a user-specified number of predominant colors and shapes. The natural patterns that the system extracts from a given environment can then be used to design new camouflage patterns.

Natick also has a laser-based body-scanning and digitizing

A soldier is scanned in Natick's Whole Body Digitizer (above) to collect data that will be used to optimize the design and sizing of clothing and equipment. (Right) Soldiers and their equipment undergo testing in the center's Doriot Climatic Chambers, which can simulate climatic extremes ranging from a tropical monsoon to a polar deep freeze.

system to pursue its research into three-dimensional anthropometry, the study of the geometry of the human form and its differences among populations. Both military and private industry often use anthropometric data to assess the range of body sizes within populations of interest. At Natick the scanning and digitizing system, which measures and records a body's 3-D surface coordinates, is used to optimize the design and sizing of uniforms and equipment. For instance, researchers recently surveyed the surface coordinates of the heads and faces of about 90 male and female soldiers in order to get the best possible fit from chemical protective masks.

By incorporating 3-D digital models of the human form into computer-aided design software, Natick researchers can design and evaluate clothing and equipment prior to creating actual physical prototypes. This improved understanding of human shape differences makes it possible for better-fitting clothing to be developed for the army's diverse population. Over the long term, whole-body modeling of individuals could lead to custom apparel design, commonly referred to as "apparel on demand" or "mass-produced custom." In other words, if an accurate image of an individual's surface coordinates existed, clothing then could be designed and fabricated specif-

ically for that individual. Such technology could form the basis of a manufacturing system having great potential value to both the military and private industry.

Perhaps Natick's most essential facility is the Doriot Climatic Chambers, where soldiers test themselves and their equipment against worldwide climate extremes. The facility houses two wind tunnels, each 18.3 meters long, 3.4 meters high, and 4.6 meters wide (60×11×15 feet). Temperatures inside the tropic tunnel range from −18° to 74° C (0° to 165° F); inside the arctic tunnel the temperature range is −57° to 49° C (−70° to 120° F). With an ability to simulate rainfall at rates up to 10 centi-

meters (four inches) an hour and winds up to 65 kilometers (40 miles) per hour, the chambers provide valuable insight into how new items will perform in just about any environment. They also generate information on human performance relative to acclimation, dehydration, and work rates—information that has provided critical field guidance to U.S. commanders in the Persian Gulf and Somalia. The work done in the chambers is at the heart of Natick's mission, for it helps to ensure that soldiers will be fully protected, sustained, and effective wherever they are called into action.

FROM LAB BENCHES TO BATTLEFIELDS

Through programs devoted to the pursuit of basic science, Natick has often been able to nurture technologies from infancy to maturation. In a recent, ongoing example of that process, the center's scientists have employed a technique called electrospinning to produce an experimental new fabric that could one day be used to make seamless garments. Electrospinning is a process by which a polymer solution is charged to high voltage. At a certain voltage level a fine jet shoots out from the solution and travels through air toward an electrically grounded target, forming a continuous polymer fiber made of numerous filaments. As it reaches its target, the fiber splays into its component filaments and dries, which results in a web of fine, interconnected filaments—*i.e.,* a nonwoven fabric.

Electrospinning gives scientists the ability to bring together a variety of polymer types and fiber forms into a single material and to produce ultrathin membranes. Microporous thin membranes are used in protective garments, sport clothing, and even diapers, and they offer significant advantages in weight reduction, comfort, and protection against toxic substances. Depending on the specific polymer used, fabric properties such as strength, weight, and porosity could be customized in the resulting electrospun textile. Natick scientists hope to incorporate into one fabric desired values of such diverse properties as electrical conductivity, chemical reactivity, flammability, and resistance to wind and water. Ultimately they would like to be able to electrospin fibers directly onto 3-D garment forms obtained through whole-body scanning and modeling. Made with the help of computer-aided design and manufacturing processes, the resulting garments would be not only custom-fit but also seamless, which would reduce a soldier's risk of chemical exposure during battle.

In another instance of cutting-edge basic science, Natick researchers are helping to realize a longtime goal of fiber-industry specialists: the duplication of spider silk for potential use in ballistic protective clothing. The fiber used in such clothing must be high in strength, in modulus (a mathematical term that in this case refers to a fiber's stiffness), and in extensibility (the amount it can elongate under tension before breaking). In other words, it must be very tough. Currently the army's protective vests and helmets incorporate fibers of Kevlar, the trademarked name of an aramid polymer made by Du Pont. Although Kevlar fibers are tough, spider silk is three times tougher. A major reason for spider silk's preeminence lies in its superior extensibility. Consequently, it can absorb more mechanical energy without breaking and, theoretically, stop a projectile more effectively. The superior qualities of spider silk also make it a highly attractive material for such applications as parachute cords, fiber-composite materials, and surgical sutures.

In a major breakthrough in the long struggle to duplicate spider silk, Natick researchers have successfully cloned the gene that codes for the protein constituting the dragline silk of the golden orb weaver spider (*Nephila clavipes*). In addition, they have made synthetic genes, based on the natural gene, whose protein products mimic spider dragline silk. By means of recombinant DNA technology, both natural and synthetic genes have been inserted into *Escherichia coli* bacteria, which in turn have been induced to produce small quantities of silks in a fermenter. Fibers have been spun from the bacterially produced silks, and several patent applications on the technology are in the works.

Scientists still must overcome many challenges before the worth of spider silk as a

This nonwoven polymer membrane is a product of electrospinning, a technology being developed by Natick scientists. Electrospinning offers the ability to create ultrathin protective fabrics having customized properties.

ballistic protective material can be proved. Perhaps most significant is the need to ascertain how the recombinant bacteria can be coaxed into producing larger quantities of the silk. Spider silk protein has proved to be uncommonly difficult to work with, both for humans and for the normally prolific *E. coli.*

LIFESAVING CLOTHING

Natick's world leadership in providing superior protective clothing is especially notable in the area of ballistics. The center's engineers have to develop gear that meets the twin challenges of protecting the soldier as thoroughly as possible from shrapnel and bullets while being light enough to avoid unduly restricting the soldier's mobility. Currently researchers are developing a new ballistic protective vest, the Modular Body Armor system, as a lighter-weight replacement for the army's present body armor. Its weight reduction will not only increase a soldier's mobility and survivability but also reduce the likelihood of heat stress.

Modular Body Armor combines two ballistic protection features. It has a "soft" component, the vest itself, that protects against fragmentation—shrapnel and other explosive

Natick scientists have cloned the gene for the dragline silk protein of the golden orb weaver spider (right) and have inserted it into bacteria, which then have been induced to make small amounts of silk in a fermenter (bottom right). The broken end of a silk strand (bottom left) has been magnified thousands of times for studies of silk's toughness.

debris—and handgun bullets. The army's current vest is made of 13 layers of a particular Kevlar weave. The materials under investigation for the new vest include a variety of other weaves of Kevlar and additional high-performance fibers such as ultrahigh-molecular-weight polyethylene, liquid-crystal polymers, and other aramid-based fibers.

Modular Body Armor also has a "hard" component, a set of removable plates inserted into front and back pockets on the vest, for protection against rifle bullets. The hard plates currently designated for the system are made of a ceramic material, although researchers are investigating the performance of metal plates, primarily titanium, as well. The plates are backed up by a fiber-reinforced composite with a plasticized resin that supports the ceramic against the force of a ballistic impact.

With chemical and biological weapons—toxic chemical agents and infectious microbes, respectively—posing a particularly ominous battlefield threat, work is also under way to develop comprehensive protection for soldiers against those less-traditional forms of warfare. Two areas of research are being pursued. The Joint Service Lightweight Integrated Suit Technology (JSLIST) pro-

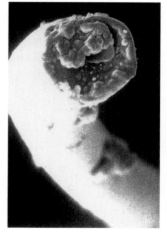 

(Top) Stephen Krasemann—Tony Stone Images; (above, left and right) Photographs, U.S. Army SSCOM

gram, based at Natick, is a consolidated effort of the four major branches of the U.S. military to design and develop the next generation of protective garments based on materials that are permeable to air and water vapor yet effectively block chemical and biological agents.

Such materials employ two layers of fabric. The outer layer has all the typical attributes of good environmental protection, including water resistance, low flammability, and the ability to be imprinted with a camouflage pattern. The inner layer contains activated carbon that adsorbs the toxin and prevents it from getting through to the skin. If the toxin is delivered as a liquid rather than a vapor, the water-repellent outer-shell fabric causes the liquid to bead on the surface and evaporate without penetration. Since the layers pass air and water vapor, body sweat can evaporate and leave, which vastly minimizes the risk of heat stress among soldiers wearing protective clothing in warm climates.

The JSLIST program has already developed an overgarment that reduces the weight and bulk associated with protective clothing, is launderable, and is durable enough for 45 days of wear. It also has an integrated hood and thus offers improved protection where the soldier's mask meets the garment. The accompanying boot is durable enough for 60 days of wear and is fire-retardant and petroleum-, oil-, and lubricant-resistant.

The second avenue of research pursued by Natick scientists involves clothing that incorporates a so-called perm-selective barrier, which would be particularly effective against biological agents and would re- duce weight even more. The fabric of the garment would still consist of two layers, but the inner layer, made of a polymeric film, would be much thinner and lighter than the activated-carbon–based fabrics. The film would act as a diffusion barrier with selective permeability; it would be impermeable to air and would retard the penetration of organic chemical toxins, but it would permit sweat to evaporate and leave. This inner layer would offer protection not only against liquid and vapor chemical toxins but also against aerosols, the primary method of delivering biological agents. Since permeation rates of organic compounds differ from

Modular Body Armor (left) combines a "soft" vest made of Kevlar and other high-performance fibers with "hard" ceramic or metal plates that slip into front and back pockets on the vest. (Below) Designed for tent support, these inflatable fabric arches, or airbeams, are made by means of a new seamless three-dimensional weaving and braiding technology developed at Natick.

one permselective barrier to another, it is the ability to predict the properties of these barriers that lies at the cutting edge of research in the field.

NEW TEXTILE TECHNOLOGY

One of the more significant avenues of research being pursued by Natick's experts in soft-shelter systems is a textile technology that promises new levels of mobility and protection to soldiers in the field as well as broad applications in areas beyond the world of tents. Natick has developed techniques for weaving and braiding fabrics in three dimensions to make seamless fabric

tubes. When inflated under high pressure, the tubes can function as arches, or airbeams, in place of metal frames for tent structural support. Airbeams allow for rapid, easy deployment and for tents that are significantly lighter than traditional shelters.

The high-strength structural fabric tube produced by the new technology is unlike that used to make commercial inflatable shelters. Most commercial inflatables are seamed—conventional flat-manufactured fabrics are coated, cut into patterns, and then glued or heat-welded together. Application of this technique to military shelters has shown that air inevitably

leaks out through the seams, which reduces the pressure and the strength of the inflatable. The new seamless 3-D weaving and braiding techniques result in high-strength structures with improved reliability and durability.

The U.S. Navy is interested in extending the technology beyond airbeams to build lightweight, high-strength water and fuel-transfer containers and ejection-seat stabilizers for aircraft. Seamless fabric tubes could serve a variety of other military and civilian needs as well—for example, in constructing dams and other flood-control devices, safer breakwaters for offshore bases, ammunition barricades, inflatable

space antennas, pollution-control devices, humanitarian-relief shelters, inflatable boats, and aircraft escape slides.

THE ARMY'S KITCHEN

State-of-the-art food facilities have solidified Natick's standing as the army's kitchen. In fact, all of the recipes used by the U.S. armed forces in military dining facilities around the world are tested in kitchens located in the Natick Labs. New recipes are developed and tested according to new findings in nutrition, new trends in taste, and the changing dietary needs of the religiously and ethnically diverse military population. All army field rations are also tested on the premises, as are commercial products that may one day be included in those rations.

Its extensive food-testing, processing, and packaging capabilities have allowed Natick to take the lead in innovative ration design. It was a pioneer in the development of freeze-dehydrated foods, and it developed early cake mixes during World War II. In the 1960s it was also a leader in perfecting high-altitude feeding systems like Tube Foods, which are semisolid entrees and desserts contained in aluminum containers that resemble toothpaste tubes. Originally used by astro-

Hot pasta and chicken entrees (above) are among the menu choices for the shelf-stable Meal, Ready-to-Eat (MRE) field ration. A soldier (right) activates a chemical ration heater with water to warm his MRE.

nauts in the Mercury, Gemini, and Apollo programs, Tube Foods are now designed for pilots who fly at high altitudes and must eat while wearing oxygen masks. More recently, Natick was the birthplace of the Meal, Ready-to-Eat (MRE), the standard army field ration that has been served to soldiers since 1980, when it began replacing the Meal, Combat Individual, or C ration. More than 100 million of these meals were sent to troops in Saudi Arabia during the Persian Gulf War in 1990–91.

The groundbreaking MRE, which meets the calorie- and protein-intensive standards of the military's recommended-daily-allowance guidelines set by the U.S. surgeon general, is designed for long-lasting freshness. Owing to a triple-laminate foil packaging technique that protects the food from oxygen and moisture, two primary culprits in spoilage, MREs are shelf-stable for a minimum of three years at 27° C (80° F) and a minimum of six months at 38° C (100° F). The packaging process, which incorporates heat pasteurization, oxygen scavengers that absorb excess oxygen, and vacuum seals that keep out food spoilants, makes the use of chemical preservatives unnecessary.

Soldiers heat their MREs in the field, using "flameless ration heaters," which the Natick Labs developed so that troops in remote locations could enjoy hot food. Pouring a small amount of water in the polyethylene bag containing the heating mixture—a blend of food-grade magnesium, iron, and salt—triggers a chemical reaction that causes the water to boil. Simply by adding water to the heating bag and dropping in an entree pouch, a hungry soldier can have a fully heated meal in 10 minutes' time.

Natick continues to make new advances in ration design. One is the development of Mobility Enhancing Ration Components (MERCs), a flexible ration system that gives soldiers all the eat-on-the-run convenience of sandwiches. MERCs are nutritious shelf-stable pocket sandwiches—barbecued chicken, salami, and peanut butter and jelly are among current offerings—that require no heating, stay fresh in storage, and are suitable for all climates. They represent a breakthrough in the state-of-the-art technology of intermediate moisture foods.

In addition, efforts are under way to develop and engineer foods that will enhance the physical and mental performance of combat soldiers during extended operations and under all climatic conditions. Referred to as Performance Enhancing Ration Components (PERCs), these foods will be formulated with a balance of ingredients that have a proven potential to enhance performance. Incorporating complex carbohydrates, caffeine, glutamine, tyrosine, and choline as possible enhancements, PERCs will be designed to provide extra energy, delay fatigue, improve response time and decision making, and minimize declines in performance under stress. Products developed to date include a high-energy food bar called the HooAH! Bar and a beverage called the ERGO (Energy Rich, Glucose Optimized) Drink that acts as a source of supplemental carbohydrates. Both products will be issued to soldiers in the near future.

COMING DOWN EASY

Parachutes have long played an important role in the deployment of soldiers and supplies, and airdrop technology will become even more vital as humanitarian operations increase in frequency and create a demand for the quick delivery of food, medicine, and relief shelters. Parachutes also have become integral to the completion of space missions, such as the landing of Mars Pathfinder on the Martian surface in 1997 and the descent of the Galileo probe into Jupiter's atmosphere in 1995. For such reasons Natick is constantly looking at ways to improve airdrop capabilities. Using the considerable

Photographs, U.S. Army SSCOM

The HooAH! Bar is one of a line of Performance Enhancing Ration Components (PERCs) developed by Natick's food experts to boost a soldier's energy and delay fatigue under stress.

Natick's Advanced Precision Aerial Delivery System uses a wing-shaped parafoil canopy and an automatic navigation system to deliver payloads from high altitudes precisely where needed.

number-crunching power of new supercomputers, the center's aerospace engineers are conducting leading-edge research that should pave the way for more efficient and better targeted parachute design

and safer parachute deployment.

Understanding the aerodynamic forces that govern the deployment, inflation, terminal descent, and impact of airdrop systems is important to designing parachutes. The physics of these events are very complex, however, because they involve not only the motion of the airdrop system itself but also the turbulent and unsteady airflow around and through the para-

chute. Analytic or numerical models describing and predicting parachute deployment and inflation have thus been difficult to construct, and designers have traditionally relied on trial-and-error field tests to reveal the effects of the interaction of these physical forces on their creations. Natick is overcoming that limitation, developing analytic computer models that accurately predict the physics of parachutes.

The aerodynamic forces influencing parachute inflation are characterized by the interaction between fluid dynamics—that is, the velocity and pressure distribution caused by the airflow in and around the parachute's canopy—and structural dynamics, which involves the solid parts of the airdrop system, including the fabric of the canopy, the suspension lines, and the payload. This interaction makes it impossible to predict the pressure distribution on a canopy surface without an accurate representation of the canopy's shape. At the same time, however, the shape of the canopy cannot be described without an accurate representation of the pressure distribution on the surface.

Along with colleagues across the country, Natick researchers are attempting to numerically integrate software that predicts fluid dynamics with software that predicts structural dynamics. They have developed a two-dimensional model for an airdrop system featuring this integration and are working with researchers at the University of Connecticut to apply the approach in three dimensions. Advances in high-performance computing are making such intricate simulations possible. Researchers hope that one day they will be able to offer engineers a rela-

U.S. Army SSCOM Photo

On the digitized battlefield of the future, soldiers will have computer technology incorporated into their uniforms and equipment. Each soldier will be a complete weapons platform whose equipment is united by design into a single, performance-optimized system.

tively user-friendly design tool that will predict parachute performance ahead of field testing.

THE SOLDIER AS FIGHTING SYSTEM

On the battlefield of the future, as threats become more sophisticated, soldiers will have computer technology at their fingertips, even incorporated into their uniforms. Clothing and equipment design, therefore, is entering a renaissance, and opportunities abound for advances in soldier protection and comfort. Natick's researchers are investigating so-called smart textiles, fabrics with built-in sensors that can identify and adapt to various threats. The center is also taking a leading role in developing protective countermeasures to threats from directed-energy weapons, such as lasers, which produce beams of concentrated energy. Eye protection in the form of a device that guards against tunable lasers is at the center of present research, but there will be a greater need for directed-energy protection if weapons capable of projecting destructive levels of microwave energy become a significant part of the battlefield.

The project that stands at the forefront of these efforts, weaving together the strands of all of Natick's research, is

Land Warrior, a revolutionary program to develop a totally integrated soldier fighting system for the 21st century. The concept behind Land Warrior is the view of the soldier as a complete weapons platform—the soldier whose individual equipment is united by design into a single, performance-optimized system. One of the most striking elements of the system is its helmet, which has a mounted computer and sensor display that acts as the soldier's interface to the other components of the system and to the battlefield. Through the

display, the soldier can view computer-generated graphic data, digital maps, intelligence information, troop locations, and imagery from a heat-sensing Thermal Weapon Sight and video camera on the soldier's weapon. The weapon-mounted imaging devices allow a soldier to aim and fire at a target around a corner without exposing more than hands and arms.

As the concept of the soldier changes, as the individual's role on the battlefield becomes more complex, Natick's research becomes at once more sophisticated and more hum-

ble, focused, as always, on an understanding of the soldier as a human being. By continuing to support and sustain soldiers in comfort, by placing a premium on their nutritional needs, and by designing equipment to keep them safe, Natick will be able to shape a 21st-century military force that is technologically driven but people-centered.

INTERNET RESOURCE

• U.S. Army SSCOM home page
  http://www.sscom.army.mil

179

Pebbles around a hole
KIINAGASHIMA-CHO, JAPAN
7 DECEMBER 1987

Enchanting the Earth

Essay by Chet Raymo

Sculptures and photographs by Andy Goldsworthy

Sculptor Andy Goldsworthy creates artworks in the open air, using ordinary materials at hand. Intentionally ephemeral and quietly unfamiliar, his earthworks lead viewers to probe the human and natural forces at work in the world.

Chet Raymo is Professor of Physics and Astronomy at Stonehill College, Easton, Massachusetts. His most recent books include Honey from Stone: A Naturalist's Search for God; The Soul of the Night: An Astronomical Pilgrimage; *and* Skeptics and True Believers.

Andy Goldsworthy is a renowned artist who has created site-specific earthworks in landscapes throughout the world, including the North Pole, the Australian Outback, and the seacoast near his home in Dumfriesshire, Scotland. Photographs of his work have been collected in numerous publications, including Andy Goldsworthy: A Collaboration with Nature; Black Stones, Red Pools: Dumfriesshire Winter 1994–5; Stone; *and* Wood.

Imagine that you are walking through the countryside— on a hill overlooking a rolling valley or in a ravine alongside a tumbling stream—and you come upon a sculpture by British artist Andy Goldsworthy. It might be a hole in the earth ringed with pebbles sorted by color or an arch of river ice across a stream or a pool of water filled with floating flower heads of dandelions. You have never seen a Goldsworthy creation before, nor have you heard of the artist. Indeed, you are not certain that what you have stumbled across is the work of human hands.

Perhaps this thing that you have found is a product of gravity, wind, or moving water. Inanimate forces often create forms that give the appearance of artifice: wave-sorted pebbles on a sloping beach, a desert arch carved by windblown sand, or river ice heaped by the force of water into towers at a weir. But the pebbles are too obviously sorted by color, the ice sheets too purposefully placed, the dandelions too far from any likely source.

Then perhaps you have stumbled upon the work of an animal architect, something as instinctively contrived as the beaver's lodge or the spider's spiral web. Your mind races for an explanation. What animal? For what purpose?

You conclude that the thing you have found is a human artifact.

Now you are swept by other emotions. You are curious about the mind that dreamed up such a thing. You wonder at the need that drove the maker to spend so much time on a fragile construction in a remote place. Then you feel pleasure—for the beauty of the thing, for the way this unanticipated work of art forces you to

Stacked sticks
Assisted by Cécile Panzieri and Peter Raczeck
CENTRAL PARK, NEW YORK
JUNE 1993

see the world afresh, and for a heightened awareness of the mystery that you suddenly sense all around you.

All at once you know the meaning of the word *enchantment.*

If Goldsworthy's sculptures sometimes appear to be products of natural forces or animal instinct, it is because they have something in common with both. His art exploits the creative agencies of inanimate, animate, and conscious forces. This melding of constructive possibilities, from passive gravity to active intellect, makes his art an open door into a world of primeval connectedness—a world we have largely forgotten in our increasingly human-centered society.

A physicist will feel at home with Goldsworthy's art. As an artist, Goldsworthy intuitively understands the physical principles that the scientist describes mathematically: gravity, force vectors, angles of repose, buoyancy, fracture, phase change. His work often resembles natural sculptures, not because he mimics nature's forms but because he allows inanimate forces to play a role in the act of creation.

Students of animal behavior also will experience in Goldsworthy's art a sense of recognition. Animal architects use natural materials found on the spot, put together by stacking, weaving, mud daubing, and cementing with bodily fluids. Goldsworthy sometimes uses spit to freeze together sheets or spires of ice or to plaster leaves to mud or stones. In his journal he records having used warm urine to unfreeze sticks and stones that served as temporary supports for ice sculptures. While working in the Arctic, he once stained snowballs pink with the blood of a seal killed by a native hunter. Although he does not possess the geneti-

Sheep and kangaroo bones bleached white by the sun enclosing a boulder snake
MOUNT VICTOR STATION, SOUTH AUSTRALIA
11 FEBRUARY 1992

cally coded building instincts of the animal architect, he is certainly attuned to impulses that are deeply biological.

It is a small but significant step from the beaver's timber lodge or the cliff swallow's mud nest to the ancient cairns and barrows that crown the hilltops of Goldsworthy's Britain and so often seem to inspire his art. These human-built structures fill needs that are more than merely biological; they are responses to the mysteries of life and death, the cycles of the Sun and Moon, and the beckoning infinity of the night sky. With these most ancient surviving examples of human architecture, we have left the world of instinct and entered a world of conscious contrivance.

The attraction of Goldsworthy's art is that it encompasses

all of these worlds—the physical, biological, and intellectual. It recapitulates our past, from the cosmic forces that gathered and segregated the materials of the planet through billions of years of organic evolution to the spark of conscious intellect that created religion, art, sci-

twenty-three in the second both taken down intact incorporated into a third work one hundred and fourteen sticks
ANCHORAGE, ALASKA
26, 27–28, 29 NOVEMBER 1995

ence, and ultimately the full paraphernalia of modern technological civilization—air, water, earth, stone, wood touched by mind.

Andy Goldsworthy was born in Cheshire, England, in 1956 and raised in Yorkshire. He studied at the Bradford College of Art in Yorkshire and Preston Polytechnic in Lancashire. Since his student days, he has worked mostly in the open air, using natural materials. Some of his creations last for only fractions of a second, such as

water or colored earth flung into the air to catch a particular light. Ice or sand sculptures might endure for minutes or hours before being reclaimed by the sun or tide. Once he lined up stones on the tidal flats of Britain's Morecambe Bay. They are still there, although buried under the sand, like the fossil vertebrae of some ancient sea serpent that will endure through geologic time.

In geologic time, 100 years is no different from a second. This is the timetable that Goldsworthy keeps; human clocks seem particularly irrelevant to his artistic temperament. He has described his art as a "celebration of the transience of nature." Whether he is creating for seconds or for millennia, a camera is the one essential technological accessory that he carries into the field. His extensive body of work is best known through a series of splendid photographic books.

Goldsworthy now lives in the village of Penpont in Dumfriesshire, Scotland, where he has a studio in an old stone granary. Although his work has taken him as far afield as Japan and the North Pole, his home environment remains his deepest source of inspiration. "What is important to me is that at the heart of whatever I

do are a growing understanding and a sharpening perception of the land," Goldsworthy writes.

His work is important to us for the same reasons.

Certainly we have become estranged from the land by technology and the economic exploitation of natural resources. Goldsworthy is sympathetic to environmental concerns, and his art has been warmly embraced by environmentalists. But there is a deeper importance to his art, something that goes beyond the present environmental crisis. We also face a spiritual crisis, a faltering of confidence concerning who we are and why we are here. Having surrounded ourselves with the artificial, we have forgotten our connection with nonhuman nature, forgotten that we are made of massy atoms, spun on the spindles of DNA, fed on starlight.

What is required is a new alliance with the land, informed by science and technique yet open to mystery. What is required is a reenchantment of the Earth.

In an essay on fairy stories in his book *Tree and Leaf,* the

English writer J.R.R. Tolkien, creator of the Middle-earth fantasy novels, outlined a program for this reenchantment through fantasy. By the forging of magic swords in fantasy, the true nature of iron is revealed, Tolkien says. By the making of a Pegasus, all horses are ennobled; by inventing the mythical Trees of the Sun and Moon, "root and stock, flower and fruit are manifested in glory." Tolkien's observations about the magical landscapes of fairy tales and fantasy novels could apply with equal truthfulness to Goldsworthy's art. A Goldsworthy cairn of balanced stones ennobles all stones; a hanging screen of woven reeds invests every

meadow with mystery; an arch of snow at the North Pole celebrates the root of winter's chill.

Goldsworthy creates what Tolkien calls a "Secondary World," made of the stuff of the Primary World of nature but put together in imaginative ways. "The mind that thought of *light, heavy, grey, yellow, still, swift,* also conceived of magic that would make heavy things light and able to fly, turn grey lead into yellow gold, and the still rock into a swift water," Tolkien writes. In the enchanted worlds of fantasy, for example, we find the rare and terrible blue moon, the ram with fleece of gold, and hot fire in the belly of the worm. The

artist who would create such worlds, he observes, requires an "elvish craft."

"Elvish craft" is what Andy Goldsworthy possesses in abundance. His art is fun, whimsical, fey. It is impossible to look at a Goldsworthy creation—a hanging tapestry of iris and laurel leaves stitched together with thorns or a river boulder wrapped in red poppy petals—without feeling that one has entered the world of faerie. The artist is playing with our sense of what is natural, teasing us into imagining that what we see has been conjured from the materials of the earth as if by incantation—not through a suspension of nature's laws but by use of those

SWINDALE BECK WOOD, CUMBRIA
10 DECEMBER **1984**
Rushes and grass stalks
thin end of one pushed up wider hollow end of another
lines secured with thorns and clay
drawing rocks on calm days

laws in ways that nature has not yet imagined.

For a museum installation in Japan, Goldsworthy filled a room with spherical river boulders wrapped in thick clay. As the clay slowly dried, it cracked and fell away in chunks to reveal the rock cores. Even in photographs, they give the impression of dragon eggs hatching before our eyes.

In another work the artist took dandelion flowers, pinned them with thorns to willow stalks, and laid them in a ring on forked sticks above a meadow of bluebells—a fairy circle if ever there was one. Goldsworthy's earthworks evoke the "fairy forts" of the Celtic countryside, remnants of human habitation whose origins have been lost in the mists of time.

The successful creator of fantasy must be a good craftsman who "loves his material, and has a knowledge and feeling for clay, stone and wood which only the art of making can give," Tolkien writes. Goldsworthy exhibits in his work an uncommon knowledge and feeling for the materials of the Earth. He understands the raw creative power of heat, cold, water, wind, and gravity, and he seems to intuit the spider's skill with silk and the dauber wasp's knowledge of mud. His enchanted creations

strike through the artificial barriers we have erected between ourselves and nature.

"We need, in any case, to clean our windows," Tolkien advises, "so that the things seen clearly may be freed from the drab blur of triteness or familiarity—from possessiveness." Many commentators have suggested that our deepening environmental crisis springs from our sense of possessing nature: what is ours is there to be used—and abused. The freeing of nature—and ourselves—from the cage of human dominion is a responsibility we all share, but we can especially learn from those artists who through their "elvish craft" help wipe our windows clean, letting us see clearly the universe by which we are possessed against all our conscious pretensions to the contrary.

In an interview with the English novelist John Fowles, Goldsworthy said: "The most rewarding thing ever said to me was by a Dutch woman of a shape I had carved in sand. She said, 'Thank you for showing me that was there.' That is what my work does for me myself, the discovering 'what was there.' If it does it for others, then so much the richer."

Enchantment of the sort practiced by Goldsworthy lets us see how precious—how permeated with power and maj-

esty, darkness and light—is the Primary World that we are rapidly paving over, chopping down, polluting, draining dry. Goldsworthy has no quarrel with technology. In the introduction to one of the monographs of his work, he writes: "Technology, travel and tools are part of my life and if needed should be part of my work also. A camera is used to document, an excavator to move earth, snowballs are carried cross country by articulated truck." Nature goes beyond the countryside, he says, existing even indoors. His work is an attempt to discover honest nature even in urban and industrial materials.

But when Goldsworthy works indoors or with materials that are far removed from their source, he soon feels the need to return to nature, to put "hand to earth." He sees his work not as an expression of his own ideas but as a process of discovery. He rejects the bankrupt notion of possession. What he seems to be seeking is

the enchanter's secret knowledge of the Earth's own truth, and through the Earth he hopes to come to a more truthful understanding of himself.

Goldsworthy's visionary art should be better known by scientists, technologists, landscape architects, city planners, civil engineers, industrial farmers, and others who have the power to unalterably transform the land. Its unique melding of inanimate, animate, and conscious creative energies provides a timely antidote to our modern self-absorption, our isolation from nature, and our unnatural sense of possessiveness. Only when we again come to understand that each thing—each tree and leaf, each stone, each handful of earth—has its own truth will we respect the integrity of the environment and know what it means to live as part of an enchanted landscape.

At the onset of a rain or snow shower, Goldsworthy often will drop to the earth, spread wide his arms and legs, and use his body as a kind of mask as the ground around him is dampened with rain or whitened with snow. The resulting shadows of his presence, preserved in photographs, are haunting metaphors for how lightly our touch should be on the land—unmistakably human but fittingly ephemeral.

185

Beech leaves
SCAUR WATER, DUMFRIESSHIRE
OCTOBER 1992

Blades of grass
creased and arched
secured with thorns
PENPONT, DUMFRIESSHIRE
14 AUGUST 1988

Fine dry sand
edges and ridges
softened by the breeze
ARIZONA
21 NOVEMBER 1989

Broken pebbles
scratched white with another stone
ST ABBS, THE BORDERS
1 JUNE 1985

Iris blades pinned together with thorns
filled in five sections with rowan berries
fish attacking from below
difficult to keep all the berries in
nibbled at by ducks
YORKSHIRE SCULPTURE PARK, WEST BRETTON
29 AUGUST 1987

Slate dome hole
Wall by Joe Smith
Photograph by Catriona Grant
ROYAL BOTANIC GARDENS, EDINBURGH
SUMMER 1990

Proposal (unrealised)
for cliff top enclosure
to collapse a little each year
as the cliff eroded
SCARBOROUGH BLUFFS, CANADA
1992

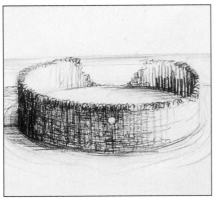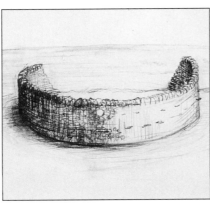

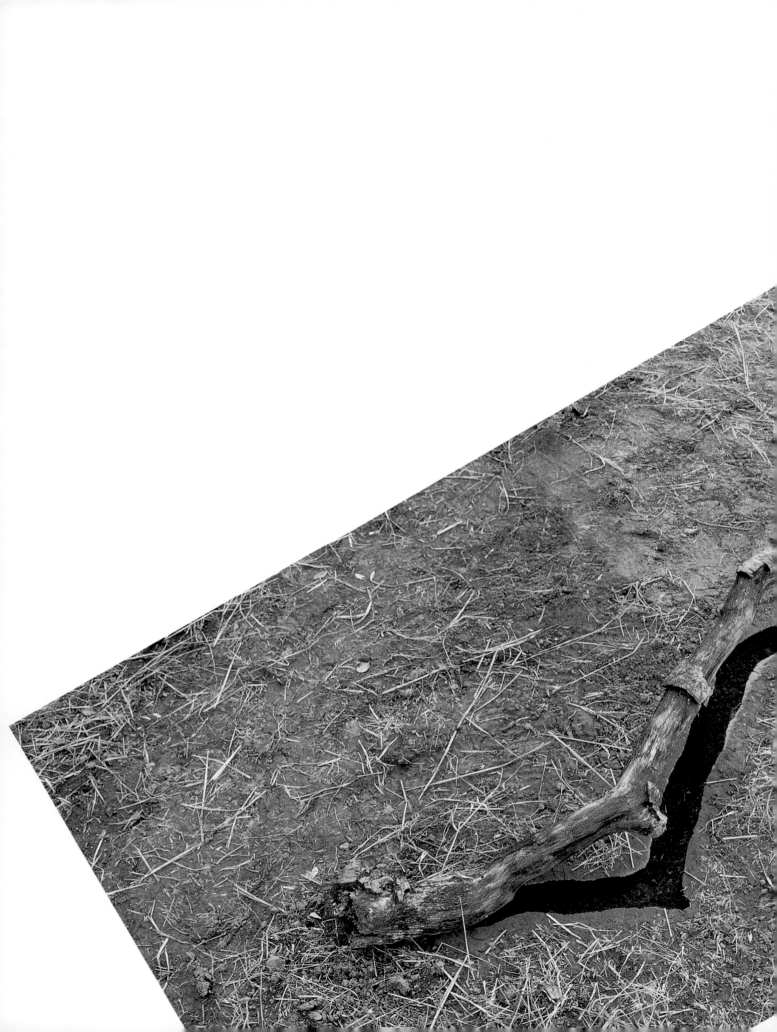

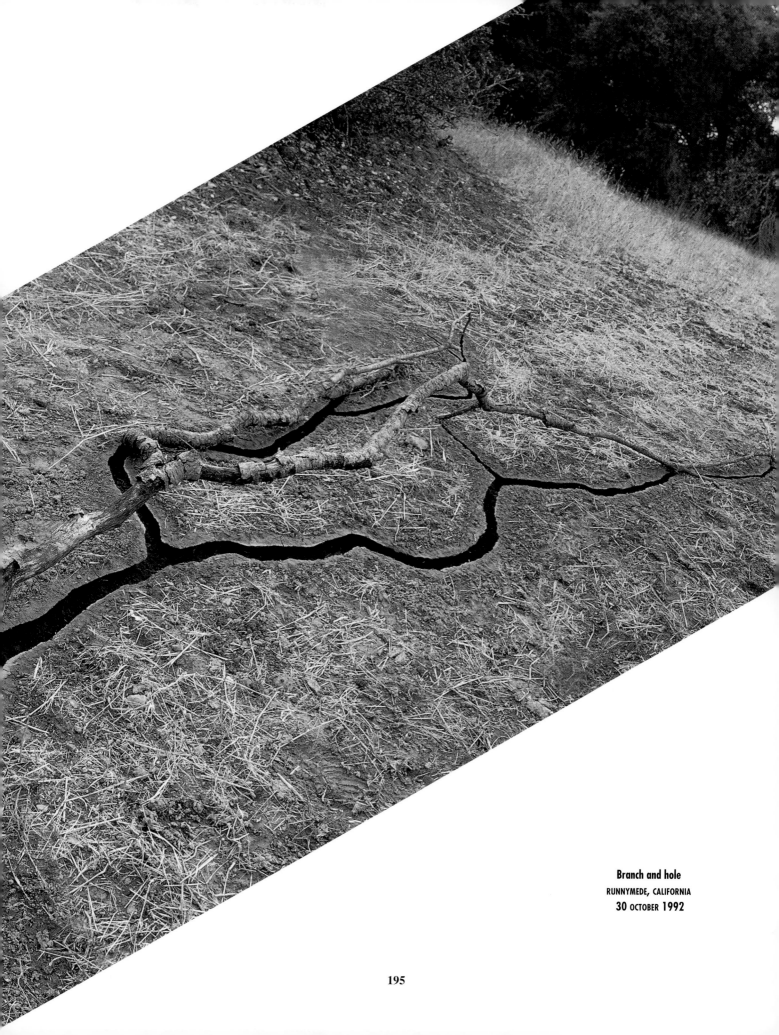

Branch and hole
RUNNYMEDE, CALIFORNIA
30 OCTOBER 1992

A stone
laid on previously
for several hours
slow rain dried
as quickly
as it wetted
returned in summer
sun and showers
five shadows
in three days
GATELAWBRIDGE, DUMFRIESSHIRE
JULY 1993

Oak leaves in holes
ILKLEY, YORKSHIRE
1978

ENCYCLOPÆDIA BRITANNICA
SCIENCE UPDATE

Major New Revisions from *Encyclopædia Britannica* and *Britannica Online*™

This section introduces to readers of the *Yearbook of Science and the Future* selected articles or portions of them that have been revised or written anew for *Encyclopædia Britannica* or *Britannica Online*™, an electronic version of the encyclopædia.

Selections from two encyclopædia articles, SENSORY RECEPTION—specifically, a major portion of the section *Human hearing and balance: structure and function of the ear*—and INDUSTRIAL POLYMERS, have

been chosen. They appear in the 1998 printing and are also available to *Britannica Online*™ subscribers. A third selection, Orville and Wilbur WRIGHT, is taken from the current version of *Britannica Online*™. (*Britannica Online*™ may be accessed on the Internet at http://www.eb.com.) Each selection is the work of distinguished scholars, and each represents the continuing dedication of *Encyclopædia Britannica* to bringing such articles to the general reader.

Sensory Reception

HUMAN HEARING AND BALANCE: STRUCTURE AND FUNCTION OF THE EAR

Parts of the ear

The human ear, like that of other mammals, contains sense organs that serve two quite different functions: that of hearing and that of postural equilibrium and coordination of head and eye movements. Anatomically the ear has three distinguishable parts: the outer, middle, and inner ear (Figure 52). The outer ear consists of the visible portion called the auricle, or pinna, which projects from the side of the head, and the short external auditory ca-

nal, the inner end of which is closed by the tympanic membrane, commonly called the eardrum. The function of the outer ear is to collect sound waves and guide them to the tympanic membrane. The middle ear is a narrow, air-filled cavity in the temporal bone. It is spanned by a chain of three tiny bones—the malleus (hammer), incus (anvil), and stapes (stirrup), collectively called the auditory ossicles. This ossicular chain conducts sound from

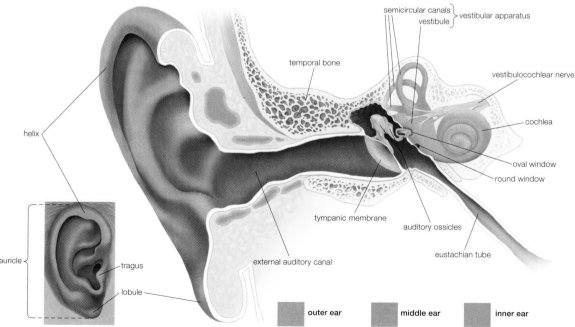

Figure 52: Structure of the human ear.
Encyclopædia Britannica, Inc.

the tympanic membrane to the inner ear, which has been known since the time of Galen (2nd century AD) as the labyrinth. It is a complicated system of fluid-filled passages and cavities located deep within the rock-hard petrous portion of the temporal bone. The inner ear consists of two functional units: the vestibular apparatus, consisting of the vestibule and semicircular canals, which contains the sensory organs of postural equilibrium; and the snail-shell-like cochlea, which contains the sensory organ of hearing. These sensory organs are highly specialized endings of the eighth cranial nerve, also called the vestibulocochlear nerve.

Anatomy of the human ear

OUTER EAR

The most striking differences between the human ear and the ears of other mammals are in the structure of the outermost part, the auricle (Figure 52). In humans the auricle is an almost rudimentary, usually immobile shell that lies close to the side of the head. It consists of a thin plate of yellow fibrocartilage covered by closely adherent skin. The cartilage is molded into clearly defined hollows, ridges, and furrows that form an irregular, shallow funnel. The deepest depression, which leads directly to the external auditory canal, or acoustic meatus, is called the concha. It is partly covered by two small projections, the tonguelike tragus in front and the antitragus behind. Above the tragus a prominent ridge, the helix, arises from the floor of the concha and continues as the incurved rim of the upper portion of the auricle. An inner, concentric ridge, the antihelix, surrounds the concha and is separated from the helix by a furrow, the scapha, also called the fossa of the helix. In some ears a little prominence known as Darwin's tubercle is seen along the upper, posterior portion of the helix; it is the vestige of the folded-over point of the ear of a remote human ancestor. The lobule, the fleshy lower part of the auricle, is the only *External auditory canal* area of the outer ear that contains no cartilage. The external auditory canal is a slightly curved tube that extends inward from the floor of the concha and ends blindly at

the tympanic membrane (Figure 52). In its outer third the wall of the canal consists of cartilage; in its inner two-thirds, of bone. The entire length of the passage (24 millimetres, or almost 1 inch) is lined with skin, which also covers the outer surface of the tympanic membrane. Fine hairs directed outward and modified sweat glands that produce earwax, or cerumen, line the canal and discourage insects from entering it.

TYMPANIC MEMBRANE AND MIDDLE EAR

Tympanic membrane. The thin, semitransparent tympanic membrane, or eardrum, which forms the boundary between the outer and middle ear, is stretched obliquely across the end of the external canal. Its diameter is about 9 millimetres (0.35 inch), its shape that of a flattened cone with its apex directed inward. Thus, its outer surface is slightly concave. The edge of the membrane is thickened and attached to a groove in an incomplete ring of bone, the tympanic annulus, which almost encircles it and holds it in place. The uppermost small area of the membrane where the ring is open is slack and is called the pars flaccida, but the far greater portion is tightly stretched and is called the pars tensa. The appearance and mobility of the tympanic membrane are important for the diagnosis of middle-ear disease, which is especially common in young children. When viewed with the otoscope, the healthy membrane is translucent and pearl-gray in colour, sometimes with a pinkish or yellowish tinge.

Middle-ear cavity. The cavity of the middle ear is a narrow, air-filled space. A slight constriction divides it into an upper and a lower chamber, the tympanum (tympanic cavity) proper below and the epitympanum above. These chambers also are referred to as the atrium and attic, respectively. The middle-ear space roughly resembles a rectangular room with four walls, a floor, and a ceiling. The outer (lateral) wall of the middle-ear space is formed by the tympanic membrane. Its ceiling (superior wall) is a thin plate of bone that separates it from the cranial cavity and brain above. The floor (inferior wall) is also a thin bony plate separating the cavity from the jugular vein and carotid artery below. The back (posterior) wall partly separates it from another cavity, the mastoid antrum, but an opening in this wall leads to the antrum and to the small air cells of the mastoid process, which is the roughened, slightly bulging portion of the temporal bone just behind the external auditory canal and the auricle. In the front (anterior) wall is the opening of the eustachian, or auditory, tube, which connects the middle ear with the nasopharynx (see below *Eustachian tube*). The inner (medial) wall, which separates the middle ear from the inner ear, or labyrinth, is a part of the bony otic capsule of the inner ear. It has two small openings, or fenestrae, one above the other. The upper one is the oval window, which is closed by the footplate of the stapes. The lower one is the round window, which is covered by a thin membrane.

Auditory ossicles. Crossing the middle-ear cavity is the short ossicular chain formed by three tiny bones that link the tympanic membrane with the oval window and inner ear (Figure 53). From the outside inward they are the malleus (hammer), the incus (anvil), and the stapes (stirrup). These bones are suspended by ligaments, which leave the chain free to vibrate in transmitting sound from the tympanic membrane to the inner ear.

The malleus consists of a handle and a head. The handle is firmly attached to the tympanic membrane from the centre (umbo) to the upper margin (Figure 53). The head of the malleus and the body of the incus are joined tightly and are suspended in the epitympanum just above the upper rim of the tympanic annulus, where three small ligaments anchor the head of the malleus to the walls and roof of the epitympanum. Another minute ligament fixes the short process (crus) of the incus in a shallow depression, called the fossa incudis, in the rear wall of the cavity. The long process of the incus is bent near its end and bears a small bony knob that forms a loose, ligament-enclosed joint with the head of the stapes. The stapes is the smallest bone in the body. It is about 3 millimetres

Tympanum and epitympanum

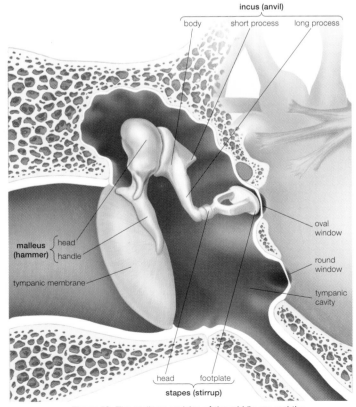

incus (anvil)
body   short process   long process

malleus (hammer) { head / handle

tympanic membrane

oval window

round window

tympanic cavity

head   footplate
stapes (stirrup)

Figure 53: The auditory ossicles of the middle ear and the structures surrounding them.
Encyclopædia Britannica, Inc.

(0.1 inch) long and weighs scarcely 3 milligrams (0.0001 ounce). It lies almost horizontally, at right angles to the process of the incus. Its base, or footplate, fits nicely in the oval window and is surrounded by the elastic annular ligament, although it remains free to vibrate in transmitting sound to the labyrinth.

Muscles. Two minuscule muscles are located in the middle ear. The longer muscle, called the tensor tympani, emerges from a bony canal just above the opening of the eustachian tube and runs backward then outward as it changes direction in passing over a pulleylike projection of bone. The tendon of this muscle is attached to the upper part of the handle of the malleus. When contracted, the tensor tympani tends to pull the malleus inward and thus maintains or increases the tension of the tympanic membrane. The shorter, stouter muscle, called the stapedius, arises from the back wall of the middle-ear cavity and extends forward and attaches to the neck of the head of the stapes. Its reflex contractions tend to tip the stapes backward, as if to pull it out of the oval window. Thus it selectively reduces the intensity of sounds entering the inner ear, especially those of lower frequency.

Eustachian tube. The eustachian tube, about 45 millimetres (1.75 inches) long, leads downward and inward from the tympanum to the nasopharynx, the space that is behind and continuous with the nasal passages and is above the soft palate. At its upper end the tube is narrow and surrounded by bone. Nearer the pharynx it widens and becomes cartilaginous. Its mucous lining, which is continuous with that of the middle ear, is covered with cilia, small hairlike projections whose coordinated rhythmical sweeping motions speed the drainage of mucous secretions from the tympanum to the pharynx.

The eustachian tube helps to ventilate the middle ear and to maintain equal air pressure on both sides of the tympanic membrane. The tube is closed at rest and opens during swallowing so that minor pressure differences are adjusted without conscious effort.

INNER EAR

The membranous and bony labyrinths

There are actually two labyrinths of the inner ear, one inside the other—the membranous labyrinth contained within the bony labyrinth (Figure 54). The bony labyrinth consists of a central chamber called the vestibule, the three semicircular canals, and the spirally coiled cochlea. Within each structure, and filling only a fraction of the available space, is a corresponding portion of the membranous labyrinth: the vestibule contains the utricle and saccule, each semicircular canal its semicircular duct, and the cochlea its cochlear duct. Surrounding the membranous labyrinth and filling the remaining space is the watery fluid called perilymph. It is derived from blood plasma and resembles but is not identical with the cerebrospinal fluid of the brain and the aqueous humour of the eye. Like most of the hollow organs, the membranous labyrinth is lined with epithelium (a sheet of specialized cells that covers internal and external body surfaces). It is filled with a fluid called endolymph, which has a markedly different ionic content from perilymph. Because the membranous labyrinth is a closed system, the endolymph and perilymph do not mix.

Vestibular system. The vestibular system is the apparatus of the inner ear involved in balance. It consists of two structures of the bony labyrinth, the vestibule and the semicircular canals, and the structures of the membranous labyrinth contained within them (Figure 54).

Vestibule. The two membranous sacs of the vestibule, the utricle and the saccule, are known as the otolith organs (Figure 55). Because they respond to gravitational forces, they are also called gravity receptors. Each sac has on its inner surface a single patch of sensory cells called a macula, which is about 2 millimetres (0.08 inch) in diameter and which monitors the position of the head relative to the vertical (see below *The physiology of balance: vestibular function: Detection of linear acceleration: static equilibrium*). In the utricle the macula projects from the anterior wall of that tubular sac and lies primarily in the horizontal plane. In the saccule the macula is in the verti-

cal plane and directly overlies the bone of the inner wall of the vestibule. In shape it is elongated and resembles the letter J. Each macula consists of neuroepithelium, a layer that is made up of supporting cells and sensory cells, as well as a basement membrane, nerve fibres and nerve endings, and underlying connective tissue. The sensory cells are called hair cells because of the hairlike cilia—stiff, nonmotile stereocilia and flexible, motile kinocilia—that project from their apical ends. The nerve fibres are from the superior, or vestibular, division of the vestibulocochlear nerve. They pierce the basement membrane and, depending on the type of hair cell, either end on the basal end of the cell or form a calyx, or cuplike structure, that surrounds it.

Each of the hair cells of the vestibular organs is topped by a hair bundle, which consists of about 100 fine, nonmotile stereocilia of graded lengths and a single motile kinocilium. The stereocilia are anchored in a dense cuticular plate at the cell's apex. The single kinocilium, which is larger and longer than the stereocilia, rises from a noncuticular area of the cell membrane at one side of the cuticular plate. The tallest stereocilia are those closest to the kinocilium, and they decrease in length in stepwise fashion away from the kinocilium. Minute filamentous strands link the tips and shafts of neighbouring stereocilia to each other. When the hair bundles are deflected—*e.g.,* because of a tilt of the head—the hair cells are stimulated to alter the rate of the nerve impulses that they are constantly sending via the vestibular nerve fibres to the brain stem. Covering the entire macula is a delicate acellular structure, the otolithic, or statolithic, membrane. This membrane is sometimes described as gelatinous, although it has a fibrillar pattern. The surface of the membrane is covered by a blanket of rhombohedral crystals, referred to as otoconia, or statoconia, and which consist of calcium carbonate in the form of calcite. These crystalline particles, which range in length from 1 to 20 micrometres (there are about 25,000 micrometres in an inch), are much denser than the membrane—their specific gravity is almost three times that of the membrane and the endolymph—and thus add considerable mass to it.

The vestibular hair cells are of two types. Type I cells have a rounded body enclosed by a nerve calyx; type II cells have a cylindrical body with nerve endings at the base. They form a mosaic on the surface of the maculae, with the type I cells dominating in a curvilinear area (the striola) near the centre of the macula and the cylindrical

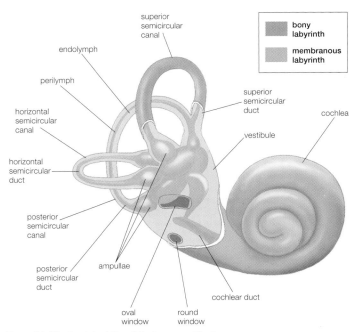

Figure 54: The two labyrinths of the inner ear. The bony labyrinth is partially cut away to show the membranous labyrinth within.

Encyclopædia Britannica, Inc.

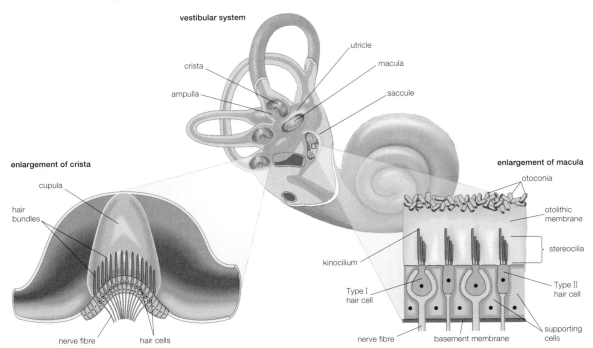

Figure 55: (Centre) the membranous labyrinth of the vestibular system, which contains the organs of balance: (lower left) the cristae of the semicircular ducts and (lower right) the maculae of the utricle and saccule.
Encyclopædia Britannica, Inc.

cells around the periphery. The significance of these patterns is poorly understood, but they may increase sensitivity to slight tiltings of the head.

Semicircular canals. The three semicircular canals of the bony labyrinth are designated, according to their position, superior, horizontal, and posterior (Figure 54). The superior and posterior canals are in diagonal vertical planes that intersect at right angles. Each canal has an expanded end, the ampulla, which opens into the vestibule. The ampullae of the horizontal and superior canals lie close together, just above the oval window, but the ampulla of the posterior canal opens on the opposite side of the vestibule. The other ends of the superior and posterior canals join to form a common stem, or crus, which also opens into the vestibule. Nearby is the mouth of a canal called the vestibular aqueduct, which opens into the cranial cavity. The other end of the horizontal canal has a separate opening into the vestibule. Thus, the vestibule completes the circle for each of the semicircular canals.

Each of the three bony canals and their ampullae encloses a membranous semicircular duct of much smaller diameter that has its own ampulla. The membranous ducts and ampullae follow the same pattern as the canals and ampullae of the bony labyrinth, with their openings into the utricle and with a common crus for the superior and posterior ducts. Like the other parts of the membranous labyrinth, they are filled with endolymph and surrounded by perilymph. The narrow endolymphatic duct passes from the utricle through the vestibular aqueduct into the cranial cavity, carrying excess endolymph to be absorbed by the endolymphatic sac.

Each membranous ampulla contains a saddle-shaped ridge of tissue called the crista, the sensory end organ that extends across it from side to side. It is covered by neuroepithelium, with hair cells and supporting cells. From this ridge rises a gelatinous structure, the cupula, which extends to the roof of the ampulla immediately above it, dividing the interior of the ampulla into two approximately equal parts. Like the hair cells of the maculae, the hair cells of the cristae have hair bundles projecting from their apices. The kinocilium and the longest stereocilia extend far up into the substance of the cupula, occupying fine parallel channels. Thus, the cupula is attached at its base to the crista but is free to incline toward or away from the utricle in response to the slightest flow of endolymph or a change in pressure. The tufts of cilia move

with the cupula and, depending on the direction of their bending, cause an increase or decrease in the rate of nerve impulse discharges carried by the vestibular nerve fibres to the brain stem.

Cochlea. *Structure of the cochlea.* The cochlea contains the sensory organ of hearing. It bears a striking resemblance to the shell of a snail and in fact takes its name from the Greek word for this object. The cochlea is a spiral tube that is coiled two and one-half turns around a hollow central pillar, the modiolus. It forms a cone approximately 9 millimetres (0.35 inch) in diameter at its base and 5 millimetres in height. When stretched out, the tube is approximately 30 millimetres in length; it is widest—2 millimetres—at the point where the basal coil opens into the vestibule and tapers until it ends blindly at the apex. The otherwise hollow centre of the modiolus contains the cochlear artery and vein, as well as the twisted trunk of fibres of the cochlear nerve. This nerve, a

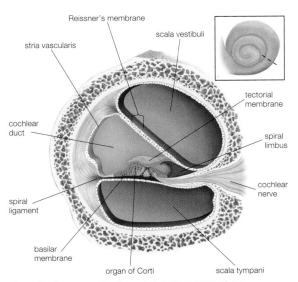

Figure 56: A cross section through one of the turns of the cochlea (inset) showing the scala tympani and scala vestibuli, which contain perilymph, and the cochlear duct, which is filled with endolymph.
Encyclopædia Britannica, Inc.

Marginal note: Semicircular ducts

division of the very short vestibulocochlear nerve, enters the base of the modiolus from the brain stem through an opening in the petrous portion of the temporal bone called the internal meatus. The spiral ganglion cells of the cochlear nerve are found in a bony spiral canal winding around the central core.

A thin bony shelf, the osseous spiral lamina, winds around the modiolus like the thread of a screw. It projects about halfway across the cochlear canal, partly dividing it into two compartments, an upper chamber called the scala vestibuli (vestibular ramp) and a lower chamber called the scala tympani (tympanic ramp). The scala vestibuli and scala tympani, which are filled with perilymph, communicate with each other through an opening at the apex of the cochlea, called the helicotrema, which can be seen if the cochlea is sliced longitudinally down the middle. At its basal end, near the middle ear, the scala vestibuli opens into the vestibule. The basal end of the scala tympani ends blindly just below the round window. Nearby is the opening of the narrow cochlear aqueduct, through which passes the perilymphatic duct. This duct connects the interior of the cochlea with the subdural space in the posterior cranial fossa (the rear portion of the floor of the cranial cavity).

Cochlear duct   A smaller scala, called the cochlear duct (scala media), lies between the larger vestibular and tympanic scalae; it is the cochlear portion of the membranous labyrinth. Filled with endolymph, the cochlear duct ends blindly at both ends—*i.e.*, below the round window and at the apex. In cross section this duct resembles a right triangle (Figure 56). Its base is formed by the osseous spiral lamina and the basilar membrane, which separate the cochlear duct from the scala tympani. Resting on the basilar membrane is the organ of Corti, which contains the hair cells that give rise to nerve signals in response to sound vibrations. The side of the triangle is formed by two tissues that line the bony wall of the cochlea, the stria vascularis, which lines the outer wall of the cochlear duct, and the fibrous spiral ligament, which lies between the stria and the bony wall of the cochlea. A layer of flat cells bounds the stria and separates it from the spiral ligament. The hypotenuse is formed by the transparent vestibular membrane of Reissner, which consists of only two layers of flattened cells. A low ridge, the spiral limbus, rests on the margin of the osseous spiral lamina. Reissner's membrane stretches from the inner margin of the limbus to the upper border of the stria.

Basilar membrane   In humans the basilar membrane is about 30 to 35 millimetres in length. It widens from less than 0.001 millimetre near its basal end to 0.005 millimetre near the apex. The basilar membrane is spanned by stiff, elastic fibres that are connected at their basal ends in the modiolus. Their distal ends are embedded in the membrane but are not actually attached, which allows them to vibrate. The fibres decrease in calibre and increase in length from the basal end of the cochlea near the middle ear to the apex, so that the basilar membrane as a whole decreases remarkably in stiffness from base to apex. Furthermore, at the basal end the osseous spiral lamina is broader, the stria vascularis wider, and the spiral ligament stouter than at the apex. In contrast, however, the mass of the organ of Corti is least at the base and greatest at the apex. Thus, a certain degree of tuning is provided in the structure of the cochlear duct and its contents. With greater stiffness and less mass, the basal end is more attuned to the sounds of higher frequencies. Decreased stiffness and increased mass render the apical end more responsive to lower frequencies.

Organ of Corti.   Arranged on the surface of the basilar membrane are orderly rows of the sensory hair cells, which generate nerve impulses in response to sound vibrations. Together with their supporting cells they form a complex neuroepithelium called the basilar papilla, or organ of Corti. The organ of Corti is named after the Italian anatomist Alfonso Corti, who first described it in 1851. Viewed in cross section (Figure 57) the most striking feature of the organ of Corti is the arch, or tunnel, of Corti, formed by two rows of pillar cells, or rods. The pillar cells furnish the major support of this structure. They separate

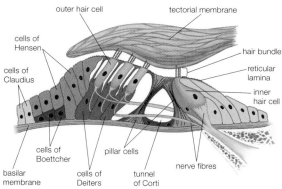

Figure 57: Structure of the organ of Corti.
Encyclopædia Britannica, Inc.

a single row of larger, pear-shaped, inner hair cells from three or more rows of smaller, cylindrical, outer hair cells. The inner hair cells are supported and enclosed by the inner phalangeal cells, which rest on the thin outer portion, called the tympanic lip, of the spiral limbus. On the inner side of the inner hair cells and the cells that support them is a curved furrow called the inner sulcus. This is lined with more or less undifferentiated cuboidal cells.

Each outer hair cell is supported by a phalangeal cell of Deiters, or supporting cell, which holds the base of the hair cell in a cup-shaped depression (Figure 57). From each Deiters' cell a projection extends upward to the stiff membrane, the reticular lamina, that covers the organ of Corti. The top of the hair cell is firmly held by the lamina, but the body is suspended in fluid that fills the space of Nuel and the tunnel of Corti.

Each hair cell has a cytoskeleton composed of filaments of the protein actin, which imparts stiffness to structures in which it is found. The hair cell is capped by a dense cuticular plate, composed of actin filaments, which bears a tuft of stiffly erect stereocilia, also containing actin, of graded lengths arranged in a staircase pattern. This so-called hair bundle has rootlets anchored firmly in the cuticular plate. On the top of the inner hair cells 40 to 60 stereocilia are arranged in two or more irregularly parallel rows. On the outer hair cells approximately 100 stereocilia form a W pattern. At the notch of the W the plate is incomplete, with only a thin cell membrane taking its place. Beneath the membrane is the basal body of a kinocilium, although no motile ciliary (hairlike) portion is present as is the case on the hair cells of the vestibular system.

The stereocilia are about three to five micrometres in length. The longest make contact with but do not penetrate the tectorial membrane (Figure 57). This membrane is an acellular, gelatinous structure that covers the top of the spiral limbus as a thin fibrillar layer, then becomes thicker as it extends outward over the inner sulcus and the reticular lamina. Its fibrils extend radially and somewhat obliquely to end at its lateral border, just above the junction of the reticular lamina and the cells of Hensen. In the upper turns of the cochlea, the margin of the membrane ends in fingerlike projections that make contact with the stereocilia of the outermost hair cells. **Stereocilia**

The myelin-ensheathed fibres of the vestibulocochlear nerve fan out in spiral fashion from the modiolus to pass into the channel near the root of the osseous spiral lamina, called the canal of Rosenthal. The bipolar cell bodies of these neurons constitute the spiral ganglion. Beyond the ganglion their distal processes extend radially outward in the bony lamina beneath the limbus to pass through an array of small pores directly under the inner hair cells, called the habenula perforata. Here the fibres abruptly lose their multilayered coats of myelin and continue as thin, naked, unmyelinated fibres into the organ of Corti. Some fibres form a longitudinally directed bundle running beneath the inner hair cells and another bundle just inside the tunnel, above the feet of the inner pillar cells. The majority of the fibres (some 95 percent in the human ear) end on the inner hair cells. The remainder cross the tunnel to form longitudinal bundles beneath the rows of the outer hair cells on which they eventually terminate.

The endings of the nerve fibres beneath the hair cells are of two distinct types. The larger and more numerous endings contain many minute vesicles, or liquid-filled sacs, containing neurotransmitters, which mediate impulse transmission at neural junctions. These endings belong to a special bundle of nerve fibres that arise in the brain stem and constitute an efferent system, or feedback loop, to the cochlea. The smaller and less numerous endings contain few vesicles or other cell structures. They are the terminations of the afferent fibres of the cochlear nerve, which transmit impulses from the hair cells to the brain stem (see below *The physiology of hearing: Cochlear nerve and central auditory pathways*).

The total number of outer hair cells in the cochlea has been estimated at 12,000 and the number of inner hair cells at 3,500. Although there are about 30,000 fibres in the cochlear nerve, there is considerable overlap in the innervation of the outer hair cells. A single fibre may supply endings to many hair cells, which thus share a "party line." Furthermore, a single hair cell may receive nerve endings from many fibres. The actual distribution of nerve fibres in the organ of Corti has not been worked out in detail, but it is known that the inner hair cells receive the lion's share of afferent fibre endings without the overlapping and sharing of fibres that are characteristic of the outer hair cells.

Viewed from above, the organ of Corti with its covering, the reticular lamina, forms a well-defined mosaic pattern. In humans the arrangement of the outer hair cells in the basal turn of the cochlea is quite regular, with three distinct and orderly rows; but in the higher turns of the cochlea the arrangement becomes slightly irregular, as scattered cells form fourth or fifth rows. The spaces between the outer hair cells are filled by oddly shaped extensions (phalangeal plates) of the supporting cells. The double row of head plates of the inner and outer pillar cells cover the tunnel and separate the inner from the outer hair cells. The reticular lamina extends from the inner border cells near the inner sulcus to the Hensen cells but does not include either of these cell groups. When a hair cell degenerates and disappears as a result of aging, disease, or noise-induced injury, its place is quickly covered by the adjacent phalangeal plates, which expand to form an easily recognized "scar."

Endolymph and perilymph. The perilymph, which fills the space within the bony labyrinth surrounding the membranous labyrinth, is similar, but not identical, in composition to other extracellular fluids of the body, such as cerebrospinal fluid. The concentration of sodium ions in the perilymph is high (about 150 milliequivalents per litre), and that of potassium ions is low (about 5 milliequivalents per litre), as is true of other extracellular fluids. Like these fluids, the perilymph is apparently formed locally from the blood plasma by transport mechanisms that selectively allow substances to cross the walls of the capillaries. Although it is anatomically possible for cerebrospinal fluid to enter the cochlea by way of the perilymphatic duct, experimental studies have made it appear unlikely that the cerebrospinal fluid is involved in the normal production of perilymph.

The membranous labyrinth is filled with endolymph, which is unique among extracellular fluids of the body, including the perilymph, in that its potassium ion concentration is higher (about 140 milliequivalents per litre) than its sodium ion concentration (about 15 milliequivalents per litre).

The physiology of hearing

Hearing is the process by which the ear transforms sound vibrations in the external environment into nerve impulses that are conveyed to the brain, where they are interpreted as sounds. Sounds are produced when vibrating objects, such as the plucked string of a guitar, produce pressure pulses of vibrating air molecules, better known as sound waves. The ear can distinguish different subjective aspects of a sound, such as its loudness and pitch, by detecting and analyzing different physical characteristics of the waves. Pitch is the perception of the frequency of sound waves—*i.e.*, the number of wavelengths that pass a fixed point in a unit of time. Frequency is usually measured in cycles per second, or hertz. The human ear is most sensitive to and most easily detects frequencies of 1,000 to 4,000 hertz, but at least for normal young ears the entire audible range of sounds extends from about 20 to 20,000 hertz. Sound waves of still higher frequency are referred to as ultrasonic, although they can be heard by other mammals. Loudness is the perception of the intensity of sound—*i.e.*, the pressure exerted by sound waves on the tympanic membrane. The greater their amplitude or strength, the greater is the pressure or intensity, and consequently the loudness, of the sound. The intensity of sound is measured and reported in decibels (dB), a unit that expresses the relative magnitude of a sound on a logarithmic scale. Stated in another way, the decibel is a unit for comparing the intensity of any given sound with a standard sound that is just perceptible to the normal human ear at a frequency in the range to which the ear is most sensitive. On the decibel scale, the range of human hearing extends from 0 dB, which represents a level that

Loudness and pitch

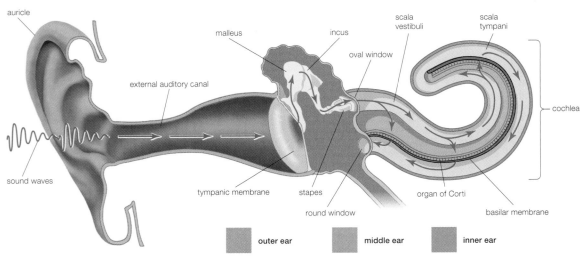

Figure 58: The mechanism of hearing. Sound waves enter the outer ear and travel through the external auditory canal until they reach the tympanic membrane, causing the membrane and the attached chain of auditory ossicles to vibrate. The motion of the stapes against the oval window sets up waves in the fluids of the cochlea, causing the basilar membrane to vibrate. This stimulates the sensory cells of the organ of Corti, atop the basilar membrane, to send nerve impulses to the brain.
Encyclopædia Britannica, Inc.

is all but inaudible, to about 130 dB, the level at which sound becomes painful.

In order for a sound to be transmitted to the central nervous system, the energy of the sound undergoes three transformations (Figure 58). First, the air vibrations are converted to vibrations of the tympanic membrane and ossicles of the middle ear. These, in turn, become vibrations in the fluid within the cochlea. Finally, the fluid vibrations set up traveling waves along the basilar membrane that stimulate the hair cells of the organ of Corti. These cells convert the sound vibrations to nerve impulses in the fibres of the cochlear nerve, which transmits them to the brain stem, from which they are relayed, after extensive processing, to the primary auditory area of the cerebral cortex, the ultimate centre of the brain for hearing. Only when the nerve impulses reach this area does the listener become aware of the sound.

TRANSMISSION OF SOUND WAVES THROUGH THE OUTER AND MIDDLE EAR

Transmission of sound by air conduction.   The outer ear directs sound waves from the external environment to the tympanic membrane (Figure 52). The auricle, the visible portion of the outer ear, collects sound waves and, with the concha, the cavity at the entrance to the external auditory canal, helps to funnel sound into the canal. Because of its small size and virtual immobility, the auricle in humans is less useful in sound gathering and direction finding than it is in many animals. The canal helps to enhance the amount of sound that reaches the tympanic membrane. This resonance enhancement works only for sounds of relatively short wavelength—those in the frequency range between 2,000 and 7,000 hertz—which helps to determine the frequencies to which the ear is most sensitive, those important for distinguishing the sounds of consonants.

Sounds reaching the tympanic membrane are in part reflected and in part absorbed. Only absorbed sound sets the membrane in motion. The tendency of the ear to oppose the passage of sound is called acoustic impedance (see below). The magnitude of the impedance depends on the mass and stiffness of the membrane and the ossicular chain and on the frictional resistance they offer.

When the tympanic membrane absorbs sound waves, its central portion, the umbo, vibrates as a stiff cone, bending inward and outward. The greater the force of the sound waves, the greater the deflection of the membrane and the louder the sound. The higher the frequency of a sound, the faster the membrane vibrates and the higher the pitch of the sound is. The motion of the membrane is transferred to the handle of the malleus, the tip of which is attached to the umbo. At higher frequencies the motion of the membrane is no longer simple, and transmission to the malleus may be somewhat less effective.

The malleus and incus are suspended by small elastic ligaments and are finely balanced, with their masses evenly distributed above and below their common axis of rotation. The head of the malleus and the body of the incus are tightly bound together, with the result that they move as a unit in unison with the tympanic membrane. At moderate sound pressures, the vibrations are passed on to the stapes, and the whole ossicular chain moves as a single mass. However, there may be considerable freedom of motion and some loss of energy at the joint between the incus and the stapes because of their relatively loose coupling. The stapes does not move in and out but rocks back and forth about the lower pole of its footplate, which impinges on the membrane covering the oval window in the bony plate of the inner ear. The action of the stapes transmits the sound waves to the perilymph of the vestibule and the scala vestibuli (Figure 58).

Function of the ossicular chain.   In order for sound to be transmitted to the inner ear, the vibrations in the air must be changed to vibrations in the cochlear fluids. There is a challenge involved in this task that has to do with difference in impedance—the resistance to the passage of sound—between air and fluid. This difference, or mismatch, of impedances reduces the transmission of sound. The tympanic membrane and the ossicles function

Matching of impedances

to overcome the mismatch of impedances between air and the cochlear fluids, and thus the middle ear serves as a transformer, or impedance matching device.

Ordinarily, when airborne sound strikes the surface of a body of water, almost all of its energy is reflected and only about 0.1 percent passes into the water. In the ear this would represent a transmission loss of 30 decibels, enough to seriously limit the ear's performance, were it not for the transformer action of the middle ear. The matching of impedances is accomplished in two ways, primarily by the reduction in area between the tympanic membrane and the stapes footplate and secondarily by the mechanical advantage of the lever formed by the malleus and incus. Although the total area of the tympanic membrane is about 69 square millimetres (0.1 square inch), the area of its central portion that is free to move has been estimated at about 43 square millimetres. The sound energy that causes this area of the membrane to vibrate is transmitted and concentrated in the 3.2-square-millimetre area of the stapes footplate. Thus, the pressure is increased at least 13 times. The mechanical advantage of the ossicular lever (which exists because the handle of the malleus is longer than the long projection of the incus) amounts to about 1.3. The total increase in pressure at the footplate is, therefore, not less than 17-fold, depending on the area of the tympanic membrane that is actually vibrating. At frequencies in the range of 3,000 to 5,000 hertz, the increase may be even greater because of the resonant properties of the ear canal.

The ossicular chain not only concentrates sound in a small area but also applies sound preferentially to one window of the cochlea, the oval window (Figure 58). If the oval and round windows were exposed equally to airborne sound crossing the middle ear, the vibrations in the perilymph of the scala vestibuli would be opposed by those in the perilymph of the scala tympani, and little effective movement of the basilar membrane would result. As it is, sound is delivered selectively to the oval window, and the round window moves in reciprocal fashion, bulging outward in response to an inward movement of the stapes footplate and inward when the stapes moves away from the oval window. The passage of vibrations through the air across the middle ear from the tympanic membrane to the round window is of negligible importance.

Function of the muscles of the middle ear.   The muscles of the middle ear, the tensor tympani and the stapedius, can influence the transmission of sound by the ossicular chain. Contraction of the tensor tympani pulls the handle of the malleus inward and, as the name of the muscle suggests, tenses the tympanic membrane. Contraction of the stapedius pulls the stapes footplate outward from the oval window and thereby reduces the intensity of sound reaching the cochlea. The stapedius responds reflexly with quick contraction to sounds of high intensity applied either to the same ear or to the opposite ear. The reflex has been likened to the blink of the eye or the constriction of the pupil of the eye in response to light and is thought to have protective value. Unfortunately, the contractions of the middle-ear muscles are not instantaneous, so that they do not protect the cochlea against damage by sudden intense noise, such as that of an explosion or of gunfire. They also fatigue rather quickly and thus offer little protection against injury sustained from high-level noise, such as that experienced in rock concerts and many industrial workplaces.

Transmission of sound by bone conduction.   There is another route by which sound can reach the inner ear: by conduction through the bones of the skull. When the handle of a vibrating tuning fork is placed on a bony prominence such as the forehead or mastoid process behind the ear, its note is clearly audible. Similarly, the ticking of a watch held between the teeth can be distinctly heard. When the external canals are closed with the fingers, the sound becomes louder, indicating that it is not entering the ear by the usual channel. Instead, it is producing vibrations of the skull that are passed on to the inner ear, either directly or indirectly, through the bone. The higher audible frequencies cause the skull to vibrate in segments, and these vibrations are transmitted to the

Compression and inertial bone conduction

cochlear fluids by direct compression of the otic capsule, the bony case enclosing the inner ear. Because the round window membrane is more freely mobile than the stapes footplate, the vibrations set up in the perilymph of the scala vestibuli are not canceled out by those in the scala tympani, and the resultant movements of the basilar membrane can stimulate the organ of Corti. This type of transmission is known as compression bone conduction.

At lower frequencies—i.e., 1,500 hertz and below—the skull moves as a rigid body. The ossicles are less affected and move less freely than the cochlea and the margins of the oval window because of their inertia, their suspension in the middle-ear cavity, and their loose coupling to the skull. The result is that the oval window moves with respect to the footplate of the stapes, which gives the same effect as if the stapes itself were vibrating. This form of transmission is known as inertial bone conduction. In otosclerosis the fixed stapes interferes with inertial, but not with compressional, bone conduction.

TRANSMISSION OF SOUND WITHIN THE INNER EAR

Transmission of sound waves in the cochlea. The mechanical vibrations of the stapes footplate at the oval window creates pressure waves in the perilymph of the scala vestibuli of the cochlea. These waves move around the tip of the cochlea through the helicotrema into the scala tympani and dissipate as they hit the round window (Figure 58). The wave motion is transmitted to the endolymph inside the cochlear duct. As a result the basilar membrane vibrates, which causes the organ of Corti to move against the tectoral membrane, stimulating generation of nerve impulses to the brain.

Analysis of sound

Within the cochlea the different frequencies of complex sounds are sorted out, or analyzed, and the physical energy of these sound vibrations is converted, or transduced, into electrical impulses that are transmitted to the brain stem by the cochlear nerve. The cochlea analyzes sound frequencies (distinguishes pitch) by means of the

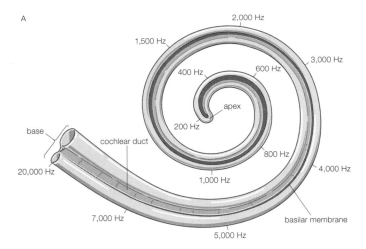

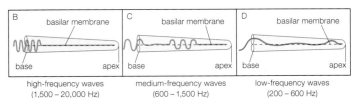

Figure 59: The analysis of sound frequencies by the basilar membrane. (A) The fibres of the basilar membrane become progressively wider and more flexible from the base of the cochlea to the apex. As a result, each area of the basilar membrane vibrates preferentially to a particular sound frequency. (B) High-frequency sound waves cause maximum vibration of the area of the basilar membrane nearest to the base of the cochlea, (C) medium-frequency waves affect the centre of the membrane, (D) low-frequency waves preferentially stimulate the apex of the basilar membrane. (The locations of cochlear frequencies along the basilar membrane shown are a composite drawn from different sources.)
Encyclopædia Britannica, Inc.

basilar membrane, which exhibits different degrees of stiffness, or resonance, along its length (Figure 59).

Pitch is distinguished because of the continuous changes that occur along the length of the basilar membrane, which increases in width and mass and decreases in stiffness from its base near the oval window to its apex. Each region of the membrane is most affected by a specific frequency of vibrations. Low-frequency sounds cause the apical end of the membrane to vibrate, and high-frequency sounds cause the basal end to vibrate (Figure 59). Vibrations reaching the basal end through the perilymph proceed along the membrane as traveling waves that attain their maximum amplitude at a distance corresponding to their frequency and then rapidly subside. The higher the frequency of the sound imposed, the shorter the distance the waves travel. Thus, a tone of a given frequency causes stimulation to reach a peak at a certain place on the basilar membrane. The region that vibrates most vigorously stimulates the greatest number of hair cells in that area of the organ of Corti, and these hair cells send the most nerve impulses to the auditory nerve and the brain (see below). The brain recognizes the place on the basilar membrane and thus the pitch of the tone by the particular group of nerve fibres activated. For the lower frequencies—up to about 3,000 hertz—the rate of stimulation is also an important indicator of pitch. This means that the auditory nerve fibres convey information to the brain about the timing of the sound frequency as well as its place of maximum vibration on the membrane. For higher frequencies place alone seems to be decisive.

Loudness also is determined at this level by the amplitude, or height, of the vibration of the basilar membrane. As a sound increases, so does the amplitude of the vibration. This increases both the number of hair cells stimulated and the rate at which they generate nerve impulses.

Transduction of mechanical vibrations. The hair cells located in the organ of Corti transduce mechanical sound vibrations into nerve impulses. They are stimulated when the basilar membrane, on which the organ of Corti rests, vibrates. The hair cells are held in place by the reticular lamina, a rigid structure supported by the pillar cells, or rods of Corti, which are attached to the basilar fibres. At the base of the hair cells is a network of cochlear nerve endings, which lead to the spiral ganglion of Corti in the modiolus of the cochlea. The spiral ganglion sends axons into the cochlear nerve. At the top of the hair cell is a hair bundle containing stereocilia, or sensory hairs, that project upward into the tectorial membrane, which lies above the stereocilia in the cochlear duct. (The single kinocilium, which is found on the hair cells of the vestibular system, is not found on the receptor cells of the cochlea.) When the basilar membrane moves upward, the reticular lamina moves upward and inward; when the membrane moves downward, the reticular lamina moves downward and outward. The resultant shearing forces between the reticular lamina and the tectorial membrane displace or bend the longest of the stereocilia, exciting the nerve fibres at the base of the hair cells.

The mechanism the hair cell uses to convert sound into an electrical stimulus is not completely understood, but certain key features are known. One of the most important aspects of this process is the endocochlear potential, which exists between the endolymph and perilymph. This direct current potential difference is about +80 millivolts and results from the difference in potassium content between the two fluids. It is thought to be maintained by the continual transport of potassium ions from the perilymph into the cochlear duct by the stria vascularis. The endolymph, which has a high potassium level and a positive potential, is contained in the cochlear duct and thus bathes the tops of the hair cells. The perilymph, which has a low potassium level and a negative potential, is contained in the scala vestibuli and scala tympani and bathes the lower parts of the hair cells. The inside of the hair cell has a negative intracellular potential of −60 millivolts with respect to the perilymph and −140 millivolts with respect to the endolymph. This rather steep gradient, especially at the tip of the cell, is thought to sensitize the cell to the slightest sound.

Endocochlear potential

The stereocilia are graded in height, becoming longer on the side away from the modiolus. All the stereocilia are interlinked so that, when the taller ones are moved against the tectorial membrane, the shorter ones move as well. The mechanical movement of this hair bundle generates an alternating hair cell receptor potential. This occurs in the following manner. When the stereocilia are bent in the direction of increasing stereocilia length, ion channels in the membrane open, allowing potassium ions to move into the cell. The influx of potassium ions excites, or depolarizes, the hair cell. However, when the stereocilia are deflected in the opposite direction, the ion channels are shut and the hair cell is inhibited, or hyperpolarized. The depolarization of the cell stimulates the release of chemicals called neurotransmitters from the base of the hair cell. The neurotransmitters are absorbed by the nerve fibres located at the basal end of the hair cell, stimulating them to send an electrical signal along the cochlear nerve.

COCHLEAR NERVE AND CENTRAL AUDITORY PATHWAYS

Auditory nerve fibres. The vestibulocochlear nerve consists of two anatomically and functionally distinct parts: the cochlear nerve, which innervates the organ of hearing, and the vestibular nerve, which innervates the organs of equilibrium. The fibres of the cochlear nerve originate from an aggregation of nerve cell bodies, the spiral ganglion, located in the modiolus of the cochlea. The neurons of the spiral ganglion are called bipolar cells because they have two sets of processes, or fibres, that extend from opposite ends of the cell body. The longer, central fibres, also called the primary auditory fibres, form the cochlear nerve, and the shorter, peripheral fibres extend to the bases of the inner and outer hair cells. They extend radially from the spiral ganglion to the habenula perforata, a series of tiny holes beneath the inner hair cells. At this point they lose their myelin sheaths and enter the organ of Corti as thin, unmyelinated fibres. There are only about 30,000 of these fibres, and the greater number of them—about 95 percent—innervate the inner hair cells. The remainder cross the tunnel of Corti to innervate the outer hair cells. The longer central processes of the bipolar cochlear neurons unite and are twisted like the cords of a rope to form the cochlear nerve trunk. These primary auditory fibres exit the modiolus through the internal meatus, or passageway, and immediately enter the part of the brain stem called the medulla.

Auditory pathways. *Ascending pathways.* The central auditory pathways extend from the medulla to the cerebral cortex. They consist of a series of nuclei (groups of nerve cell bodies in the central nervous system similar to a peripheral ganglion) connected by fibre tracts made up of their axons (processes that convey signals away from the cell bodies). This complex chain of nerve cells helps to process and relay auditory information, encoded in the form of nerve impulses, directly to the highest cerebral levels in the cortex of the brain. To some extent different properties of the auditory stimulus are conveyed along distinct parallel pathways. This method of transmission, employed by other sensory systems, provides a means for the central nervous system to analyze different properties of the single auditory stimulus, with some information processed at low levels and other information at higher levels. At lower levels of the pathway, information as to pitch, loudness, and localization of sounds is processed, and appropriate responses, such as the contraction of the intra-aural muscles, turning of the eyes and head, or movements of the body as a whole, are initiated.

In the medulla the fibres of the cochlear nerve terminate when they reach a collection of nerve cells called the cochlear nucleus. The cochlear nucleus consists of several distinct cell types and is divided into the dorsal and ventral cochlear nucleus. Each cochlear nerve fibre branches at the cochlear nucleus, sending one branch to the dorsal and the other branch to the ventral cochlear nucleus.

Some fibres from the ventral cochlear nucleus pass across the midline to the cells of the superior olivary complex, whereas others make connection with the olivary cells of the same side. Together, these fibres form the

Processing of auditory information

trapezoid body. Fibres from the dorsal cochlear nucleus cross the midline to end on the cells of the nuclei of the lateral lemniscus. There they are joined by the fibres from the ventral cochlear nuclei of both sides and from the olivary complex. The lemniscus is a major tract, most of the fibres of which end in the inferior colliculus, the auditory centre of the midbrain, although some fibres may bypass the colliculus and end, together with the fibres from the colliculus, at the next higher level, the medial geniculate body. From the medial geniculate body there is an orderly projection of fibres to a portion of the cortex of the temporal lobe.

In humans and other primates the primary acoustic area in the cerebral cortex is the superior transverse temporal gyri of Heschl, a ridge in the temporal lobe, on the lower lip of the deep cleft between the temporal and parietal lobes, known as the sylvian fissure.

Because about half of the fibres of the auditory pathways cross the midline while others ascend on the same side of the brain, each ear is represented in both the right and left cortex. For this reason, even when the auditory cortical area of one side is injured by trauma or stroke, binaural hearing may be little affected. Impaired hearing due to bilateral cortical injury involving both auditory areas has been reported, but it is extremely rare.

Descending pathways. Parallel with the pathway ascending from the cochlear nuclei to the cortex is a pathway descending from the cortex to the cochlear nuclei. In both pathways some of the fibres remain on the same side, while others cross the midline to the opposite side of the brain. There is also evidence of a "spur" line ascending from the dorsal cochlear nucleus to the cerebellum and another descending from the inferior colliculus to the cerebellum. The significance of these cerebral connections is not clear, but they may antedate the evolutionary development of the cerebral cortex. In general, the descending fibres may be regarded as exercising an inhibitory function by means of a sort of "negative feedback." They also may determine which ascending impulses are to be blocked and which are allowed to pass on to the higher centres of the brain.

Function of descending fibres

From the superior olivary complex, a region in the medulla oblongata, there arises also a fibre tract called the olivocochlear bundle. It constitutes an efferent system, or feedback loop, by which nerve impulses, thought to be inhibitory, reach the hair cells. This system, which uses acetylcholine as a neurotransmitter, is presumably involved in sharpening, or otherwise modifying, the analysis that is made in the cochlea.

Analysis of sound by the auditory nervous system. Evidence of orderly spatial representations of the organ of Corti at the lower levels of the auditory pathway has been reported by many investigators. These patterns seem to be in accord with the place theory of the cochlear analysis of sound. Physiological evidence of tuning of the auditory system also has been obtained by recording with the electrical potentials from individual neurons at various levels. Most neurons of the auditory pathway show a "best frequency"—*i.e.,* a frequency to which the individual neuron responds at minimal intensity. This finding is entirely compatible with experimental evidence of frequency tuning of the hair cells (see above *Transmission of sound within the inner ear*). With each increase in the intensity of the sound stimulus, the neuron is able to respond to a wider band of frequencies, thus reflecting the broad tuning of the basilar membrane. With sounds of lower frequency, the rate of impulses fired by the neuron reflects the stimulus frequency, and the response often reveals phase-locking with the stimulus; that is, the nerve fibres are stimulated at regularly recurring intervals, corresponding to a particular position or phase, of each sound wave. Increased intensity of stimulation causes a more rapid rate of responding. In general, the pitch of a sound tends to be coded in terms of which neurons are responding, and its loudness is determined by the rate of response and the total number of neurons activated.

It appears likely that in humans the cortex is not involved in frequency recognition but is reserved for the analysis of more complex auditory stimuli, such as speech and music, for which the temporal sequence of sounds is equally important. Presumably it is also at the cortical level that the meaning of sounds is interpreted and behaviour is adjusted in accordance with their significance. Such functions were formerly attributed to an "auditory association area" immediately surrounding the primary area, but they probably should be thought of as involving much more of the cerebral cortex, thanks to the multiple, parallel interconnections between the various areas.

Localization of sound
The localization of sounds from a stationary source in the horizontal plane is known to depend on the recognition of minute differences in the intensity and time of arrival of the sound at the two ears. A sound that arrives at the right ear a few microseconds sooner than it does at the left or that sounds a few decibels louder in that ear is recognized as coming from the right. In a real-life situation the head may also be turned to pinpoint the sound by facing it and thus canceling these differences. For low-frequency tones a difference in phase at the two ears is the criterion for localization, but for higher frequencies the difference in loudness caused by the sound shadow of the head becomes all-important. Such comparisons and discriminations appear to be carried out at brain stem and midbrain levels of the central auditory pathway. The spectral shapes of sounds have been shown to be most important for determining the elevation of a source that is not in the horizontal plane. Localization of sound that emanates from a moving source is a more complicated task for the nervous system and apparently involves the cerebral cortex and short-term memory. Experiments in animals have shown that injury to the auditory area of the cortex on one side of the brain interferes with the localization of a moving sound source on the opposite side of the body.

Each cochlear nucleus receives impulses only from the ear of the same side. A comparison between the responses of the two ears first becomes possible at the superior olivary complex, which receives fibres from both cochlear nuclei. Electrophysiological experiments in animals have shown that some neurons of the accessory nucleus of the olivary complex respond to impulses from both ears. Others respond to impulses from one side exclusively, but their response is modified by the simultaneous arrival of impulses from the other side.

The system appears to be capable of making the extraordinarily fine discriminations of time and intensity that are necessary for sound localization. By virtue of such bilateral neural interconnections in the brain, the two ears together can be much more effective than one ear alone in picking out a particular sound in the presence of a background of noise. They also permit attention to be directed to a single source of sound, such as one instrument in an orchestra or one voice in a crowd.

HEARING TESTS

Before the development of electroacoustic equipment for generating and measuring sound, the available tests of hearing gave approximate answers at best. A person's hearing could be specified in terms of the ability to distinguish the ticking of a watch or the clicking of coins or the distance at which conversational speech or a whispered voice could be understood. The examiner also might note the length of time the person could hear the gradually diminishing note of a tuning fork, comparing the performance with his own.

Tuning fork tests. A qualitative assessment of hearing loss can be carried out with a tuning fork. These tests exploit the ability of sound to be conducted through the bones of the skull (see above *Transmission of sound waves through the outer and middle ear: Transmission of sound by bone conduction*).

One example of a tuning fork test is the Weber test, in which the fork is simply placed on the person's forehead, and the examiner asks in which ear the person hears it. If a sensorineural lesion is present in one ear, the person will localize the sound in the opposite, or "better," ear. If a conductive defect is present, the person will localize it in the "worse" ear—*i.e.*, the one that is protected from interference by extraneous sounds. This simple test has

been a valuable aid in the diagnosis of otosclerosis for many years.

Audiometry. With the introduction of the electric audiometer in the 1930s, it became possible to measure an individual's hearing threshold for a series of pure tones ranging from a lower frequency of 125 hertz to an upper frequency of 8,000 or 10,000 hertz. This span includes the three octaves between 500 and 4,000 hertz that are most important for speech.

The audiometer consists of an oscillator or signal generator, an amplifier, a device called an attenuator, which controls and specifies the intensity of tones produced, and an earphone or loudspeaker. The intensity range is usually 100 decibels in steps of 5 decibels. The "zero dB" level represents normal hearing for young adults under favourable, noise-free laboratory conditions. It was established in 1964 as an international standard.

Pure-tone audiometry
In pure-tone audiometry each ear is tested separately, while the other is shielded against sound. The person being tested wears an earphone or sits in front of a loudspeaker in a quiet test chamber, with instructions to give a hand signal whenever a brief tone is sounded. The audiologist proceeds to determine the lowest intensity for each frequency at which the person reports being just able to hear the tone 50 percent of the time. For example, one who hears the tone of 4,000 hertz only half the time at the 40-decibel setting has a 40-decibel hearing level for that frequency—*i.e.*, a threshold 40 decibels above the normal threshold. A graph showing the hearing level for each ear by octaves and half octaves across the frequency range of 125 to 8,000 hertz is called an audiogram. The shape of the audiogram for an individual who is hard-of-hearing can provide the otologist or audiologist with important information for determining the nature and cause of the hearing defect.

A calibrated bone-conduction vibrator usually is furnished with the audiometer so that hearing by bone conduction also can be measured. When an individual has otosclerosis or another conductive defect of the middle ear, there may be a sizable difference between the air-conduction and bone-conduction audiograms, the so-called air-bone gap. This difference is a measure of the loss in transmission across the middle ear and indicates the maximum improvement that may be obtained through successful corrective surgery. When the defect is confined to the organ of Corti, the bone-conduction audiogram shows the same degree of loss as the air-conduction audiogram. In such cases of sensorineural impairment, surgery is seldom capable of improving hearing, but a hearing aid may be helpful.

Recruitment
Although faint sounds may not be heard at all by the ear with a sensorineural impairment, more intense sounds may be as loud as they are to a healthy ear. This rapid increase in loudness above the threshold level is called recruitment. When the opposite ear has normal hearing, recruitment can be measured by the alternate binaural loudness balance test. The subject is asked to set the controls so that the loudness of the tone heard in the defective ear matches that of the tone heard in the normal ear. By repeating the comparison at several intensity levels, the presence or absence of recruitment can be demonstrated. When recruitment is excessive, the range of useful hearing between the threshold and the level at which loudness becomes uncomfortable or intolerable may be narrow, so that the amplification provided by a hearing aid is of limited value to the subject.

Although hearing thresholds for pure tones give some indication of the person's ability to hear speech, direct measurement of this ability is also important. Two types of tests are used most often. In one test the speech reception threshold is measured by presenting words of spondee pattern—*i.e.*, words containing two syllables of equal emphasis, as in "railway" or "football"—at various intensity levels until the level is found at which the person can just hear and repeat half the words correctly. This level usually corresponds closely to the average of the person's thresholds for frequencies of 500, 1,000, and 2,000 hertz. A more important measure of socially useful hearing is the discrimination score. For this test a list of selected monosyllabic words is presented at a comfortable intensity level, and the subject is scored in terms of the percentage of words heard correctly. This test is helpful in evaluating certain forms of hearing impairment in which the sounds may be audible but words remain unintelligible. Such tests usually are carried out in a quiet, sound-treated room that excludes extraneous noise. These tests may give an overly optimistic impression of the ability of the individual with a sensorineural impairment to understand speech in ordinary noisy surroundings. For this reason speech tests are best carried out against a standardized noise background as well as in the quiet. A person with a conductive defect may be less disturbed by the noisy environment than a healthy subject. More elaborate tests, which often involve speech or sound localization, are available for evaluating hearing when central defects of the auditory system are suspected as a result of aging, disease, or injury. Their interpretation may be difficult, however, and the diagnostic information they furnish may be unclear.

When the hearing of infants or others who are unable to cooperate in standard audiometric tests must be measured, their thresholds for pure tones can be established by electrophysiological means. One type of test is the electrocochleogram (ECoG). Electric potentials representing impulses in the cochlear nerve are recorded from the outer surface of the cochlea by means of a fine, insulated needle electrode inserted through the tympanic membrane to make contact with the promontory of the basal turn. This test provides a direct sampling of cochlear function.

A noninvasive, painless, and more frequently used test is brain-stem-evoked response audiometry (BERA). In this test electrodes are pasted to the skin (one placed behind the ear) and are used to record the neural responses to brief tones. The minute potentials evoked by a train of brief sound stimuli are suitably amplified and averaged by a small computer to cancel out background activity, such as potentials from muscles or the cerebral cortex. The typical recording shows a series of five or six waves that represent the responses of successive neural centres of the auditory pathway of the brain stem and provide information about the strength and timing of their activity.

The physiology of balance: vestibular function

The vestibular system is the sensory apparatus of the inner ear that helps the body maintain its postural equilibrium. The information furnished by the vestibular system is also essential for coordinating the position of the head and the movement of the eyes. There are two sets of end organs in the inner ear, or labyrinth: the semicircular canals, which respond to rotational movements (angular acceleration); and the utricle and saccule within the vestibule, which respond to changes in the position of the head with respect to gravity (linear acceleration; see Figure 60). The information these organs deliver is proprioceptive in character, dealing with events within the body itself, rather than exteroceptive, dealing with events outside the body, as in the case of the responses of the cochlea to sound. Functionally these organs are closely related to the cerebellum and to the reflex centres of the spinal cord and brain stem that govern the movements of the eyes, neck, and limbs. For anatomical descriptions of the vestibular apparatus see above *Anatomy of the human ear: Inner ear: Vestibular system.*

Although the vestibular organs and the cochlea are derived embryologically from the same formation, the otic vesicle, their association in the inner ear seems to be a matter more of convenience than of necessity. From both the developmental and the structural point of view, the kinship of the vestibular organs with the lateral line system of the fish is readily apparent. The lateral line system is made up of a series of small sense organs located in the skin of the head and along the sides of the body of fishes. Each organ contains a crista, sensory hair cells, and a cupula, as found in the ampullae of the semicircular ducts. The cristae respond to waterborne vibrations and to pressure changes.

Organs of balance

The anatomists of the 17th and 18th centuries assumed that the entire inner ear, including the vestibular apparatus, is devoted to hearing. They were impressed by the orientation of the semicircular canals, which lie in three planes more or less perpendicular to one another, and believed that the canals must be designed for localizing a source of sound in space. The first investigator to present evidence that the vestibular labyrinth is the organ of equilibrium was a French experimental neurologist, Marie-Jean-Pierre Flourens, who in 1824 reported a series of experiments in which he had observed abnormal head movements in pigeons after he had cut each of the semicircular canals in turn. The plane of the movements was always the same as that of the injured canal. Hearing was not affected when he cut the nerve fibres to these organs, but it was abolished when he cut those to the basilar papilla (the bird's uncoiled cochlea). It was not until almost half a century later that the significance of his findings was appreciated and the semicircular canals were recognized as sense organs specifically concerned with the movements and position of the head.

DETECTION OF ANGULAR ACCELERATION: DYNAMIC EQUILIBRIUM

Because the three semicircular canals—superior, posterior, and horizontal—are positioned at right angles to one another, they are able to detect movements in three-

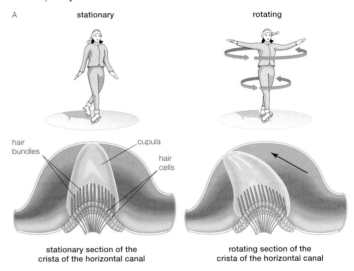

Figure 60: The physiology of balance. Each of the two sensory organs of balance, the cristae of the semicircular ducts and the maculae of the utricle and saccule, evaluates different aspects of equilibrium, but both function in a similar way. (A) The cristae respond to rotational movements and are involved in dynamic equilibrium. (B) The maculae respond to gravitational pull and help to maintain static equilibrium.
Encyclopædia Britannica, Inc.

dimensional space (see above *Anatomy of the human ear: Inner ear: Semicircular canals*). When the head begins to rotate in any direction, the inertia of the endolymph causes it to lag behind, exerting pressure that deflects the cupula in the opposite direction. This deflection stimulates the hair cells by bending their stereocilia in the opposite direction (Figure 60A). The German physiologist Friedrich Goltz formulated the "hydrostatic concept" in 1870 to explain the working of the semicircular canals. He postulated that the canals are stimulated by the weight of the fluid they contain, the pressure it exerts varying with the head position. In 1873 the Austrian scientists Ernst Mach and Josef Breuer and the Scottish chemist Crum Brown, working independently, proposed the "hydrodynamic concept," which held that head movements cause a flow of endolymph in the canals and that the canals are then stimulated by the fluid movements or pressure changes. The German physiologist J.R. Ewald showed that the compression of the horizontal canal in a pigeon by a small pneumatic hammer causes endolymph movement toward the crista and turning of the head and eyes toward the opposite side. Decompression reverses both the direction of endolymph movement and the turning of the head and eyes. The hydrodynamic concept was proved correct by later investigators who followed the path of a droplet of oil that was injected into the semicircular canal of a live fish. At the start of rotation in the plane of the canal the cupula was deflected in the direction opposite to that of the movement and then returned slowly to its resting position. At the end of rotation it was deflected again, this time in the same direction as the rotation, and then returned once more to its upright stationary position. These deflections resulted from the inertia of the endolymph, which lags behind at the start of rotation and continues its motion after the head has ceased to rotate. The slow return is a function of the elasticity of the cupula itself.

These opposing deflections of the cupula affect the vestibular nerve in different ways, which have been demonstrated in experiments involving the labyrinth removed from a cartilaginous fish. The labyrinth, which remained active for some time after its removal from the animal, was used to record vestibular nerve impulses arising from one of the ampullar cristae. When the labyrinth was at rest there was a slow, continuous, spontaneous discharge of nerve impulses, which was increased by rotation in one direction and decreased by rotation in the other. In other words, the level of excitation rose or fell depending on the direction of rotation.

The deflection of the cupula excites the hair cells by bending the cilia atop them: deflection in one direction depolarizes the cells; deflection in the other direction hyperpolarizes them. Electron-microscopic studies have shown how this polarization occurs. The hair bundles in the cristae are oriented along the axis of each canal. For example, each hair cell of the horizontal canals has its kinocilium facing toward the utricle, whereas each hair cell of the superior canals has its kinocilium facing away from the utricle. In the horizontal canals deflection of the cupula toward the utricle—*i.e.,* bending of the stereocilia toward the kinocilium—depolarizes the hair cells and increases the rate of discharge. Deflection away from the utricle causes hyperpolarization and decreases the rate of discharge. In superior canals these effects are reversed.

DETECTION OF LINEAR ACCELERATION: STATIC EQUILIBRIUM

The gravity receptors that respond to linear acceleration of the head are the maculae of the utricle and saccule (see above *Anatomy of the human ear: Inner ear: Vestibule*). The left and right utricular maculae are in the same, approximately horizontal, plane and because of this position are more useful in providing information about the position of the head and its side-to-side tilts when a person is in an upright position. The saccular maculae are in parallel vertical planes and probably respond more to forward and backward tilts of the head.

Both pairs of maculae are stimulated by shearing forces between the otolithic membrane and the cilia of the hair cells beneath it (Figure 60B). The otolithic membrane is covered with a mass of minute crystals of calcite (otoconia), which add to the membrane's weight and increase the shearing forces set up in response to a slight displacement when the head is tilted. The hair bundles of the macular hair cells are arranged in a particular pattern—facing toward (in the utricle) or away from (in the saccule) a curving midline—that allows detection of all possible head positions. These sensory organs, particularly the utricle, have an important role in the righting reflexes and in reflex control of the muscles of the legs, trunk, and neck that keep the body in an upright position. The role of the saccule is less completely understood. Some investigators have suggested that it is responsive to vibration as well as to linear acceleration of the head in the sagittal (fore and aft) plane. Of the two receptors, the utricle appears to be the dominant partner. There is evidence that the mammalian saccule may even retain traces of its sensitivity to sound inherited from the fishes, in which it is the organ of hearing.

(Joseph E. Hawkins)

Discovery of the function of the semicircular canals [margin note]

Stimulation of the maculae [margin note]

Industrial Polymers

Polymers are chemical compounds that consist of long, chainlike molecules made up of multiple repeating units. The term polymer was coined in 1832 by the Swedish chemist Jöns Jacob Berzelius from the Greek *polys,* or "many," and *meros,* or "parts." Polymers are also referred to as macromolecules, or "giant molecules"—a term introduced by the German chemist Hermann Staudinger in 1922. Some giant molecules occur naturally. Proteins, for example, are natural polymers of amino acids that make up much of the structural material of animals; and the polymers deoxyribonucleic acid (DNA) and ribonucleic acid (RNA) are linear strands of nucleotides that define the genetic makeup of living organisms. Other examples of natural polymers are silk, wool, natural rubber, cellulose, and shellac. These materials have been known and exploited since ancient times. Indeed, people in what is now Switzerland cultivated flax, a source of polymeric cellulose fibres, during the Neolithic Period, or New Stone Age, some 10,000 years ago, while other ancient people collected proteinaceous wool fibres from sheep and silk fibres from silkworms. About five millennia ago, tanners produced leather through the cross-linking of proteins in animal skins by means of gallic acid—forming the basis of the oldest industry in continuous production. Even embalming, the art for which ancient Egypt is famous, is based on the condensation and cross-linking of proteins with formaldehyde.

Early developments in polymer technology, taking place in the 19th century, involved the conversion of natural polymers to more useful products—for example, the conversion of cellulose, obtained from cotton or wood, into celluloid, one of the first plastics. Before the 1930s only a small number of synthetically produced polymers were available commercially, but after that period—and especially after World War II—synthetic compounds came to dominance. Derived principally from the refining of petroleum and natural gas, synthetic polymers are made into the plastics, rubbers, man-made fibres, adhesives, and surface coatings that have become so ubiquitous in modern life.

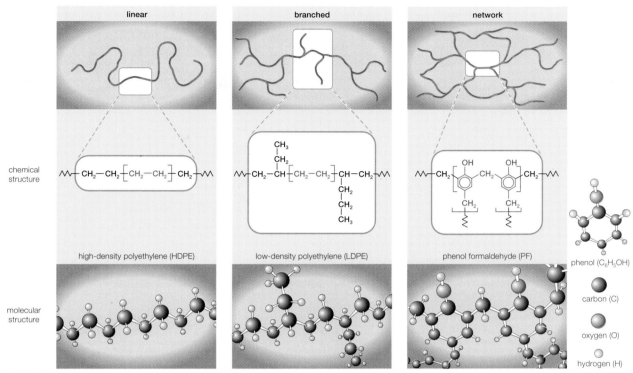

Figure 1: *Three common polymer structures.*
The linear, branched, and network architectures are represented at the top, respectively, by high-density polyethylene (HDPE), low-density polyethylene (LDPE), and phenol formaldehyde (PF). The chemical structure and molecular structure of highlighted regions are also shown.
Encyclopædia Britannica, Inc.

It is with these modern industrially produced polymers—of both natural and synthetic origin—that this article is concerned. The article begins with a discussion of the chemistry of industrial polymers. Following this introduction to the structure and formation of macromolecules, there is a section on the composition, properties, and applications of the major polymer compounds. The article then proceeds with sections on the principal classes of polymer materials—plastics (thermoplastic and thermosetting resins), elastomers (natural and synthetic rubbers), man-made fibres, adhesives, and surface coatings.

The chemistry of industrial polymers

What distinguishes polymers from other types of compounds is the extremely large size of the molecules. The size of a molecule is measured by its molecular weight, which is equal to the sum of the atomic weights of all the atoms that make up the molecule. Atomic weights are given in atomic mass units; in the case of water, for example, a single water molecule, made up of one oxygen atom (16 atomic mass units) and two hydrogen atoms (1 atomic mass unit each), has a molecular weight of 18 atomic mass units. Polymers, on the other hand, have average molecular weights ranging from tens of thousands up to several million atomic mass units. It is to this vast molecular size that polymers owe their unique properties, and it is the reason that Staudinger referred to them as macromolecules.

The atoms composing macromolecules are held together by covalent chemical bonds, formed by the sharing of electrons. Individual molecules are also attracted to one another by electrostatic forces, which are much weaker than covalent bonds. These electrostatic forces increase in magnitude, however, as the size of the molecules increases. In the case of polymers, they are so strong that agglomerates of molecules can be molded into permanent shapes, as in the case of plastics, or drawn out into fibres, as in the textile industry. The chemical composition and structure of polymers thus make them suitable for industrial applications. The distinctive properties of polymers and their formation from chemical precursors are the subject of this section.

THE STRUCTURE OF MACROMOLECULES

Linear, branched, and network. Polymers are manufactured from low-molecular-weight compounds called monomers by polymerization reactions, in which large numbers of monomer molecules are linked together. Depending on the structure of the monomer or monomers and on the polymerization method employed, polymer molecules may exhibit a variety of architectures. Most common from the commercial standpoint are the linear,

Monomers

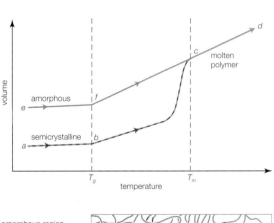

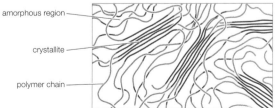

Figure 2: *Amorphous and semicrystalline polymer morphologies.*
(Top) Volume-temperature diagram for amorphous and and semicrystalline polymers, showing volume increasing with temperature; (bottom) schematic diagram of the semicrystalline morphology, showing amorphous regions and crystallites.
Encyclopædia Britannica, Inc.

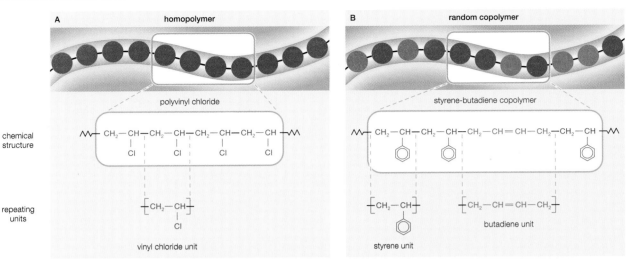

Figure 3: *Homopolymer and copolymer arrangements of polymer repeating units.*
The five possible arrangements are represented by (A) polyvinyl chloride, (B) styrene-butadiene
copolymer, (C) styrene-maleic anhydride copolymer, (D) styrene-isoprene copolymer, and
(E) ethylene-acrylonitrile copolymer. Each coloured ball represents the repeating unit of the
same colour below.
Encyclopædia Britannica, Inc.

branched, and network structures, shown in Figure 1 on page 211. The linear structure shown is illustrated by high-density polyethylene (HDPE), a chainlike molecule made from the polymerization of ethylene. With the chemical formula $CH_2{=}CH_2$, ethylene is essentially a pair of double-bonded carbon atoms (C), each with two attached hydrogen atoms (H). As the repeating unit making up the HDPE chain, it is shown in brackets, as $+CH_2-CH_2+$. A polyethylene chain from which other ethylene repeating units branch off is known as low-density polyethylene (LDPE); this polymer demonstrates the branched structure, in Figure 1. The network structure shown is that of phenol-formaldehyde (PF) resin. PF resin is formed when molecules of phenol (C_6H_5OH) are linked by formaldehyde (CH_2O) to form a complex network of interconnected branches. The PF repeating unit is represented in the figure by phenol rings with attached hydroxyl (OH) groups and connected by methylene groups (CH_2).

Branched polymer molecules cannot pack together as closely as linear molecules can; hence, the intermolecular forces binding these polymers together tend to be much weaker. This is the reason why the highly branched LDPE is very flexible and finds use as packaging film, while the linear HDPE is tough enough to be shaped into such objects as bottles or toys. Polymers having a dense network, such as PF resin, are very rigid—even brittle—whereas network polymers containing long, flexible branches connected at only a few sites along the chains exhibit elastic properties.

Amorphous and semicrystalline. Polymers exhibit two types of morphology in the solid state: amorphous and semicrystalline. In an amorphous polymer the molecules are oriented randomly and are intertwined, much like cooked spaghetti, and the polymer has a glasslike, transparent appearance. In semicrystalline polymers, the molecules pack together in ordered regions called crystallites, as shown in Figure 2 on page 211. As might be expected, linear polymers, having a very regular structure, are more likely to be semicrystalline. Semicrystalline polymers tend to form very tough plastics because of the strong intermolecular forces associated with close chain packing in the crystallites. Also, because the crystallites scatter light, they are more opaque than amorphous polymers. Crystallinity may be induced by stretching polymers in order to align the molecules—a process called drawing. In the plastics industry, polymer films are commonly drawn to increase the film strength.

At low temperatures the molecules of an amorphous or semicrystalline polymer vibrate at low energy, so that they are essentially frozen into a solid condition known as the glassy state. In the volume-temperature diagram

shown in Figure 2, this state is represented by the points e (for amorphous polymers) and a (for semicrystalline polymers). As the polymer is heated, however, the molecules vibrate more energetically, until a transition occurs from the glassy state to a rubbery state. The onset of the rubbery state is indicated by a marked increase in volume, caused by the increased molecular motion. The point at which this occurs is called the glass transition temperature; in the volume-temperature diagram it is indicated by the vertical dashed line labeled T_g, which intersects the amorphous and semicrystalline curves at points f and b. In the rubbery state above T_g, polymers demonstrate elasticity, and some can even be molded into permanent shapes. One major difference between plastics and rubbers, or elastomers, is that the glass transition temperatures of rubbers lie below room temperature—hence their well-known elasticity at normal temperatures. Plastics, on the other hand, must be heated to the glass transition temperature or above before they can be molded. The glass transition temperature

When brought to still higher temperatures, polymer molecules eventually begin to flow past one another. The polymer reaches its melting temperature (T_m in the phase diagram) and becomes molten (progressing along the line from c to d). In the molten state polymers can be spun into fibres. Polymers that can be melted are called thermoplastic polymers. Thermoplasticity is found in linear and branched polymers, whose looser structures permit molecules to move past one another. The network structure, however, precludes the possibility of molecular flow, so that network polymers do not melt. Instead, they break down upon reheating. Such polymers are said to be thermosetting.

Copolymers and polymer blends. When a single monomer is polymerized into a macromolecule, the product is called a homopolymer. Copolymers, on the other hand, are made from two or more monomers. Procedures have been developed to make copolymers in which the repeating units are distributed randomly, in alternating fashion, in blocks, or as grafts of one monomer block onto the backbone chain of another. Representatives of the homopolymer and the various copolymer types are shown in Figure 3. The molecular structure of each type is shown schematically, along with the chemical structure of the representative polymer and its monomer repeating units. Such structural variety affords the polymer manufacturer considerable latitude in tailoring polymers to satisfy a diversity of applications.

In the industrial marketplace, polymers are blended to modify their properties in much the same way that metals are alloyed. The blended polymers may or may not dissolve in one another; most, in fact, do not. Where they are miscible, the properties of the homogeneous blend are often a weighted average of those of the individual poly-

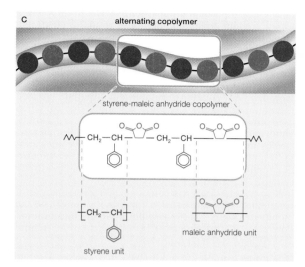

C alternating copolymer

styrene-maleic anhydride copolymer

chemical structure

repeating units

styrene unit

maleic anhydride unit

D block copolymer

styrene-isoprene copolymer

chemical structure

repeating units

styrene unit

isoprene unit

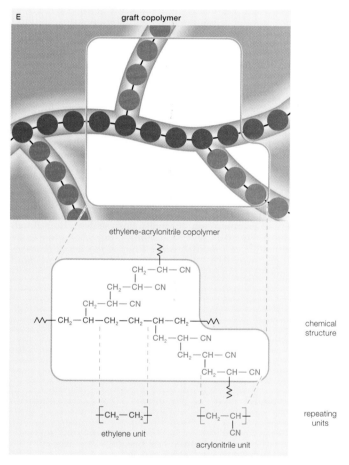

E graft copolymer

ethylene-acrylonitrile copolymer

chemical structure

repeating units

ethylene unit

acrylonitrile unit

mers, although sometimes a synergistic relationship is exhibited that leads to improved properties.

In the case of immiscible polymer blends, a variety of strategies have been developed to keep the separate phases together when the blends are subjected to stress. One is to synthesize two or more interlocking network polymers—an arrangement referred to as an interpenetrating polymer network (IPN).

Inter-penetrating polymer networks

POLYMERIZATION REACTIONS

Monomers are converted to polymers by two distinctly different mechanisms. One is by successive addition of monomer molecules onto the reactive ends of a growing polymer. This process, similar to adding links onto a chain, is called chain-growth polymerization or addition polymerization. Chain-growth polymerization is most commonly applied to vinyl monomers (that is, monomers containing carbon-carbon double bonds) and to certain types of cyclic monomers (that is, monomers in which the double bond is contained in ring-shaped molecules). The other process, called step-growth polymerization, involves the build-up of molecular weight not in a chainlike fashion but in a stepwise fashion, by the random combination of monomer molecules containing reactive functional groups. Chain-growth and step-growth polymerization are described in some detail below.

Chain-growth polymerization. *Free-radical initiation.* Chain-growth polymerization reactions require the presence of an initiator, a compound that reacts with the monomer to form another reactive compound, which begins the linking process. The most widely used initiators are compounds such as peroxides that break down to an unstable species called a radical (or free radical). A radical is a reactive compound that contains an unpaired electron; it is commonly given the designation R·.

Free-radical polymerization of ethylene

The first step in polymerization involves addition of the initiator radical (R·) to the monomer to form a new radical having the unpaired electron on a carbon atom, as can be seen in the polymerization of ethylene ($CH_2{=}CH_2$):

$$R \cdot + CH_2{=}CH_2 \longrightarrow R{-}CH_2{-}\dot{C}H_2$$

The new radical then adds to a second ethylene molecule:

$$R{-}CH_2{-}\dot{C}H_2 + CH_2{=}CH_2 \longrightarrow R{-}CH_2{-}CH_2{-}CH_2{-}\dot{C}H_2$$

Ethylene molecules are added successively to the chain until very little ethylene is left. At this point the chain is terminated, either by a combination of two chains

$$R{\fplus}CH_2{-}CH_2{\fplus}_n CH_2{-}\dot{C}H_2 + \dot{C}H_2{-}CH_2{\fplus}CH_2{-}CH_2{\fplus}_n R \longrightarrow$$
$$R{\fplus}CH_2{-}CH_2{\fplus}_n CH_2{-}CH_2{-}CH_2{-}CH_2{\fplus}CH_2{-}CH_2{\fplus}_n R$$

or by a disproportionation reaction involving the transfer of a hydrogen atom from one of the growing chains to the other:

$$R{\fplus}CH_2{-}CH_2{\fplus}_n CH_2{-}\dot{C}H_2 + \dot{C}H_2{-}CH_2{\fplus}CH_2{-}CH_2{\fplus}_n R \longrightarrow$$
$$R{\fplus}CH_2{-}CH_2{\fplus}_n CH_2{-}CH_3 + CH_2{=}CH{\fplus}CH_2{-}CH_2{\fplus}_n R$$

The structure enclosed in brackets, ${\fplus}CH_2{-}CH_2{\fplus}_n$, is the repeating unit of the polymer chain. The number of repeating units, *n*, varies according to the length of the polymer chain or, in other words, the molecular weight. Because polymer chains do not all terminate at the same length, reference is normally made to a polymer's average molecular weight.

The polymer produced by reactions such as that outlined above is named by adding the prefix "poly-" to the monomer name—in this case, polyethylene. A monomer name that contains more than one word can be enclosed in parentheses—*e.g.,* poly(vinyl chloride)—although in industrial usage the parentheses are often omitted. (This article follows common industrial usage by omitting the parentheses.) Abbreviations are commonly used for polymer names, such as HDPE for high-density polyethylene or PVC for polyvinyl chloride.

Because growing polyethylene chains are very flexible, the radical at the chain end may curl around and abstract a hydrogen atom from a CH_2 group at some point in the middle of the chain, thus forming a new radical site from which chain growth continues. This reaction, shown in Figure 4, is referred to as backbiting or, more technically, chain transfer. The result is a polymer chain with the branched structure of low-density polyethylene (LDPE), also shown in Figure 1. Chain-transfer reactions may also occur intermolecularly.

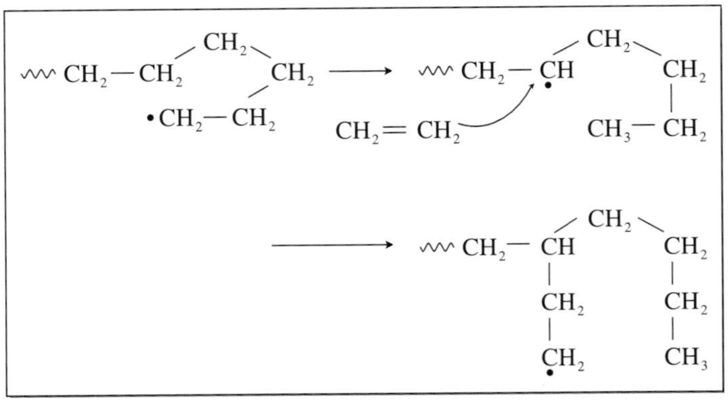

Figure 4: The formation of a branched polyethylene structure through the process of backbiting, or chain transfer.

Organometallic catalysis. In the early 1950s the German chemist Karl Ziegler discovered a method for making almost entirely linear HDPE at low pressures and low temperatures in the presence of complex organometallic catalysts. (The term catalyst may be used with these initiators because, unlike free-radical initiators, they are not consumed in the polymerization reaction.) In the Ziegler process the polymer chain grows from the catalyst surface by successive insertions of ethylene molecules, as shown in Figure 5. When polymerization is complete, the polymer chains detach from the catalyst surface. A great variety of complex organometallic catalysts have been developed, but the most commonly used are formed by combining a transition metal compound such as titanium trichloride, $TiCl_3$, with an organo-aluminum compound such as triethylaluminum, $Al(CH_2CH_3)_3$.

The Ziegler process

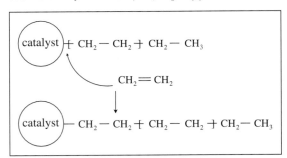

Figure 5: The polymerization of ethylene ($CH_2{=}CH_2$) using a complex organometallic catalyst (see text).

Soon after Ziegler made his discovery, the Italian chemist Giulio Natta and his coworkers discovered that Ziegler-type catalysts could polymerize propylene, $CH_2{=}CHCH_3$, to yield a polymer having the same spatial orientation for all the methyl (CH_3) groups attached to the polymer chain:

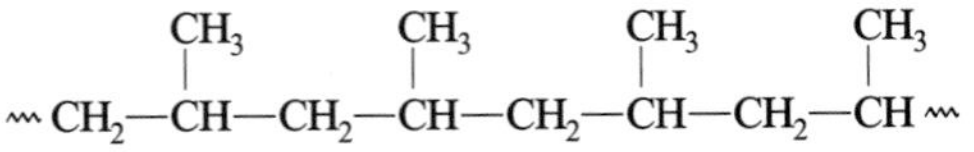

Because all the methyl groups are located on the same side of the chain, Natta called the polymer isotactic polypropylene. With vanadium-containing catalysts, Natta was also able to synthesize polypropylene containing methyl groups oriented the same way on alternate carbons—an arrangement he called syndiotactic.

Isotactic and syndiotactic polymers are referred to as stereoregular—that is, polymers having an ordered arrangement of pendant groups along the chain. A polymer with a random orientation of groups is said to be atactic. Stereoregular polymers are usually high-strength materials because the uniform structure leads to close packing of the polymer chains and a high degree of crystallinity. The catalyst systems employed to make stereoregular polymers are now referred to as Ziegler-Natta catalysts. More recently, new soluble organometallic catalysts, termed metallocene catalysts, have been developed that are much more reactive than conventional Ziegler-Natta catalysts.

Ionic initiation. Vinyl monomers may also be polymerized by ionic initiators, although these are usedless widely in the polymer industry than their radical or organometallic counterparts. Ionic initiators may be cationic (positively charged) or anionic (negatively charged). Cationic initiators are most commonly compounds or combinations of compounds that can transfer a hydrogen ion, H^+, to the monomers, thereby converting the monomer into a cation. Polymerization of styrene ($CH_2{=}CHC_6H_5$) with sulfuric acid (H_2SO_4) typifies this process:

$$H_2SO_4 + CH_2{=}CHC_6H_5 \longrightarrow CH_3{-}\underset{\displaystyle C_6H_5}{\underset{|}{CH}}{}^{+}HSO_4^{-}$$

$$CH_3{-}\underset{\displaystyle C_6H_5}{\underset{|}{CH}}{}^{+}HSO_4^{-} + CH_2{=}CHC_6H_5 \longrightarrow CH_3{-}\underset{\displaystyle C_6H_5}{\underset{|}{CH}}{-}CH_2{-}\underset{\displaystyle C_6H_5}{\underset{|}{CH}}{}^{+}HSO_4^{-}$$

Polymerization then proceeds by successive additions of the cationic chain end to monomer molecules. Note that, in ionic polymerization, an oppositely charged ion (in this case, bisulfate ion $[HSO_4^-]$) is associated with the chain end to preserve electrical neutrality.

One type of anionic initiator is an alkali metal such as sodium (Na), which transfers an electron to the styrene monomer to form a radical anion:

$$Na + CH_2{=}CHC_6H_5 \longrightarrow \cdot CH_2{-}\underset{\displaystyle C_6H_5}{\underset{|}{CH^{-}}}\ Na^{+}$$

Two radical anions combine to form a dianion:

$$2\ \cdot CH_2{-}\underset{\displaystyle C_6H_5}{\underset{|}{CH^{-}}}\ Na^{+} \longrightarrow Na^{+}\ {}^{-}\underset{\displaystyle C_6H_5}{\underset{|}{CH}}{-}CH_2{-}CH_2{-}\underset{\displaystyle C_6H_5}{\underset{|}{CH^{-}}}\ Na^{+}$$

The polymer chain then grows from both ends of the dianion by successive additions of monomer molecules.

Under carefully controlled conditions, ionic polymers retain their charged chain ends once all the monomer has reacted. Polymerization resumes when more monomer is added to yield a polymer of yet higher molecular weight. Alternatively, a second type of monomer can be added, leading to a block copolymer.

Polymerization of dienes. Each of the monomers whose polymerization is described above—ethylene, propylene, and styrene—contain one double bond. Another category of monomers are those containing two double bonds separated by a single bond. Such monomers are referred to as diene monomers. Most important are butadiene ($CH_2{=}CH{-}CH{=}CH_2$), isoprene ($CH_2{=}C[CH_3]{-}CH{=}CH_2$), and chloroprene ($CH_2{=}C[Cl]{-}CH{=}CH_2$). When diene monomers such as these undergo polymerization, a number of different repeating units may be formed. Isoprene, for example, forms four, having the following designations:

Structural variations of isoprene

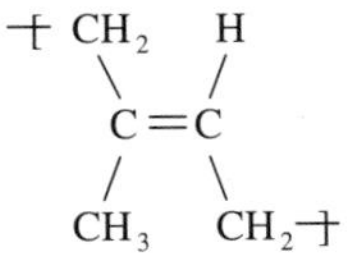

trans-1,4 polymer

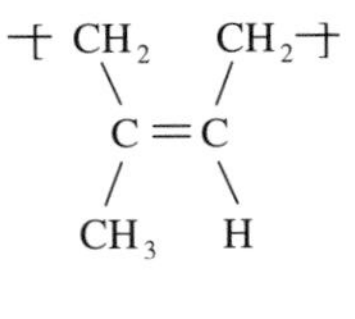

cis-1,4 polymer

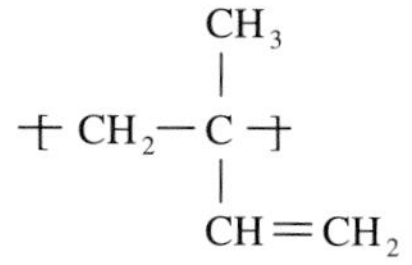

$$\text{CH}_3$$
$$+\text{CH}_2-\underset{|}{\overset{|}{\text{C}}}+ \qquad \text{1,2 polymer}$$ 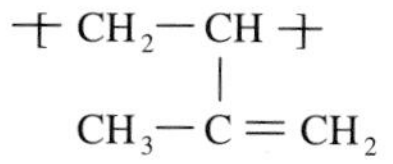
$$\text{CH}=\text{CH}_2$$

$$+\text{CH}_2-\underset{|}{\text{CH}}+ \qquad \text{3,4 polymer}$$
$$\text{CH}_3-\text{C}=\text{CH}_2$$

Under free-radical conditions the *trans*-1,4 polymer predominates, although any of the other structural variations may be present to a smaller extent in the polymer chains. With the appropriate choice of complex organometallic or ionic initiator, however, any one of the above repeating units may be formed almost exclusively. Low-temperature anionic polymerization of isoprene, for example, leads almost exclusively to the *cis*-1,4 polymer. Given the fact that *Hevea* rubber, the most common variety of natural rubber, consists of *cis*-1,4 polyisoprene, it is possible, through anionic polymerization, to manufacture a synthetic isoprene rubber that is virtually identical to natural rubber.

In commercial use, diene polymers are invariably converted to thermosetting elastomeric network polymers by a process called cross-linking or vulcanization.

Ring-opening metathesis polymerization. A relatively new development in polymer chemistry is polymerization of cyclic monomers such as cyclopentene in the presence of catalysts containing such metals as tungsten, molybdenum, and rhenium. The action of these catalysts yields linear polymers that retain the carbon-carbon double bonds that were present in the monomer:

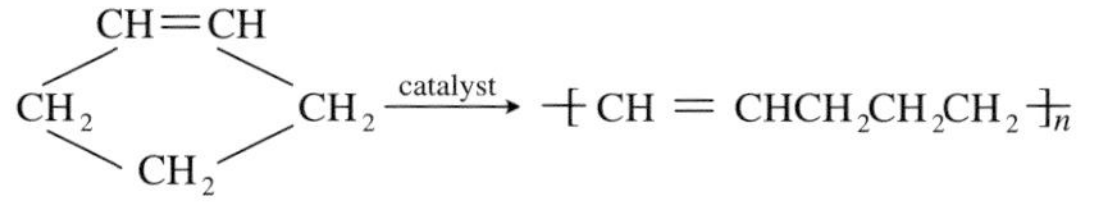

$$\overset{\text{CH}=\text{CH}}{\underset{\text{CH}_2}{\overset{\text{CH}_2}{\diagup}}\underset{\text{CH}_2}{\diagdown}} \xrightarrow{\text{catalyst}} +\text{CH}=\text{CHCH}_2\text{CH}_2\text{CH}_2\text{+}_n$$

Such reactions are called ring-opening metathesis polymerization (ROMP) because a redistribution of the chemical bonds of the monomer occurs in forming the polymer. As is the case with polydienes, polymers synthesized by ROMP techniques may be cross-linked for elastomeric applications.

Step-growth polymerization. Step-growth polymerization typically takes place between monomers that contain functional groups which react in high yield to form new functionalities. Examples of such functional groups are carboxylic acids, which react with alcohols to form esters and with amines to form amides:

$$\underset{\text{carboxylic acid}}{\text{R}-\overset{\text{O}}{\overset{\|}{\text{C}}}-\text{OH}} + \underset{\text{alcohol}}{\text{R}'-\text{OH}} \longrightarrow \underset{\text{ester}}{\text{R}-\overset{\text{O}}{\overset{\|}{\text{C}}}-\text{O}-\text{R}'} + \underset{\text{water}}{\text{H}_2\text{O}}$$

$$\underset{\text{carboxylic acid}}{\text{R}-\overset{\text{O}}{\overset{\|}{\text{C}}}-\text{OH}} + \underset{\text{amine}}{\text{R}'-\text{NH}_2} \longrightarrow \underset{\text{amide}}{\text{R}-\overset{\text{O}}{\overset{\|}{\text{C}}}-\text{NH}-\text{R}'} + \underset{\text{water}}{\text{H}_2\text{O}}$$

Here R and R′ represent two different organic molecular groups.

When monomers containing two of one type of functional group react with monomers containing two of another, linear polymers are formed. One commercially important example is the reaction of the dicarboxylic acid terephthalic acid (containing two CO—OH groups) with the dialcohol ethylene glycol (containing two OH groups) to form polyethylene terephthalate (PET), a very important polyester:

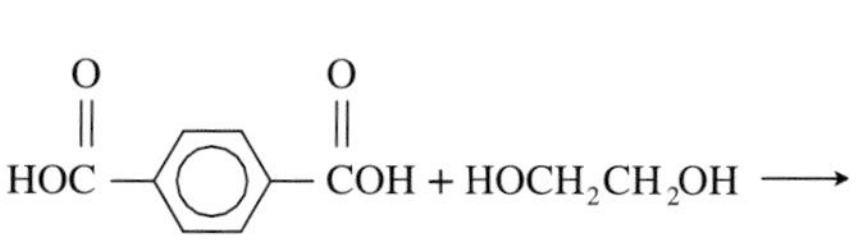

$$\underset{\text{terephthalic acid}}{\text{HOC}-\hspace{-4pt}\underset{}{\bigcirc}\hspace{-4pt}-\overset{\text{O}}{\overset{\|}{\text{COH}}}} + \underset{\text{ethylene glycol}}{\text{HOCH}_2\text{CH}_2\text{OH}} \longrightarrow$$

$$+\overset{\text{O}}{\overset{\|}{\text{C}}}-\hspace{-4pt}\underset{}{\bigcirc}\hspace{-4pt}-\overset{\text{O}}{\overset{\|}{\text{COCH}_2\text{CH}_2\text{O}}}+ + 2\text{H}_2\text{O}$$
$$\underset{\text{PET}}{} \qquad \underset{\text{water}}{}$$

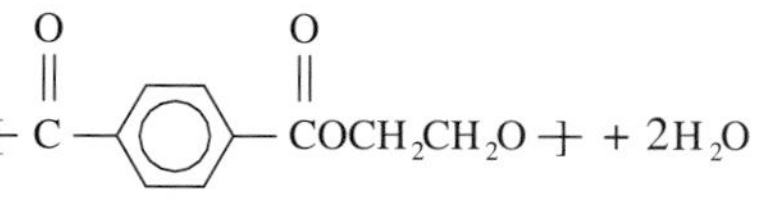

Another important reaction is that of adipic acid (containing two CO—OH groups) with 1,6-hexamethylenediamine (containing two NH$_2$ groups) to form polyhexamethylene adipamide, also called nylon 6,6:

$$\underset{\text{adipic acid}}{\text{HOC(CH}_2)_4\overset{\text{O}}{\overset{\|}{\text{COH}}}} + \underset{\text{1,6-hexamethylenediamine}}{\text{H}_2\text{N(CH}_2)_6\text{NH}_2} \longrightarrow$$

$$+\overset{\text{O}}{\overset{\|}{\text{C}}}\text{(CH}_2)_4\overset{\text{O}}{\overset{\|}{\text{C}}}\text{NH(CH}_2)_6\text{NH}+ + 2\text{H}_2\text{O}$$
$$\underset{\substack{\text{polyhexamethylene adipamide}\\\text{(nylon 6,6)}}}{} \qquad \underset{\text{water}}{}$$

All the step-growth reactions outlined above yield a byproduct and are therefore called condensation reactions. Not all step-growth reactions are condensation reactions, however; some do not yield any by-product. One example is the reaction between benzene-1,4-diisocyanate and ethylene glycol to form a polyurethane:

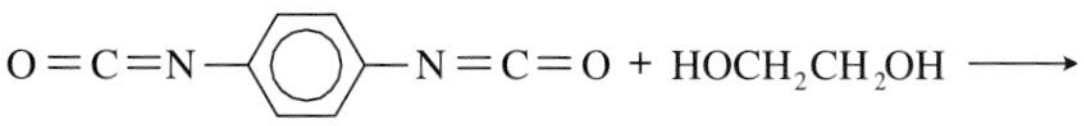

Condensation reactions

$$\underset{\text{benzene-1,4-diisocyanate}}{\text{O}=\text{C}=\text{N}-\hspace{-4pt}\underset{}{\bigcirc}\hspace{-4pt}-\text{N}=\text{C}=\text{O}} + \underset{\text{ethylene glycol}}{\text{HOCH}_2\text{CH}_2\text{OH}} \longrightarrow$$

$$+\overset{\text{O}}{\overset{\|}{\text{C}}}\text{NH}-\hspace{-4pt}\underset{}{\bigcirc}\hspace{-4pt}-\text{NH}\overset{\text{O}}{\overset{\|}{\text{C}}}\text{OCH}_2\text{CH}_2\text{O}+$$

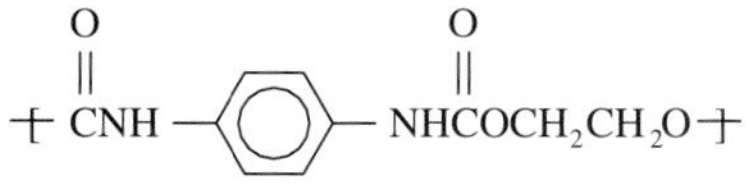

$$\underset{\text{polyurethane}}{}$$

Monomers containing more than two functional groups yield network polymers. An example is glyptal, a polyester formed from a reaction of phthalic anhydride with the trialcohol glycerol:

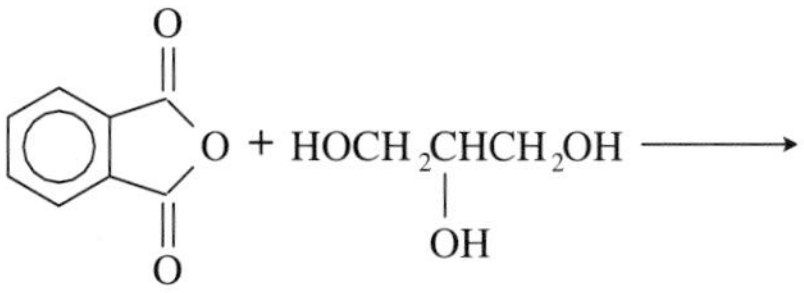

phthalic anhydride + $\text{HOCH}_2\overset{|}{\underset{\text{OH}}{\text{CH}}}\text{CH}_2\text{OH}$ →

glycerol

glyptal

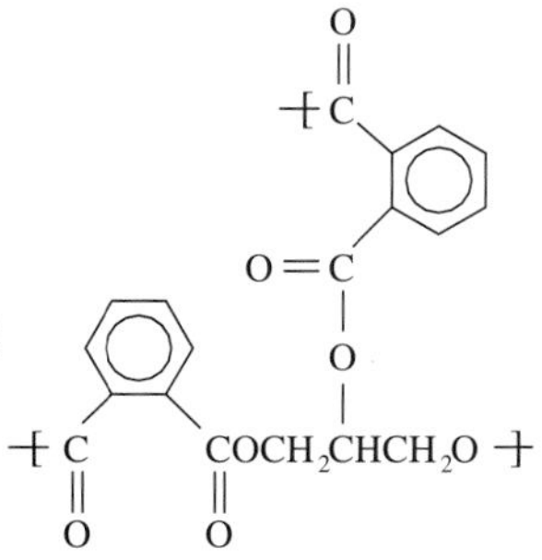

INDUSTRIAL POLYMERIZATION METHODS

The addition polymerization reactions described above are usually exothermic—that is, they generate heat. Heat generation is seldom a problem in small-scale laboratory reactions, but on a large industrial scale it can be dangerous, since heat causes an increase in the reaction rate, and faster reactions in turn produce yet more heat. This phenomenon, called autoacceleration, can cause polymerization reactions to accelerate at explosive rates unless efficient means for heat dissipation are included in the design of the reactor.

Condensation polymerization, on the other hand, is endothermic—that is, the reaction requires an input of heat from an external source. In these cases the reactor must supply heat in order to maintain a practical reaction rate.

Reactor design must also take into account the removal or recycling of solvents and catalysts. In the case of condensation reactions, reactors must provide for the efficient removal of volatile by-products.

Polymerization on an industrial scale is conducted using five basic methods: bulk, solution, suspension, emulsion, and gas-phase.

Bulk polymerization. Bulk polymerization is carried out in the absence of any solvent or dispersant and is thus the simplest in terms of formulation. It is used for most step-growth polymers and many types of chain-growth polymers. In the case of chain-growth reactions, which are generally exothermic, the heat evolved may cause the reaction to become too vigorous and difficult to control unless efficient cooling coils are installed in the reaction vessel. Bulk polymerizations are also difficult to stir because of the high viscosity associated with high-molecular-weight polymers.

Solution polymerization. The conducting of polymerization reactions in a solvent is an effective way to disperse heat; in addition, solutions are much easier to stir than bulk polymerizations. Solvents must be carefully chosen, however, so that they do not undergo chain-transfer reactions with the polymer. Because it can be difficult to remove solvent from the finished viscous polymer, solution polymerization lends itself best to polymers that are used commercially in solution form, such as certain types of adhesives and surface coatings. Polymerization of gaseous monomers is also conducted with the use of solvents, as in the production of polyethylene illustrated in Figure 6.

Suspension polymerization. In suspension polymerization the monomer is dispersed in a liquid (usually water) by vigorous stirring and by the addition of stabilizers such as methyl cellulose. A monomer-soluble initiator is added in order to initiate chain-growth polymerization. Reaction heat is efficiently dispersed by the aqueous medium. The polymer is obtained in the form of granules or beads, which may be dried and packed directly for shipment.

Emulsion polymerization. One of the most widely used methods of manufacturing vinyl polymers, emulsion polymerization involves formation of a stable emulsion (often referred to as a latex) of monomer in water using a soap or detergent as the emulsifying agent. Free-radical initiators, dissolved in the water phase, migrate into the stabilized monomer droplets (known as micelles) to initiate polymerization. The polymerization reaction is not terminated until a second radical diffuses into the swelling micelles, with the result that very high molecular weights are obtained. Reaction heat is effectively dispersed in the water phase.

The major disadvantage of emulsion polymerization is that the formulating of the mix is complex compared with the other methods, and purification of the polymer after coagulation is more difficult. Purification is not a problem, however, if the finished polymer is to be used in the form of an emulsion, as in latex paints or adhesives.

Gas-phase polymerization. This manufacturing method is used with gaseous monomers such as ethylene, tetrafluoroethylene, and vinyl chloride. The monomer is introduced under pressure into a reaction vessel containing a polymerization initiator. Once the polymerization reaction begins, monomer molecules diffuse to the growing polymer chains. The resulting polymer is obtained as a granular solid.

(Malcolm P. Stevens)

The major polymers

In the commercial production of plastics, elastomers, man-made fibres, adhesives, and surface coatings, (the subjects of other sections of this article), a tremendous variety of polymers are used. In this section, the major commercially employed polymers are divided by the composition of their "backbones," the chains of linked repeating units that make up the macromolecules. Classified according to composition, industrial polymers are either carbon-chain polymers (also called vinyls) or heterochain polymers (also called noncarbon-chain, or nonvinyls). In carbon-chain polymers, as the name implies, the backbones are made up of linkages between carbon atoms; in heterochain polymers a number of other

Poly-
ethylene
production

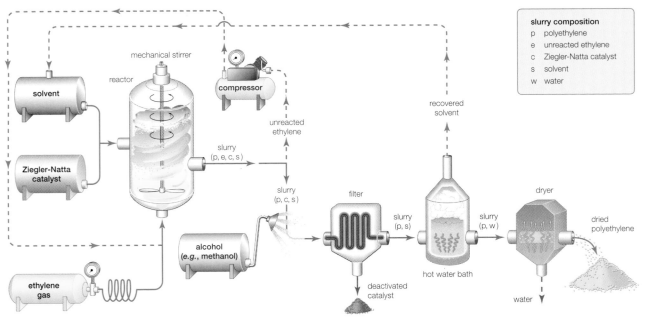

Figure 6: *Solution polymerization of ethylene, using Ziegler-Natta catalysts.*
Gaseous ethylene is pumped under pressure into a reactor vessel, where it polymerizes under the influence of a Ziegler-Natta catalyst in the presence of a solvent. A slurry of polyethylene, unreacted ethylene monomer, catalyst, and solvent exits the reactor. Unreacted ethylene is separated and returned to the reactor, while the catalyst is neutralized by an alcohol wash and filtered out. Solvent is recovered from a hot water bath and recycled, and polyethylene is dried and obtained as a crumb.
Encyclopædia Britannica, Inc.

elements are linked together in the backbones, including oxygen, nitrogen, sulfur, and silicon.

CARBON-CHAIN POLYMERS

Polyolefins and related polymers. Olefins are hydrocarbons whose molecules contain a pair of carbon atoms linked together by a double bond. Most often derived from natural gas or from low-molecular-weight constituents of petroleum, they include ethylene, propylene, and butene (butylene).

Structure of the olefin repeating unit

Olefin molecules are commonly represented by the chemical formula $CH_2=CHR$, with R representing an atom or pendant molecular group of varying composition. As the repeating unit of a polymeric molecule, their chemical structure can be represented as:

$$+CH_2-CH+ \text{ or } +\overset{\displaystyle H}{\underset{\displaystyle R}{C}}-\overset{\displaystyle H}{\underset{\displaystyle R}{C}}+$$

Polyethylene (PE). Ethylene, commonly produced by the cracking of ethane gas, forms the basis for the largest single class of plastics, the polyethylenes. Ethylene monomer has the chemical composition $CH_2=CH_2$; as the repeating unit of polyethylene it has the following chemical structure:

$$+CH_2-CH_2+$$

This simple structure can be produced in linear or branched forms such as those illustrated in Figure 1. Branched versions are known as low-density polyethylene (LDPE) or linear low-density polyethylene (LLDPE); the linear versions are known as high-density polyethylene (HDPE) and ultrahigh molecular weight polyethylene (UHMWPE).

In 1935 the British chemists Eric Fawcett and Reginald Gibson obtained waxy, solid PE while trying to react ethylene with benzaldehyde at high pressure. Because the product had little potential use, development was slow. It was left to Karl Ziegler of the Kaiser Wilhelm (now Max Planck) Institute for Coal Research at Mülheim an der Ruhr, Ger., to win the Nobel Prize for Chemistry in 1963 for inventing linear HDPE—which Ziegler actually produced with Erhard Holzkamp in 1953, catalyzing the reaction at low pressure with an organometallic compound henceforth known as a Ziegler catalyst.

LDPE is prepared from gaseous ethylene under very high pressures and high temperatures in the presence of peroxide initiators. These processes yield a polymer structure with both long and short branches, as shown in Figure 1 (centre). As a result, LDPE is only partly crystalline, yielding a material of high flexibility. Its principal uses are in packaging film, trash and grocery bags, agricultural mulch, wire and cable insulation, squeeze bottles, toys, and housewares.

Some LDPE is reacted with chlorine (Cl) or with chlorine and sulfur dioxide (SO_2) to produce chlorinated polyethylene (CM) or chlorosulfonated polyethylene (CSM), a virtually noncrystalline and elastic material. Because their main polymer chains are saturated, CM and CSM elastomers are highly resistant to oxidation and ozone attack, and their chlorine content gives some flame resistance and resistance to swelling by hydrocarbon oils. They are mainly used for hoses, belts, heat-resistant seals, and coated fabrics.

LLDPE is structurally similar to LDPE. It is made by copolymerizing ethylene with 1-butene and smaller amounts of 1-hexene and 1-octene, using Ziegler-Natta or metallocene catalysts. The resulting structure has a linear backbone, but it has short, uniform branches that, like the longer branches of LDPE, prevent the polymer chains from packing closely together. Overall, LLDPE has similar properties to LDPE and competes for the same markets.

High-density polyethylene

HDPE is manufactured at low temperatures and pressures using Ziegler-Natta and metallocene catalysts or ac-

tivated chromium oxide (known as a Phillips catalyst). The polymer has the linear structure illustrated in Figure 1 (left). The lack of branches allows the polymer chains to pack closely together, resulting in a dense, highly crystalline material of high strength and moderate stiffness. Uses include blow-molded bottles for milk and household cleaners and injection-molded pails, bottle caps, appliance housings, and toys.

UHMWPE is made with molecular weights of 3 million to 6 million atomic units, as opposed to 500,000 atomic units for HDPE. These polymers can be spun into fibres and drawn, or stretched, into a highly crystalline state, resulting in high stiffness and a tensile strength many times that of steel. Yarns made from these fibres are woven into bulletproof vests.

Polypropylene (PP). This highly crystalline thermoplastic resin is built up by the chain-growth polymerization of propylene ($CH_2=CHCH_3$). The polymer repeating unit has the following structure:

$$+CH_2-\underset{\displaystyle CH_3}{CH}+$$

Only the isotactic form of polypropylene is marketed in significant quantities. (In isotactic polypropylene, all the methyl [CH_3] groups are arranged along the same side of the polymer chain.) It is produced at low temperatures and pressures using Ziegler-Natta catalysts.

Polypropylene shares some of the properties of polyethylene, but it is stiffer, has a higher melting temperature, and is slightly more oxidation-sensitive. A large proportion goes into fibres, where it is a major constituent in fabrics for home furnishings such as upholstery and indoor-outdoor carpets. However, because of its very low moisture absorption, limited dyeability, and low softening point (an important factor when ironing clothing), polypropylene is not an important apparel fibre.

As a plastic, polypropylene is blow-molded into bottles for foods, shampoos, and other household liquids. It is also injection-molded into many products, such as appliance housings, dishwasher-proof food containers, toys, automobile battery casings, and outdoor furniture.

Discovery of polypropylene by Giulio Natta

It is generally accepted that isotactic polypropylene was discovered in 1954 by the Italian chemist Giulio Natta and his assistant Paolo Chini, working in association with Montecatini (now Montedison SpA) and employing catalysts of the type recently invented by Karl Ziegler for synthesizing polyethylene. (Partly in recognition of this achievement, Natta was awarded the Nobel Prize for Chemistry in 1963 along with Ziegler.)

Polystyrene (PS). This rigid, relatively brittle thermoplastic resin is polymerized from styrene ($CH_2=CHC_6H_5$). Styrene, also known as phenylethylene, is obtained by reacting ethylene with benzene in the presence of aluminum chloride to yield ethylbenzene, which is then dehydrogenated to yield clear, liquid styrene. The styrene monomer is polymerized using free-radical initiators primarily in bulk and suspension processes, although solution and emulsion methods are also employed. The structure of the polymer repeating unit can be represented as:

$$+CH_2-\underset{\displaystyle C_6H_5}{CH}+ \text{ or } +CH_2-\underset{\displaystyle \bigcirc}{CH}+$$

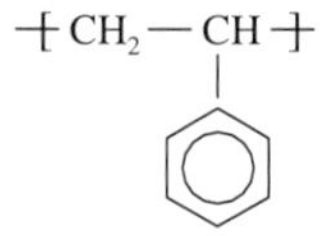

The presence of the pendant phenyl (C_6H_5) groups is key to the properties of polystyrene. These large, ring-shaped groups prevent the polymer chains from packing into close, crystalline arrangements, so that solid polystyrene is transparent. In addition, the phenyl rings restrict rotation of the chains around the carbon-carbon bonds, thus lending the polymer its noted rigidity.

Foamed polystyrene is made into insulation, packaging, and food containers such as beverage cups, egg cartons, and disposable plates and trays. Solid polystyrene products include injection-molded eating utensils, audiocassette holders, and cases for packaging compact discs. Many foods are packaged in clear, vacuum-formed polystyrene trays, owing to the high gas permeability and good water-vapour transmission of the material.

More than half of all polystyrene produced is blended with 5 to 10 percent polybutadiene to reduce brittleness and improve impact strength. This blend is marketed as high-impact polystyrene.

Polyvinyl chloride (PVC). Second only to PE in production and consumption, PVC is manufactured by bulk, solution, suspension, and emulsion polymerization of vinyl chloride monomer, using free-radical initiators. Vinyl chloride (CH_2=CHCl) is most often obtained by reacting ethylene with oxygen and hydrogen chloride over a copper catalyst. It is a carcinogenic gas that must be handled with special protective procedures. As a polymer repeating unit, its chemical structure is:

$$\left[CH_2 - \underset{\underset{Cl}{|}}{CH} \right]$$

The repeating units take on the linear homopolymer arrangement illustrated in Figure 3.

PVC was first prepared by the German chemist Eugen Baumann in 1872, but it was not patented until 1913, when Friedrich Heinrich August Klatte used sunlight to initiate the polymerization of vinyl chloride. Commercial application of this plastic was limited by its extreme rigidity. In 1926, while trying to dehydrohalogenate PVC in a high-boiling solvent in order to obtain an unsaturated polymer that might bond rubber to metal, Waldo Lonsbury Semon, working for the B.F. Goodrich Company in the United States, serendipitously obtained what is now called plasticized PVC. The discovery of this flexible, inert product was responsible for the commercial success of the polymer.

Rigid and plasticized PVC

Pure PVC finds application in the construction trades, where its rigidity and low flammability are useful in pipe, conduit, siding, window frames, and door frames. In combination with plasticizer (sometimes in concentrations as high as 50 percent), it is familiar to consumers as floor tile, garden hose, imitation leather upholstery, and shower curtains.

Acrylic polymers. Acrylic is a generic term denoting derivatives of acrylic and methacrylic acid, including acrylic esters and compounds containing nitrile and amide groups. A flexible acrylic ester, polymethyl acrylate, was produced commercially by Rohm and Haas AG in Germany beginning in 1927 and by the Rohm and Haas Company in the United States beginning in 1931; used in sheets for laminated safety glass, it was sold under the trademarked name Plexigum. In the early 1930s a more rigid plastic, polymethyl methacrylate, was discovered in England by Rowland Hill and John Crawford at Imperial Chemical Industries, which gave the material the trademarked name Perspex. At the same time, Otto Röhm attempted to produce safety glass by polymerizing methyl methacrylate between glass layers; the polymer separated from the glass as a clear plastic sheet, which Röhm gave the trademarked name Plexiglas. Both Perspex and Plexiglas were commercialized in the late 1930s. (DuPont subsequently introduced its own product under the trademark Lucite.)

Polyacrylonitrile (PAN). Acrylonitrile (CH_2=CHCN), a compound obtained by reacting propylene with ammonia (NH_3) and oxygen in the presence of catalysts, is polymerized to polyacrylonitrile through suspension methods using free-radical initiators. The structure of the polymer repeating unit is:

$$\left[CH_2 - \underset{\underset{CN}{|}}{CH} \right]$$

Acrylic fibres

Most of the polymer is employed in the production of acrylic fibres, which are defined as fibres that contain 85 percent or more PAN. Because PAN is difficult to dissolve in organic solvents and is highly resistant to dyeing, very little fibre is produced containing PAN alone. On the

other hand, a copolymer containing PAN and 2 to 7 percent of a vinyl comonomer such as vinyl acetate can be readily spun to fibres that are soft enough to allow penetration by dyestuffs. Acrylic fibres are soft and flexible, producing lightweight, lofty yarns. Such properties closely resemble those of wool, and hence the most common use of acrylics in apparel and carpets is as a wool replacement—for example, in knitwear such as sweaters and socks.

Acrylics modified by halogen-containing comonomers such as vinyl chloride or vinylidene chloride are classified as modacrylics. (By definition, modacrylics contain more than 35 and less than 85 percent PAN.) Chlorine imparts a notable flame resistance to the fibre—an advantage that makes modacrylics desirable for such products as children's sleepwear, blankets, awnings, and tents.

Polymethyl methacrylate (PMMA). Methyl methacrylate is polymerized in bulk or suspension methods using free-radical initiators. As a polymer repeating unit, its structure is:

$$\left[CH_2 - \underset{\underset{CO_2CH_3}{|}}{\overset{\overset{CH_3}{|}}{C}} \right]$$

The presence of the pendant methyl (CH_3) groups prevents the polymer chains from packing closely in a crystalline fashion and from rotating freely around the carbon-carbon bonds. As a result, PMMA is a transparent and rigid plastic. Because it retains these properties over years of exposure to ultraviolet radiation and weather, PMMA is an ideal substitute for glass. A most successful application is in internally lighted signs for advertising and directions. PMMA is also employed in domed skylights, swimming pool enclosures, aircraft canopies, instrument panels, and luminous ceilings. For these applications the plastic is sold in the form of sheets that are machined or thermoformed, but it is also injection-molded into headlights and taillights and lighting-fixture covers.

Polymethyl acrylate and polyethyl acrylate. These materials are polymers of acrylic esters (CH_2=CHCO$_2$R), which have the following repeating unit structure:

$$\left[CH_2 - \underset{\underset{CO_2R}{|}}{CH} \right]$$

R may be a methyl (CH_3) or ethyl (CH_2CH_3) group or a longer carbon chain. The polymers are generally prepared in solution- and emulsion-polymerization methods using free-radical initiators. They are employed as fibre modifiers and in adhesives and surface coatings. Acrylic ester polymers are the film-forming components of acrylic paints.

Acrylic paints

Polyacrylate elastomers. Acrylic esters, copolymerized with small amounts (approximately 5 percent) of another monomer containing a reactive halogen, can form polymer chains that interlink at the halogen sites. These so-called polyacrylate elastomers display good heat resistance (almost as good as silicone rubbers and fluoroelastomers) and resistance to swelling by hydrocarbon oils. They are mainly used for O-rings, seals, and gaskets.

Fluorinated polymers. *Polytetrafluoroethylene (PTFE).* PTFE was discovered serendipitously in 1938 by a DuPont chemist, Roy Plunkett, who found that a tank of gaseous tetrafluoroethylene (CF_2=CF$_2$) had polymerized to a white powder. During World War II it was applied as a corrosion-resistant coating to protect metal equipment used in the production of radioactive material. DuPont released its trademarked Teflon-coated nonstick cookware in 1960.

PTFE is made from the gaseous monomer, tetrafluoroethylene, using high-pressure suspension or solution methods in the presence of free-radical initiators. The polymer is similar in structure to polyethylene, consisting of a carbon chain with two fluorine atoms bonded to each carbon:

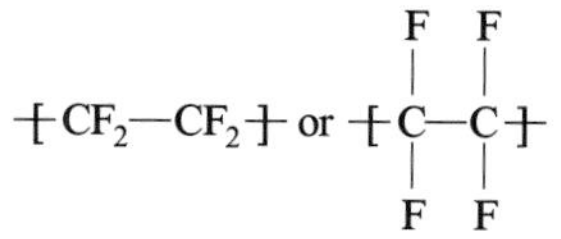

$$+CF_2-CF_2+ \text{ or } +\underset{\underset{F}{|}}{\overset{\overset{F}{|}}{C}}-\underset{\underset{F}{|}}{\overset{\overset{F}{|}}{C}}+$$

The fluorine atoms surround the carbon chain like a sheath, giving a chemically inert and relatively dense product with very strong carbon-fluorine bonds. The polymer is inert to most chemicals, does not melt below 300° C (575° F), and has a very low coefficient of friction. These properties allow it to be used for bushings and bearings that require no lubricant, as liners for equipment used in the storage and transportation of strong acids and organic solvents, as electrical insulation under high-temperature conditions, and in its familiar application as a cooking surface that does not require the use of fats or oils.

Fluoroelastomers. A number of fluorinated polymers or copolymers having elastomeric properties are produced that incorporate the monomers vinylidene fluoride (CH_2=CF_2), hexafluoropropylene (CF_2=$CFCF_3$), and chlorotrifluoroethylene (CF_2=$CFCl$) in addition to tetrafluoroethylene. These elastomers have outstanding resistance to oxygen, ozone, heat, and swelling by oils, chlorinated solvents, and fuels. With service temperatures up to 250° C (480° F), they are elastomers of choice for use in industrial and aerospace equipment subjected to severe conditions. Principal applications are as temperature-resistant O-rings, seals, and gaskets.

Diene polymers. As stated above in *The chemistry of industrial polymers: Polymerization reactions,* dienes are compounds whose molecules contain two carbon-carbon double bonds separated by a single bond.

Polybutadiene (butadiene rubber, BR). Butadiene (CH_2=CH—CH=CH_2) is produced by the dehydrogenation of butene or butane or by the cracking of petroleum distillates. It is polymerized to polybutadiene by solution methods, employing either anionic or Ziegler-Natta initiators. Like the other diene polymers, polybutadiene is isomeric; that is, it can be produced with more than one molecular structure. A common elastomeric structure is *cis*-1,4 polybutadiene, whose repeating unit has the following structure:

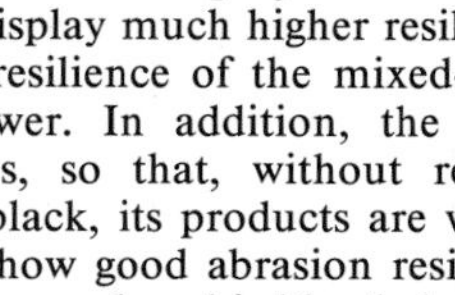

$$+CH_2 \qquad\qquad CH_2+$$
$$\diagdown\qquad\qquad\diagup$$
$$C = C$$
$$\diagup\qquad\qquad\diagdown$$
$$H \qquad\qquad H$$

Two other structures are the *trans*-1,4 and the 1,2 "side vinyl" isomers.

Polybutadienes are made either with high *cis* content (95 to 97 percent) or with only 35 percent *cis* content along with 55 percent *trans* and 10 percent "side vinyl." The properties of the two polymers are quite different. Although both display much higher resilience than other elastomers, the resilience of the mixed-isomer polymer is somewhat lower. In addition, the mixed polymer never crystallizes, so that, without reinforcing fillers such as carbon black, its products are weak and brittle. Both materials show good abrasion resistance. Much of the polybutadiene produced is blended with natural rubber (polyisoprene) or with styrene-butadiene rubber to give improved resilience and lower rolling resistance. More than half of all usage is in tires; other applications are footwear, wire and cable insulation, and conveyor belts.

Polychloroprene (chloroprene rubber, CR). Polychloroprene is the polymer name for the synthetic rubber known as neoprene (a proprietary trade name of DuPont that has become generic). One of the first successful synthetic elastomers, neoprene was first prepared in 1931 by Arnold Collins, a chemist in Wallace Hume Carothers' research group at DuPont, while he was investigating by-products of divinylacetylene.

Polychloroprene is prepared by emulsion polymerization of chloroprene, or 2-chlorobutadiene, which is obtained by the chlorination of butadiene or isoprene. Of the sev-

eral structures adopted by the chloroprene repeating unit, the most common is *trans*-1,4 polychloroprene, which can be represented as follows:

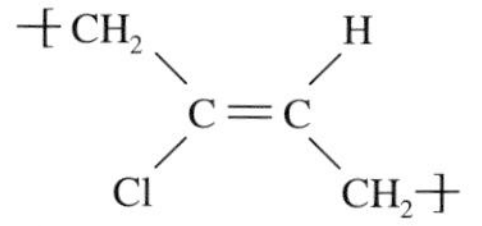

$$+CH_2 \qquad\qquad H$$
$$\diagdown\qquad\qquad\diagup$$
$$C = C$$
$$\diagup\qquad\qquad\diagdown$$
$$Cl \qquad\qquad CH_2+$$

This polymer tends to crystallize and harden slowly at temperatures below about 10° C (50° F). It also crystallizes on stretching, so that cured components are strong even without fillers. The presence of chlorine in the molecular structure causes this elastomer to resist swelling by hydrocarbon oils, to have greater resistance to oxidation and ozone attack, and to possess a measure of flame resistance. Principal applications are in products such as hoses, belts, springs, flexible mounts, and gaskets where resistance to oil, heat, flame, and abrasion are required.

Polyisoprene (natural rubber, NR; isoprene rubber, IR). Of the several isomeric forms that polyisoprene can adopt, NR consists almost exclusively of the *cis*-1,4 polymer, the structure of which is shown above in *The chemistry of industrial polymers: Chain-growth polymerization: Dienes.* The uniqueness of NR lies in its remarkable extensibility and toughness, as evidenced by its ability to be stretched repeatedly to seven or eight times its original length. The polymer chains crystallize readily on stretching, lending greater strength, so that NR is a self-reinforcing material. In its natural state, however, NR is greatly affected by temperature: it crystallizes on cooling, taking only several hours to do so at −25° C (−13° F), and it becomes tacky and inelastic above approximately 50° C (120° F). In addition, like other diene elastomers, it is swollen and weakened by hydrocarbon oils, and it reacts with oxygen and ozone in the atmosphere, leading to rupture of the polymer molecules and softening of the material over time. These disadvantages are overcome to a great extent by vulcanizing and compounding processes.

IR is manufactured by solution polymerization methods, using both anionic and Ziegler-Natta catalysts. The product is at most 98 percent *cis*-1,4 polyisoprene, and therefore its structure is not as regular as NR. As a result, it does not crystallize as readily as the natural material, and it is not as strong or as tacky in the raw (unvulcanized) state. In all other respects, though, IR is a complete substitute for NR. For both IR and NR, the principal usage is in tires, although these elastomers are also preferred for rubber springs and mountings owing to their good fatigue resistance and high resilience. Footwear is an important application, and NR is still used in adhesives (such as rubber cement).

Vinyl copolymers. In addition to the copolymers mentioned above (*e.g.,* fluoroelastomers, modacrylics), a number of important vinyl (carbon-chain) copolymers are manufactured. These include most of the important synthetic elastomers not described above in *Diene polymers,* along with several specialty plastics and thermoplastic elastomers. These copolymers are described in this section.

Acrylonitrile-butadiene-styrene (ABS). ABS is a graft copolymer made by dissolving styrene-butadiene copolymer in a mixture of acrylonitrile and styrene monomers, then polymerizing the monomers with free-radical initiators in an emulsion process. Grafting of acrylonitrile and styrene onto the copolymer chains occurs by chain-transfer reactions. ABS was patented in 1948 and introduced to commercial markets by the Borg-Warner Corporation in 1954.

ABS is a tough, heat-resistant thermoplastic. The three structural units provide a balance of properties, the butadiene groups (predominantly *trans*-1,4) imparting good impact strength, the acrylonitrile affording heat resistance, and the styrene units giving the copolymer its rigidity. ABS is widely used for appliance and telephone housings, luggage, sporting helmets, pipe fittings, and automotive parts.

Styrene-butadiene rubber (SBR). During World War II the United States, cut off from its East Asian supplies of natural rubber, developed a number of synthetics, includ-

Neoprene

Properties of synthetic polyisoprene

ing a copolymer of butadiene and styrene. This general-purpose rubber, which had been called Buna S by the German chemists Eduard Tschunkur and Walter Bock, who had patented it in 1933, was given the wartime designation GR-S (Government Rubber-Styrene) by the Americans, who improved upon its production. Now known as SBR, this copolymer has become the most important synthetic rubber, representing about one-half of total world production.

A mixture of approximately 75 percent butadiene and 25 percent styrene, SBR is polymerized either in an emulsion process in the presence of free-radical initiators or in a solution process under anionic conditions. The styrene and butadiene repeating units are arranged in a random manner along the polymer chain, as shown schematically in the illustration of the styrene-butadiene copolymer in Figure 3.

Properties of styrene-butadiene rubber

SBR is weak and unusable without reinforcement by carbon black, but with carbon black it is strong and abrasion-resistant. Like natural rubber, it is swollen and weakened by hydrocarbon oils and attacked by atmospheric oxygen and ozone. In SBR, however, the main effect of oxidation is increased interlinking of the polymer chains, so that the rubber tends to harden with age instead of softening.

Because of its excellent abrasion resistance, SBR is widely used in automobile and truck tires, more so than any other synthetic rubber. A large amount of SBR is produced in latex form as a rubbery adhesive for use in applications such as carpet backing. Other applications are in belting, flooring, wire and cable insulation, and footwear.

Nitrile rubber (nitrile-butadiene rubber, NBR). Buna N, a group of acrylonitrile-butadiene copolymers, was patented in the United States in 1934 by IG Farben chemists Erich Konrad and Eduard Tschunkur. Produced in the United States during World War II as GR-N (Government Rubber-Nitrile), it has become valued for its outstanding resistance to oil.

NBR is prepared in emulsion processes using free-radical initiators. The amount of acrylonitrile present in the copolymer varies from 15 to 50 percent. With increasing acrylonitrile content the rubber shows higher strength, greater resistance to swelling by hydrocarbon oils, and lower permeability to gases—although the glass transition temperature is also raised, with the result that the rubber is less flexible at lower temperatures. The main uses of NBR are in fuel hoses, gaskets, rollers, and other products in which oil resistance is required.

Butyl rubber (isobutylene-isoprene rubber, IIR). Butyl rubber is a copolymer of isobutylene and isoprene that was first produced by William Sparks and Robert Thomas at the Standard Oil Company (New Jersey) (now Exxon Corporation) in 1937. During World War II the copolymer was called GR-I, for Government Rubber-Isobutylene.

IIR is produced by copolymerizing isobutylene in solution with low concentrations (1.5 to 4.5 percent) of isoprene. The polymer repeating units have the following structures:

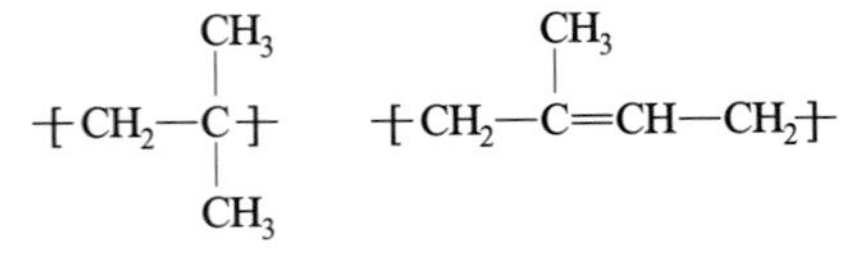

isobutylene   isoprene

Because the base polymer, polyisobutylene, is stereoregular (that is, with its pendant groups arranged in a regular order along the polymer chains), and because the chains crystallize rapidly on stretching, IIR containing only a small amount of isoprene is strong like natural rubber and polychloroprene—even without carbon-black reinforcement. Butyl rubber shows an unusually low rate of molecular motion well above the glass transition temperature, probably because of restricted flexibility of the molecules. This lack of motion is reflected in the copolymer's unusually low permeability to gases as well as its out-

Gas-retention properties of butyl rubber

standing resistance to attack by ozone. IIR is relatively resistant to oxidation because there are few unsaturated groups per molecule.

Because of its excellent air retention, butyl rubber quickly replaced natural rubber as the preferred material for inner tubes in all but the largest sizes. It also plays an important part in the inner liners of tubeless tires. It is also used for many other automobile components, such as window strips, because of its resistance to oxidation.

Styrene-butadiene and styrene-isoprene block copolymers. These "triblock" copolymers, also known as styrene-butadiene-styrene (SBS) and styrene-isoprene-styrene (SIS) rubber, consist of polystyrene sequences (or blocks) at each end of the chain and a butadiene or isoprene sequence in the centre. Polystyrene end-blocks of adjacent chains collect together in small "domains," so that clusters of polystyrene are distributed through a network of butadiene or isoprene. Such a structure makes SBS and SIS into thermoplastic elastomers, blends that exhibit the elasticity and resilience of polybutadiene or polyisoprene along with the permanence of the fixed ends. SBS and SIS are easily processed and reprocessed, owing to the thermoplastic properties of polystyrene, and they are remarkably strong at room temperature. They are frequently used for injection-molded parts, as hot-melt adhesives (especially in shoes), and as an additive to improve the properties of bitumen.

Ethylene-propylene copolymers. There are two major types of ethylene-propylene copolymers with elastomeric properties: those made with the two monomers alone and those made with small amounts (approximately 5 percent) of a diene—usually ethylidene norbornene or 1,4-hexadiene. Both copolymers are prepared in solution using Ziegler-Natta catalysts. The former are known as EPM (ethylene-propylene monomer) and the latter as EPDM (ethylene-propylene-diene monomer). The copolymers contain approximately 60 percent by weight ethylene. A pronounced advantage of EPDM is that the residual carbon-carbon double bond (*i.e.,* the double bond that remains after polymerization) is attached to the polymer chain rather than being made part of it. EPDM, with the double bonds located in the side groups, is much less susceptible to degradation by weathering and sunlight, because any breaking of the double bonds by ozonolysis, thermal deterioration, or oxidation leaves the main chains intact.

The principal uses of EPM are in automobile parts and as an impact modifier for polypropylene. EPDM is employed in flexible seals for automobiles, wire and cable insulation, weather stripping, tire sidewalls, hoses, and roofing film.

EPDM-propylene blend

EPDM is also mixed with polypropylene to make a thermoplastic elastomer. These polymer blends, which usually contain 30 to 40 mole percent polypropylene, can be processed and reprocessed, and they are resistant to oxidation, ozone attack, and weathering. They are therefore used in such low-severity applications as shoes, flexible covers, and sealing strips. The trademarked product Santoprene, produced by Advanced Elastomer Systems, L.P., is an example.

Styrene-maleic anhydride copolymer. Styrene and maleic anhydride can be copolymerized in a bulk process using free-radical initiators to yield an alternating-block copolymer, as is illustrated schematically in Figure 3. The copolymer repeating unit can be represented as:

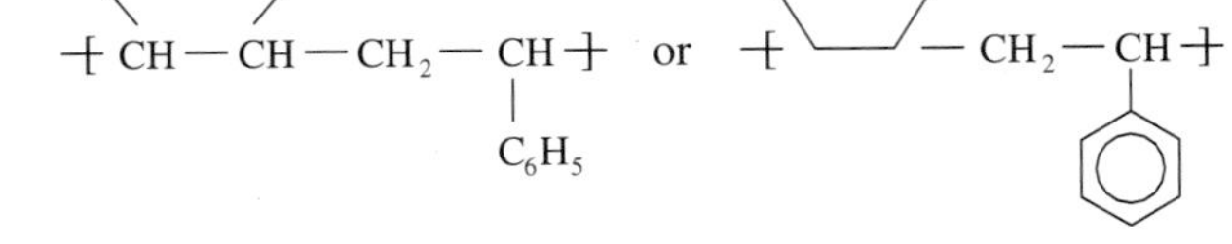

In practice, most of the copolymers contain about 5 to 20 percent maleic anhydride, depending on the application, and some grades also contain small amounts of butadiene as a comonomer. The plastic is used in automobile parts, small appliances, and food-service trays.

HETEROCHAIN POLYMERS

A wide variety of heterochain polymers—that is, polymers in which the backbone contains elements such as oxygen, nitrogen, sulfur, or silicon in addition to carbon—are in commercial use. Many of these compounds are complex in structure. In this section the major heterochain polymer families are presented in alphabetic order, with important representatives of each family described in turn.

Aldehyde condensation polymers. Aldehyde condensation polymers are compounds produced by the reaction of formaldehyde with phenol, urea, or melamine. The polymerization reactions of these monomers produce complex, thermosetting network polymers with the following general structures (in which CH_2 groups connected to the units are provided by the formaldehyde):

phenol formaldehyde

urea formaldehyde

melamine formaldehyde

The network structure of phenol-formaldehyde resin is also illustrated in Figure 1.

Phenol formaldehyde. Many people date the beginning of the modern plastics industry to 1907, when Leo Hendrik Baekeland, a Belgian-born American chemist, applied for a patent on a phenol-formaldehyde thermoset that eventually became known by the trademarked name Bakelite. Also known as phenolic resins, phenol-formaldehyde polymers were the first completely synthetic polymers to be commercialized.

Two methods are used to make phenol-formaldehyde polymers. In one, an excess of formaldehyde is reacted with phenol in the presence of a base catalyst in water solution to yield the resole, which is a fusible, soluble low-molecular-weight prepolymer with CH_2OH groups attached to the phenol rings. On heating, the resole condenses further, with loss of water and formaldehyde, to yield thermosetting network polymers. The other method involves reacting formaldehyde with an excess of phenol using an acid catalyst to produce prepolymers called novolacs. Novolacs resemble the polymer except that they are of much lower molecular weight and are still thermoplastic. Curing to network polymer is accomplished by the addition of more formaldehyde or, more commonly, of compounds that decompose to formaldehyde on heating.

Phenol-formaldehyde polymers make excellent wood adhesives for plywood and particleboard. Because their colour frequently stains the wood, they are not suitable for interior decorative paneling. They are the adhesive of choice for exterior plywood, however, owing to their good moisture resistance.

Phenolic resins, invariably reinforced with fibres or flakes, are also molded into heat-resistant objects such as electrical connectors and appliance handles.

Urea-formaldehyde polymers. Resins made from urea-formaldehyde polymers are processed in much the same way as are resoles (*i.e.,* using excess formaldehyde). Like phenolics, the polymers are used as wood adhesives, but, because they are lighter in colour, they are more suitable for interior plywood and decorative paneling. They are less durable, however, and do not have sufficient weather resistance to be used in exterior applications.

Urea-formaldehyde polymers are also blended with alkyd paints in order to improve the surface hardness of the coating.

Melamine-formaldehyde polymers. These compounds are similar to urea-formaldehyde resins in their processing and applications. In addition, their greater hardness and water resistance makes them suitable for decorative dinnerware and for fabrication into the tabletop and countertop product sold under the trademarked name Formica.

Melamine-based polymers have also been extensively employed in automobile topcoats and in finishes for appliances and metal furniture. However, their use in coatings is decreasing because of restrictions on the emission of formaldehyde, a major component of these coatings.

Cellulosics. Cellulose ($C_6H_7O_2[OH]_3$) is a naturally occurring polymer made up of repeating glucose units. Although it is a linear polymer, cellulose is thermosetting; that is, it forms permanent, bonded structures that cannot be loosened by heat or solvents without causing chemical decomposition. Its thermosetting behaviour arises from strong dipolar attractions that exist between cellulose molecules, imparting properties similar to those of interlinked network polymers.

In the 19th century, methods were developed to separate cellulose from other constituents of wood and then to regenerate the cellulose back to its original composition for use as both a fibre (rayon) and a plastic (cellophane). Ester and ether derivatives of cellulose were also developed and used as fibres and plastics. The most important compounds were cellulose nitrate and cellulose acetate. Both of these chemical derivatives were based on the cellulose structure

with X being NO_2 in the case of the nitrate and $COCH_3$ in the case of the acetate.

Rayon. The development of rayon as a practical fibre began in France, with the work of Louis-Marie-Hilaire Bernigaud, comte de Chardonnet. In 1889 Chardonnet exhibited fibres made by squeezing a nitrocellulose solution through spinnerettes, hardening the emerging jets in warm air, and then reconverting them to cellulose by chemical treatment. Manufacture of Chardonnet silk, later known as rayon, the first commercially produced man-made fibre, began in 1891 at a factory in Besançon. Another type of cellulose—and the most popular type in use today—was produced in 1891 from a syrupy yellow liquid that three British chemists, Charles Cross, Edward Bevan, and Clayton Beadle, discovered by the dissolution of cellulose xanthate in dilute sodium hyroxide. By 1905 Courtaulds Ltd., the British silk firm, was producing this fibre, which became known as viscose rayon (or simply viscose).

Modern manufacture of viscose rayon has not changed in its essentials. Purified cellulose is first treated with caustic soda (sodium hydroxide). After the alkali cellulose has aged, carbon disulfide is added to form cellulose xanthate, which is dissolved in sodium hydroxide. This viscous solution (viscose) is forced through spinnerettes. Emerging from the holes, the jets enter a coagulating bath

Bakelite

Thermosetting qualities of cellulose

of acids and salts, in which they are reconverted to cellulose and coagulated to form a solid filament.

Rayon fibre remains an important fibre, although production has declined in industrial countries because of environmental concerns connected with the release of carbon disulfide into the air and salt by-products into streams. It has many properties similar to cotton and can also be made to resemble silk. In apparel, it is used alone or in blends with other fibres in applications where cotton is normally used. High-strength rayon, produced by drawing (stretching) the filaments during manufacture to induce crystallization of the cellulose polymers, is made into tire cord for use in automobile tires.

Cellulose nitrate. In 1846, the German chemist Christian Friedrich Schönbein accidentally treated cotton with a mixture of nitric and sulfuric acids and obtained cellulose nitrate, which soon became commonly known as nitrocellulose. In 1861 the British inventor Alexander Parkes patented Parkesine, a plastic made from a liquid solution of nitrocellulose in wood naphtha, and in the United States, John W. Hyatt produced the first commercially successful plastic in 1869 by mixing solid cellulose nitrate and camphor. The solid solution could be heated until soft and then molded into shapes. Hyatt's Celluloid Manufacturing Company made it into a variety of products, including combs, piano keys, and knife handles. Beginning in the 1880s, celluloid acquired one of its most prominent uses in detachable collars and cuffs for men's clothing, and the development of superior solvents allowed the material to be made into flexible film for photography.

In the 1920s and '30s celluloid began to be replaced in most of its applications by less flammable and more versatile materials such as cellulose acetate, Bakelite, and the new vinyl polymers. By the end of the 20th century its only unique application of note was in table tennis balls. It also continued to be used as a film-forming polymer in some solvent-based clear coatings and paints and in fingernail polishes.

Cellulose acetate. In 1865 Paul Schützenberger and Laurent Naudin of the Collège de France in Paris discovered the acetylation of cellulose by acetic anhydride. An important commercial contribution was made by the British chemist George Miles in 1903-05 with the discovery that, when the highly acetylated cellulose was subjected to hydrolysis, it became transformed to a less highly acetylated compound (cellulose diacetate) that was soluble in cheap organic solvents such as acetone. The full exploitation on a commercial scale of the acetone-soluble material was accomplished by two Swiss brothers, Henri and Camille Dreyfus, who in 1921 began commercial manufacture of a diacetate fibre trademarked as Celanese. Acetate fabrics found wide favour for their softness, graceful drape, wrinkle resistance, and resistance to staining. In 1950 Courtaulds Ltd. began to develop triacetate fibres, which became known for their greater shape retention, resistance to shrinking, and ease of washing and drying.

Production of acetate fibres has declined since the mid-20th century partly because of competition from polyester fibres. Nevertheless, acetate fibres are still used in "easy care" garments and for the inner linings of clothing because of their high sheen. Cellulose diacetate tow (bundles of fibre) has become the principal material for cigarette filters.

The first commercial use of cellulose diacetate as a plastic was in so-called safety film, which began to replace celluloid film in motion-picture photography in the 1920s. Cellulose acetate became widely used in the automotive industry because of its mechanical strength, toughness, wear-resistance, transparency, and ease of moldability. With the introduction of newer polymers beginning in the 1930s and '40s, however, cellulose acetate plastic went into decline. It is still extruded or cast into film or sheet used in packaging, membrane filters, and photographic film, and it is injection-molded into small parts such as toothbrushes and eyeglass frames.

Polyamides. A polyamide is a polymer that contains recurring amide groups (R—CO—NH—R′) as integral parts of the main polymer chain. The most important amide polymers are the nylons, an extremely versatile class of material that is an indispensable fibre and plastic. In this section the aramids, "aromatic polyamides" that contain benzene rings in their carboxylic-acid portions, are also described.

Nylon. In October 1938, DuPont announced the invention of the first wholly synthetic fibre ever produced. Given the trade name Nylon (which has now become a generic term), the material was actually polyhexamethylene adipamide, also known as nylon 6,6 for the presence of six carbon atoms in each of its two monomers. Soon after the DuPont fibre was marketed, nylon 6 (polycaprolactam) was produced in Europe based on the polymerization of caprolactam. Nylon 6 and nylon 6,6 have almost the same structure and similar properties and are still the most important polyamide fibres worldwide. Their repeating units have the following structure:

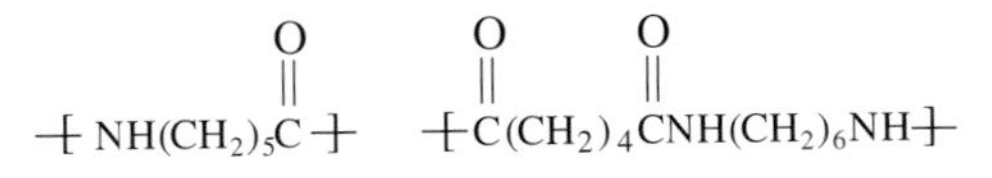

$$+NH(CH_2)_5\overset{\overset{\displaystyle O}{\|}}{C}+ \qquad +\overset{\overset{\displaystyle O}{\|}}{C}(CH_2)_4\overset{\overset{\displaystyle O}{\|}}{C}NH(CH_2)_6NH+$$

nylon 6   nylon 6,6

Nylon 6,6 was first synthesized at DuPont in 1935 by Wallace Hume Carothers by the condensation reaction of adipic acid and 1,6-hexamethylenediamine. (This reaction is illustrated above in *The chemistry of industrial polymers: Step-growth polymerization.*) The high strength, elasticity, abrasion resistance, mildew resistance, lustre, dyeability, and shape-holding properties of the material made it a very important fibre, and its market has grown greatly since its introduction. In apparel and home furnishings, nylon is important in hosiery, lingerie, stretch fabrics and sports garments, soft-sided luggage, furniture upholstery, and carpets. (For carpeting the nylon fibre is made in large-diameter filaments.) Industrial uses of nylon fibre include vehicle tires, ropes, seat belts, parachutes, substrates for coated fabrics such as artificial leather, water hoses, nonwoven fabrics for carpet underlayments, and disposable garments for the healthcare industry. As plastics the nylons still find employment as an engineering plastic—for example, in bearings, pulleys, gears, zippers, and automobile fan blades.

Other polyamides of commercial importance include nylons 4,6; 6,10; 6,12; and 12,12—each prepared from diamines and dicarboxylic acids; nylon 11, prepared by step-growth polymerization from the amino acid $H_2N(CH_2)_{10}COOH$; and nylon 12, made by ring-opening polymerization of a cyclic amide.

Aramids. Following the success of nylons, aramids (aromatic nylons) were prepared by condensation of a diamine and terephthalic acid, a carboxylic acid that contains a hexagonal benzene ring in its molecules. The close packing of the aromatic polymer chains produced a strong, tough, stiff, high-melting fibre for radial tires, heat- or flame-resistant fabrics, bulletproof clothing, and fibre-reinforced composite materials. DuPont began to produce Nomex (its trademark for poly-*meta*-phenylene isophthalamide) in 1961 and Kevlar (the trademarked name of poly-*para*-phenylene terephthalamide) in 1971. These two compounds are distinguished by the structure of their polymer chains, Kevlar containing *para*-oriented phenyl rings and Nomex containing *meta*-oriented rings:

Nomex

Kevlar

Margin notes:
Celluloid

Acetate fibre

Synthesis of nylon by Carothers

Nomex and Kevlar

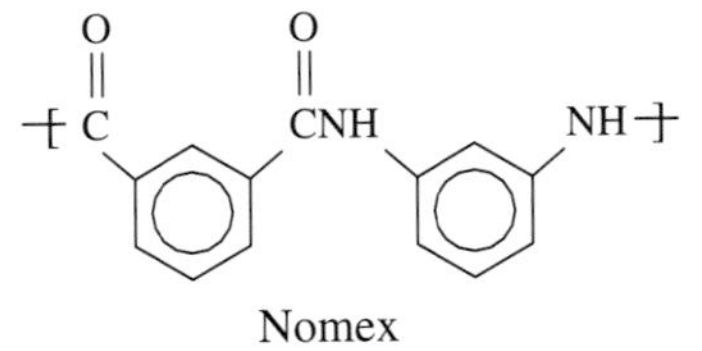

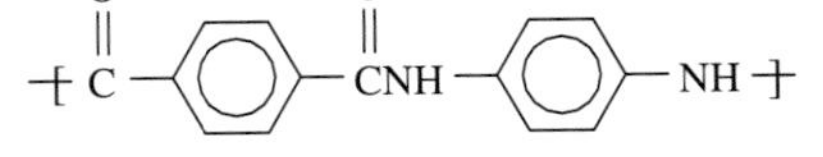

Because of the rodlike structure of the *para*-oriented aramids, a "liquid-crystalline" solution is obtained that pre-orients the molecules even before they are spun, leading to as-spun fibres of ultrahigh stiffness.

Polyesters. Polyesters are polymers made by a condensation reaction taking place between monomers in which the linkage between the molecules occurs through the formation of ester groups. The esters, which in almost all cases link an organic alcohol to a carboxylic acid, have the general structure

$$R—\overset{\overset{\displaystyle O}{\|}}{C}—O—R'$$

where R and R' are any organic combining groups. The major industrial polyesters include polyethylene terephthalate, polycarbonate, alkyds, and unsaturated polyesters.

Polyethylene terephthalate (PET). PET is produced by the step-growth polymerization of ethylene glycol and terephthalic acid as shown, above in *The chemistry of industrial polymers: Polymerization reactions*. The presence of the large benzene rings in the repeating units

gives the polymer notable stiffness and strength, especially when the polymer chains are aligned with one another in an orderly arrangement by drawing (stretching). In this semicrystalline form, PET is made into a high-strength textile fibre marketed under such trademarked names as Dacron (DuPont) and Terylene (Imperial Chemical Industries Ltd.). The stiffness of PET fibres makes them highly resistant to deformation, so that they impart excellent resistance to wrinkling when incorporated in fabrics. They are often used in durable-press blends with other fibres such as rayon, wool, and cotton, reinforcing the inherent properties of those fibres while contributing to the ability of the fabric to recover from wrinkling. PET is the most important of the man-made fibres in weight produced and in value.

At a slightly higher molecular weight, PET is made into a high-strength plastic that can be shaped by all the common methods employed with other thermoplastics. Recording tape and magnetic film is produced by extrusion of PET film (often sold under the trademarks Mylar and Melinex). Molten PET can be blow-molded to create a transparent container that possesses not only high strength and rigidity but also good impermeability to gas and liquid. In this form PET has become widely used in carbonated-beverage bottles and in jars for food that is processed at low temperatures. It is the most widely recycled plastic.

PET was first prepared in England by J. Rex Whinfield and James T. Dickson of the Calico Printers Association during a study of phthalic acid begun in 1940. Because of wartime restrictions, patent specifications for the new material, named Terylene, were not published, and production by ICI did not begin until 1954. Meanwhile, by 1945 DuPont had independently developed a practical preparation process from terephthalic acid, and in 1953 the company began to produce Dacron.

Polycarbonate (PC). Marketed under the trademarked names Lexan and Merlon, among others, polycarbonate is a special type of polyester used as an engineering plastic. It possesses exceptional stiffness, mainly by virtue of having more aromatic rings incorporated into the polyester chain:

This structure is arrived at by reacting bisphenol A, an aromatic derivative of benzene, with phosgene, a highly reactive and toxic gas.

Polycarbonate is highly transparent, has an impact strength considerably higher than most plastics, and can be injection-molded, blow-molded, and extruded. These properties lead to its fabrication into large carboys for water, shatter-proof windows, safety shields, and safety helmets. It is the favoured plastic for injection-molding into compact discs.

Alkyds and oil-free coating polyesters. Alkyds, or alkyd resins, are highly complex network polyesters that are manufactured for the paint industry. Developed from research conducted at the General Electric Co. in the 1920s, they are made from dicarboxylic acids or their anhydrides and polyfunctional alcohols such as glycerol. (The polymerization of such a network polyester, glyptal, is shown above in *The chemistry of industrial polymers: Step-growth polymerization.*) To the ester-forming monomers are added modifiers consisting of unsaturated oils such as tung oil, linseed oil, or dehydrated castor oil. The resulting polymers are thus branched polyesters with fatty-acid side groups.

When an alkyd-based coating is applied to a surface, the oil portion of the polyester undergoes a free-radical cross-linking reaction in the presence of oxygen from the surrounding air; this process, known as drying, yields a tack-free surface. A typical alkyd paint consists of the oil-modified polyester to form the coating film, a solvent such as hexane or mineral spirits to aid in application, metal naphthenates to catalyze the drying reaction, and pigment.

The term polyester, when used in the context of organic surface coatings, indicates a polyester free of natural-oil modifiers. Such polyesters are used extensively in coatings.

Unsaturated polyesters. Unsaturated polyesters are linear copolymers containing carbon-carbon double bonds that are capable of undergoing further polymerization in the presence of free-radical initiators. The copolyesters are prepared from a dicarboxylic acid or its anhydride (usually phthalic anhydride) and an unsaturated dicarboxylic acid or anhydride, along with one or more dialcohols. The linear polymers are subsequently dissolved in a monomer such as styrene and are copolymerized with the styrene in a mold to form a network structure.

Glass-fibre reinforcement is almost always used in products made of unsaturated polyesters. The principal applications are boat hulls, appliances, business machines, automobile parts, and building components.

Polyethers. Polyethers are polymers that are formed by the joining of monomers through ether linkages—*i.e.*, two carbon atoms connected to an oxygen atom. A variety of polyethers are manufactured, ranging from engineering plastics to elastomers. The compounds also differ markedly in their structures, though they all retain the C—O—C linkage.

Polyacetal. Also called polyoxymethylene (POM) or simply acetal, polyacetal has the simplest structure of all the polyethers. It is manufactured in a solution process by anionic or cationic chain-growth polymerization of formaldehyde ($H_2C{=}O$), a reaction analogous to vinyl polymerization. It is a high-strength, highly crystalline engineering plastic that exhibits a low coefficient of friction and excellent resistance to oils, greases, and solvents.

Polyacetyl has been used as a replacement for metal in plumbing and automotive parts. Principal uses include appliance parts, electronics components, gears, bushings, bearings, plumbing fixtures, zippers, and belt buckles.

Polyetherketone (PEK) and polyetheretherketone (PEEK). PEK and PEEK are high-strength, radiation-resistant engineering plastics whose structures combine both ether and ketone groups. Both are thermally stable and highly resistant to chemicals. Principal uses are in machine parts, nuclear power-plant equipment, automobile parts, aerospace components, cable insulation, and pump parts.

Epoxies (epoxy resins). Epoxies are polyethers built up from monomers in which the ether group takes the form

Polyester fibres [margin note]

Alkyd-based surface coating [margin note]

Engineering properties of polyacetal [margin note]

of a three-membered ring known as the epoxide ring:

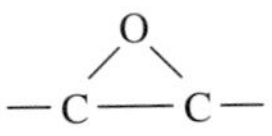

$$\underset{-C-C-}{\overset{\displaystyle O}{\diagup\diagdown}}$$

While many variations exist, the most common epoxy resin is formed from epichlorohydrin and bisphenol A. These two monomers first form an epoxy prepolymer that retains two terminal epoxide rings:

$$\underset{CH_2-CHCH_2}{\overset{O}{\diagup\diagdown}} \!\!\left[O-R-\underset{OH}{\overset{}{O\text{CH}_2\text{CHCH}_2}}\right]_{\!n} \!\!O-R-O\text{CH}_2\underset{}{\overset{O}{\diagup\diagdown}}CH-CH_2$$

$$R = -\!\!\left\langle \bigcirc \right\rangle\!\!-\underset{CH_3}{\overset{CH_3}{\underset{|}{\overset{|}{C}}}}\!\!-\!\!\left\langle \bigcirc \right\rangle\!\!-$$

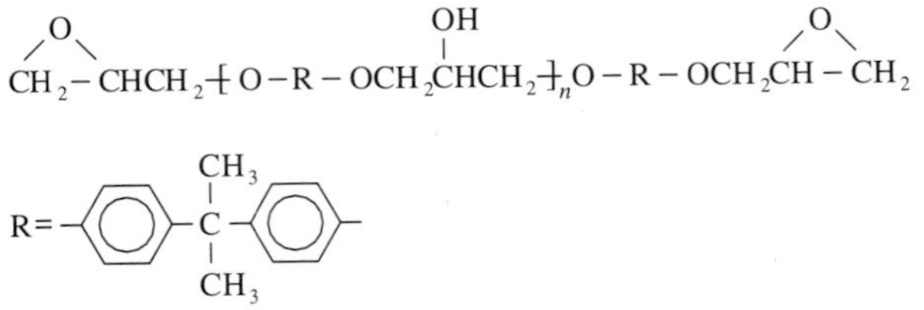

In the above structure, n varies from about 2 to 25 repeating units; such low-molecular-weight prepolymers as these are called oligomers. Depending on their average chain length, the prepolymers vary from dense liquids to solids.

In a typical epoxy reaction, the prepolymers are further polymerized through the opening of the terminal epoxide rings by amines or anhydrides. This process, called curing, yields complex, thermosetting network polymers in which the repeating units are linked by linear ether groups. The highly polar network polymers characteristically exhibit excellent adhesive properties. In addition, because the curing reaction is easy to initiate and proceeds quite readily at room temperature, epoxy resins make very useful surface coatings. Most commonly a two-component system is used, in which one component is a low-molecular-weight polymer with amine endgroups and the other component is an epoxide-terminated polymer. The two components are mixed before application to the surface, where the polymer is allowed to cure.

Epoxy resins are also made into structural parts such as laminated circuit boards, laminates and composites for aerospace applications, and flooring. For these applications epoxies show high strength when reinforced with fibres of glass, aramid, or carbon.

Polysiloxanes (silicones). Polysiloxanes are polymers whose backbones consist of alternating atoms of silicon and oxygen. They can exist as elastomers, greases, resins, liquids, and adhesives. Their great inertness, resistance to water and oxidation, and stability at high and low temperatures have led to a wide range of applications.

Siloxanes were first characterized as macromolecules by the English chemist Frederic Stanley Kipping in 1927. In 1943 Eugene George Rochow at the General Electric Company Laboratories in Schenectady, N.Y., U.S., prepared silicones by the hydrolysis of dialkyldimethoxysilane—a ring-opening process that he patented in 1945 and that remains the basis of modern polymerization methods.

The most common siloxane polymer, polydimethylsiloxane, has the following structure:

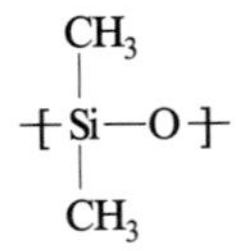

$$\left[\!\!\begin{array}{c} CH_3 \\ | \\ Si-O \\ | \\ CH_3 \end{array}\!\!\right]$$

Flexibility and stability of silicone — Siloxane molecules rotate freely around the Si—O bond, so that, even with vinyl, methyl, or phenyl groups attached to the silicon atoms, the molecule is highly flexible. In addition, the Si—O bond is highly heat-resistant and is not readily attacked by oxygen or ozone. On the other hand, the Si—O bond is susceptible to hydrolysis and attack by acids and bases, and the rubber vulcanizates are relatively weak and readily swollen by hydrocarbon oils.

Nonvulcanized, low-molecular-weight polysiloxanes make excellent lubricants and hydraulic fluids and are known as silicone oils. Vulcanized silicone rubber is used mainly in O-rings, heat-resistant seals, caulks and gaskets, electrical insulators, flexible molds, and (owing to its chemical inertness) surgical implants.

Polysulfides. Polysulfides are polymers that contain one or more groups of sulfur atoms in their backbones. They fall into two types: compounds containing a single sulfur atom per repeating unit and compounds containing two or more. Of the former type, polyphenylene sulfide is the most important. The latter type is known generically as polysulfide rubber or by its trade name, thiokol.

Polyphenylene sulfide (PPS). PPS is a high-strength, highly crystalline engineering plastic that exhibits good thermal stability and chemical resistance. It is polymerized by reacting dichlorobenzene monomers with sodium sulfide at about 250° C (480° F) in a high-boiling, polar solvent. Polymerization is accompanied by loss of sodium chloride.

When electron-donor or electron-acceptor dopants are added to PPS, the polymer becomes a conductor of electricity. PPS is used principally in automotive and machine parts, appliances, electronic and electrical processing equipment, and coatings.

Polysulfide rubber. Polysulfide rubber was discovered in 1926 by an American chemist, Joseph Cecil Patrick, while he was attempting to obtain ethylene glycol for use as an antifreeze. The elastomer was commercialized under the trade name Thiokol (after the Greek *theion,* "brimstone" [sulfur] and *kommi,* "gum"), which eventually became generic.

The polymer is mainly used in the form of a low-molecular-weight liquid that cures in place to create an elastomeric sealant. It typically consists of sulfur-sulfur linkages connecting short sequences of ethylene, the molecular chain being terminated by reactive mercaptan groups that are also used for interlinking. The principal uses of thiokols are in oil-resistant and weather-resistant seals and gaskets. They are also used in gasoline hoses and as binders for solid rocket propellants.

Polyurethanes. Polyurethanes are a class of extremely versatile polymers that are made into flexible and rigid foams, fibres, elastomers, and surface coatings. They are formed by reacting an isocyanate (a compound having the functional group NCO) with an alcohol (having the functional group OH).

During the late 1930s Otto Bayer, manager of the IG Farben laboratories in Leverkusen, Ger., prepared many polyurethanes by condensation reaction of dihydric alcohols such as 1,4-butanediol with difunctional diisocyanates. A major breakthrough in the commercial application of polyurethane did not occur until 1941, when a trace of moisture reacted with isocyanate to produce carbon dioxide. The production of this gas resulted in many small empty areas, or cells, in the product (which was subsequently called "imitation Swiss cheese").

Polyurethane foams. The largest segment of the market for polyurethanes is in rigid and flexible foams. Flexible foams are usually made with polyols and an excess of toluene diisocyanate (TDI). Foam is manufactured by adding water, which reacts with the terminal isocyanate groups to increase the molecular weight through urea linkages while simultaneously releasing carbon dioxide. The carbon dioxide gas, referred to as the blowing agent, is trapped as bubbles in the increasingly viscous polymer. The principal uses of flexible foam are in upholstery, bedding, automobile seats, crash panels, carpet underlays, textile laminates, and sponges.

Rigid foams are made with polymeric isocyanate (PMDI) and polyether glycols, along with low-molecular-weight dialcohols to increase the rigidity. Use of PMDI, which contains a larger number of reactive functional groups, results in a network polyurethane. A blowing agent such as pentane is normally added to augment the foaming. Rigid polyurethane foam is used in insulation, packaging, marine flotation equipment, and lightweight furnishings.

Polyurethane fibres. Spandex is a segmented polyurethane—that is, a fibre composed of alternating rigid and flexible segments that display different stretch-resistance characteristics. The rigid segments are normally prepared from MDI and a low-molecular-weight dialcohol such as

Spandex

ethylene glycol or 1,4-butanediol, while the flexible segments are made with MDI and a polyether or polyester glycol. The rigid segments have a tendency to aggregate, and the flexible segments act as springs connecting the rigid segments. As a result, spandex fibres can be stretched to great lengths, yet they also display a greater stretch-resistance than other rubbers and do not break down on repeated stretching. Spandex is well suited for garments with high stretch requirements, such as support hose, swimsuits, and sportswear.

Polyurethane elastomers. Two types of polyurethane elastomers are marketed: thermosetting network polymers and thermoplastic elastomers. The latter are block copolymers formulated in much the same way as are polyurethane fibres. The former make use of polyfunctional monomers such as PMDI or glycerol; further cross-linking occurs via reactions involving isocyanate and urethane groups.

The polymerization of monomers to form network polyurethanes is so rapid that articles may be fabricated by injecting the reacting monomers directly into a mold, a technology known as reaction injection molding. Polyurethane elastomers are made into automobile parts, industrial rollers, flexible molds, forklift tires, roller-skate and skateboard wheels, medical equipment, and shoe soles.

Polyurethane surface coatings. Polyurethanes form some of the highest-performance coatings available. A variety of formulations is marketed. One type is a one-component (one-pot) prepolymer containing excess isocyanate groups. Upon application of the liquid to a surface, these groups react with water from the atmosphere to form a urea, which further reacts with other isocyanate groups to provide the cross-linking necessary to cure the coating. Alkyd-type one-pot coatings, in which the polyurethane is modified with drying oils, are also available.

Polyurethane surface coatings are applied to wood, concrete, and automobile and machine parts. They also have marine applications.

(Gordon P. Bierwagen; Alan N. Gent; George B. Kauffman; J. Preston; Ferdinand Rodriguez; Malcolm P. Stevens)

Orville and Wilbur **Wright**

American brothers, inventors, and aviation pioneers (respectively b. Aug. 19, 1871, Dayton, Ohio, U.S.—d. Jan. 30, 1948, Dayton; b. April 16, 1867, near Millville, Ind.—d. May 30, 1912, Dayton), who achieved the first powered, sustained, and controlled airplane flight (1903) and built and flew the first fully practical airplane (1905).

Orville Wright
Brown Brothers

Early family life. Orville and Wilbur were the sons of Milton Wright, an ordained minister of the Church of the United Brethren in Christ, and Susan Catherine Koerner Wright, whom Milton had met while he was training for the

Wilbur Wright
Brown Brothers

ministry and while Susan was a student at a United Brethren college in Hartsville, Ind. Two boys, Reuchlin (1861–1920) and Lorin (1862–1939), were born to the couple before Wilbur was born on a farm near Millville, Ind. The young family then moved to Dayton, Ohio, so that Milton could take up duties as the editor of a church newspaper. In that city a pair of twins, Otis and Ida, were born and died in 1870. Orville arrived a year later, followed by Katharine (1874–1929).

Elected a bishop of the church in 1877, Milton spent long periods of time away from home visiting the Brethren congregations for which he was responsible. The family moved often: to Cedar Rapids, Iowa, in 1878; to a farm near Richmond, Ind., in 1881; and back to Dayton in 1884. The Wright children were educated in public schools and grew up, as Orville later explained, in a home where "there was always much encouragement to children to pursue intellectual interests; to investigate whatever aroused curiosity." In a less nourishing environment, Orville believed, "our curiosity might have been nipped long before it could have borne fruit."

These were not tranquil years for Bishop Wright. As the leader of a conservative faction opposed to modernization in the church, he was involved in a 20-year struggle that led to a national schism in 1889 and was followed by multiple lawsuits for possession of church property. Even as these decades of crisis were approaching a conclusion, an entirely new conflict developed, this time within the small schismatic branch that Bishop Wright had led away from the original church. The resulting church disciplinary hearings and civil court cases continued up to the time of the bishop's retirement in 1905.

Bishop Wright exercised an extraordinary influence on the lives of his children. Wilbur and Orville, like their father, were independent thinkers with a deep confidence in their own talents, an unshakable faith in the soundness of their judgment, and a determination to persevere in the face of disappointment and adversity. Those qualities, when combined with their unique technical gifts, help to explain the success of the Wright brothers as inventors. At the same time, the bishop's rigid adherence to principle and disinclination to negotiate disputes may have had some influence on the manner in which the brothers, later in life, conducted the marketing of their invention.

Printers and bicycle makers. Wilbur and Orville were the only members of the Wright family who did not attend college or marry. Wilbur's plans to enter college came to an end when he was injured in a hockey accident in the winter of 1885–86. He spent the following three years recovering his health, reading extensively in his father's library, assisting the bishop with his legal and church problems, and caring for his invalid mother, who died of tuberculosis in 1889.

Following their mother's death, Orville, who had spent several summers learning the printing trade, persuaded Wilbur to join him in establishing a print shop. In addition to normal printing services, the brothers edited and published two short-lived local newspapers, and they also developed a local reputation for the quality of the presses that they designed, built, and sold to other printers. These printing presses were one of the first indications of the Wright brothers' extraordinary technical ability and their unique approach to the solution of problems in mechanical design.

In 1892 the brothers opened a bicycle sales and repair shop, and they began to build bicycles on a small scale in 1896. They developed their own self-oiling bicycle wheel hub and installed a number of light machine tools in the shop. Profits from the print shop and the bicycle operation eventually were to fund the Wright brothers' aeronautical experiments from 1899 to 1905. In addition, the experience of designing and building lightweight, precision machines of wood, wire, and metal tubing was ideal preparation for the construction of flying machines.

In later years the Wrights dated their fascination with flight to a small helicopter toy that their father had brought home from his travels when the family was living in Iowa. A decade later, they had read accounts of the work of the German glider pioneer Otto Lilienthal. But it was news reports of Lilienthal's death in a glider crash in August 1896 that marked the beginning of their serious interest in flight. By 1899 the brothers had exhausted the resources of the local library and had written to the Smithsonian Institution for suggestions as to further reading in aeronautics. The following year they wrote to introduce themselves to Octave Chanute, a leading civil engineer and an authority on aviation who would remain a confidant of the brothers during the critical years from 1900 to 1905.

Early glider experiments.   The ability of the Wright brothers to analyze a mechanical problem and move toward a solution was apparent from the outset of their work in aeronautics. The brothers realized that a successful airplane would require wings to generate lift, a propulsion system to move it through the air, and a system to control the craft in flight. Lilienthal, they reasoned, had built wings capable of carrying him in flight, while the builders of self-propelled vehicles were developing lighter and more powerful internal combustion engines. The final problem to be solved, they concluded, was that of control.

Most aeronautical experimenters up to that time had sought to develop flying machines incorporating a measure of inherent stability, so that the aircraft would tend to fly a straight and level course unless the pilot intervened to change altitude or direction. As experienced cyclists, the Wrights preferred to place complete control of their machine in the hands of the operator. Moreover, aware of the dangers of weight-shifting control (a means of controlling the aircraft by shifting the position of the pilot), the brothers were determined to control their machine through a precise manipulation of the centre of pressure on the wings. After considering various mechanical schemes for obtaining such control, they decided to try to induce a helical twist across the wings in either direction. The resulting increase in lift on one side and decrease on the other would enable the pilot to raise or lower either wing tip at will.

Their first experiments with "wing warping," as the system would be called, were made with a small biplane kite flown in Dayton in the summer of 1899. Discovering that they could cause the kite to climb, dive, and bank to the right or left at will, the brothers began to design their first full-scale glider using Lilienthal's data to calculate the amount of wing surface area required to lift the estimated weight of the machine and pilot in a wind of given velocity.

Realizing that Dayton, with its relatively low winds and flat terrain, was not the ideal place to conduct aeronautical experiments, the Wrights requested of the U.S. Weather Bureau a list of more suitable areas. They selected Kitty Hawk, an isolated village on the Outer Banks of North Carolina, which offered high average winds, tall dunes from which to glide, and soft sand for landings.

Tested in October 1900, the first Wright glider was a biplane featuring 165 square feet (15 square m) of wing area and a forward elevator for pitch control. The glider developed less lift than expected, however, and very few free flights were made with a pilot on board. The brothers flew the glider as a kite, gathering information on the performance of the machine that would be critically important in the design of future aircraft.

Eager to improve on the disappointing performance of their 1900 glider, the Wrights increased the wing area of their next machine to 290 square feet. Establishing their camp at the foot of the Kill Devil Hills, 4 miles (6.5 km) south of Kitty Hawk, the brothers completed 50 to 100 glides in July and August of 1901. As in 1900, Wilbur made all the glides, the best of which covered nearly 400 feet (120 m). The 1901 Wright aircraft was an improvement over its predecessor, but it still did not perform as well as their calculations had predicted. Moreover, the experience of 1901 suggested that the problems of control were not fully resolved.

Discouraged, but determined to preserve a record of their aeronautical work to date, Wilbur accepted Chanute's invitation to address the prestigious Western Society of Engineers. Wilbur's talk was delivered in Chicago on Sept. 18, 1901, and was published as "Some Aeronautical Experiments" in the journal of the society. It indicated the extent to which the Wright brothers, in spite of their disappointments, had already moved beyond other flying machine experimenters.

Solving the problems of lift and control.   Realizing that the failure of their gliders to match calculated performance was the result of errors in the experimental data published by their predecessors, the Wrights constructed a small wind tunnel with which to gather their own information on the behaviour in an air stream of model wings of various shapes and sizes. The brilliance of the Wright brothers, their ability to visualize the behaviour of a machine that had yet to be constructed, was seldom more apparent than in the design of their wind tunnel balances, the instruments mounted inside the tunnel that actually measured the forces operating on the model wings. During the fall and early winter of 1901 the Wrights tested between 100 and 200 wing designs in their wind tunnel, gathering information on the relative efficiencies of various airfoils and determining the effect of different wing shapes, tip designs, and gap sizes between the two wings of a biplane.

With the results of the wind tunnel tests in hand, the brothers began work on their third full-scale glider. They tested the machine at the Kill Devil Hills camp in September and October of 1902. It performed exactly as the design calculations predicted. For the first time, the brothers shared the flying duties, completing 700–1,000 flights, covering distances up to 622.5 feet, and remaining in the air for as long as 26 seconds. In addition to gaining significant experience in the air, the Wrights were able to complete their control system by adding a movable rudder linked to the wing-warping system.

Powered, sustained flight.   With the major aerodynamic and control problems behind them, the brothers pressed forward with the design and construction of their first powered machine. They designed and built a four-cylinder internal combustion engine with the assistance of Charles Taylor, a machinist whom they employed in the bicycle shop. Recognizing that propeller blades could be understood as rotary wings, the Wrights were able to design twin pusher propellers on the basis of their wind tunnel data.

The brothers returned to their camp near the Kill Devil Hills in September 1903. They spent the next seven weeks assembling, testing, and repairing their powered machine and conducting new flight tests with the 1902 glider. Wilbur made the first attempt at powered flight on December 14, but he stalled the aircraft on take-off and damaged the forward section of the machine. Three days were spent making repairs and waiting for the return of good weather. Then, at about 10:35 on the morning of Dec. 17, 1903, Orville made the first successful flight, covering 120 feet through the air in 12 seconds. Wilbur flew 175 feet in 12 seconds on his first attempt, followed by Orville's second effort of 200 feet in 15 seconds. During the fourth and final

Orville Wright piloting the "Flyer" at Kill Devil Hills, Dec. 17, 1903.

By courtesy of National Air and Space Museum, Smithsonian Institution, Washington, D.C.

flight of the day, Wilbur flew 852 feet over the sand in 59 seconds. The four flights were witnessed by five local citizens. For the first time in history, a heavier-than-air machine had demonstrated powered and sustained flight under the complete control of the pilot.

Determined to move from the marginal success of 1903 to a practical airplane, the Wrights in 1904 and 1905 built and flew two more aircraft from Huffman Prairie, a pasture near Dayton. They continued to improve the design of their machine during these years, gaining skill and confidence in the air. By October 1905 the brothers could remain aloft for up to 39 minutes at a time, performing circles and other maneuvers. Then, no longer able to hide the extent of their success from the press, and concerned that the essential features of their machine would be understood and copied by knowledgeable observers, the Wrights decided to cease flying and remain on the ground until their invention was protected by patents and they had negotiated a contract for its sale.

Making the invention public. The claim of the Wright brothers to have flown was widely doubted during the years 1906–07. During that period a handful of European and American pioneers struggled into the air in machines designed on the basis of an incomplete understanding of Wright technology. Meanwhile the brothers, confident that they retained a commanding lead over their rivals, continued to negotiate with financiers and government purchasing agents on two continents.

In February 1908 the Wrights signed a contract for the sale of an airplane to the U.S. Army. They would receive $25,000 for delivering a machine capable of flying for at least one hour with a pilot and passenger at an average speed of 40 miles (65 km) per hour. The following month, they signed a second agreement with a group of French investors interested in building and selling Wright machines under license.

With the new aircraft that they would fly in America and France ready for assembly, the Wright brothers returned to the Kill Devil Hills in May 1908, where they made 22 flights with their old 1905 machine, modified with upright seating and hand controls. On May 14, Wilbur carried aloft the first airplane passenger—mechanic Charles Furnas.

Wilbur then sailed to France, where he captured the European imagination with his first public flight; this took place over the Hunaudières Race Course near Le Mans on Aug. 8, 1908. During the months that followed, the elite of the continent traveled to watch Wilbur fly at Le Mans and Pau in France and at Centocelle near Rome.

Orville began the U.S. Army trials at Fort Myer, Va., with a flight on Sept. 3, 1908. Fourteen days later a split propeller precipitated a crash that killed his passenger, Lieutenant Thomas E. Selfridge, and badly injured the pilot. During the course of his recovery, Orville and his sister Katharine visited Wilbur in Europe. Together, the brothers returned to Fort Myer to complete the Army trials in 1909. Having exceeded the required speed of 40 miles per hour, the Wrights earned a bonus of $5,000 beyond the $25,000 contract price.

Following the successful Fort Myer trials, Orville traveled to Germany, where he flew at Berlin and Potsdam. Wilbur made several important flights as part of New York City's Hudson-Fulton Celebration, then went to College Park, Md., where he taught the first three U.S. Army officers to fly.

Going into business. In November 1909 the Wright Company was incorporated with Wilbur as president, Orville as one of two vice presidents, and a board of trustees that included some of the leaders of American business. The Wright Company established a factory in Dayton and a flying field and flight school at Huffman Prairie. Among the pilots trained at the facility was Henry H. "Hap" Arnold, who would rise to command of the U.S. Army Air Forces during World War II.

The brothers also formed the Wright Exhibition Company in March 1910, with A. Roy Knabenshue, an experienced balloon and airship pilot, as manager. Although the Wrights were not eager to enter what they regarded as a "mountebank business," they recognized that an exhibition team would generate steady revenues to supplement funds received from the sale of aircraft, flight instruction, and license fees. Orville began training pilots for the exhibition team at Montgomery, Ala., and continued instruction at Huffman Prairie. The exhibition company made its first appearance at Indianapolis, Ind., in June 1910 and remained in business until November 1911, by which time the deaths of several team members convinced the Wright brothers to discontinue operations.

After the summer of 1909, Wilbur focused his energies on business and legal activities. He took the lead in bringing a series of lawsuits against rival aircraft builders in the United States and Europe whom the brothers believed had infringed upon their patent rights. In Germany, the Wright claims were disallowed on the basis of prior disclosure. Even in France and America, where the position of the Wright brothers was upheld in virtually every court judgment, the defendants were able to manipulate the legal process in such a manner as to avoid substantial payments. Moreover, the Wrights' spirited pursuit of their international patent rights significantly complicated their public image. Once inaccurately regarded as a pair of naive mechanical geniuses, they were now unfairly blamed for having retarded the advance of flight technology by bringing suit against other talented experimenters. The era of the lawsuits came to an effective end in 1917, when the Wright patents expired in France and the U.S. government created a patent pool in the interest of national defense.

Orville carries on the legacy. Exhausted by business and legal concerns and suffering from typhoid fever, Wilbur died in his bed early on the morning of May 30, 1912. Wilbur had drawn Orville into aeronautics and had taken the lead in business matters since 1905. Upon Wilbur's decease, Orville assumed leadership of the Wright Company, remaining with the firm until 1915, when he sold his interest in the company to a group of financiers. He won the 1913 Collier Trophy for his work on an automatic stabilizer for aircraft, and he worked as a consulting engineer during World War I, helping the Dayton-Wright Company plan for the production of foreign aircraft designs and assisting in the development of a pilotless aircraft bomb.

One of the most celebrated Americans of his time, Orville received honorary degrees and awards from universities and organizations across America and Europe. He remained active in aeronautics as a member of the National Advisory Committee for Aeronautics (1920–48) and as a leader of other organizations, notably the advisory board of the Daniel and Florence Guggenheim Fund for the Promotion of Aeronautics. Orville disliked public speaking, however, and enjoyed nothing more than spending time with friends and family in the privacy of his home and laboratory in Dayton or his vacation retreat on Georgian Bay, off of Lake Huron in Ontario, Can. During the last four decades of his life he devoted considerable energy to defending the priority of the Wright brothers as the inventors of the airplane. A long-running feud with the leadership of the Smithsonian Institution was particularly noteworthy. During the years prior to World War I, Smithsonian officials claimed that the third secretary of the institution, S.P. Langley, had constructed a machine "capable" of flight prior to the Wrights' success of December 1903. Unable to obtain a retraction of this claim by 1928, Orville lent the restored 1903 airplane to the Science Museum in London and did not consent to bringing the machine to Washington, D.C., until after the Smithsonian offered an apology in 1942.

On Jan. 27, 1948, Orville suffered a heart attack; he died three days later in a Dayton hospital. There is perhaps no better epitaph for both of the Wright brothers than the words crafted by a group of their friends to appear as a label identifying the 1903 Wright airplane on display at the Smithsonian: "By original scientific research, the Wright brothers discovered the principles of human flight. As inventors, builders and flyers, they further developed the aeroplane, taught man to fly, and opened the era of aviation."

(Tom D. Crouch)

SCIENCE
YEAR IN REVIEW

CONTENTS

THE YEAR IN SCIENCE:
AN OVERVIEW

by Robert P. Crease

Science, as its practitioners know, is a deeply engaging activity. The image of scientists as detached and aloof is one that is often promoted by movies and TV, but this stereotype is the result of a misreading of professional care and vigilance. Books and interviews reveal many scientists to be deeply passionate about their work. Science, of course, also provokes a range of strong reactions in the general public.

Indeed, if anything characterized the year in science, it was how many key developments evoked particularly extreme reactions. Some of these developments were natural occurrences, some technological feats, and some both, there being no clear boundary between the natural and technological. Reactions to them ranged the full spectrum from awe and wonder to fear and terror.

Natural phenomena

Of the natural wonders of 1997, the most visible—literally—was Comet Hale-Bopp, which was witnessed by more individuals than any other comet in history. One of the most spectacular comets of the century, Hale-Bopp appeared in the skies early in the year. Distinguished by its elongated plasma tail, the comet was easily seen by the naked eye and remained visible for several months, making its closest approach to Earth on March 23, when it was about 193 million km (120 million mi)

Robert P. Crease is Associate Professor and Director of the graduate program in the philosophy department of the State University of New York at Stony Brook. He is the author of a forthcoming book on the early history of Brookhaven National Laboratory, Upton, N.Y.

away. At its brightest, Hale-Bopp was outshone only by the Moon and a handful of bright planets and stars. By April more than 80% of the U.S. population had seen the comet.

Among scientists, many shared the awed reaction of Dale Cruikshank, a research scientist at the NASA Ames Research Center, Moffett Field, California. In the March 28 issue of *Science,* which was devoted partly to the comet, Cruikshank noted that the knowledge gained by studying Hale-Bopp "bears not only upon the origin of these icy transients from beyond the planetary region of the solar system but upon our own origins as well." Because comets are thought to have contributed most or all key ingredients for life (including water, carbon dioxide, and nitrogen) to the Earth's crust after its formation and to have been responsible for several mass extinctions on the planet, Cruikshank hailed comets as "the givers and takers of life," reminders that "life on Earth is connected to stardust."

Other reactions to the comet were disturbing. Outside San Diego, Calif., 39 members of a doomsday cult known as

Heaven's Gate committed mass suicide in March. According to a videotape left behind by the cult members, they believed that a giant alien spacecraft lurked behind the comet and that after death they would board the spacecraft and ride to heaven. Hale-Bopp thus demonstrated that comets, considered supernatural omens since ancient times, are still able to inspire fanatic reactions on the eve of the 21st century.

Another event that captured the public imagination during the past year was the exploration of the planet Mars. On July 4 NASA's Mars Pathfinder spacecraft landed on the Martian surface, the first spacecraft to do so since Vikings 1 and 2 released landers that touched down on Mars in 1976. Once down, Pathfinder deployed solar arrays, a color stereo camera, and instruments for atmospheric and meteorologic studies. The images that it transmitted were immediately posted on the Internet and eagerly viewed by millions of people. While some marveled at NASA's technological achievement, others hoped that the expedition would turn up evidence of extraterrestrial beings. (None materialized.) On Pathfinder's second day,

Newspeople swarm an examiner at the site near San Diego, Calif., where 39 Heaven's Gate cult members committed mass suicide in March 1997. The members had hoped to board a spacecraft they believed was hiding behind Comet Hale-Bopp. The incident showed that comets are still able to inspire fanatic reactions.

KRT

it deployed the Sojourner land rover, which explored the rocks and soil of the surrounding area. In September the Mars Global Surveyor began orbiting the planet in preparation for yet another series of studies of its climate and surface.

Using NASA's Hubble Space Telescope, astronomers observed several other celestial marvels, including two colliding galaxies, each containing up to a million stars. In September astronomers used the telescope to photograph what may be the brightest star in our galaxy; the star— 25,000 light-years from Earth—appeared to radiate 10 million times the luminosity of the Sun. In addition, astronomers recorded what was apparently an eruption from a black hole in a microquasar in our galaxy known as GRS 1915+105.

Terrestrial events also generated strong reactions in 1997. Of all the animals that inspire fear and wonder in humans, *Tyran-*

nosaurus rex must certainly be the most formidable. "Sue," the largest, most complete *Tyrannosaurus rex* skeleton known, was auctioned in October for $8,360,000. Although the high price suggested a soaring interest in fossils, many paleontologists worried about harm to their profession should the commercialization of their research material continue. Still other terrestrial marvels studied in 1997 ranged from sandcastles (the question "What keeps them up?" was the subject of a cover article in *Nature* in June) to Yellowstone National Park's famous geyser Old Faithful, whose interior was studied via a miniature video camera lowered down its insides.

Controversial births: lambs and septuplets

The single most dramatic and controversial technological achievement of 1997 was the

birth of a lamb. In a report entitled "Viable Offspring Derived from Fetal and Adult Mammalian Cells," which appeared in the journal *Nature* in February, Scottish embryologist Ian Wilmut and his team of researchers at the Roslin Institute, near Edinburgh, described having taken a cell from the udder of a six-year-old Finn Dorset ewe to create a genetic duplicate of the animal, a lamb they named Dolly. Because biologists had all but ruled out the possibility that a cell from a mature animal could be manipulated to generate an exact replica of the donor, the achievement by Wilmut and his colleagues was regarded as a major scientific breakthrough, although it still needed to be confirmed by others.

The predictable media frenzy that ensued was peppered by equally predictable jokes, from various puns ("Ewe Again?" and "Send in the Clones") to advertisements that cashed in on the attention ("Big deal," ran one for a copier company, underneath two identical pictures of Dolly, "We've been making perfect copies for years"). News of a successful attempt at cloning a sheep immediately prompted criticism, however. Many people were disturbed by the potential extension of the cloning technique to humans. Some critics, warning of the possibility that cloning could one day be abused, invoked Aldous Huxley's *Brave New World* and Mary Shelley's *Frankenstein* as cautionary tales, and others conjured nightmare scenarios involving the resurrection of tyrants and the creation of armies of sinister clones. Around the world, governments debated legislation to ban or severely restrict cloning.

In December the Roslin team announced the creation of two other cloned lambs,

Jeff Danziger, Los Angeles Times Syndicate

"Dr. Ian Wilmut is grilled by a Congressional Panel (Science marches on.)"

Molly and Polly, from fetal cells bearing a human gene that codes for factor IX, a protein that helps blood to clot. The work opened up vast new possibilities in medical therapy and research; for instance, the scientists hoped that once the lambs matured, their milk would contain useful quantities of factor IX. Once extracted, the protein would be valuable to patients who lacked it, such as people with hemophilia.

To many nonscientists the reported breakthrough in cloning seemed a sudden wake-up call for humanity, ethically speaking ("a little like splitting the atom," said one theologian). Actually, neither the science nor the ethical discussions were all that new. Scientifically, to many, Dolly and company represented only additional and inevitable steps in a revolutionary advance in recombinant DNA technology that began a quarter of a century ago. Ethically, too, the issues and rhetoric were only incrementally different; many arguments were recycled from the controversies that arose after the first heart-transplant operations, the first gene splicing, and the first steps toward cloning. The real surprise about Dolly's birth is how many of us were surprised.

By the end of the year, the debate over cloning appeared to grow more rational as scientists showed themselves willing to accept a reasonable set of regulations in view of the popular concerns, and legislators showed themselves willing to allow scientists a reasonable degree of freedom, given the potential scientific benefits. Then, in December, the debate took a bizarre turn. Chicago physicist Richard Seed claimed that he could—and would—clone a human being. Seed (critics could not resist calling him the "bad seed") said he eventually

wanted to open a cloning clinic for humans. Not surprisingly, his plans revived the media frenzy over cloning, rallied the fearful, and reinvigorated the case for extreme measures and outright bans.

Several other births in 1997 also aroused mixed emotions. One such reaction occurred in April when doctors at the University of Southern California announced that they had helped a 63-year-old woman to become pregnant (with an egg donated by a younger woman) and that the woman had been successful in giving birth. The news led to a heated discussion of the ethics of late parenthood. In October researchers in Atlanta, Ga., reported a successful pregnancy and birth from human eggs that had been initially frozen, thawed, and then fertilized, and more debate about the ethics of reproductive technology was provoked. Still more controversial was the birth, to Bobbi and Kenny McCaughey in Des Moines, Iowa, in November, of the first known living set of septuplets. The parents and others were quoted as calling the birth a gift of God, a miracle. Not so fast, others pointed out. Not only were fertility drugs (which often produce multiple eggs) involved, but so was the huge hospital support staff, which delivered the babies two months prematurely and kept them alive in intensive care after birth. "This is not any more of a miracle than winning the lottery," sniffed one doctor.

The desire to call the birth of the McCaughey septuplets a miracle illustrates how much the human control that already extends over the facts and forms of human life is taken so completely for granted. When the Vatican, in criticizing the cloning work, blasted its potential extension to humans, saying that human beings have a

Although Bobbi and Kenny McCaughey (top), the parents of the first known living set of septuplets, called the birth a gift of God, others credited the use of fertility drugs, which often produce multiple eggs. One of the famous infants, Kenneth Robert McCaughey, is pictured above in intensive care.

right to be "born in a human way, and not in a laboratory," it failed to address what being born "in a human way" means in the technologically enriched hospital environments in which most babies in Western industrial nations are born. It was also silent about the lengths to which many childless couples are now able to go to achieve pregnancies. Some doctors had extremely harsh things to say about the septuplets' birth, pointing out that trying to carry all seven fetuses to term without aborting some ran an unacceptable risk of killing several and severely damaging those who survived.

Mir and Deep Blue

Forty years after launching Sputnik, the first artificial satellite, Russia had a major embarrassment on its hands in a yearlong epic involving its space station *Mir.* In February a flash fire forced the crew to retreat to the Soyuz escape module; in March the oxygen system failed; and in April the cooling system broke. The worst single blow, literally, occurred in June when a docking cargo ship plowed into *Mir,* smashing a solar panel array, punching a hole in the station, and leading to the severing of power cables. In July the navigation system broke; the oxygen system failed again; a 24-hour power outage took place after the crew accidentally unplugged the wrong power cable; and the pressure finally got to the *Mir* commander, who began suffering physical symptoms of stress. For the rest of the year, the crew members spent much of the time in the Soyuz escape module, accommodating themselves to a seemingly endless string of computer glitches, hardware failures, and patchwork repairs.

Reactions to *Mir*'s troubles varied widely. Some saw humor, one American commentator comparing the saga to a combination of *2001: A Space Odyssey* and the Three Stooges. *Mir* was, however, a sticky topic for NASA, which subsidizes the space station. *Mir*'s troubles raised awkward questions about the much-needed Russian participation in the international space station, whose rationale (like that of *Mir*) is largely political rather than scientific, and NASA responded by trying to celebrate the *Mir* astronauts' daring and heroism. Many American science commentators were appalled by the huge amount of money devoted to a project with

a tiny scientific return. When most of *Mir*'s onboard science experiments ground to a halt in June, Robert L. Park, the top conscience-gadfly of U.S. science and author of "What's New," a weekly newsletter put out by the American Physical Society, caustically observed that "science has not suffered noticeably."

Gary Kasparov contemplates his next move against IBM's Deep Blue computer program during the second game of their six-game rematch in May 1997. Kasparov, who lost the game and eventually lost the match, admitted to being awed and terrified by Deep Blue's extraordinary capabilities.

A more successful technological marvel was IBM's Deep Blue computer program, which defeated Gary Kasparov, the world chess champion, in a six-game match in May. It marked the first time a computer program had defeated a reigning champion in a tournament, and it was Kasparov's first tournament loss since becoming

champion. The significance of Deep Blue's victory was hotly debated by cognitive scientists. Some called it a triumph for artificial intelligence, or AI (chess has been called the drosophila of AI), whereas others said it revealed only that as an exemplar of thought, chess is trivial.

Uncharacteristically, Kasparov seemed to suffer an emotional and mental collapse in the match's final game, which he resigned after only 19 moves, puzzling and shocking friends, associates, and chess fans. He later admitted to being awed and terrified by the machine's extraordinary capabilities. "I'm a human being," Kasparov said, groping for an explanation. "When I see something that is well beyond my understanding, I'm afraid."

Reactions and overreactions

The past year witnessed a number of frightening close calls with disease. A strain of influenza (avian flu) that jumped directly from birds to people appeared in Hong Kong, and officials responded by ordering over a million chickens and other poultry killed as a preventive measure. The U.S. government ordered the largest recall of hamburger meat in its history—some 11.3 million kg (25 million lb) of ground beef produced at the Hudson Foods plant in Columbus, Neb.—after tests showed that some of the meat was contaminated by a potentially deadly strain of bacterium.

Some forms of science and technology, rather than being embraced for their uses in society, tend to generate fear and resistance. Nuclear technology is a case in point. Not only is research into the nucleus capable of inspiring peculiar kinds of anxieties ("nuclear fear," science historians

The most ambitious planetary spacecraft yet built, Cassini (left) is launched at Cape Canaveral, Fla., on Oct. 15, 1997, and will arrive at Saturn in 2004. Because Cassini was powered by plutonium-containing radioisotope thermoelectric generators, antinuclear protesters objected to the launch.

call it), but missteps and coverups by the nuclear industry and its government sponsors also have generated an understandable amount of distrust. For instance, in September a watchdog group revealed that in the 1950s the U.S. Atomic Energy Commission had privately warned film manufacturers that radioactive fallout from nuclear weapons tests could damage their products, although the government publicly claimed that there was no health threat from the same material. Small wonder that episodes involving nuclear-research and technology give rise to extreme reactions.

Earlier in the year, a fire and subsequent explosion took place at a nuclear-fuel-reprocessing plant operated by Japan's state-run nuclear power company. It was the worst nuclear accident in the nation's history. Many analysts said the vigorous public outcry far exceeded the severity of the situation; still, it was partly understandable, given evidence that the response to

the accident had been slow and sloppy, that official statements had been erroneous, and that photographic evidence had been destroyed. Ontario Hydro, a Canadian company that is the largest power utility in North America, closed several of its reactors in response to a report criticizing management at its nuclear facilities. In Germany thousands of antinuclear protesters staged a series of demonstrations intended to disrupt the transport of a load of spent reactor fuel from a nuclear power plant in Bavaria to a storage facility at Gorleben, located 95 km (60 mi) from Hamburg. Some 30,000 policemen were enlisted to guard the cargo, which reached Gorleben on March 6.

Cassini, the most ambitious planetary spacecraft yet built, was launched in October. The internationally built craft will arrive at Saturn in 2004, releasing a probe that will touch down on the Saturnian moon Titan. Antinuclear protesters objected to the launch because Cassini was

powered by plutonium-containing radioisotope thermoelectric generators that could rupture in a launch accident. Such power sources are considered indispensable to extended solar missions; they powered Pioneer 10, Galileo, and other missions and are planned for the Europa Orbiter and the Pluto-Kuiper Express.

In January 1997 the discovery of a leak of water containing a small amount of tritium at a reactor at Brookhaven National Laboratory, Upton, N.Y., was announced. The leak was never considered a hazard either to the general public or to Brookhaven employees, and the total amount of radioactivity was a quarter of that found in a typical tritium-powered

(Below) AP/Wide World; (opposite page) UPI

A controversial exhibition of human specimens was mounted by the Museum of Technology and Work in Mannheim, Ger., during the past year. Although the exhibition was denounced by religious groups as a violation of human dignity, many people praised the educational value of the show.

emergency exit sign. In combination with worries about safety and in a highly charged political environment, however, the discovery triggered a chain of events, including the shutdown of the reactor, the Department of Energy's cancellation of the contract to manage the lab, legislation by Rep. Michael Patrick Forbes and Sen. Alfonse D'Amato to disallow funding for restarting the reactor, and an unprecedented competition for a new contractor. Brookhaven's scientists put together their own response to those events with petitions, protests, and placards ("Forbes/D'Amato: Over-Reactors"). (Meanwhile, in June, a New Jersey teenager broke open a tritium-powered exit sign and inhaled some of the material, which did not constitute a health hazard. The incident was not widely reported in the media.) Somehow amid all the turmoil, lab scientists—who often on their way to work had to battle protesters denouncing them as environmental criminals—continued to churn out good science. Brookhaven's achievements of 1997 included the discoveries of a rare decay of the K^+ meson, the rarest decay of a subatomic particle yet detected, and of an unusual meson, the first whose building blocks appeared to be quarks and gluons. Moreover, work at Brookhaven's state-of-the-art medical imaging center included pathbreaking studies of cocaine and addiction.

Genetic engineering is another powerful symbol able to attract fear and resistance. Dolly was only one example; another took place in France, where a government decision to ban cultivation of a transgenic strain of corn led one of that nation's leading geneticists, Axel Kahn, to resign the presidency of its regulatory committee

on genetically modified organisms. Another kind of fear was in play in Alaska, where scientists were dumbfounded to discover activists and local residents vehemently objecting to an ionospheric research lab owing to fears of harm to neighbors and of participation in a conspiracy to manipulate the weather.

One fear—that electromagnetic fields are cancer-causing—may have been laid to rest in 1997. A study by a team of epidemiologists published in the July 3 issue of *The New England Journal of Medicine* found "little support" for a correlation between electromagnetic fields and acute lymphoblastic leukemia in children. An editorial that accompanied the report pointed out that "hundreds of millions of dollars have gone into studies that never had much promise of finding a way to prevent the tragedy of cancer in children....It is time to stop wasting our research resources." Another fear may be on the wane following the U.S. Food and Drug Administration's approval in December of the irradiation of red meat as a means of ensuring food safety.

In November the U.S. CIA released a dramatic computer simulation of the crash

of TWA Flight 800, which had gone down in the Atlantic Ocean off Long Island, N.Y., 16 months earlier following an explosion in its center fuel tank. All 230 persons aboard the jet were killed. Despite an extraordinarily thorough investigation, the cause of the explosion remained undetermined, though the FBI concluded that the crash had not been caused by a criminal act of sabotage. During the investigation numerous conspiracy theories had circulated, including accusations that the U.S. military had fired a missile at the plane. An FBI assistant director who led the inquiry had been quoted as saying, "Science will overpower the question mark." In this case it did not, and the human imagination rushed in to fill the vacuum.

An almost amusing example of a potentially disastrous glitch in a complicated technological system is the so-called millennium bug (also known as the Y2K problem), the design flaw—unanticipated when computers were first set up—that makes many computers, in everything from data banks to pacemakers, unable to cope with the year 2000 without extensive and expensive alterations. In 1997 the first Y2K case was taken to court. Problems like the Y2K are inevitable concomitants of large technological systems. As *The Economist* pointed out, "The correct response to the millennium bug is not dismay but humility."

Pseudoscience events

A number of important anniversaries were celebrated in 1997: the discovery of the electron (100th), the development of aspirin (100th), the invention of the transistor (50th), and the establishment of the U.S.

national laboratory system (50th). Another was the 50th anniversary of the UFO craze, which effectively began with the "Roswell incident," the thoroughly debunked claim that a UFO crash occurred in Roswell, N.M., in July 1947 and then was covered up in a huge government conspiracy. Media fascination with aliens and UFOs lasted throughout the year.

A few courageous and responsible souls launched counterattacks against pseudoscience. Ian Plimer, a geology professor at the University of Melbourne, Australia, sued Ark Search Inc., an organization claiming to have found Noah's Ark in Turkey, on the basis that its "misleading and deceptive" fundraising activities violated Australia's Fair Trading Act. Plimer's suit was unsuccessful, and he was left with staggering legal fees. On Oct. 23, 1997, Stephen Jay Gould wrote a delightful op-ed piece in the *New York Times,* pointing out that according to a famous and once widely accepted prediction based on the work of the Anglican prelate James Ussher in 1650, the world would end that day. (The prediction went unfulfilled.) The cruelest jab against pseudoscience, however, was made by Park in a "What's New" item headlined, "Paparazzi unfairly singled out." Citing reports that Diana, princess of Wales, had consulted her personal astrologer just hours before she was killed in an automobile accident on August 31, Park demanded to know why she had not been warned. "It would appear to be malpractice," he wrote, only half tongue-in-cheek.

Poets, painters, and scientists

It is not difficult to understand why scientific and technological achievements arouse controversy and emotion. Science affects not just what we know but how we understand ourselves. How we handle cloning, which reproductive decisions we make, how smart we can make our machines, how we cope with risk, and even how seriously we credit astrologers are important decisions that affect who we are. To the extent that it affects human self-understanding, the pursuit of science shares much with the pursuit of the humanities.

That, in fact, was the point of one of the most interesting—and controversial—science editorials of the year. In the November 21 issue of *Science,* Mark Emmert, chancellor of the University of Connecticut, argued that scientists should come to the aid of the beleaguered National Endowment for the Arts (NEA), which had been targeted for extinction by certain politicians. Science and the arts, he maintained, are similar kinds of activities that ought to be defended together. As Emmert wrote:

The divide between art and science does not seem to me to be so great that the attacks on the NEA could not be extended easily to any intellectual work—artistic, humanistic, or scientific—where the economic payoffs are not obvious and the results are occasionally contrary to popular views or values. Scientists need to worry about poets and painters because they work toward the same end, simply with different intellectual tools.

Emmert's claim provoked a flood of letters. Some respondents argued that science contributes far more to human welfare than the humanities, whereas others took the opposing viewpoint. The episode revealed that the ability to arouse heated controversy is not limited to certain developments in science, but even extends to the general role of science in society.

Tourists peer through the portholes of a flying saucer at a festival celebrating the 50th anniversary of the "Roswell incident," the claim that a UFO crash occurred in Roswell, N.M., in July 1947 and then was covered up in a government conspiracy. The fascination with UFOs showed no signs of waning in 1997.

ANTHROPOLOGY

Debate in physical anthropology in 1997 focused primarily on the last 1.5 million years of human evolution and the emergence of modern humans. As is common in the field of anthropology, the discovery of fossils makes dramatic news when it is announced, but the real controversy begins when the first studies of those remains are published. Reports of three fossil discoveries made between 1993 and 1995 were published during the past year. First, detailed publication of the finds from the Sima de los Huesos site in Atapuerca, Spain, provided important evidence relating to human evolution between 200,000 and 300,000 years ago. Second, on the basis of data from the Gran Dolina site, also in Atapuerca, where human remains about 780,000 years old were discovered, a bold hypothesis about the evolution of modern humans was offered. Finally, an international research team in Africa reported on the discovery of the remains of nine members of *Australopithecus boisei* (dating to about 1.4 million years ago) that provide information on physical variability within the species. The most significant laboratory discovery of 1997 came when researchers in Germany and the U.S. reported success in extracting mitochondrial DNA (mtDNA) from a Neanderthal fossil between 30,000 and 100,000 years old, which fueled the debate over whether Neanderthals evolved gradually into modern humans or were replaced by them.

Branching out

Once relatively sparse, the human evolutionary tree of the last million years is becoming bushier. Traditional views of human evolution assumed that *Homo erectus* emerged about 1.8 million years ago in eastern Africa and spread throughout Africa, Europe, and Asia over the next million years. Until recently there was little evidence that Europe was occupied much before 500,000 years ago, but finds at Gran Dolina have pushed that date back dramatically. Remains dating to 200,000–500,000 years ago were generally lumped into a generic "ancient *Homo sapiens*" category. They consisted of fragments from many different sites scattered all over Europe. These remains were believed to represent the ancestors of Neanderthals (*H. sapiens neanderthalensis*) and modern humans (*H. sapiens sapiens*). Modern humans were assumed to have evolved gradually all over the world, more or less simultaneously.

In 1987 this view was shaken when Rebecca Cann, Mark Stoneking, and Allan Wilson, all at the University of California, Berkeley, at the time, reported their analysis of modern human mtDNA and suggested that all living humans shared a common ancestor who lived in Africa some 100,000–200,000 years ago. This ancestor was widely reported in the press as "Eve," since mtDNA is inherited only through the female line. Cann, Stoneking, and Wilson concluded that one early population of modern humans had spread out of Africa and eventually replaced all other populations of *Homo* worldwide, a theory known as the "single-origin" model. Although this model was challenged on various technical grounds, additional genetic analyses have tended to support the initial finding. Some paleoanthropologists doubted the conclusions because they were able to identify clusters of skeletal traits in Neanderthals

Juan Luis Arsuaga (right, in red) of the Complutensian University of Madrid and members of his archaeological team perform excavation work at the Sima de los Huesos site in Atapuerca, Spain. The remains of at least 32 Middle Pleistocene hominids have been recovered at the site since 1993.

and modern humans from Europe and the Middle East that seemed to suggest a gradual transformation of Neanderthals into modern humans. Their theory, the "regional-continuity" model, assumes that ancestral *H. erectus* populations throughout the world gradually evolved first through archaic *H. sapiens,* then to fully modern humans, and that interbreeding between these populations was sufficient to prevent humans from developing into separate species. In the past year several published studies directly challenged the regional-continuity model, suggesting that the patterns of skeletal traits in Neanderthal and early human remains are compatible with the replacement of Neanderthals by modern humans. One of the studies argued that on the basis of facial traits, Upper Paleolithic and Mesolithic samples were similar to one another but clearly different from Lower Paleolithic and Neanderthal samples. Increasing evidence that Neanderthals may represent a separate species has led to the creation of the new taxa *H. heidelbergensis* and *H. neanderthalensis* as distinct from *H. sapiens.*

Human skeletal remains bearing directly on this controversy have recently been discovered at two cavern sites in the Atapuerca region of northern Spain. These collapsed limestone caverns were first exposed at the turn of the century by railroad workers who were cutting a route through the Atapuerca Hills. Under the direction of Juan Luis Arsuaga of the Complutensian University of Madrid, José María Bermúdez de Castro of the National Museum of Natural Sciences, Madrid, and Eudald Carbonell of the University Rovira i Virgili, Tarragona, work at several locations in the caverns has significantly in-creased scientists' understanding of human evolution in Europe.

At Sima de los Huesos, Spanish archaeologists have recovered the remains of at least 32 individuals since 1993. Detailed publication of the finds came during the past year. The collection comprises more than 1,600 human skeletal fragments, including the remains of a complete skull, that were estimated to be 200,000–300,000 years old; it is by far the largest sample of Middle Pleistocene hominids from a single location. The site is a large limestone cavern accessible only through a 14-m (46-ft) vertical shaft. It was apparently not a living site, since tools and food remains have not been found in the deposits, only an accumulation of human and carnivore (primarily bear) bones. At least 158 adult bears and several other kinds of carnivores are represented. Exactly how the human and carnivore bones came to rest in the cavern is not entirely clear, since the deposits have been disturbed by water flowing through the cavern. Many of the human bones have been chewed by canids (probably wolves). The human fossils were classified as *H. heidelbergensis,* a group thought to be ancestral to Neanderthals. The age range of the individuals at Sima de los Huesos is unusual in the relatively large number of adolescent and young adults represented. Most are estimated to have died between the ages of 12 and 20. Normally individuals at these ages suffer lower mortality than younger children and older adults. The mystery of how the fossils came to rest in the cavern may be resolved as further excavations are conducted.

Less than one kilometer (0.62 mi) away at Gran Dolina, Spanish archaeologists uncovered evidence of even older humans—

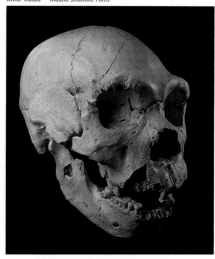

Photographs (below and opposite page), Javier Trueba—Madrid Scientific Films

Among the more than 1,600 human skeletal fragments unearthed by Spanish archaeologists at the Sima de los Huesos site were the remains of a complete *Homo heidelbergensis* skull, the best-preserved pre-Neanderthal skull ever discovered. Publication of finds from the site came during 1997.

to date, about 80 bone fragments representing at least six different individuals. Paleomagnetic dating of the deposits indicated that they are more than 780,000 years old. Most dramatic, however, was the find of skull bones revealing the partial face of a juvenile. The face appears strikingly modern for its age and has touched off a debate regarding its place in human evolution. Recently the Spanish researchers proposed that the finds from Gran Dolina are different enough to warrant identifying them as a new species, *H. antecessor* (from a Latin word meaning "explorer" or "one who goes first"). *H. antecessor* is defined on the basis of 29 traits that distinguish it from its ancestor in eastern Africa, *H. ergaster* (classified by many paleoanthropologists as a form of *H. erectus*), and its descendants, *H. heidelbergensis* and *H. sapiens.*

German researcher Matthias Krings poses with part of the skull from a Neanderthal skeleton discovered near Düsseldorf, Ger., in 1856. Analysis of data from DNA extracted from the bones suggested that Neanderthals did not contribute to the modern human gene pool.

Two elements of these proposals have stirred up controversies that will be debated intensely over the next several years. First, the creation of a new taxon on the basis of remains from only six individuals has been challenged on the grounds of insufficient data. Moreover, the traits used to define the new taxon depend heavily on a juvenile facial fragment that may not accurately characterize the features of adults. Second, unless evidence of *H. antecessor* can be found in Africa, the claim that *H. antecessor* is ancestral to both Neanderthals and modern humans is not compatible with the view that modern humans appeared less than 200,000 years ago in Africa. Some of the bones unearthed at the Gran Dolina site appear to have cut marks, which suggests that they were defleshed prior to burial. These unusual features point to the possibility of cannibalism, a possibility that will require more complete study of the remains than has been done so far.

Hominid evolution

Although *A. boisei* is not ancestral to modern humans, it lived in eastern Africa at the same time as *H. erectus* (between 1.4 million and 2 million years ago) before becoming extinct. Study of the species provides an opportunity to determine how their diet and social organization might have differed from *H. erectus*. Both species walked upright. While *H. erectus* had the larger brain and made stone tools, *A. boisei* was larger but had a smaller brain. At least part of the *H. erectus* diet came from meat, whereas *A. boisei* appears to have been a vegetarian. An international team consisting of researchers from Japan, Ethiopia, and the U.S. has been examining the deposits at Konso, Eth., since the site was discovered in 1991. Between volcanic deposits that have been dated to 1,410,000–1,430,000 years ago, the remains of nine *A. boisei* individuals have been found to date. These discoveries significantly increase the number of the known specimens of *A. boisei* and offer data on the range of variation in *A. boisei* during a relatively short period of time within a single geographic location. This is important because it provides comparative information on the degree of variation in physical characteristics that can be found in a single ancient species. Among the remains is a nearly complete skull. Information on the physical variability within *A. boisei* will help paleoanthropologists resolve outstanding controversies regarding how much variability within a group of fossils is needed before a new species should be defined. A second interesting feature of the finds is that they come from deposits characterized by dry grassland. Previous studies had suggested that *A. boisei* preferred a mixed woodland habitat. Remains of *H. erectus* and Acheulean (Lower Paleolithic) stone tools have been found in the same stratigraphic intervals.

Mitochondrial DNA study

A recent study cast new light on the origin of modern humans and Neanderthals and on the long-disputed relationship between the two. In a report published in the July 11, 1997, issue of the journal *Cell*, researchers in Germany and the U.S. described the successful extraction of mtDNA from a Neanderthal fossil. Matthias Krings of the Ludwig Maximilian University of Munich, Anne Stone of Pennsylvania State University, Ralf W. Schmitz of the Rhineland Museum, Bonn, and colleagues extracted the mtDNA from a Neanderthal-type specimen found in 1856 near Düsseldorf, Ger. In 1991 Schmitz had initiated an interdisciplinary project to focus on the fossil material. The mtDNA sequence extracted from the fossil was carefully examined to ensure its authenticity and the absence of contamination from modern mtDNA. Comparison of the Neanderthal sample with modern samples from Europe, Asia, America, and Oceania indicated that the Neanderthal mtDNA fell outside the variation of modern humans. Moreover, the Neanderthal mtDNA was not more similar to that of Europeans, as would be expected if Neanderthals had evolved gradually into modern humans in Europe. In order to estimate the age of a common ancestor between modern humans and Neanderthals, the researchers compared modern human and Neanderthal mtDNA with chimpanzee mtDNA. Assuming a human-chimpanzee divergence of four million to five million years ago, the researchers calculated that modern humans and Neanderthals diverged about 550,000–690,000 years ago and that all modern humans share a common ancestor who lived about 120,000–150,000 years ago. On the basis of these results, the researchers concluded that Neanderthals became extinct without contributing mtDNA to modern humans. The researchers pointed out that care must be taken to test associated nonhuman fossils for the potential to produce ancient mtDNA before removing samples from the much rarer human fossils. The findings are certain to be controversial over the next few years. If the extraction of ancient mtDNA can be independently confirmed by other laboratories, paleoanthropologists will have a powerful new tool for exploring the origin of modern humans.

—David L. Carlson

ARCHAEOLOGY

A number of exciting developments in archaeology occurred during the past year. Forensic archaeology emerged as a valuable weapon in criminal investigations. Earthen mounds at a site near Monroe, La., were found to be the earliest-known remnants of human construction in North America. The mounds dated to about 5,400

years ago, almost 2,000 years earlier than the next oldest mounds in the region. Other news of note came from Turkey, where recent archaeological excavation of Catalhuyuk, possibly the largest Neolithic settlement in the world, brought forth remarkable evidence of village life about 9,000 years ago. New evidence also indicated that swarms of earthquakes were responsible for the destruction of many Bronze Age cities in the eastern Mediterranean, including the legendary Jericho and Troy. Finally, recent advances in radiocarbon calibration pushed back the ages of known early American cultures by about 2,000 years.

Forensic archaeology

One of the major focuses of archaeologists is on context, which is the term for the often complex relationship between the material remains of past human life and activities and the surrounding matrix of environmental data in which those remains are found. Preserving context is the primary reason that preservation laws have been passed in the U.S. and other countries around the world. These laws are intended to protect archaeological sites from collectors and unauthorized diggers and from rampant and thoughtless destruction by developers. Because of the constant awareness and emphasis on context, archaeologists pay attention to details of all kinds as they describe, classify, and analyze relevant data. This process makes archaeologists especially good at solving puzzles and thus useful allies to authorities involved in the collection of evidence related to criminal investigations.

Two notable examples in the growing field of forensic archaeology are from opposite sides of the globe. Recently archae-

Forensic experts uncover corpses in a mass grave near Sarajevo, Bosnia and Herzegovina. Evidence gathered by archaeologists working for the International Criminal Tribunal for the Former Yugoslavia led to indictments of Serbian officers of the Yugoslav People's Army for crimes against humanity.

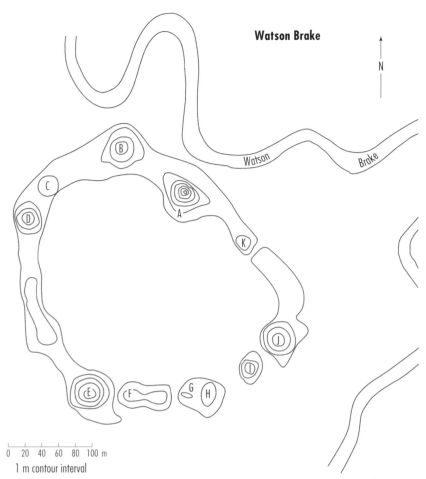

Watson Brake

N

Watson   Brake

0   20   40   60   80   100 m
1 m contour interval

A contour map of the Watson Brake site near Monroe, La., depicts the oval-shaped complex of 11 low earthen mounds that archaeologists have dated to about 5,400 years ago. The mounds are the earliest-known remnants of human construction in North America.

Adapted from information obtained from Belmont and Jones

ologists working for the International Criminal Tribunal for the Former Yugoslavia excavated several mass graves in the Srebrenica region of Bosnia and Herzegovina. The systematic excavation of these graves provided evidence that led to the indictments of Serbian officers of the Yugoslav People's Army for crimes against humanity. In San Antonio, Texas, graduate students and professors from the University of Texas painstakingly gathered hundreds of fragments of human remains scattered across an urban backyard. The remains turned out to be those of four murder victims. The process of the criminal investigation was monitored with great interest by the local news media, and archaeologists had citywide attention for several weeks during mid-1997. Although archaeologists and physical anthropologists helped determine the identities of

some of the victims through DNA studies and facial reconstruction performed on at least one of the skulls, the case remained unsolved.

Earliest North American mound site

Mounds constructed by human beings are relatively common in the eastern U.S. along or near major rivers like the Mississippi. Almost all of them are the remains of villages and towns occupied by pottery-making peoples whose diet consisted primarily of domesticated corn, beans, and squash. Until 1997 no mound site in North America had been dated to more than 3,400 years ago. It was thought that the hunter-gatherers who roamed the continent beginning about 10,000 years ago could neither have afforded the energy nor have harnessed enough labor to build such sites.

A recent find, however, showed that these assumptions were wrong. Joe W. Saunders, a professor of geosciences at Northeast Louisiana University, found that an oval-shaped complex of 11 low earthen mounds near Monroe dated to about 5,400 years ago, almost 2,000 years earlier than the next oldest mounds in the region. The site, called Watson Brake, had been seasonally occupied by hunter-gatherers who had relied to a large extent on fish and other riverine animals. The site's occupants had not yet learned to make pottery.

The mounds comprise earth and gravel dug from nearby areas and presumably transported to the site in baskets or hide bags. The 11 mounds contain several hundred tons of such material, which indicates that the occupants had organized large numbers of people over a long period of time to construct the site according to a specific plan. One mound is 7.5 m (24.6 ft) tall, and the others are 1–4.5 m (3.3–14.8 ft) in height. They are arranged in an oval about 280 m (918.6 ft) in diameter and are connected by low narrow ridges.

What were the mounds used for? In other parts of North and Central America, earthen mounds were often used to support temples or administrative buildings associated with high levels of cultural complexity. The mounds at Watson Brake contain no evidence of wooden or other superstructures, and their exact function remains unknown.

What is clear is that a relatively powerful person, or a group of such people, was able to plan the layout and organize the necessary labor to begin construction of the site. Because it was seasonally occupied and built upon for several hundred years, Watson Brake reflects a long-lived dedication to the original plan and the continuation of the organizational power over several generations.

Renewed excavation of Catalhuyuk

After a 30-year lull, archaeologists revived and expanded excavation of a 13.5-ha (33-ac) grassy mound located about 240 km (150 mi) south of Ankara, Turkey. The mound is the site of a 9,000-year-old settlement called Catalhuyuk, perhaps the largest settlement of the Neolithic Period. The first archaeological research at the site had been led by British archaeologist James Mellaart between 1961 and 1965. The settlement was found to have housed 10,000 occupants in tightly packed mud-brick houses, each of which had rooftop entrances. Mellaart suggested that life at Catalhuyuk revolved around elaborate rituals involving communal shrines, bull horns, and wall paintings of terrifying wild animals. Clay figurines and wall paintings also depicted powerful females who were interpreted to represent a mother-goddess cult of fertility somewhat similar to later cults in the eastern and northern Mediterranean region. Mellaart saw the settlement as politically complex, with priestly and elite classes in positions of authority.

Recent archaeological excavation of Catalhuyuk, led by Ian Hodder of the University of Cambridge, shed an entirely different light on life in the ancient city. Hodder contended that the social structure in Catalhuyuk was much simpler than believed earlier, with both reinterpreted and fresh evidence pointing to a very crowded city that had little political complexity and no elite, priestly, or functionally specialized classes. Instead, Hodder argued, each

family was independent, and ritual was confined to each household. He found no evidence of organized religion that unified the city through communal rites, as is common in cities and communities throughout the world.

Hodder based his argument primarily on the fact that each house his team excavated seemed to be divided into ritual and domestic activity areas. The latter was always in the southern portion of the room around the cooking area, whereas the household shrines were found in the northern, eastern, or western portions of the rooms. Wall paintings, bull horns, and offerings of finely made objects, such as a 20-cm (8-in) flint dagger, marked shrines in excavated dwellings. No communal areas where large rituals or administrative functions would have been performed were found in the city.

If Hodder was correct in his interpretation, Catalhuyuk is highly unusual in that it represents a large, tightly packed concentration of people who were not organized or controlled by political and priestly elites yet managed the social cohesion necessary to maintain a city for several hundred years.

Of conquerors and earthquakes

Most of the late Bronze Age cities of the eastern Mediterranean, including the legendary Jericho, Troy, Megiddo (also known as Armageddon), Knossos, and Mycenae, were destroyed in a relatively short period, between 1225 and 1175 BC. Most scholars had assumed that invading seafaring warriors, as described in myths and biblical tales, destroyed these once-great cities, but recently Amos Nur, a geo-

physicist at Stanford University, found strong evidence that earthquakes caused severe damage and left many of the crippled cities vulnerable to marauders, who finished them off. Nur noticed that archaeological excavations at many Bronze Age cities in the region had revealed that mud-brick and stone walls seemed to have fallen simultaneously within each city, burying people along with their belongings. Although it is possible that invaders might have pushed down walls to destroy a city, it is not likely that they would do so before pillaging gold and other precious objects from the inhabitants.

Nur thought that earthquakes were the more likely culprits, so he deciphered the region's seismic history. He showed that epicenters of 20th-century temblors with the power necessary to knock down walls correlated very well with the locations of Bronze Age cities. He then traced major faults in the region and showed that the destroyed cities were located along or near the most active earthquake zones. Nur reasoned that these faults have been active for many thousands of years and concluded that temblors along the faults were responsible for the periods of destruction. The archaeological evidence of nearly simultaneous damaging earthquakes in the region suggested to Nur that, as in the present, major earthquakes occurred in swarms, with periods of quiet between them.

Nur also explored the Qumran caves where the Dead Sea Scrolls were discovered. One of the caves, known as the "Cave of Letters," where fragments of the Psalms and the Book of Numbers were found, contained a human skeleton buried beneath huge boulders that had fallen from the ceiling of the cave. Nur maintains that

An artist's rendering of Catalhuyuk as it may have looked 9,000 years ago shows the tightly packed mud-brick houses with rooftop entrances that made up perhaps the largest settlement of the Neolithic Period. Each house seems to have been divided into ritual and domestic activity areas.

portions of the cave collapsed in an earthquake that occurred around 31 BC. In addition, he believes that many important documents and other material dating back more than 2,000 years lie buried under the pile of rubble. Nur hopes to organize a large expedition to excavate the cave, which may contain documents related to

the emergence of Christianity and of rabbinic Judaism and on the relationship between early Christianity and Jewish religious traditions.

Dating early peoples in the Americas

Radioactive carbon-14, or radiocarbon, dating is a primary tool in interpreting the past. Both radiocarbon and stable carbon exist in the Earth's atmosphere as carbon dioxide, and their ratio has remained fairly constant for many thousands of years. As a result of plant photosynthesis, this ratio is reflected in the food chain. As long as

a plant or animal is respiring and taking in food, radiocarbon and stable carbon are continually replenished in its tissues. After the organism dies, however, the amount of stable carbon in its tissues remains constant, but the amount of radiocarbon decreases as it decays into stable nitrogen. Radiocarbon dating is possible because one can determine how long an organism has been dead on the basis of the steady decay of radiocarbon in the long-lasting hard tissues—for example, bones, shells, and teeth—that remain. The ratio of radiocarbon to stable carbon in the atmosphere was once thought to be quite steady from year to year, but tree-ring studies since the 1960s have shown that stable carbon and radiocarbon fluctuate in the atmosphere owing to changes in solar activity, cosmic radiation, the Earth's magnetic field, and the amount of carbon trapped in the oceans at any given time. Direct dating of the rings of long-lived trees in the U.S. and Europe has given rise to calibration curves that allow more accurate determinations of calendrical dates based on radiocarbon ages. Calibrations based on tree rings are ever more sophisticated and accurate but are limited to the last 10,000 years.

Until recently, radiocarbon ages older than 10,000 years have not had the benefit of calibrated corrections. Radiocarbon ages associated with the Late Pleistocene (10,000–22,000 years ago) are beyond tree-ring calibration curves and, consequently, are inaccurate in relation to calendrical time. This poses problems for archaeologists interested in the timing of the last climatic events of the Quaternary Ice Age and the movements of peoples into and across the Americas.

Archaeologists, physicists, and other scientists have used two different kinds of evidence to refine the radiocarbon "clock." As noted by archaeologist Stuart J. Fiedel, the first evidence came from counting the yearly layers of accumulated ice on the Greenland ice sheet. These layers offer a detailed record of atmospheric activity during the past 100,000 years. Specific events are recorded in the ice layers. One important event is the sudden steep drop in Northern Hemisphere temperature that signifies the onset of the last major cooling period, called the Younger Dryas, that occurred at the end of the Pleistocene. Scientists have recorded evidence of the

Younger Dryas in many kinds of data throughout the Northern Hemisphere but have not been able to accurately date its onset and duration in relation to the activities of humans, particularly in the Americas. Previous radiocarbon ages on organic remains from lake beds of Europe and the Americas indicated that the Younger Dryas began some 10,600–10,900 years ago. Cores taken from the Greenland ice sheets indicate that the correct date is 2,000 years older, at around 12,900 years ago. Uncorrected radiocarbon ages indicated that the Younger Dryas lasted only 400 years, but the ice sheet cores show that the correct period was 1,300 years. Dramatic increases in oceanic carbon due to the much colder water temperatures and a corresponding decrease in atmospheric carbon caused this discrepancy. The discrepancy provides an accurate way to calibrate Late Pleistocene radiocarbon ages.

The second kind of evidence—and a corroboration of the ice sheet corrections to the radiocarbon clock—came from the tropical coral reefs off Barbados in the West Indies. Samples of coral known to be old were dated, using both uranium-thorium and radiocarbon methods. Comparison of the two independent methods showed that radiocarbon dating underestimates the true age of Late Pleistocene coral by about 2,000 years, the same amount indicated by the Greenland ice cores.

Fiedel compiled a chronology of Late Pleistocene climatic events recorded in the Greenland ice: Oldest Dryas (cold); Bolling (warm); Older Dryas (cold); Allerød (warm); Intra-Allerød Cold Period (cold); End of Allerød (warm); Younger Dryas (cold). The warm period after the Younger

Dryas is the post-Pleistocene epoch called the Holocene, which continues to the present time. Some of the best evidence in North America for the environments associated with early Americans, collectively called Paleoindians, is found in the southwestern U.S. Fiedel used cultural sequences from that area to correlate the climatic events with these archaeological cultures.

His proposed chronology pushes back the ages of these well-known Paleoindian cultures by about 2,000 years. The earliest well-documented culture in North America is called Clovis, after a city in New Mexico near one of the biggest archaeological sites. Clovis peoples are represented by a relatively large number of sites throughout North America. Abundant radiocarbon ages from Clovis-associated materials suggested that these peoples lived between 10,800 and 11,200 years ago. The recent calibrations indicate that more accurate dates would fall between 12,500 and 13,200 years ago. This correction puts the Clovis period in the Allerød warming period. Later North American Paleoindian cultures, such as Folsom (also named for a town in New Mexico), appear to correlate to the first half of the Younger Dryas cold period. Folsom was previously dated to between 9,900 and 10,500 years ago but now appears to date more accurately to between 11,900 and 12,500 years ago.

Mass extinctions of species of large Pleistocene animals occurred primarily during the Allerød and Younger Dryas periods. The Late Pleistocene was a complex time, and undoubtedly the convenient 2,000-year correction is too simple to stand as a highly accurate radiocarbon calibration technique throughout the Northern

Hemisphere. By early 1998 it was already being refined and tested. Interpreting the climatic events associated with the end of the Ice Age is even more complex, but the Greenland ice cores and the tropical coral ages, along with a host of other data, including those from archaeological sites, will clarify scientists' understanding of this important period of the past.

—James D. Wilde

ARCHITECTURAL AND CIVIL ENGINEERING

The 1997 exhibition "Mechanical Marvels: Invention in the Age of Leonardo," organized by the Institute and Museum of History of Science in Florence and Finmeccanica in Rome, provided a

historical context for the year's achievements in architecture and engineering. The venerable connection between design and technological ingenuity was demonstrated by Renaissance inventions ranging from Filippo Brunelleschi's ribbed dome for the Florence Cathedral, at the time the largest dome ever built without temporary wooden structural supports, to Francesco di Giorgio's monograph of designs for harbor-dredging machines and mechanical column lifters, considered the world's first modern technical treatise.

Architectural engineering

Following the 1995 earthquake that severely damaged Kobe, Japan, Kisho Kurokawa Architect & Associates and struc-

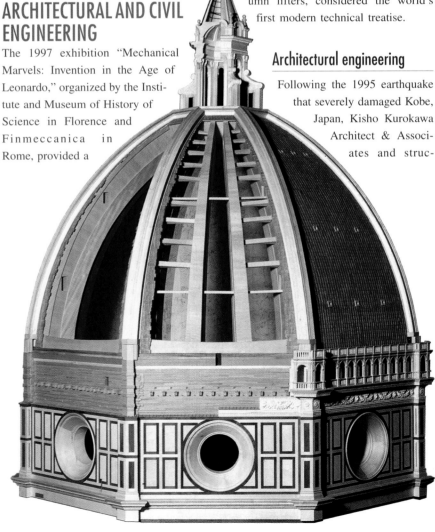

tural engineers Ove Arup & Partners reconsidered their seismic-protection design for the 67,000-sq m (721,000-sq ft) Osaka Convention Center, to be completed in 2000. The confined site precluded a horizontal scheme, which forced the architects to design a 13-story building.

The unusually strong horizontal forces of the Kobe earthquake, however, prompted architects and engineers to redesign additional protection for the vertical building. Using a supercomputer modeling program normally employed to analyze damage caused by vehicle collisions, engineers simulated the effects of an earthquake's abrupt horizontal forces on each structural component. To minimize welded connections, the building was supported by six vertical towers and framed with massive H-shaped steel columns. The columns were reinforced with diagonal steel-frame energy-absorbing braces. These braces were designed to slip freely at their connections, forming a kind of flexible exoskeleton that would absorb an earthquake's force before it affected the building's main structure. The solution ran counter to American engineering practices, which called for designing a building's main load-bearing members to absorb seismic energy.

A major earthquake that hit Los Angeles in 1994 with unusually strong horizontal forces similar to the Kobe shock prompted Robert Englekirk Consulting Structural Engineers to rethink its seismic scheme for the city's Getty Center, an arts complex of

The model of Filippo Brunelleschi's ribbed dome for the Florence Cathedral was part of a 1997 exhibition that showcased Renaissance design and technology.

buildings and gardens that opened in December 1997. Central to the seismic plan was the use of innovative lateral reinforcements.

In Spain the Guggenheim Museum Bilbao opened its doors in October 1997. Designed by American architect Frank O. Gehry, the international art museum had the architect's distinctive style—walls that appeared to be a jumble of intersecting curves and irregular forms defying structural reason. Much of the building's design daring was made possible by the technological ingenuity of structural engineers Skidmore, Owings & Merrill. The engineers used computerized design-to-production techniques to make a direct electronic link between Gehry's office and the steel-frame fabricators. The designers' computer models created curved sections of truss-braced walls that were composed of stock members in a minimum number of sizes. The building's exterior cladding—sheets of titanium rolled to a thickness of only 0.38 mm (0.015 in)—pushed manufacturing technologies to new limits of minimum tolerances.

In 1997 architects gave life and form to some of the most mundane civil-engineering projects. A design by the Hillier Group for the main building of the new Cogeneration Plant at John F. Kennedy International Airport in Jamaica, N.Y., combined utility and elegance in a curve-roofed and glass-walled structure that revealed the plant's monumental mechanical workings.

In Seattle, Wash., landscape architects Danadjieva & Koenig Associates wrapped the grounds of the city's sewage-treatment plant in kilometers of tiered, sinuously curved concrete retaining walls. Planted

(Opposite page) Institute and Museum of History of Science, Florence and Finmeccanica; (below) Timothy Hursley

The jumble of intersecting curves and irregular forms in Frank O. Gehry's exuberant design for the Guggenheim Museum Bilbao challenged the ingenuity of architectural engineers.

with cascading vegetation, the berms created a narrow, winding urban park around the facility's perimeter.

In the London Docklands, a redevelopment district located on the site of a former East London port, the architectural firm Future Systems designed an 84-m (1 m=3.28 ft) arched bridge across the Thames, supported by gracefully crossed steel legs resting on pontoons.

Civil engineering

Despite environmental concerns and public opposition to costs, Switzerland awarded construction contracts for the first phase of a $160 million project to build the world's longest tunnel—the 57-km (1 km=0.62 mi) Gothard Tunnel—through the Alps. The world's longest bridge—the 3,910-m Akashi Kaikyo suspension bridge in Japan—neared its 1998 completion date. In Greece, after nearly a decade of delays, final design planning began for a $900 million cable-stayed bridge across the Gulf

Timothy Hursley

Rafael Viñoly Architects' design for the Tokyo International Forum featured a lobby with a 225-m-long skylight supported by a colossal reverse-barrel truss.

of Corinth. The French-financed bridge, scheduled for completion in 2004, would span the 2.9-km-wide gulf with four traffic lanes. Poland announced the first phase of a $2.5 billion highway-construction program that would link major cities at opposite ends of the nation. Intense opposition by environmentalists failed to halt construction on a 1.1-km earthen dam on Cardiff Bay, Wales. Designed to block the world's second largest tidal wash across 200 ha (500 ac) of mudflats, the $340 million project would allow the city of Cardiff to develop the flats as part of its program to revitalize 1,000 ha (2,500 ac) of abandoned commercial waterfront.

In the U.S. builders completed the first 11 km of a 37-km reconstruction of the Chesapeake Bay Bridge-Tunnel. At John F. Kennedy International Airport, an ambitious modernization and expansion program was revived after having been on hold since 1989. The most recent proposal, however, scaled back the original plan, which had included designs for a mega-terminal. The program called for replacing the airport's congested single-loop system with a new traffic plan. The revised design divided the airport into five sections, each accessed by its own road. In Boston Harbor engineers implemented an environmental technique for disposal of dredged materials that they hoped would be transferable to other sites around the world. The $65 million dredging program placed contaminated silt from the harbor into disposal cells—about 28,000–57,000-cu m (1,000,000–2,000,000-cu ft) holes dug into the bottoms of navigation channels. To prevent the soil from being washed into harbor waters, the cells were capped with 0.9 m of granular fill. The technique would

replace the traditional practice of dumping contaminated soil at sea, a practice that had adversely affected marine life and threatened shorelines with deposits of contaminated drift.

Honors and awards

Projects that received 1997 Honor Awards from the American Institute of Architects (AIA), Washington, D.C., used many of the latest technologies. Several projects were renovations or restorations that benefited from the recent flurry of research into more long-lasting and efficient building technologies. Awards went to architects Venturi, Scott Brown and Associates for renovations and additions to the 1874 Memorial Hall at Harvard University, Hardy Holzman Pfeiffer Associates for the firm's renovation of Dillingham Hall in Honolulu and the New Victory Theater in New York City, Steven Ehrlich Architects for conversion of an industrial building in Culver City, Calif., into offices for Sony Pictures Entertainment, and Herbert Lewis Kruse Blunck Architecture for conversion of a former warehouse into office space for Praxair Distribution in Ankeny, Iowa.

Other AIA awards were granted to projects exhibiting ingenuity in environmentally sensitive design. Among these was Skidmore, Owings & Merrill's plan for a housing development in Ho Chi Minh City, Vietnam, which provided shelter for up to one million people while protecting the tidal region's water quality and hydrology. Also recognized was Communitas Architecture's plan for Parco San Giuilano in the Venetian suburb of Mestre, an urban park that reclaimed marshy land at the edge of an industrial mainland with water-

ways and tree-lined public walkways. Also recognized for its environmental achievement was Walter Chatham's design for a 180-sq m (1,940-sq ft) guest house for the Delta and Pine Land Co. in Scott, Miss. Constructed on pilings to allow water to pass unobstructed under the house during seasonal floods, the building also took advantage of natural ventilation and daylight.

Other award-winning designs played down their cutting-edge architectural technology with traditional-looking exteriors that conformed to the style of neighboring structures, including Kallmann McKinnell & Wood Architects' molecular and structural biology center for Yale University. Some buildings openly celebrated their great technological virtuosity, such as Rafael Viñoly Architects' Tokyo International Forum, which featured a lobby with a 225-m-long skylight supported by a colossal reverse-barrel truss.

In January 1998 *Engineering News-Record* recognized outstanding achievements in civil engineering and related technologies by naming its 1997 Top 25 Newsmakers. Among those honored was Leslie

E. Robertson of the structural engineering firm Leslie E. Robertson Associates, New York City. His landmark engineering for a 120-m pedestrian bridge to the Miho Museum near Kyoto, Japan, featured unusually thin structural components whose use was made possible by a unique combination of cantilevered, cable-stayed, and posttensioned systems.

Also recognized was Michael Abrahams, head of the structures department of the multinational construction company Parsons Brinckerhoff, who spanned Pearl Harbor, Hawaii, with a 1.6-km bridge, one of the largest pontoon structures in the world.

Antonio Nanni, a professor of civil engineering at the University of Missouri at Rolla, imported and improved a high-speed, nondestructive testing system from Europe that used hydraulic jacks and computers to verify the need for concrete-beam upgrades in parking structures. The new system slashed testing time from days to minutes.

Dennis G. Majors, reservoir-project manager for the Metropolitan Water Dis-

trict of southern California, was honored for having located a seismically stable site for the construction of the new $1.9 billion Eastside Reservoir near the city of Los Angeles.

Engineer Armin B. Mehrabi with Construction Technology Laboratories, Inc., Skokie, Ill., developed a nondestructive diagnostic laser system to measure the force distribution on existing cable-stayed bridges.

Geotechnical engineers for Mueser Rutledge Consulting Engineers, New York City, coordinated the design of the world's longest deep-ocean sewage pipe in Ponce, P.R. The 5.6-km pipe was designed to discharge 167 million liters (44 million gal) per day of treated wastewater into the ocean.

—Charles King Hoyt

ASTRONOMY

From the surface of Mars to the far reaches of deep space, exciting breakthroughs and achievements marked the past year in astronomy. The first probe to land on Mars in more than 20 years revealed that the planet had once experienced crustal melting, and an extensive study of supernovas resulted in a new estimate for the age of the universe.

Solar system

After a seven-month voyage, the unmanned Pathfinder spacecraft arrived at Mars on July 4, 1997. The first probe to land on the Martian surface since the Vikings in 1976, Pathfinder sent to Earth a stream of weather data and panoramic, stereoscopic images of a red desertlike surface. (*See* SPACE EXPLORATION: *Space Probes.*) During the Martian night the temperatures dipped to −79° C (−110° F). This was almost as cold as the lowest recorded temperature at the Earth's South Pole. During the day the Sun warmed the ground to about −12° C (10° F). Clouds of carbon dioxide crystals were visible at heights of 15 km and were moving 25 km/h in an atmosphere thinner and drier than that above any desert on Earth (1 km = 0.62 mi).

Astronomers had targeted this particular site, Ares Vallis, for investigation because it appears to be an ancient floodplain. In the early 1970s an orbiting probe, Mariner 9, showed that the surface of Mars reveals evidence of erosion caused by water from massive floods. There are, however, no signs of liquid water on the planet today. In fact, most of Mars is far too cold for water to exist in liquid form. The reasons for this change are unknown. It has been

suggested that at one time the planet's internal heat or a drastic climate change thawed great reserves of subsurface ice. Scientist reasoned that a floodplain, such as Ares Vallis, would contain a diversity of rock carried from many locations and deposited by the ancient floodwaters. The Pathfinder images did, indeed, reveal rocks with a great variety in size, shape, and texture.

Pathfinder carried a companion to Mars: an 11.5-kg (25-lb) solar-powered rover called Sojourner, which was nestled on one of the solar panels. On the second day on Mars Sojourner rolled down a ramp and began to explore the surface. Its primary mission was to image and chemically analyze the rocks and soil at the landing site. The nearby rocks were given whimsical names such as Yogi and Barnacle Bill. Analysis revealed that Barnacle Bill is similar to the quartz-rich rock called andesite. On Earth andesite is formed by the melting of the Earth's crust by volcanic activity.

Shortly after landing on Mars, the Pathfinder spacecraft transmitted images that showed a rock-strewn landscape (above). The still-undeployed six-wheeled Sojourner rover is seen nestled on an unfolded solar panel. During its mission Sojourner visited and chemically analyzed nearby rocks, such as the one nicknamed Yogi (left) by scientists.

This implies that Mars once had significant crustal melting.

In the year 1610 the Italian astronomer Galileo Galilei focused one of the first telescopes on the planet Jupiter. It revealed the planet as a disk that looked distinctly different from the pointlike stars. Galileo also discovered four moons that circle Jupiter. Today these objects are referred to as the Galilean satellites. They are the largest moons in the Jupiter system, each comparable in size to the planet Mercury. The densities of these moons suggested that water ice is a major component of their composition, and the images returned by the Voyager flyby missions of 1979 suggested that the outer three Galilean moons have an ice crust. During the past year significant evidence for the existence of liquid water in the frigid outer solar system was obtained. Since its arrival at Jupiter in 1995, the Galileo spacecraft has completed 11 orbits of Jupiter on trajectories designed for close encounters with the Galilean moons. The images returned have been of much higher resolution than those returned by the Voyager probes. During an especially close pass of the moon Europa, features as small as 20 km across were seen.

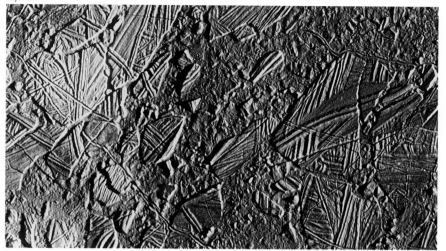

Ice slabs on the surface of Jupiter's moon Europa, imaged by the Galileo spacecraft, show similarities to broken pack ice seen in Earth's polar regions. Such fracturing led some planetary scientists to suspect the presence of a huge ocean of liquid water beneath the ice crust. The suggestion of liquid water on Europa fueled speculation about the possibility of life in the outer solar system.

Images of a region intersected by two large surface fractures revealed a jumble of ice slabs. Planetary scientist Paul Geissler of the University of Arizona found in the Europa images many similarities with broken pack ice seen in Earth's polar regions. He suspected that an ocean of liquid water exists just one to two kilometers beneath the surface of the ice crust. Both Io and Europa have significantly elliptical orbits. The stretching and pulling of these moons by Jupiter's gravity changes throughout the orbital cycle. The internal heat this generates produces almost constant volcanic eruptions on Io. The effects are less severe for Europa, but the heating may keep the interior water in liquid form and account for the moon's fractured surface.

The suggestion of liquid water on Europa fueled speculation about the possibility of life in the outer solar system. Some scientists reasoned that the gravitational stress may produce volcanic vents on the floor of Europa's ocean. On Earth such vents are the location for colonies of life forms that survive by using thermal energy in place of sunlight. The test of these ideas will have to await an actual landing on Europa by an automated probe designed to penetrate the ice crust.

Water was recently discovered much closer to home. NASA's Lunar Prospector probe, which went into lunar orbit in early 1998, detected water ice at the Moon's poles. This confirmed an earlier detection of water by the U.S. Defense Department–NASA Clementine probe. Most likely the lunar ice does not sublimate because it is located in the bottoms of craters that are permanently in shadow. Although the total volume of ice was difficult to estimate, it did appear to be a potential resource for future lunar colonies.

Stellar astronomy

From the Earth's Southern Hemisphere there is a remarkable star that can be seen with the unaided eye. Although it is not especially bright now, for a few months in the year 1843 this star, Eta Carinae, was one of the brightest stars in the night sky. It has roughly 100 times the mass of the Sun, which makes it one of the most massive stars known. During the 1843 outburst it ejected several solar masses of material into space at speeds of almost 1,000 km per second. This ejected material can be seen today with the Hubble Space Telescope as two lobes of gas expanding in opposite directions from the star. Eta Carinae is believed to be a blue supergiant with a luminosity four million times that of the Sun. Its outburst activity is related to the fact that it is entering the latter stages of its evolution.

Astronomers poorly understand this phase in the life of a massive star, and Eta Carinae is one of the few examples available for study. Consequently, they became excited in 1997 as it showed signs of increasing activity. Eta Carinae is a source of X-ray emissions that are believed to be associated with high-speed stellar winds of charged particles driven from the star by its intense light pressure. The X-rays may be produced when this wind collides with and heats external clouds of gas. Another possibility is that the stellar wind is colliding with another stellar wind from a binary companion star. This suggestion cannot be tested directly because at its distance of 7,500 light-years, Eta Carinae appears as an unresolved point. The binary star model might explain the five-year periodicity in its activity level. If the stars move on highly elliptical orbits, the X-ray emission may peak when the stars reach minimum separation at five-year intervals. A peak in the activity level was predicted for late 1997 or early 1998. As if on cue, throughout 1997 there was a steady increase in the X-ray emission. In the binary star model, as the stars draw closer together, their winds collide with more intensity, and the X-ray emission is thereby increased. No one knows if this is correct. Nor do astronomers understand the 85-day periodicity in X-ray flares. The X-ray flux continued to increase in early 1998, and there were changes in the optical and ultraviolet spectra like those seen in previous outbursts. Although the outburst was not as violent as the one in 1843, observations of this event may help astronomers determine if Eta Carinae is a binary system and what the cause of its X-ray emissions is.

The Hubble Space Telescope was used to study an even more massive star located near the center of our galaxy. At visible wavelengths this star is heavily obscured by interstellar dust. The Hubble observations were made in the near-infrared wavelengths that penetrate the dust more freely. Astronomer Don F. Figer of the University of California, Los Angeles, estimated a

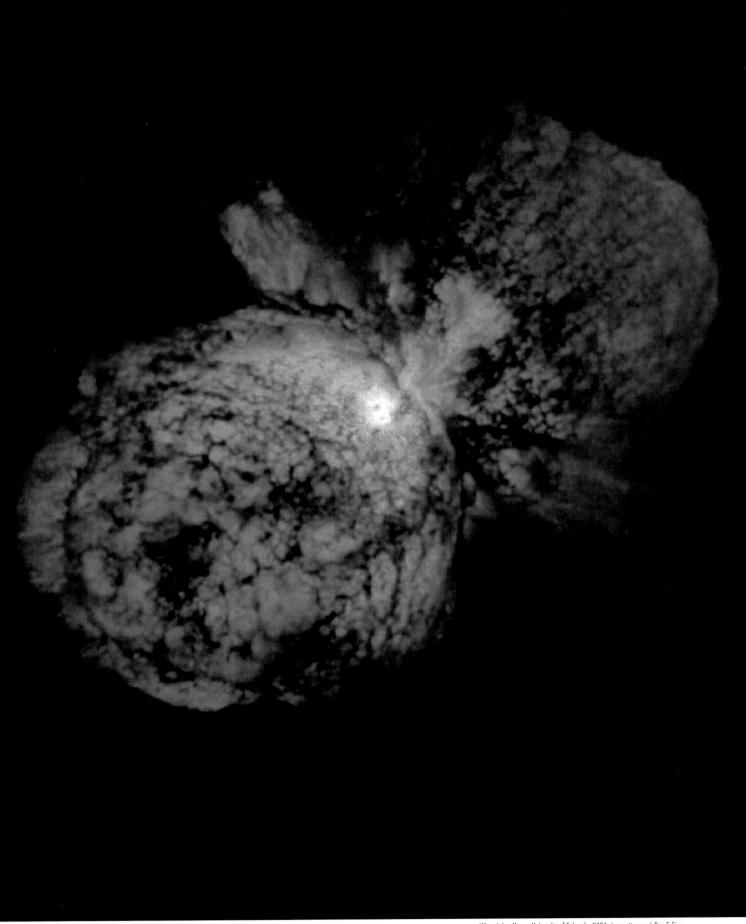

luminosity of 10 million times that of the Sun. This means that despite its distance of 25,000 light-years, the star would be visible to the unaided eye if the interstellar dust was absent. This luminosity implies a mass of at least 100 times that of the Sun and possibly more mass than Eta Carinae. Figer and his colleagues concluded that during the last few million years, strong stellar winds and explosive outbursts have ejected half of the star's original mass into space. This material can be seen in a cloud of material that surrounds the star. The cloud has been nicknamed the Pistol Nebula because of its shape, and the star has been nicknamed the Pistol Star. Stars of such great mass are prime candidates for a far more violent event, called a supernova, which marks the end of a star's life. Explosions triggered by the catastrophic collapse of the massive stellar core cause most of the star to be ejected explosively into space and can outshine 10 million Suns. The collapsed core becomes a neutron star or a black hole.

A supernova was seen in 1987 in the Large Magellanic Cloud, a satellite galaxy of the Milky Way Galaxy. The view from the Hubble Space Telescope revealed that the explosion site was surrounded by three circular rings of gas that were glowing owing to the ionizing radiation from the still-cooling supernova. These rings were not produced by the supernova but were formed long ago by the ejection gas clouds during outburst events like those seen in Eta Carinae and the Pistol Star. The material ejected from the supernova blast left the star at one-tenth the speed of light and is still expanding. It is expected to reach the inner ring soon after the year 2000. This will produce a significant brightening of the ring. There are already some indications that this display of cosmic fireworks has begun. Peter Garnavich and Robert P. Kirshner of the Harvard-Smithsonian Center for Astrophysics and colleagues imaged a spot on the inner edge of the ring that has begun to glow brightly. This spot may be an inward-pointing ring protrusion that was struck early by the expanding supernova blast wave. During the next year or two, there should be many more such hot spots throughout the inner ring.

Extragalactic astronomy

A group of astronomers led by Michael Hauser of the Space Telescope Science Institute accomplished a remarkable feat during the past year. They found a way to detect radiation from nearly all the stars in the visible universe, even those long dead. A star's light travels in all directions into space. Even after the star ends its life and fades away, all the light it ever emitted still exists in space. Eventually, this light is absorbed by interstellar dust grains that are warmed and then reradiate the energy at infrared wavelengths. This infrared radiation is absorbed and reradiated countless times by other dust grains. The net effect is that nearly all starlight is eventually converted to infrared radiation and "stored" in this form. Some of this radiation will escape from the dust in the galaxies and reach intergalactic space. This gives the universe a diffuse infrared background glow. A measurement of this glow provides a census of the stars, both past and present. The Hauser team used data collected by the Cosmic Background Explorer satellite to search for the background glow. They spent more than four years working from a database of two billion infrared measurements of 400,000 locations spread throughout the sky. Because of the bright emissions from other sources, it was difficult to detect the glow. The team mathematically modeled and subtracted the glow from objects in our solar system and from the stars and clouds of dust in our galaxy. The result was a smooth background of residual radiation coming from intergalactic space.

The strength of this emission was larger than expectations based on estimates of the stellar population. In fact, the results suggested that as many as two-thirds of the stars in the universe cannot be seen directly by optical telescopes. It may be that

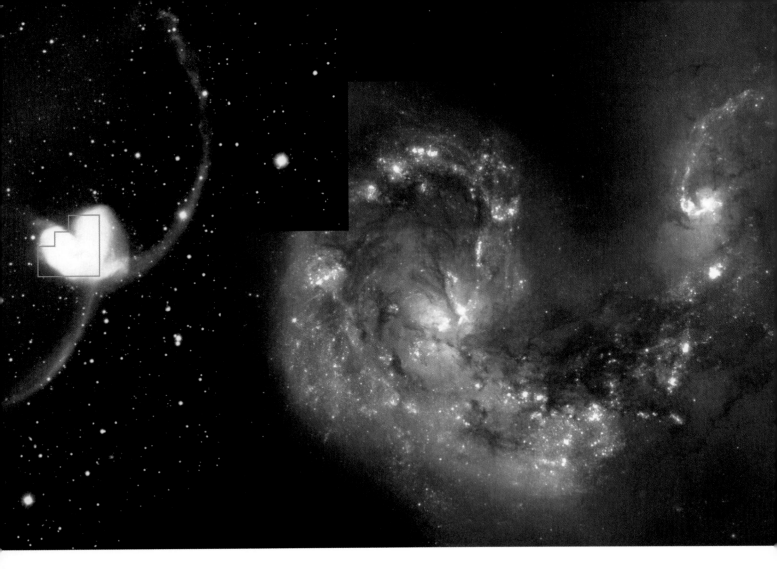

the universe is very dusty and that many stars are thus hidden from view. Alternatively, in the early universe many stars were produced that have long since ended their lives. The results of this study may place important constraints on the models of the universe.

The "most beautiful picture of the year award" arguably goes to the Hubble Space Telescope's image of a galaxy collision. For several decades astronomers had suspected that an unusual object, nicknamed the Antennae Galaxy, was actually two galaxies that were colliding. The nickname was derived from the object's long luminous tails of matter which resemble an insect's antennae. They most likely mark the arcing trajectories the galaxies followed as they fell toward one another.

Galaxy collisions are common. Previous Hubble deep-space images indicated that nearly one-third of all very distant galaxies are involved in collisions and near collisions. The Antennae Galaxy is the nearest example of such an encounter. The Hubble Telescope image shows the collision in remarkable detail, revealing more than 1,000 bright, young star clusters produced by the collision. These were formed when giant interstellar clouds (tens to hundreds of light-years across) were compressed during the collision, which caused them to collapse under their own gravity. After they collapsed, the clouds fragmented and their individual components were heated until they ignited nuclear fusion reactions at their centers to become stars. Star formation caused by galaxy collisions had never before been seen in such detail. It had been commonly believed that compact star clusters, called globular clusters, were produced only when the galaxies formed, soon after the big bang. The images of the Antennae Galaxy clearly showed, however, that they could be formed much later by galaxy collisions.

During the past year the answer to a perplexing mystery began to take shape. More than 20 years ago, Earth satellites launched by the United States to detect the gamma-ray emissions from nuclear testing discovered instead bursts of gamma rays from deep space. These occurred at a rate of one or two per day and typically lasted for a few seconds to a few minutes. Their origin was a mystery. In 1991, hoping to solve the puzzle, NASA launched the Compton Gamma Ray Observatory (GRO) satellite. By 1998 the GRO had detected approximately 1,700 bursts. They were distributed in a completely random pattern across the sky. This strongly argued that the bursters are extragalactic in origin. In order for this conclusion to be confirmed, the bursters must be observed at other wavelengths. For example, if a burst could be detected in visible light, its position might coincide with a known star or galaxy. The problem was that the bursts ended very quickly, which caused the position information from the GRO to be very coarse. In 1996 an Italian-Dutch satellite, BeppoSAX, was launched into orbit. It was able to achieve a 50-fold increase in positional accuracy over the GRO and also established that there is a longer-duration X-ray emission associated with the bursts. This raised the hope that the bursts could be detected with ground-based optical telescopes. In February 1997 the position of a gamma-ray burst in Orion was quickly transmitted to optical astronomers, who found a faint, fading point of light. It appeared at the edge of a faint, fuzzy patch of light that could be a very distant galaxy. Another gamma-ray burst was seen in visible light in May 1997. Although it was not associated with a visible galaxy, its spectrum showed that the light had passed through intervening gas clouds at least four billion light-years away. Consequently, the burst source had to be at least that distant, and so the extragalactic nature of gamma-ray bursters seemed established. Many astronomers believed that the most likely source of the bursters was the collision of a pair of neutron stars, the highly compressed cores of stars that remain after supernova explosions.

The distances between galaxies and between galaxy clusters are increasing with time. This expansion implies that the universe was once much denser and hotter. The big bang marked the start of the expansion. Astronomers can estimate the age of the universe by calculating the time taken for the galaxies to reach their present positions. This requires a measurement of the expansion rate, which in turn requires measurement of the distances to galaxies. In recent years several studies, using variable stars in the galaxies, have determined expansion rates that imply an age of the universe of 8 billion to 14 billion years. Unfortunately, this is at least two billion years less than the estimated age of the oldest stars. This contradiction appeared to be moving toward a resolution on two fronts. First, the data coming from the Hipparcos satellite, which gives very precise distances to nearby stars, indicated that the luminosity of the oldest stars had been overestimated. As a result, their age was also overestimated. Second, a recent study revealed a slower expansion rate for the universe. In order to get the best estimate of the expansion rate, it is necessary to measure the distances to the farthest possible galaxies. A research group led by astronomer Saul Perlmutter of the Lawrence Berkeley National Laboratory, Berkeley, Calif., used ground-based and orbiting telescopes to study supernova explosions in distant galaxies. One particular subtype of supernova is extremely consistent in its luminosity during eruption. By comparing the apparent brightness of such a supernova with its known luminosity, the distance to its host galaxy was found. The expansion rate determined from this work implied an age of the universe of 15 billion years, in good agreement with the revised age of the oldest stars of 13 billion years.

The supernova observations also hinted at a curious effect. The most distant galaxies in the sample appear to be moving away at speeds greater than expected, given their distances. In other words, at great distances the expansion of the universe appears to be accelerating rather than coasting or decelerating. A few months later these observations were confirmed by a research group led by Brian Schmidt of Mount Stromlo and Siding Spring Observatories in Australia. The observations suggest that an unknown repulsive, or "antigravity," force is driving the acceleration. Albert Einstein's general theory of relativity predicts a nonstatic universe, but at the time that he developed the theory, the expansion of the universe had not yet been discovered. To make his theory consistent with a static universe, he added a term, called the cosmological constant, to his equations, but he later dropped it when the expanding universe was recognized. Astronomers were considering the reintroduction of the term to account for the currently observed acceleration, although it would not explain the origin of the new force. If a fundamental antigravity force does exist, the implications would be profound.

In 1997 the field of astronomy recognized the passing of two researchers who were well known to the public. Gene Shoemaker, who died in July, was the co-discoverer (with his wife, Carolyn Spellman Shoemaker, and David H. Levy) of the comet that struck Jupiter in 1994. (*See* SCIENTISTS OF THE YEAR: *Obituaries*.) Years earlier he had fought to convince the scientific community that the craters on the Moon were caused by meteorite impacts. Carl Sagan, who died in December 1996, was the most well-known popularizer of science of our time and a champion of the search for extraterrestrial life and the exploration of our solar system.

—Ronald H. Kaitchuck

See also Feature Articles: STAR MAPS OF THE ANCIENT ORIENT; WARMING UP TO THE OUTER SOLAR SYSTEM.

CHEMISTRY

Particularly important discoveries in chemistry during the past year included insight into a key chemical process that may have enabled life to develop on primordial Earth and the identification of new chemical reactions that promise substantial reductions in chemical waste. The properties of common water continued to fascinate investigators, who confirmed the presence of intact water molecules on the Sun's surface and developed a simple method of making water behave similarly to an organic solvent. Various advances in chemistry also contributed to environmentally friendly automobiles and potential new therapies for cancer, Alzheimer's disease, and stroke, and they raised intriguing questions about the relevance of extraterrestrial organic material found in a meteorite to the fundamental biochemistry of all living things on Earth.

INORGANIC CHEMISTRY

Bioinorganic chemistry

The origin of life on Earth is one of the major mysteries confronting science. The gaining of a detailed understanding of how life developed is clouded by the extreme complexity of the environment present on Earth several billion years ago and by the fact that most of the evidence has long disappeared. Classic experiments in the 1950s demonstrated that electric discharges in a mixture of methane, ammonia, and water result in the formation of several amino acids and other organic compounds that are necessary for life. It is now thought, however, that the early atmosphere consisted mostly of carbon dioxide, nitrogen, and water and contained very

little hydrogen. This mix of chemicals could not have led to the organic compounds required for life under the conditions that were present on the surface of primordial Earth. Accordingly, there has been significant interest in developing new theories that can explain how life arose.

In the past year Günter Wächtershäuser of Munich, Ger., and Claudia Huber of the Technical University of Munich described a chemical system that promotes the formation of methyl thioacetate under conditions that are present in volcanoes and undersea hydrothermal vents. The researchers sought to develop a primordial model for the reductive acetyl-coenzyme A (acetyl-CoA) pathway found in living organisms. Probing the origins of this pathway is important to understanding the beginnings of life, since the acetyl-CoA process involves the formation of a carbon-carbon bond. The assembly of carbon-carbon bonds is a critical step in the synthesis of more complex organic molecules that are required for life.

The acetyl-CoA pathway entails the reaction of coenzyme A, carbon monoxide (CO), and a molecule that can donate a methyl group (CH_3-) and is promoted by an enzyme containing a nickel-iron-sulfur (Ni-Fe-S) reaction center. In present-day organisms carbon monoxide for the reaction is formed enzymatically from carbon dioxide or obtained from the environment, and the methyl group originates from an organic nitrogen compound able to donate one. In a primordial model all components would have to be available in the environment. Near volcanoes and underwater hydrothermal vents, the concentration of methane thiol (CH_3SH) is high. CH_3SH was therefore reasoned to be the most

likely source of a methyl group. Furthermore, iron(II) sulfide (FeS) and nickel(II) sulfide (NiS) are common minerals near volcanoes and hydrothermal vents. Finally, carbon monoxide is present in significant concentrations in volcanic emissions. Therefore, all of the ingredients for a carbon fixation pathway should have been present on primordial Earth.

The researchers found that treatment of CH_3SH with CO in the presence of a mixture of FeS and NiS in water at 100° C (212° F)—conditions intended to mimic a hydrothermal vent or a volcano—led to significant formation of acetic acid (as much as 40% yield based on CH_3SH). Acetic acid was proposed to arise through hydrolysis of a nickel-bound thioacetate ligand to form thioacetic acid (CH_3COSH), which rapidly reacts with water to form acetic acid and hydrogen sulfide. (A ligand is an atom or molecular group attached to a metal atom.) By contrast, separate use of FeS and NiS to promote the reaction led to small yields of acetic acid (no more than 15%). The results indicated that FeS and NiS interact to form a species that promotes the reaction. A mechanism proposed by the researchers is diagrammed in the Figure on the opposite page. Simple chemical reactions are proposed to lead to the penultimate Ni-Fe-S species that contains a CH_3COS group, which can react with water to afford acetic acid or with CH_3SH to give methyl thioacetate. This system therefore represents a primordial mimic of the reductive acetyl-CoA pathway and gives insight into how this process may have evolved.

The implications of the study are several. First, the acetyl-CoA pathway may be derived from very ancient processes that

Primordial Mimic of Acetyl-CoA Pathway

In the proposed mechanism, acetic acid or methyl thioacetate is produced from methane thiol (CH_3SH), carbon monoxide (CO), and water (H_2O) in the presence of a molecular species formed from iron(II) sulfide (FeS) and nickel(II) sulfide (NiS). The sulfur atoms (S) that are shown bonded to Ni and Fe are also bonded to another Ni or Fe atom or to a hydrogen atom.

predate life itself. Furthermore, the formation of activated acetyl fragments (methyl thioacetate, acetic acid, and thioacetate ligands) in water deposits near volcanic activity may have been a condition that enabled the development of life. Finally, the results suggest that life as we know it may have been able to arise on other planets in subterranean areas that contain liquid water, even though conditions on the surface may be inhospitable.

"Fluorous" organometallic chemistry

A major recent theme in synthetic chemistry has been to develop procedures that produce less chemical waste than existing protocols. Heightened awareness of the environmental effects of chemical production has led to considerable interest in developing chemical processes that use fluorocarbon solvents (organic compounds composed of carbon and fluorine). Fluoro-

carbons are appealing solvents because they are nontoxic. Moreover, whereas at room temperature liquid fluorocarbons do not form solutions with many common organic solvents, at higher temperatures they do so. Hence, if a reactant that promotes a desired reaction can be modified so that it is highly soluble in fluorocarbon solvents, it should be possible to carry out the reaction in a mixed solution of fluorocarbon and organic solvents at a higher temperature and then separate the fluorocarbon-soluble reactant from the organic product simply by cooling the reaction mixture and allowing the two solvents to separate into layers. This strategy is particularly appealing when an expensive catalyst is employed, since it is highly desirable to reuse the catalyst. (A catalyst speeds up a chemical reaction without being consumed itself.)

Several reports in the past year indicated the feasibility of using fluorocarbon-

soluble organometallic catalysts. (An organometallic compound contains at least one direct metal-carbon bond.) This work may lead to synthesis procedures that produce less solvent waste and allow more efficient recycling of precious metal catalysts.

A research team led by John A. Gladysz of the University of Utah and Istvan T. Horvath of Exxon Research and Engineering investigated the fundamental reactivity of several organometallic compounds that were modified to be highly soluble in fluorocarbon solvents. The chemists suggested using the term *fluorous* to refer to reactions that are conducted in fluorocarbon solvents, by analogy with *aqueous*, which refers to reactions conducted in water. They initially studied derivatives of a rhodium compound having the formula $RhCl(P(C_6H_5)_3)_3$, which is widely used to catalyze many types of organic reactions in traditional organic solvents such as ethanol or benzene. $RhCl(P(C_6H_5)_3)_3$ is completely insoluble in fluorocarbon solvents. If, however, the $P(C_6H_5)_3$ groups are all replaced by fluorine-containing $P(CH_2CH_2(CF_2)_5CF_3)_3$ groups, then the compound that results from the replacement, $RhCl(P(CH_2CH_2(CF_2)_5CF_3)_3)_3$, is extremely soluble in fluorous media and essentially insoluble in common organic solvents. The modified compound was shown to be a very effective catalyst in fluorous media for several transformations of organic compounds and thereby demonstrated that useful reactions can be conducted with this approach. Importantly, the investigators were able to extract almost all of the reaction products with organic solvents while leaving the catalyst dissolved in the fluorocarbon solvent. This recovered solution proved reusable without appreciable loss of catalytic activity.

The team of researchers also examined the iridium-containing complex $IrCl(CO)(P(CH_2CH_2(CF_2)_5CF_3)_3)_2$ in fluorous media to see if large differences existed in basic chemical reactivity compared with reactions run in traditional organic solvents. Owing to the extremely nonpolar nature of fluorinated solvents, reactions that involve charged transition states were found to be extremely slow. Surprisingly, certain reactions that do not involve charged or polar transition states were also found to proceed very slowly when they were carried out in fluorous media. These findings will be important for the future development of organometallic compounds that have optimized reactivity in fluorocarbon solvents.

A research team led by Gianluca Pozzi of the University of Milan reported that a cobalt porphyrin-based catalyst with perfluoroalkyl groups bonded to the porphyrin catalyzed the oxidation of several organic compounds with molecular oxygen when the reaction was conducted in fluorous media. This report is significant because oxygen's nonpolar character makes it extremely soluble in fluorocarbons. Therefore, it should be possible to achieve high concentrations of oxygen in fluorous solvents, which should greatly facilitate oxidation reactions.

New molecules

One of the holy grails of inorganic chemistry has been to synthesize a compound that contains a bond between a metal atom and the carbon-hydrogen bond of a free alkane. (Alkanes are hydrocarbon compounds whose atoms are joined together only by single bonds.) In the past year a research team led by Christopher A. Reed of the University of Southern California and Peter D.W. Boyd of the University of Auckland, N.Z., described the synthesis and characterization of the first such compound. An iron porphyrin complex was crystallized from a solution containing the alkane compound heptane to afford crystals in which heptane was coordinated to the central iron atom in the porphyrin ring. Coordination of heptane to the iron center was demonstrated by determination of the three-dimensional structure by X-ray crystallography and was further supported by calculations on model complexes. The existence of the complex suggests that even the most weakly basic functional groups can act as ligands of metals under the right conditions.

A particularly noteworthy new compound reported in the past year was $Na_2[ArGa{\equiv}GaAr]$, in which Ar represents a 2,6-disubstituted phenyl group. The claim for its unprecedented gallium-gallium triple bond was based on a very short gallium-gallium bond length as determined by X-ray crystallography. This report, by Gregory H. Robinson of the University of Georgia, received immediate worldwide attention and was the subject of both praise and skepticism. A molecular orbital study published by Karl W. Klinkhammer of the University of Stuttgart, Ger., which described the bonding within the molecule, basically supported the claim for the presence of the $Ga{\equiv}Ga$ bond, whereas others argued that its presence had yet to be conclusively established. Molecules such as $Na_2[ArGa{\equiv}GaAr]$ are extremely interesting to chemists because they illustrate deficiencies in the present understanding of chemical bonding. Compounds with short gallium-gallium bonds will certainly be the subject of much study in the next several years, and this research effort should lead to a better understanding of the bonding.

Inorganic cluster compounds containing as many as a few dozen metal atoms have been of significant interest because they represent a bridge between individual molecules and bulk solids. Although cluster compounds of many different metals have been prepared and studied since the 1960s, the chemistry of cluster compounds containing lanthanide elements remains poorly developed. (The lanthanides are elements with atomic numbers from 58 to 71.) John G. Brennan and his research group at Rutgers University, New Brunswick, N.J., reported new ways of synthesizing cluster compounds of the lanthanide element samarium. The clusters contain as many as eight samarium atoms and are held together by bridging selenium or sulfur atoms. The achievement is important because lanthanide elements have extremely useful optical properties. For example, infrared light emitted from erbium(III) ions is used to carry signals over fiber-optic networks. (Erbium, with an atomic number of 68, is a lanthanide element.) The intensity of the light emitted from single erbium(III) ions is thought to be significantly higher than that emitted from small clusters of the ions. The availability of lanthanide cluster compounds should help researchers understand how small aggregates of lanthanide metals affect the photochemical properties of the individual metal centers.

—Charles H. Winter

ORGANIC CHEMISTRY

Chemistry on the Internet

New Web sites dedicated to researching and teaching chemistry appeared on the Internet in the past year. Eastman Kodak, for example, developed the first totally Web-based laboratory information system to provide access to a variety of information for in-house use over the company intranet. General informational sites included the Intercollegiate Organic Chemistry site (http://orgchem.chem.uconn.edu/colleges/orgchem.html) developed by Michael B. Smith of the University of Connecticut and an on-line tutoring service using America Online's Academic Assistance Center. Several major chemistry journals introduced on-line versions, including *The Journal of Organic Chemistry,* and several chemical supply companies maintained Web sites through which their products could be purchased directly.

Chemotherapeutic advances

The treatment of asthma, which remained a serious problem for millions worldwide, benefited from new drug-based approaches that work to counter the body's natural

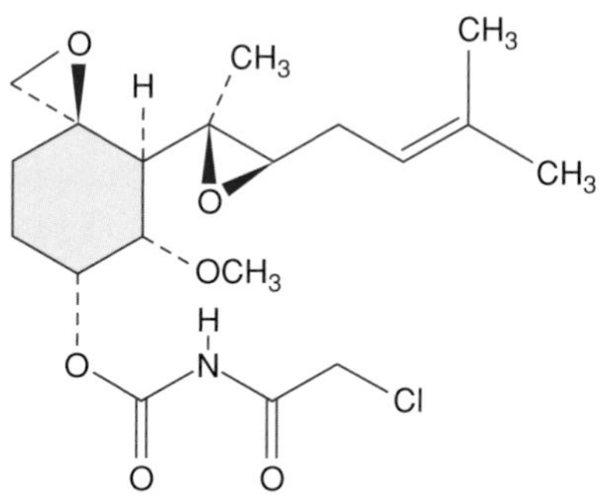

1   TNP-470

mediators of inflammation, such as leukotrienes, thromboxanes, and phosphodiesterases III and IV. Several new drugs called β_2-adrenergic agents were designed to treat the symptoms of atopy, or immediate hypersensitivity reaction, associated with asthma by acting on the body's β-adrenergic system and targeting β-receptors.

Samuel Danishefsky, Philip O. Livingston, and Kenneth O. Lloyd of Memorial Sloan-Kettering Cancer Center, New York City, developed a potential new anticancer vaccine in which a synthetically prepared carbohydrate was linked to a carrier pro-

tein. The carbohydrate, which is an analog of a structure found on the cell surface of certain kinds of tumors, was intended to trigger a natural immune response to the cancerous cells.

As cancerous tumors enlarge and proliferate, they stimulate angiogenesis, the growth of new blood vessels into the tumor mass, such that cells even deep within the tumor are nourished. Two drugs, TNP-470 (*see* 1) and ovalicin (*see* 2), were developed as antiangiogenesis agents; they act by interrupting a tumor's blood supply and thus starving it.

Donepezil, a new drug developed by the Tokyo-based company Eisai and sold under the brand name Aricept (*see* 3), was introduced to treat Alzheimer's disease. Joining tacrine (Cognex), which Parke-Davis introduced in the early 1990s, donepezil became the second agent available for improving memory and cognition in early stages of the disease. A new compound developed by NeoTherapeutics and dubbed AIT-082 (*see* 4 on p. 260) promotes nerve regeneration in areas of the brain associated with memory and thus appeared to hold promise for treating Alzheimer's. Gary S. Lynch of the University of California, Irvine, and Gary A.

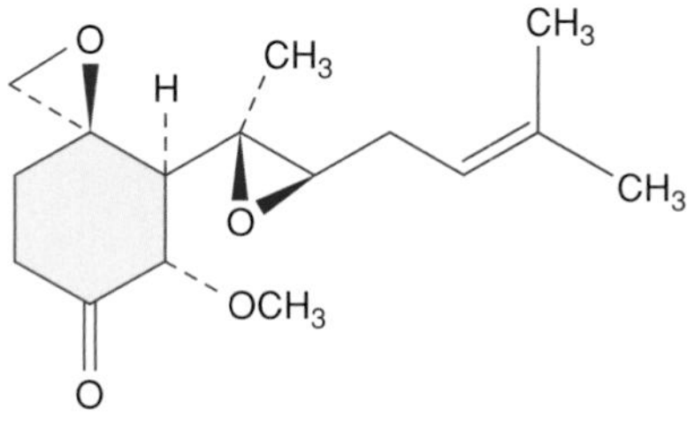

2   ovalicin

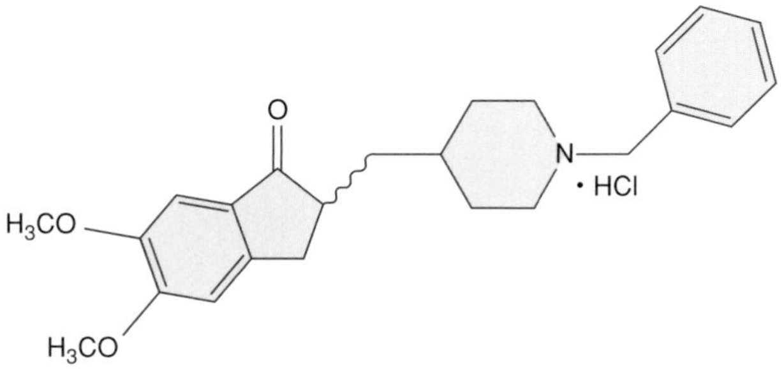

3   donepezil (Aricept)

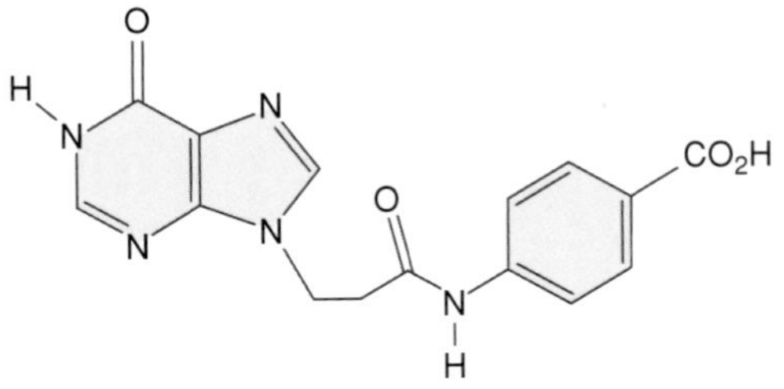

4   AIT-082

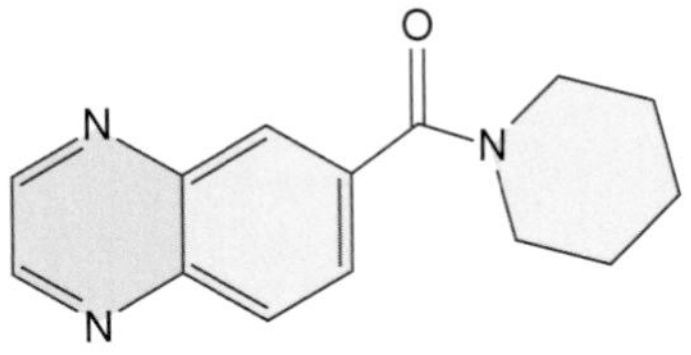

5   CX516

Rogers of Cortex Pharmaceuticals developed CX516 (*see* 5), which was designed to improve memory in people with Alzheimer's by enhancing the action of an ion-channel receptor that regulates the movement of calcium ions into nerve cells. Calcium ions are critical in the formation of certain kinds of memories.

Advances in other areas of therapeutic medicine included the development by Gilead Sciences of a compound code-named GS-4104 (*see* 6), which may prevent or treat all types of influenza, since it inhibits a key enzyme needed for replication of the flu virus in host cells. An immunosuppressant drug analog, GPI-1046 (*see* 7), prepared by Joseph P. Steiner of Guilford Pharmaceuticals, was found to stimulate regeneration of injured nerves without inhibiting the immune system.

Catalysts and catalytic processes

The development of new reagents that catalyze chemical transformations continued to play an important role in organic chemistry. Chemist Ronald Breslow of Columbia University, New York City, developed a synthetic manganese porphyrin catalyst containing four attached cyclodextrins that mimics the process by which steroids are oxidized by the liver's natural cytochrome P-450 enzyme system. K. Barry Sharpless of the Scripps Research Institute, La Jolla, Calif., discovered the first catalytic reaction for efficient epoxidation, or conversion into epoxides, of alkenes under nonacidic conditions, using hydrogen peroxide as the oxidant and methyltrioxorhenium containing pyridine ligands as the catalyst.

A new catalyst—prepared from three molecules of enantiomeric 1,1'-bi-2-naphtholate anions and three lithium ions coordinating a lanthanum(III) ion—was developed by Masakatsu Shibasaki of the University of Tokyo and Hiroaki Sasai of Osaka (Japan) University for enantioselective aldol condensations that accept unmodified ketones. (Enantioselective synthesis reactions preferentially yield one mirror-image isomer, or enantiomer, of a compound over its counterpart.) Guillermo C. Bazan of the University of Rochester, N.Y., used ethoxy boratabenzene as a catalyst to convert ethylene to 1-alkenes with 100% selectivity; the new process was cheaper and safer than those using current catalysts. Craig M. Jensen of the University of Hawaii at Manoa, William C. Kaska of the University of California, Santa Barbara, and Alan S. Goldman of Rutgers University, New Brunswick, N.J., developed a five-coordinate iridium catalyst stable to 200° C (390° F) that converts alkanes to alkenes (alkane dehydrogenation). Istvan Marko of the Catholic University of Louvain, Belg., used a copper(I) chloride solution in toluene in the presence of di-*tert*-butyl azodicarboxylate to oxidize alcohols to aldehydes or ketones, and Harvard University chemist Eric Jacobsen developed a cobalt(III) catalyst that, with water, can separate a mixture of two epoxide enantiomers into its components. That catalysts need not be complex species was demonstrated by Shantanu Chowdhury and Sujit Roy of the Indian Institute of Chemical Technology, Hyderabad, who used lithium acetate to catalyze the classic Hunsdiecker reaction, avoiding the need to boil solutions of potentially hazardous silver, thallium, or lead salts.

Synthesis of complex molecules

The total synthesis of important organic molecules was, as always, of major impor-

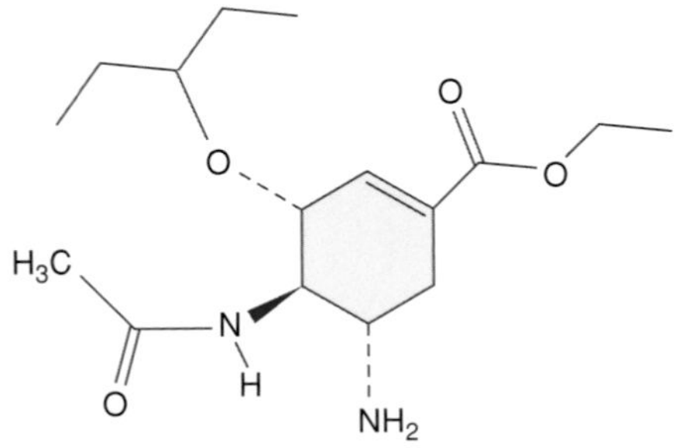

6   GS-4104

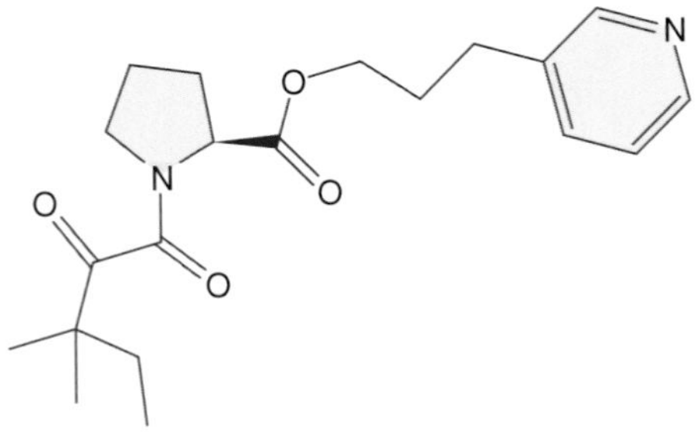

7   GPI-1046

tance in organic chemistry. Trevor C. Mc-Morris of the University of California, San Diego, synthesized hydroxymethylacylfulvene, an antitumor drug that was being evaluated in clinical trials. Shinichiro Nishimura of Hokkaido (Japan) University, synthesized a sequential glycopeptide polymer consisting of a tripeptide repeating unit, the first example of the total synthesis of a biological antifreeze glycoprotein that protects some fish against freezing in polar seas.

David H. Farb of Boston University showed that a synthetic analog of pregnanone sulfate, a naturally occurring steroid implicated in nerve cell function, protected nerve cells from damage caused by overstimulation of the N-methyl-D-aspartate ion-channel receptor, which made it potentially useful for treating stroke. A new synthesis of N-acyl amino acids was developed by Matthias Beller of the Technical University of Munich, Ger., using a high-pressure, palladium-catalyzed reaction of aldehydes, amides, and carbon monoxide.

Fundamental principles

Nobel laureate Donald J. Cram of the University of California, Los Angeles, stabilized and studied o-benzyne in solution by trapping it in a guest-host molecule. Takuzo Aida of the University of Tokyo designed a porphyrin molecule with "chirality memory" that recognized the chirality, or handedness, of certain asymmetric acids and "remembered" their absolute configuration after the acid was removed.

K. Peter C. Vollhardt of the University of California, Berkeley, probed the poten-tial of light-energy storage devices based on the reversible photochemical isomerization of (fulvene)tetracarbonyldiruthenium complexes. John A. Gladysz of the University of Utah and Istvan T. Horvath of Exxon Research and Engineering observed the HCO+ ion spectroscopically in the condensed phase under high pressure by reacting carbon monoxide with "super acid" (HF-SbF$_5$).

Organic chemical reactions

Thomas A. Moore, Ana L. Moore, and Devens Gust of Arizona State University prepared an electron acceptor (a polyene resembling carotene) and linked it to a light-sensitive "trigger" compound (a synthetic tetraarylporphyrin). This system, which mimicked natural photosynthesis, might be used to mimic a variety of energy-linked biological processes.

Nicos A. Petasis of the University of Southern California developed a convergent synthesis route to amino acids, including nonnatural amino acids. (Convergent approaches involve the preparation of precursor fragments followed by their combination to form the final product. They contrast with linear approaches, in which a reactant is converted to a product in a stepwise series of reactions.) James D. Wuest of the University of Montreal prepared a compound that crystallizes in a three-dimensional network in which a tetrahedral building block is held in position by 16 hydrogen bonds to identical units. The network contains prominent channels and essentially behaves as an "organic zeolite." (Traditional zeolites are inorganic compounds whose crystalline structure is riddled with tiny channels, which makes the materials useful as catalysts and molecular sieves.)

Richard G. Compton and Stephen G. Davies of the University of Oxford applied ultrasound to promote the electrochemical hydrogenation of water-immiscible compounds containing carbon-carbon double or triple bonds. Paul Knochel and Stefan Berger of the Philipps University of Marburg, Ger., developed organozinc reagents that transferred all of the desired alkyl substituent to aldehyde or ketone substrates and were superior to the traditional R$_2$Zn reagents. University of Montreal chemist Stephen Hanessian developed a new intramolecular reaction for forming cyclopropane rings based on a C$_5$-alkoxymethyl-N-protected 2-pyrrolidinone derivative (derived from pyroglutamate). Process chemists successfully and safely scaled up an aromatic nitration process by adding 90% nitric acid to a trifluoroacetic acid solution of the substrate at 0°–5° C (32°–41° F). Sulfuric acid-nitric acid mixtures traditionally used for nitrations often gave very poor results.

Peripheral areas

John R. Cronin and Sandra Pizzarello of Arizona State University found that four α-methyl amino acids found in the Murchison meteorite, a carbonaceous chondrite known to contain amino acids not produced on Earth, show a 2–9% enrichment in their L enantiomers, one of their two mirror-image isomers. Similar results were reported by Michael H. Engel of the University of Oklahoma and Stephen A. Macko of the University of Virginia. Because only L enantiomers of amino acids are incorporated into proteins made by life on Earth and because nonbiological chemical processes are expected to produce equal amounts of L and D enantiomers, the observed enrichment raised intriguing questions about the extraterrestrial process that may have generated it and its relevance to the handedness that is ubiquitous in life processes on Earth.

Improved reagents for visualizing fingerprints were reported by Madeleine M. Joullié of the University of Pennsylvania. Substituted 1,2-indandiones such as 5-(2-thienyl)ninhydrin react with nitrogen-containing molecules in fingerprint residues to form a fluorescent pigment and are useful reagents for fingerprint development through fluorescent pigment formation. Advances in organic chemistry can be very practical, as was exemplified by scientists at Ciba Specialty Chemicals, Basel, Switz., who developed a method for solubilizing paint pigments that are intrinsically insoluble in paint application media by converting them to "latent" pigments containing lipophilic (fat-seeking) functional groups.

Awards

Columbia University's Samuel Danishefsky received the Arthur C. Cope Award, the American Chemical Society's highest honor, for his synthesis of numerous organic compounds, including naturally occurring substances with important pharmaceutical properties, and for the development of novel approaches to organic syntheses. The James Flack Norris Award in Physical Organic Chemistry went to Peter J. Stang of the University of Utah for investigations of chemical-reaction mechanisms and, especially, for research into supramolecular chemistry—methods

of constructing giant assemblies of molecules having unique properties and applications, including nanometer-scale machinery. Joanna S. Fowler of Brookhaven National Laboratory, Upton, N.Y., took the Francis P. Garvan–John M. Olin Medal for interdisciplinary work in chemistry, biology, and medicine that provided insights into brain biochemistry, the transmission of nerve signals, and drug action.

—Michael B. Smith

See also Year in Review: MATERIALS SCIENCE AND ENGINEERING: *Polymers.*

PHYSICAL CHEMISTRY
Observing fast chemical events

The fundamental processes in chemical reactions, the breaking and forming of chemical bonds, happen so fast that the blink of an eye is an eternity by comparison. Such events take place in a trillionth of a second or less, on a timescale of hundreds of femtoseconds (a femtosecond is 10^{-15} second). In order to probe these ultrafast events, experimenters have designed laser systems that produce femtosecond pulses of light in the visible, infrared, and ultraviolet parts of the spectrum. Spectroscopy using these short pulses samples the electronic and vibrational properties of molecules. It does not, however, directly observe the positions of atoms in molecules during reactions. To follow changes in molecular structure during reactions, researchers need fast methods that make use of diffraction effects.

The diffraction of X-rays and electrons has long been used to produce three-dimensional pictures of the locations of atoms in crystalline solids and in gas-phase

molecules. Such experiments, however, typically have used continuous beams that result in a picture representing an average over time. Pulsed X-ray and electron sources have been built that produce pulses measured in nanoseconds (a nanosecond is 10^{-9} second), but these pulses are still too long to observe the basic processes involved in chemical reactions.

In the past year French researchers succeeded in extending the use of X-rays into the femtosecond regime to probe the short-timescale behavior of matter. Christian Rischel and Antoine Rousse of the Laboratory of Applied Optics, École Polytechnique, Palaiseau, led the study, aided by French and German co-workers. They observed atomic-scale motions leading to disordering of a film of a peanut-oil derivative, cadmium arachidate. This salt of a fatty acid normally forms highly ordered arrays of molecules on a surface, and their degree of order can be observed by the intense reflections that they produce when illuminated with X-rays. The investigators heated the molecular film with femtosecond pulses of infrared laser light. The energy imparted to the film caused the ordered atomic alignments to become disordered. Part of the same infrared pulse was diverted to strike a piece of silicon, which produced an ultrashort pulse of X-rays. The X-ray pulse was returned to the film and used to monitor its degree of atomic order. By making progressive changes in the delay between the infrared pulse hitting the film and the arrival of the subsequent X-ray pulse, the investigators could follow the disordering process on a femtosecond timescale. Significantly, their work showed that X-ray diffraction on an extremely short timescale is possible, us-

Figure 1: Theory and experiment suggest that the most stable form of the six-molecule water cluster is a cage structure held together by eight hydrogen bonds (dashed lines).

Cage Structure for Six-Molecule Water Cluster

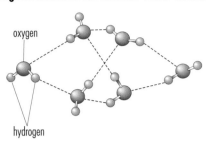

oxygen

hydrogen

ing relatively simple tabletop equipment rather than the vastly more complex and expensive synchrotron light sources that heretofore had been the only route to short X-ray pulses.

The location of atoms in molecules can also be mapped by means of electron diffraction. Experiments on samples in the gas phase previously had pushed the time resolution of this method into the nanosecond regime, but the clock stopped there because of difficulties in accurately determining the start of the experiment and in measuring the very low electron intensities involved. In the past year a new apparatus for very fast electron diffraction was reported by a group headed by Ahmed Zewail of the California Institute of Technology (Caltech). Like the French workers, the American group used a femtosecond laser pulse both to cause a change and to observe it. In this case the laser pulse removed an iodine atom from diiodomethane (CH_2I_2) and generated a short pulse of electrons that was used to determine the relative locations of the atoms in the molecule. The researchers were able to observe changes in electron diffraction with a delay of only 20 picoseconds (a picosecond is 10^{-12} second), corresponding to the loss of one iodine atom from the molecule. Actual observation of the process of carbon-iodine bond breaking, however, will necessitate a time resolution of less than one picosecond, and it remains to be seen whether such ultrafast electron diffraction experiments are possible.

Water in the laboratory and on the Sun

The details of how water performs its vital functions of dissolving solids and support-

ing life on Earth are topics that continue to engender considerable research. One fact that has long puzzled physical chemists is that the dipole moment of the molecules in liquid water—a measure of the distribution of electronic charge between the oxygen and hydrogens atoms—is about 40% larger than that of an isolated water molecule. This difference raises the question of how many water molecules must be clustered together to achieve the dipole value of the bulk liquid. A team of chemists including D.C. Clary of University College London, J.K. Gregory of the University of Cambridge, and K. Liu, M.G. Brown, and R.J. Saykally of the University of California, Berkeley, followed the evolution of the dipole moment in increasingly large clusters of water molecules via highlevel quantum mechanical calculations and spectroscopic measurements of the clusters in electric fields. They found that the dipole moment increases to the bulk value in clusters having as few as six water molecules. The structure of the six-molecule cluster appeared to have a cage structure similar to that of one of the phases of ice (*see* Figure 1).

One of the last places anyone might expect to find intact water molecules is on the surface of the Sun, where the temperature is typically 5,500° C (10,000° F). At that temperature a water molecule should be broken up into a hydroxyl (OH) radical and a hydrogen atom, or possibly into an oxygen atom and two hydrogen atoms. The existence of water on the Sun in sunspots, where the temperature is somewhat lower (about 2,900° C, or 5,300° F), was in fact reported in 1995, and new experiments by Peter Bernath of the University of Waterloo, Ont., Lloyd Wallace of the National

Optical Observatories, Tucson, Ariz., and a group led by Jonathan Tennyson of University College London supported the earlier claim. The scientists compared the spectrum of water in sunspots with that obtained in the laboratory. However, because the maximum temperature that can be reached in the laboratory is only about 2,000° C (3,600° F), they also needed to use extensive quantum mechanical calculations. The calculations were especially challenging because when a molecule is very hot, its nuclei move through large distances as the molecule undergoes massive vibrations. The results confirmed the existence of water in sunspots as the latest exotic astronomical locale for what most people regard as a very terrestrial substance.

Does the double helix behave like a wire?

The question of how electrons move through large organic molecules, such as proteins and the double helix of DNA, has been an issue since the 1970s. In the case of proteins, scientists believe that electrons move slowly along the bonds that make up the protein backbone via a low-efficiency quantum mechanical process known as tunneling. In the case of DNA, however, some researchers have argued that its unique helical structure may allow electrons to move much more freely. The movement would still involve electron tunneling, but the tunneling would occur much more easily via areas of high electron density above and below the ring-shaped bases that form the core of the DNA helix. The way in which these areas, the so-called π orbitals, stack up along the

Figure 2: A short DNA helix with a "mutation," a thymine dimer (TT) defect, is attached at one end to an electron-accepting rhodium (Rh) complex. When the system is exposed to visible light, the mutational damage is healed, and an electron is conducted down the helix to the complex.

helix would make the DNA more like a molecular wire.

A major proponent of this idea, Caltech's Jacqueline Barton, together with Peter Dandliker and Erik Holmlin, produced new evidence for a high-conductivity path in DNA. They made short DNA helices having a built-in defect in the form of a pair of adjoining bases of thymine bound directly together, a configuration called a dimer. Such a mutation can be produced in the DNA of human cells by ultraviolet radiation. They also inserted an electron-accepting complex of the metal rhodium at one end of the helix. When the system was exposed to visible light, the rhodium complex was triggered to acquire an electron from the helix. Remarkably, the electron apparently originated from the splitting apart of the thymine dimer, which was positioned at a distance from the metal complex, and was conducted down the helix to the complex (see Figure 2). Effectively the mutational damage to the DNA was healed. Furthermore, the movement of the electron did not appear to be affected by how far the metal complex was from the dimer, although it was impeded by disruptions that the researchers built into the stacking of the base pairs in some of their test samples. All of this evidence argues for a facile transport of electrons along the DNA helix.

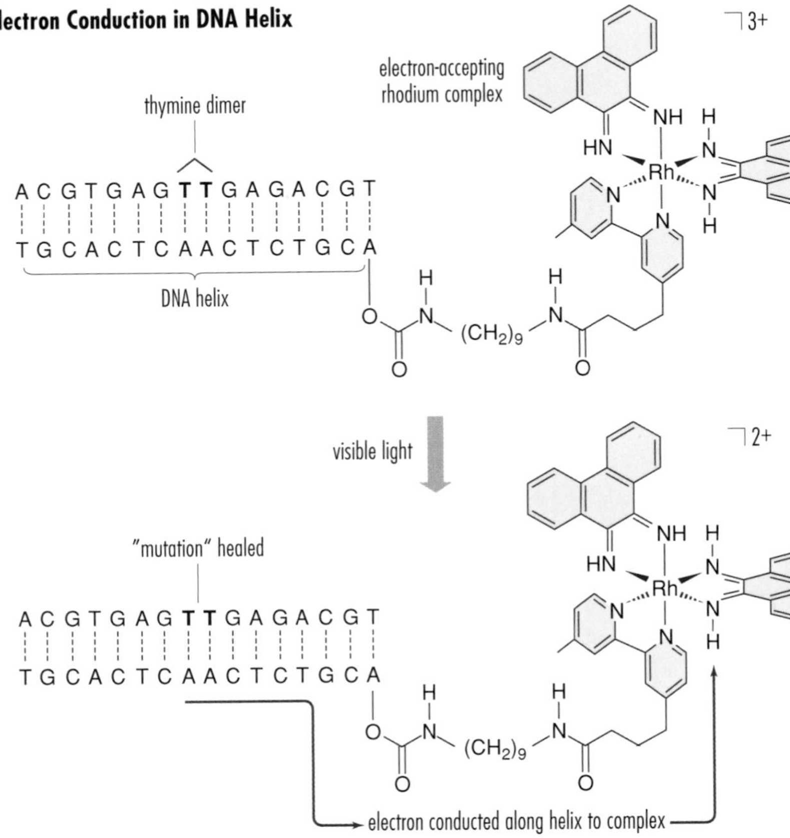

On the other hand, other scientists reported evidence that appears to argue that the DNA helix is a poor conductor. For instance, David Beratan and Satyam Priyadarshy of the University of Pittsburgh, Pa., and Steven Risser of East Texas State University calculated very slow electron transfer rates for the sort of systems used by Barton. They argued that the large sep-

aration between the π-orbital systems of the bases in DNA cannot allow fast transport. In addition, experiments by Bengt Norden, Eimer Tuite, and Per Lincoln of the Chalmers University of Technology, Göteborg, Swed., and by Thomas Meade of Caltech produced evidence for poor electron conduction in DNA.

One of the difficulties in this area of research had been in preparing enough suitable DNA test material that could be used by more than one research group. By 1998 preparative methods had improved such that comparative studies of this sort were becoming possible. If theorists and experimentalists can work together, they

may be able to better understand how DNA becomes damaged and, more important, how it can be repaired.

—Philip R. Watson

APPLIED CHEMISTRY
Tracing explosives

Calls for incorporating characteristic "taggants" into explosives to make their origin traceable even after detonation have been publicized for decades, and they became more strident after the bombings in Oklahoma City, Okla., in 1995 and in Atlanta, Ga., during the 1996 Olympics. First produced in the early 1970s in the U.S., taggants in the form of chips designed to be mixed with the explosive drew criticism that they could cause the explosives to detonate prematurely. Despite such claims, taggants have been required by law to be used in Switzerland since 1980. In 1997 10 firms presented plans for tagging as a counterterrorism measure before a U.S. National Research Council (NRC) panel.

One plan, proposed by Isotag LLC, Houston, Texas, and Cambridge Isotope Laboratories, Inc., Andover, Mass., involved replacing normal isotopes of hydrogen, carbon, nitrogen, and oxygen in one or more of the molecular components of the explosive with stable, nonradioactive isotopes of these elements differing only slightly in atomic weight. Millions of different codes can be made from the isotopic combinations, which can readily be distinguished by a mass spectrometer. According to Isotag cofounder Manny Gonzalez, compromised safety is not an issue "because we tag with the same stuff that's in there already." Two test blasts in the Nevada desert with a ton each of isotope-tagged ammonium nitrate and fuel oil (the explosive mixture used in the Oklahoma City blast) demonstrated that the tags were detectable and their coded information unaffected by the explosions.

Another plan, advanced by Poulter Laboratory, SRI International, Menlo Park, Calif., involved taggants called upconverting phosphors—particles containing pairs of rare-earth elements that on irradiation with an infrared laser emit visible light of different colors. One rare-earth element in each pair absorbs low-energy infrared photons and transfers the energy to the other element, which then emits higher-energy

visible-light photons. According to Poulter senior chemical engineer Nina Mufti, different combinations of rare-earth element pairs can provide unique spectral signatures, and only a little taggant is required for marking several tons of explosive.

The NRC panel failed to reach any definite conclusions or decisions, the main difficulties being expense, requirement for an elaborate tracking system, legal liability, and the possibility that other measures would be more effective.

Cleaning up car exhausts

In their efforts to lower air pollution, scientists and engineers have sought improvements in the catalytic converters that transform polluting automobile exhaust gases such as hydrocarbons and carbon monoxide into more acceptable compounds such as carbon dioxide and water vapor. Converters on new cars can remove as much as 98% of the polluting gases, but because they do not function well until they are warm, they allow as much as 80% of emissions to escape during the first few minutes of engine warm-up, especially on cold mornings. To address the problem, researchers at Corning (N.Y.) Inc. developed a device called a passive underbody main adsorber (PUMA) to remove these early emissions.

Situated beneath the car in the exhaust-system train, the PUMA device comprises a zeolite adsorber sandwiched between two catalytic converters. The zeolite, a highly porous inorganic aluminosilicate mineral, collects the pollutants and holds them until the converter behind it is warm enough to function efficiently. After the zeolite has reached higher temperatures, it automati-

cally releases the adsorbed pollutants into the downstream converter, where they are converted to less-hazardous compounds. The PUMA is placed under the car so that it can be integrated more easily into the vehicle design and because its distance from the engine allows the zeolite to warm slowly and continue adsorbing pollutants until the downstream converter is working well.

Manufacturers in the U.S., Europe, and Japan were testing the new device, and results for cars with a 3.8-liter engine— e.g., a six-cylinder mid-sized sedan— showed emissions 88% less than the present U.S. standard, a level that should also fall below the standard set for early in the 21st century. The year 2000 would be the earliest that the device would be installed on automobiles.

Fuel cells for electric cars

Some researchers and environmentalists have envisioned society as being on the threshold of perhaps the last great energy revolution, one that will see pollution-free hydrogen, whose only combustion product is water, displace petroleum and other fossil fuels as the world's dominant fuel. The hydrogen fuel cell, a electrochemical device with no moving parts that converts hydrogen directly into electricity, has been used in space vehicles for decades and is finding growing applications in cars, trains, and aircraft. Most of the basic research on the concept has been done; the next step is to develop more inexpensive devices and systems that will rely on hydrogen for power.

Because the weight of cylinders of compressed hydrogen is an obstacle to the use

Photographs, Reuters

of hydrogen fuel cells in electrically powered cars, Alfred Tseung and Kunyao Chen of the Chemical Energy Research Centre, University of Essex, Colchester, Eng., developed a cell that does not use hydrogen gas directly but rather uses an inexpensive organic liquid such as methanol, which is decomposed to form hydrogen on site. Carbon monoxide, an unwanted by-product of this decomposition, inactivates, or poisons, the platinum-containing catalysts that oxidize the hydrogen in the energy-releasing reaction in the fuel cell, but the researchers found that the addition of tungsten trioxide converts the carbon monoxide to innocuous carbon dioxide. Methanol should be 15–18% more efficient than gasoline and should power cars twice as far as gasoline or diesel fuel. On the other hand, as supplies of the coal and natural gas from which methanol is produced become exhausted, fuel cells will need alternative sources of hydrogen.

A proton-exchange-membrane fuel cell for cars, which derives its hydrogen from gasoline or other liquids such as ethanol or diesel fuel, was developed by researchers as a collaborative project of Arthur D. Little, Inc., Plug Power LLC, and the U.S. Department of Energy (including Los Alamos [N.M.] National Laboratory). The liquid fuel is vaporized and then combusted in air to yield a gaseous mixture of hydrogen, carbon monoxide, methane, carbon dioxide, water, and nitrogen, which is led through a series of reactors that convert the methane and carbon monoxide to produce a hydrogen-rich gas. The Chrysler Corp. was developing an onboard system using this cell to power a car, which it claimed would raise fuel efficiency to 34 km per liter (80 mi per gal) while decreasing air pollution by 95%. The firm expected to demonstrate the system in a car within two years and to produce vehicle prototypes by 2005. Costs would have to be cut drastically, however, for the system to compete with conventional gasoline engines. (For other developments in environmental technology for automobiles, *see* ENVIRONMENT: *Environmental Technology*.)

"Improved" water

Organic chemist Michael Siskin of the Exxon Research and Engineering Co. exploited the fact that the properties of ordinary water can be altered simply by heating it to 200°–300° C (392°–572° F) under pressure so that it remains liquid rather than vaporizing (the principle of the pressure cooker). Siskin noted that under those conditions water exhibited different and highly useful properties. It became similar to an organic solvent, such as acetone, with the same density and dielectric constant and was able to dissolve materials insoluble in water, such as oils or polymers.

In October 1997 U.S. Secretary of Energy Federico Peña (above left) announces the development of the first successful gasoline-to-electricity fuel cell. A collaborative project of Arthur D. Little, Inc., Plug Power LLC, and the U.S. Department of Energy, the new fuel cell (above) was seen as a major advance toward practical electric cars.

Siskin and other researchers at the University of Florida applied these observations to develop a technique called aquathermolysis, which they used to depolymerize polymers, *i.e.*, convert them back into their original monomeric components, for recycling. For example, they treated pieces of plastic soda bottles, made of polyethylene terephthalate (PET), with water at 200° C under the proper pressure for 20 minutes and obtained terephthalic acid and ethylene glycol. They also used aquathermolysis to decompose organic arsenic and organic phosphorus compounds, using them as models for chemical warfare agents. If the technique proves to work with actual chemical warfare agents, it can be used to destroy unwanted stockpiles of them by converting them into innocuous substances.

Purifying polluted water

Mesoporous silica, a form of silicon dioxide, was first prepared in the early 1990s, at which time numerous commercial applications based on its unusual properties were predicted. The porous material is honeycombed with long corridors only a few nanometers (billionths of a meter) wide, which gives it an immense surface area; a three-gram (about 0.1-oz) sample possesses the surface area of a football field. In one of the first applications of this unique material, Jun Liu and co-workers of Pacific Northwest National Laboratory, Richland, Wash., and Argonne (Ill.) National Laboratory coated it with a sulfur-containing compound, tris(methoxy)mercaptopropylsilane, to form functional monolayers (single molecular layers) with thiol groups that bond strongly to heavy-metal ions.

The spongelike material quickly adsorbed mercury, silver, and lead ions—common industrial contaminants that in humans can cause brain damage and other medical problems—from hazardous, polluted water so effectively as to render the water drinkable and within U.S. Environmental Protection Agency limits for mercury concentrations. It also did not react with sodium, zinc, barium, and other less-dangerous metal ions, which often clog conventional pollution filters. Since the coating is highly selective for certain metals, changing the coating should make the material adaptable for removing different metals. According to Liu, "You can make these things in your kitchen. The process seems simple enough to scale to large quantities."

Although the new material costs about 50% more per unit weight than commercial filter materials, it should be competitive with them because it adsorbs metals 30–10,000 times more effectively. The adsorbed mercury or lead does not leach out of the material even on heating, but the metals may be removed with concentrated acids, which will render the material reusable. Chemist Galen Stucky of the University of California, Santa Barbara, reported making mesoporous silica materials with channels twice as wide as those in the materials employed in Liu's research—large enough to contain biological molecules, such as pheromones, which would make them usable as long-acting pest lures.

In a related development DeQuan Li of Los Alamos National Laboratory produced a spongelike polymer from compounds in common starch called cyclodextrins, claiming that the material can bind organic toxins 100,000 times more strongly than activated charcoal but can be leached out completely with alcohol. Liu's and Li's new absorbent materials may prove to be inexpensive and adaptable enough for use in agriculture, manufacturing, electronics, and possibly medicine.

Edible plastic

While attempting to make "green slime" for Halloween, Gus Gray and Justin White, two 16-year-olds attending Bluestone High School, Skipwith, Va., serendipitously obtained a clear plastic residue, which their teacher Holly Nash realized might be a previously unknown material. Called "JG's edible plastic," the new substance, which requires a catalyst for its formation, is ideal for pill coatings because it is soluble in saliva but not in water. Gray and White's classmates have been consuming the material, which can be flavored with cinnamon, peppermint, and other substances.

The young inventors were paid by Fuisz Technologies Ltd., Chantilly, Va., for a one-year extendable option for the drug-delivery and food-applications firm to develop the plastic for use in what Fuisz president and CEO Kenneth W. McVey called "traditional capsules, gel caps, dermal patch and buccal patch delivery." Until the boys obtained a patent, the process and recipe were being kept secret.

Anniversaries

Numerous anniversaries related to chemistry and broader fields of human endeavor were noted in 1997. In 1597 the German chemist and alchemist Andreas Libavius published the first edition of his *Alchemia,* considered the first modern chemistry textbook. In 1797 the French chemist Nicolas-Louis Vauquelin discovered the element chromium, a metal used extensively in the production of stainless steel and other alloys. In 1897 the British physicist J.J. Thomson announced the discovery of the electron, a constituent of all atoms and the basis for myriad inventions, devices, and industries. In the same year, the German chemist Felix Hoffmann, working for Friedrich Bayer & Co., produced aspirin (acetylsalicylic acid), one of the world's most popular and most versatile drugs, and the French chemist Paul Sabatier (the 1912 Nobel Prize winner in chemistry) discovered the catalytic hydrogenation of organic compounds by nickel, a process later used to produce fuels, margarine, and shortenings. In 1947 Willard F. Libby (the 1960 Nobel Prize winner in chemistry) developed the radiocarbon, or carbon-14, dating technique.

—George B. Kauffman

See also Feature Article: CELLULOID DREAMS.

DEFENSE RESEARCH

In the continuing downward spiral of military spending following the end of the Cold War, the U.S. Department of Defense (DOD) during the past year moved to revamp its approach to research. Applied research, embodied in the large weapons programs of the past, would be downgraded, and precedence would be given instead to basic research, the mechanism for providing the technologies for the weapons of the future—should they be needed.

All three services reported plans for increasing their basic research during 1998, but the Defense Advanced Research Projects Agency (DARPA), traditionally the Pentagon's principal arm for the high-risk, high-payoff research efforts aimed at results beyond the immediate needs of military forces, began moving the opposite

way. DARPA cut its basic research budget by 16.2% (to $76 million) and increased planned spending on applied research by 16.6% (to $830 million).

The chief of U.S. naval research, Paul Gaffney, listed basic research as his top priority, with the lion's share (56%) going to universities, 38% to navy laboratories, and 6% to industry. The situation was reversed for applied research: 47% to industry, 44% to navy laboratories, and 9% to universities. Gaffney's projections called for an 8.5% increase for basic research to $382 million and an 8.5% cut in applied research to $490 million.

A. Fenner Milton, the U.S. Army's deputy assistant secretary for research and technology, said that because of tighter budgets, the army was focusing on dual-use technologies (applicable to both mili-

tary and commercial functions) and upgrades to existing weapons rather than on development of new systems. For 1998 he anticipated an 11.1% increase in basic research to $199 million and a 16.1% decline in applied research to $463 million.

At the U.S. Air Force, Helmut Helwig, deputy assistant secretary for science, technology, and engineering, reported that industry performed 50% of all air force research but only 10% of basic research. He projected a 7.6% increase in basic research to $227 million and a 9.3% decline in applied research to $593 million.

In testimony before the U.S. Congress, Anita Jones, then the director of defense research and engineering for the DOD, told the House National Security Committee that she expected to reduce the department's research infrastructure in response to the budget cuts and that several in-house laboratories would be closed as part of a program known as Base Realignment and Closure, in which unneeded military facilities are eliminated. An independent panel of academic and industry researchers was created to determine redundant laboratories and test facilities and to ascertain whether open-air testing of the actual weapons in the field could be replaced by increased use of less-costly computer simulation.

Following Jones's testimony, the DOD announced that it would trim about 60,000 positions from its 1,450,000 active-duty military personnel and, as expected, close more facilities in order to find $15 billion per year to shift to procurement as part of the Quadrennial Defense Review plan submitted to Congress. Additional funding was sought for ballistic missile defense,

The closing of California's Naval Air Station Alameda, part of a nationwide trend to decommission surplus military facilities, forced the warship USS *Carl Vinson* to leave San Francisco Bay for a new home port in Bremerton, Wash.

and the Pentagon continued its support of the tactical-aircraft program, including the air force's F-22 and the navy's F/A-18E/F fighters.

Overall, the research, development, test, and evaluation budget for the department reflected the changing priorities. The 1997 level of $36.6 billion dropped to $35.9 billion in 1998 and then would continue to decline to $32.9 billion in 2001. The department's top officials, from Defense Secretary William Cohen on down, made it clear that modernization of weapons was a remote third place on their priority list, falling behind maintenance of the operational readiness of current forces and provision of an adequate quality of life for military personnel and their families. Cohen's predecessor, William Perry, had consistently stressed the preference for readiness over new weapons in order to avoid what he called a hollow military that was well armed but incapable of operating its weapons.

To implement the new priorities, the DOD launched a new program known as the Commercial Operations and Support Savings Initiative (COSSI). COSSI was one-half of a revamped Dual Use Applications Program originally conceived by DARPA. The other half was the Science and Technology Initiative (STI), already in the hands of the services. The difference between the two was that COSSI was aimed at inserting commercial off-the-shelf technology to upgrade already fielded military systems, whereas STI looked toward implementing dual-use technology in future systems. The DOD budgeted $250 million for the total effort for 1998.

To participate in the program, a company would team with a military service

(Below and opposite page) Photographs, AP/Wide World

In the Quadrennial Defense Review plan submitted to Congress, the Pentagon continued its support of the tactical-aircraft program, including the air force's F-22 fighters.

customer to create kits, based on a commercial product or process, that would maintain the performance of a fielded system while reducing its operations and support costs. The government would share in the costs of developing and testing these kits. If the tests were successful, the company would then have the inside track for supplying operational hardware. Among the weapons systems singled out as needing this kind of upgrade were tactical airplanes and tanks and infantry fighting vehicles.

The DOD also conceded that it was having trouble staying abreast of the technologies needed for future weapons systems. Faced with a migration of leading-edge technologies to the commercial sector, the department commissioned a policy studies organization, the Potomac Institute of Policy Studies, to survey the potentially militarily critical technologies at 500 companies and about 100 federally funded research and development centers. The company looked at a variety of mechanisms,

including government-industry consortia at the state level (such as those already under way in New Mexico and New York) and greater use of cooperative research and development agreements (CRADAs), in which companies use government laboratories at a modest cost and share their technologies with the military services operating the laboratories.

One of the goals was to enable the DOD to achieve "just in time" technology investment. For example, in the case of stealth technologies, for which there were no apparent commercial markets, the department would have to make all the initial investments. Other technologies could be acquired from commercial sources, however, which would enable the military services to take advantage of industry-sponsored research. The areas in which industry was believed to be ahead included not only computer technology, advanced materials, and medical and biological technology but even aerospace technology. In the highly competitive, time-critical commercial markets, companies were reluctant to share information on research until they had a marketable product.

This situation also exacerbated the already difficult problem of intellectual property rights as companies sought to retain the results of their CRADAs and their relationships with university laboratories. Under the current reengineering and downsizing trend, companies tried to farm out basic research and seek other cost-effective mechanisms. For example, AT&T spun off its traditional research organization, Bell Laboratories, as a separate company, Lucent Technologies, and IBM moved its research operations out of their former "university environment" and attached them to operating business units.

Another method that emerged was to turn to overseas sources for the critical technologies. Development of the newest state-of-the-art spacecraft components, for example, was viewed as no longer confined to the United States. Two French companies in particular began challenging the U.S. lead: Thomson-CSF and Matra MHS. The French companies tended to stress a new semiconductor technology, known as silicon on insulation (SOI) because insulating layers within the devices improve performance. Thomson used SOI in its radiation-hardened components suitable for use in space, including a 32-bit microprocessor. Matra, with sponsorship from the European Space Agency (ESA), developed a radiation-tolerant processor.

The driving force that emerged in the international market was the post-Cold War shift toward commercial satellites, notably communications, meteorologic, and resource survey craft. Owing to high launch costs, these space programs required radiation-resistant electronics that were also reasonably cost-effective. Some nations increased their production of these devices; prominent among them was Japan, which had not previously been involved in military devices but which began research into SOI to meet commercial space needs. Japanese companies involved in this effort, under the sponsorship of the Japanese National Space Development Agency, included Mitsubishi, Hitachi, and NEC.

One high-priority area of defense research during the past year was a concept that had become known as the digital battlefield. Digital data traffic was expected to grow rapidly in order to meet command and control and reconnaissance requirements. Even before the digital systems of the future could be implemented, however,

AP/Wide World

A new method for digitizing the gun camera footage of Apache helicopters helped international observers monitor violations of the Dayton Peace Agreement that was signed in 1995 by warring factions in Bosnia and Herzegovina.

the army faced recurring problems with its voice systems. In an exercise that was intended to test 72 new technologies being considered for the Force XXI army of the future, the biggest problem was with the venerable Single Channel Ground and Airborne Radio System (SINCGARS), developed jointly by British and U.S. forces in the 1970s. The line-of-sight system that was developed for the exercise met the requirements in the digital mode; however, an estimated 10–15% of the voice messages did not reach the designated receivers.

The underlying cause of the problem was determined to be SINCGARS's response to the unusually large volume of electronic transmissions, considerably greater than it would experience in normal battlefield conditions. The NATO Implementation Force (IFOR) experienced similar problems in Bosnia and Herzegovina. The crux of the problem turned out to be that even the most sophisticated command and control system still depended on line-of-sight, packet-switched tactical communications, such as SINCGARS and the Mobile Subscriber Equipment (MSE). Even though these systems were considered an order of magnitude better than the AN/PRC systems of Korean War vintage that they replaced, they still represented 1970s technology. MSE and SINCGARS were both designed before the current acquisition reforms and represented what military planners called legacy systems that would be difficult to integrate into the digital battlefield of the future.

The former warring factions in Bosnia, meanwhile, were using cellular phones, which one U.S. brigade commander rated as better than his own communications.

Despite the inherent information security limitations of cellular phones, this technology was being considered to supplement future battlefield communications, particularly by the Special Operations Command, which was exploring acquisition of its own communications capability independent of conventional forces.

There were also problems with computers, which were expected to be at the heart of the "system of systems" concept for the future digital battlefield. Computer viruses were rampant in the Bosnian conflict; by some estimates they afflicted as many as 50% of the personal computers used by IFOR. Furthermore, the large number of single-purpose, stand-alone databases made integration of information difficult, especially in the intelligence arena. This forced the lower ranks to seek work-around solutions by adapting equipment to do jobs that were not in the original specifications.

On the positive side, a lesson learned in Bosnia was the success of innovations for the helicopters of the 1st Armored Division's 4th Brigade, which led to a new method of digitizing the Apache attack helicopter's gun camera footage for an investment of less than $1,000 in commercial software and off-the-shelf equipment. The resulting photographs documented Dayton Peace Agreement violations and, as unclassified imagery, were occasionally handed over to the former warring factions to compel compliance. The pictures displayed the exact time and location of such typical violations as tanks in the zone of separation.

The Roving Sands exercise conducted in April was focused on joint command and control for tactical missile defense against

Scuds and decoys, according to Maj. Gen. James Hill, deputy chief of staff for operations at the U.S. Army Forces Command. A variety of defensive missiles were employed, including Patriots, Hawks, Rolands, and Stingers, and for the first time three targets were attacked simultaneously. Interoperability in this case was based on the Joint Tactical Information Distribution System, which tied together more than 20,000 personnel from all the U.S. services plus participants from Canada, Germany, and The Netherlands.

In another exercise applicable to the digital battlefield, designated Spring Thunder, the U.S. Air Force in 1997 used its E-8C Joint Surveillance Target Attack Radar System aircraft to detect "red" forces at the National Training Center in Ft. Irwin, California, in a simulated surprise attack on the army's 4th Infantry Division. The exercise marked the first time the E-8C had provided mission support within 48 hours of receiving execution orders, according to the air force.

Commenting on the year's experience in trying to digitize the battlefield of the future, a task force of the Defense Science Board summed up the situation this way: "The good news is that we have made the information flow down to the forces much more robust. The related bad news is that we need to make sure that 'we don't saturate the warrior with data while starving him of useful information.' For information getting down to lower echelon and mobile forces, the 'last dirt mile is still that—the last dirt mile.'"

—John Rhea

See also Feature Article: SCIENCE FOR THE SOLDIER: THE U.S. ARMY'S NATICK LABS.

EARTH SCIENCES

The long-debated theory that the mass extinction at the end of the Cretaceous Period, some 66 million years ago, resulted from the impact of an asteroid received renewed attention during the past year. New evidence seemed to indicate that at least some dinosaurs could have survived the dark, cold period that would have followed the impact. Other studies focused on such subjects as activity within the Earth's mantle, global climate change, and plans to mine for metals on the ocean floor. One of the most powerful El Niño events of the century began to develop in 1997, and its course was followed extensively during the following months.

ATMOSPHERIC SCIENCES

On July 4, 1997, the Mars Pathfinder landed on the surface of the planet Mars. As part of the scientific mission, the Atmospheric Structure Investigation/Meteorology experiment measured the vertical structure of the Martian atmosphere from the surface to an altitude of 160 km (one kilometer is equal to 0.62 mile) and monitored the surface meteorology for 83 Martian days (one Martian day is equal to 24.7 Earth hours).

As the Pathfinder descended through the Martian atmosphere, it obtained a vertical profile (sounding) of temperature, pressure, and density. This sounding revealed a region, above an altitude of 125 km, in which the temperature increased rapidly with altitude because of heating by solar extreme ultraviolet radiation; a temperature minimum of 92 K (–181° C [–294° F]) at 80 km, the lowest temperature ever measured in the Martian atmosphere; and a large increase in temperature between 10 and 16.5 km. The temperature minimum at 80 km is below the condensation temperature for carbon dioxide, which may indicate the probability of carbon dioxide clouds at that altitude. The temperature minimum at 10 km, 181 K (–92° C [–134° F]), is below the condensation temperature for water vapor, which suggests the presence of water clouds at that level.

Data from the surface revealed a large diurnal variation in temperature; a typical maximum temperature was 263 K (–10° C [14° F]) in the early afternoon, and a typical minimum was 197 K (–76° C [–105° F]) shortly before sunrise. The surface pressure showed a diurnal oscillation of 0.2–0.3 millibar, which was associated with the large thermal tides in the Martian atmosphere. The mean pressure decreased slowly during the first part of the period, reaching a minimum at 20 Martian days, and then began a slow increase. This behavior reflected the annual cycle of pressure changes associated with condensation and sublimation of carbon dioxide at the poles.

The behavior of the Martian boundary layer was consistent with conclusions derived from measurements of the Earth's atmosphere. During the day turbulent mixing occurred as the Martian surface

After landing on Mars on July 4, 1997, NASA's Pathfinder spacecraft and its six-wheeled rover, Sojourner, beamed back images to Earth from a rocky Martian plain. Data from the planet's surface revealed a large diurnal variation in temperature. One surprising finding was the occurrence of small rotating vortices similar to dust devils on Earth.

JPL/NASA

warmed and the lower atmosphere became unstable. Surface winds revealed a diurnal variation, with downslope (drainage) winds at night and upslope winds during the day.

A remarkable finding was the occurrence during the warm, unstable afternoons of small-scale rotating vortices that looked very much like dust devils on Earth. During the passage of these vortices, the pressure fell and then rose abruptly over a period of less than a minute, and the wind shifted rapidly in a manner consistent with the passage of a clockwise-rotating vortex. (For additional information on the Mars Pathfinder mission, *see* Year in Review: SPACE EXPLORATION.)

El Niño

In 1997, under the influence of intense media coverage, El Niño became a household word around the world. At the end of the year, one of the greatest El Niño events of the century was maturing, and its impacts were being feared and felt globally.

Centered in the equatorial Pacific Ocean, El Niño is part of a naturally oc-

curring cycle of climate variability that alters storm, precipitation, and temperature patterns over much of the Earth. Effects of the 1997 El Niño likely included widespread floods in South America, dramatic suppression in the number of North Atlantic hurricanes, and increases in the frequency and intensity of eastern Pacific tropical cyclones. (For additional information, see *Oceanography,* below.)

Global climate change

Since the release of the Intergovernmental Panel on Climate Change (IPCC) Second Assessment Report, *Climate Change 1995,* which included the statement that "the balance of evidence suggests a discernible human influence on global climate," interest in global climate changes, the role of human activities in those changes, and the impacts of climate changes on society has intensified. New studies have provided further evidence that the climate is warming globally. As the concentrations in the atmosphere of carbon dioxide and other greenhouse gases continued to increase, 1997 was the warmest year and 1988–97 by far the warmest decade of the century. Temperatures in the Arctic over the past 40 years were the highest they had been in four centuries, and this warming trend caused retreats of glaciers, melting of permafrost and sea ice, and alteration of terrestrial and lake ecosystems, including faster rates of tree growth and a wider range of Arctic plant species.

NASA scientists found that precipitation over land increased during the 20th century, particularly at middle and high latitudes. The average global land precipitation rose 2.4 mm per decade, which resulted in a mean global increase during the century of slightly more than 2%. This increase was consistent with predictions from climate models that atmospheric water vapor and precipitation would increase as the atmosphere warmed and the hydrologic cycle became more active.

Kyoto conference

Climate change was recognized as a serious problem by the first World Climate Conference in 1979. That conference called for the world's governments "to foresee and prevent potential man-made changes in climate that might be adverse to the well-being of humanity." Since then there have been a number of international conferences on climate change, including the 1992 United Nations Framework Convention on Climate Change in Rio de Janeiro. The Conference of the Parties (COP), formed in 1995, held its first and second meetings in Berlin in March–April 1995 and Geneva in June 1996. The third meeting of the COP was held in Kyoto, Japan, on Dec. 1–10, 1997, and was attended by 2,200 official delegates from 159 nations.

The Kyoto Protocol expressed concern "that human activities have been substantially increasing the atmospheric concentrations of greenhouse gases, that these increases enhance the natural greenhouse

Melting ice (right) shears from the facade of Hubbard Glacier in Alaska. In December 1997 global warming was the subject of an international conference in Kyoto, Japan, chaired by Raul Estrada (below).

effect, and that this will result on average in an additional warming of the Earth's surface and atmosphere and may adversely affect natural ecosystems and humankind." Under the Kyoto Protocol, 38 industrialized nations would cut their emissions of six greenhouse gases by an average of 5.2% from 1990 levels by 2012.

Tropical Rainfall Measuring Mission (TRMM)

On Nov. 27, 1997, after more than a decade of planning and preparation, NASA and the Japan National Space Development Agency (NASDA) launched the first weather radar into space from the Tanegashima Space Center in Japan. The Tropical Rainfall Measuring Mission (TRMM) was dedicated to measuring tropical and subtropical rainfall. Tropical rainfall constitutes more than two-thirds of global rainfall and thus is a key component of the global hydrologic cycle.

The TRMM satellite, orbiting the Earth approximately once every 96 minutes, carried five instruments: a precipitation radar, a microwave imager, a visible and infrared scanner, a cloud and Earth radiant energy system, and a lightning imaging sensor. TRMM was designed to provide new details about tropical and subtropical rainfall systems, including the vertical distribution of latent heating associated with condensation of water vapor, an important aspect of the atmospheric circulations.

Fronts and Atlantic Storm-Track Experiment (FASTEX)

During January and February 1997, a major field program involving 11 countries in Europe and North America, six research aircraft, four ships, and many other observing systems such as radiosondes and drifting buoys was conducted in the Atlantic from Newfoundland to Ireland to study fierce winter storms that move eastward across the ocean and strike western Europe. Scientists hoped that the research project, called the Fronts and Atlantic Storm-Track Experiment (FASTEX), would lead to better storm forecasts for the west coasts of both Europe and North America, as well as to a better understanding of how oceanic winter storms affect world climate.

Cyclones—large-scale, low-pressure storm systems—that hit Europe often develop along cold fronts that extend across the Atlantic Ocean. Often the large-scale aspects of the cold front are well forecast, but the storms that produce gale-force winds and rain along the front are harder to predict. FASTEX researchers identified precursors in the atmosphere that trigger cyclone formation. These precursors include jet streaks (regions of maximum wind speeds inside the jet stream) and air containing high values of potential vorticity (a measure of the spin and stability of the atmosphere) in the upper troposphere, about 10–13 km above the Earth's surface.

One of the hypotheses tested in FASTEX was that targeted observations in certain sensitive regions of the atmosphere are more important in forecasting the development of cyclones than they are in other regions. Computer forecast models require initial atmospheric data (data to begin the forecast). The model forecasts are more sensitive to accurate initial data from energetically active regions upwind of the cyclone development than from relatively quiet atmospheric regions. The major goals of FASTEX were to develop better techniques for predicting the locations of these sensitive regions, to target these regions with special observations, and to evaluate how much the targeted observations improved the computer forecasts. FASTEX showed that the prime spots for enhanced observations included developing cyclones as well as their upwind precursors and that the special observations significantly improved the forecasts.

—Richard A. Anthes

GEOLOGY AND GEOCHEMISTRY

In studies of plate tectonics, true polar wander (TPW) refers to a situation in which the entire mantle of the Earth would slip over its core. During the past year Joseph Kirschvink, Robert Ripperdan, and David Evans presented evidence that in the Early to Middle Cambrian Period about 520 million–530 million years ago, the mantle and crust of the Earth slipped about 90° over the core, which caused rapid continental motion. This occurred at the same time as the sudden diversification of major animal groups in the "Cambrian explosion," and the authors suggested that the two events may be related.

The study was based on extremely well-dated paleomagnetic data from three sites in Australia, at that time part of the Gondwanaland supercontinent, and several in North America, at that time part of the Laurentia supercontinent. The Australian data revealed that Gondwanaland moved rapidly from Equator to pole over approximately 15 million years or less. The North American data indicated that Laurentia shifted from a polar to an equatorial location over the same time period. The authors speculated that these extremely rapid and uniform shifts may have been accomplished by slip of the mantle and crust over the core at a high rate of motion. Such a shift would be caused by a very large mass such as a mountain range building up at the surface and destabilizing the rotational inertia of the planet; equilibrium would be restored by movement of the large mass to the Equator by means of a mantle slip. This same process is thought to be the reason that all the giant volcanoes of Mars lie along its equator. A major feature of this motion would have been a rearrangement of ocean circulation; pronounced changes in seawater carbon and strontium isotope ratios during this interval support the hypothesis. Fragmentation of ecosystems and rapid change of ocean temperatures would have led to unusually rapid rates of evolutionary change and thus been responsible for the "Cambrian explosion."

Former location of Vancouver Island

The present model for the construction of the west coast of North America during the last 100 million years involves the addition of enormous bodies, called terranes, directly to the western leading edge of the North American tectonic plate by means of subduction and docking. Typical terrane components might be island arcs or oceanic lava plateaus. Some terranes have also clearly been faulted to the north after docking, along giant faults trending parallel to the coast, often for distances of thousands of kilometers. One such terrane, the Insular Superterrane, makes up Vancouver Island and much of the Alaska panhandle. A

long-standing dispute as to whether this terrane was faulted north after docking was resolved during the past year by Peter Ward, José Hurtado, Joseph Kirschvink, and Kenneth Verosub. The evidence for the latitude of the superterrane at the time of its formation (about 90 million years ago) comes from paleomagnetic data in its rocks; the trapped field has an inclination that corresponds to a latitude of 25° N, but at present Vancouver Island lies at about 50° N. Taken at face value, the data suggest that the rocks of the Insular Superterrane docked at the present-day latitude of Baja California, 3,500 km (2,175 mi) south of the superterrane's present position.

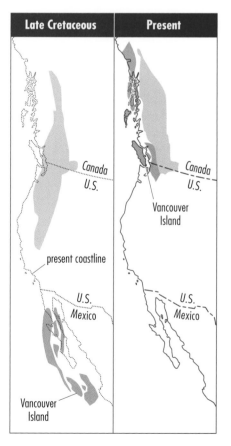

This hypothesis was attacked, however, on two fronts: first, the rocks studied earlier had perhaps been reheated and remagnetized; second, the rocks had perhaps been compacted so that the magnetic grains carrying the inclination data had been packed closer together under the pressure from deep burial, which thereby had lowered the inclination angle. The researchers fortunately found a new site where Cretaceous sediments with a strong paleomagnetic signal had clearly been cemented by rigid calcite concretions before compaction could occur and had clearly not been metamorphosed, because they contained ammonite shells whose original aragonite contained organic molecules and had not recrystallized. (Shell aragonite recrystallizes to calcite at about 100° C [212° F]). The sediments at this site indicated a paleolatitude of about 25° N, which matched the earlier determinations and confirmed the hypothesis. Consequently, it seems true that much of the northwestern coast of North America has moved thousands of kilometers north along huge faults.

Evidence for a new tectonic plate

In another major development in plate tectonics, David McAdoo and Seymour Laxon used sea-surface data obtained by satellites from the southern Pacific Ocean, including areas under ice cover, to confirm an earlier hypothesis of Joann Stock and Peter Molnar that a large plate called the Bellinghausen Plate was joined to West Antarctica and was separated from the Pacific Plate by a spreading ridge called the Bellinghausen Trough. The bearing of this trough enters Antarctica itself, which

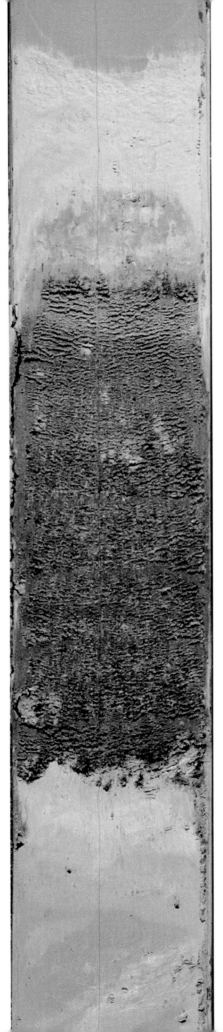

Oceanographers reported that this mud core, drilled from the ocean bed off Florida, has helped clarify the picture of the mass extinction and recovery of species that is thought to have occurred after an asteroid impact about 65 million years ago. The core reveals (bottom to top) fossil-rich white material from before the impact, a greenish zone of impact debris, and a reddish layer of material from the impacting body; this is topped by fossil-poor and then fossil-abundant layers.

shows that Antarctica was not a single continent before the beginning of the Cenozoic Era, about 66.4 million years ago. Spreading along this ridge ended about 60 million years ago.

The trough and plate were identified from bottom topography as determined by the authors. Basic data were provided by the ESR-1 satellite of the European Space Agency, which used a laser range finder to measure the height of the world sea surface to an accuracy of a few millimeters. Topographical high points on the sea bottom are matched by highs on the sea surface, and so the sea-surface map reproduces in striking detail the bottom topography of the Antarctic seas, where few ship-tracking data are available. Bottom topography can even be established in areas under the pack ice.

Iridium-bearing sediments at the Cretaceous-Tertiary boundary

For more than 20 years, the dominant hypothesis about the extinction of the dinosaurs and many other animals and plants 65 million years ago, at the end of the Cretaceous Period, has been that an asteroid struck the Earth and generated enough dust to shut out sunlight for some weeks or months to the whole Earth, which thereby caused complete collapse of all ecosystems. The assumed contact between the asteroid and the Earth is marked worldwide by a high concentration of the element iridium in the rocks of the Cretaceous-Tertiary boundary. Iridium is rare on the Earth but common in some asteroids. After the impact most species died out; a few survived, and their descendants repopulated the Earth. The crater for

this impact was recently found, most geologists believed, in the Yucatán Peninsula of Mexico. Named Chicxulub, it is a huge crater between 180 and 300 km (112 and 186 mi) in diameter, buried beneath younger rocks. For thousands of kilometers from this site, the sediments from the end of the Cretaceous contain innumerable small glass spheres called tektites, made from the impact-produced liquid.

The model seemed complete, but new research added great complexity to it during the past year. Gerta Keller, J.G. Lopez-Olivia, Wolfgang Stinnesbeck, and T. Adatte studied the boundary sections in great detail in many places, mainly in Mexico, and found clear evidence that the Chicxulub deposits were laid down about 150,000 years before the extinction of the dinosaurs and that the crater cannot have produced whatever killed them. The researchers based their conclusions on the following data. First, the sediments full of glass spheres, identified as the impact deposits, actually underlie the end-of-Cretaceous sediments by as much as a meter in most places and therefore are older. In some sections a distinctive fossil that is characteristic of the end of the Cretaceous was found in sediments above the impact deposits, which clearly confirmed that the Chicxulub deposits are older. Second, the sediments full of glass spheres, regarded as having been produced by the impact, do not appear to have been laid down all at once, as the impact hypothesis requires. Several distinct layers in this sequence contain burrows that were dug by animals like crabs and then later filled from above when the next sediments were deposited. Such a layer would be overlain by another layer, which would

Ocean Drilling Program

also be burrowed. Such burrowing takes time to accomplish, and the model for deposition determined by the researchers is that the so-called impact-ejecta sediment layers were laid down in several stages over a considerable period of time and could not be impact ejecta at all, at least not from a single event. The authors had no alternative model for deposition to propose and left the character of these unique sediments for later study.

The researchers proposed a new hypothesis, that there were two events about 150,000 years apart. The first, in which the formation of the Chicxulub structure and its related deposits occurred, was probably some type of impact. The second event produced the iridium anomaly throughout the world, and it was this impact that caused the mass extinction.

Stress measurements in the continental interior

The margins of North America contain mountain systems composed of highly deformed folded and faulted rocks, produced during continental collision or subduction. The interior, on the other hand, is made up of flat and rather featureless plains underlain by flat-lying sedimentary rocks that appear to have been undisturbed since the day they were laid down. Ben van der Pluijm, John Craddock, Brita Graham, and John Harris, however, found that not to be the case. The mineral calcite, or calcium carbonate, is the main constituent of limestones, which are in turn common in the flat-lying sediments of the interior. Calcite is easily deformed, and when strained, its crystal structure deforms along planes called twin planes. By studying a twinned

calcite crystal, one can determine the direction from which the stress that twinned it came.

The investigators wanted to see if stress from the mountain-building events at the continental margins was transmitted to the interior. They therefore collected a large number of calcite specimens from limestones at varied distances from the mountains and studied the twinning in the calcite. They found that the calcite was often twinned and that the deformation decreased as they moved inland from the mountain front; deformation was, however, still detectable thousands of kilometers inland. They concluded, therefore, that the continental interior is strained during mountain building on the continental margins. These interplate stresses may, for example, affect old faults and cause earthquakes that otherwise would be difficult to account for.

Major awards

The Geological Society of America presented its major awards at its annual meeting in October 1997 in Salt Lake City, Utah. The Penrose Medal, its most prestigious award, was given to John D. Bredehoeft of the U.S. Geological Survey (USGS) in recognition of his 32-year career in groundwater studies. (The R.A.F. Penrose, Jr., Medal is awarded in recognition of research in pure geology.) The Day Medal was awarded to Edward Irving of the Geological Survey of Canada for his pioneering work in paleomagnetism. His graduate thesis was the first work to prove that directions of magnetization could remain unchanged in rocks for a billion years. In 1954, with two associates, he

helped trace the first polar wandering path, and two years later he was the first to show that the polar wandering path from North America was displaced systematically to the west from that of Europe and concluded from this that continental drift had occurred. In 1964 he published the first book on paleoclimatology, which helped pave the way for the acceptance of plate tectonics. (The Arthur L. Day Medal is awarded for outstanding distinction in contributing to geologic knowledge through the application of physics and chemistry.)

The Young Scientist Award went to Edouard G. Bard of the University of Aix-Marseille III, Aix-en-Provence, France, in recognition of the scope and influence of his work in isotopic studies of the Quaternary Period (the last 1.6 million years). He did precise work on carbon-14 dating of foraminifera shells in deep-sea deposits and on both carbon-14 and uranium-thorium dating of corals, which allowed the precise timing of sea-level variations over the last deglaciation. This work is expected to be extremely valuable in detailing sea-level and sea-temperature changes during roughly the last 50,000 years. (The Young Scientist Award, which consists of the Donath Medal and a cash prize, is awarded to a young scientist for outstanding achievement in contributing to geologic knowledge through original research that marks a major advance in the Earth sciences.) The American Geological Institute presented the Ian Campbell Medal to M. Gordon Wolman of Johns Hopkins University, Baltimore, Md. Wolman became internationally known for his studies of watershed and river processes and the evolution of river systems over the last 40 years. Much of his work has provided the basis for

Iranian Pres. Ali Akbar Hashemi Rafsanjani (far left) visits a site in northwestern Iran damaged by a magnitude-6.0 earthquake that struck the region on Feb. 28, 1997. The quake destroyed numerous villages and killed at least 965 persons. An aftershock of magnitude 5.1 occurred two days later.

current U.S. science policy. (The Ian Campbell Medal is given in recognition of singular performance in and contribution to the profession of geology.)

—Rolfe Erickson

GEOPHYSICS

Destructive earthquakes struck China, Iran, Venezuela, and Italy during the past year. In the Caribbean Sea there was no respite for victims of the Soufrière Hills volcano on the island of Montserrat, which had begun erupting in 1995. Geophysicists monitored seismic activity at Long Valley caldera in California's Sierra Nevada and made progress in understanding the dynamics of the Earth's mantle.

Earthquakes and volcanoes

On Jan. 11, 1997, a magnitude-7.1 earthquake struck the western coast of Mexico, killing one person and causing extensive damage in Michoacán state. Shaking was felt as far inland as Mexico City. On January 21 at least 12 people were killed and thousands left homeless when a magnitude-5.9 quake struck near Jiashi in China's Xinjiang province. Most people in the area lived in earthen houses that could not withstand the ground shaking. This was the first, but not the largest, in a swarm of destructive strike-slip and normal faulting quakes that would continue in this area through the first half of 1997 (*see* below). A magnitude-6.4 earthquake struck the Iran-Turkmenistan border region on February 4, killing 79 people, injuring several hundred, and destroying or damaging more than 16,000 dwellings near Shirvan, Iran. On February 27 a magnitude-7.3

earthquake struck western Pakistan, 500 km (310 mi) north of Karachi, claiming the lives of at least 100 people, leaving thousands homeless, and causing numerous landslides that blocked roads and railroads. The main shock was followed within one week by aftershocks of magnitude 6.3, 5.9, and 5.0.

A devastating magnitude-6.0 earthquake struck the Iran-Armenia-Azerbaijan border region on February 28. Centered near Ardabil, Iran, 160 km (100 mi) east of Tabriz, this quake killed at least 965 people (some estimates ranged as high as 3,000), injured more than 2,500, left more than 35,000 homeless, and caused severe damage to roads and utility systems. The main shock was followed two days later by a destructive magnitude-5.1 aftershock. In just the first two months of 1997, the number of earthquake-related deaths worldwide had already exceeded the entire 1996 toll. On March 1 a magnitude-6.0 earthquake near Jiashi killed two people and destroyed 4,000 houses. A magnitude-4.8 earthquake on March 19 in Pakistan's Bajaur district killed at least 15 people. A magnitude-6.1 earthquake on March 26 injured more than 20 people, damaged several buildings, and

disrupted rail and air service in Kagoshima prefecture, Japan. The main shock was followed by a strong aftershock on April 2. The swarm near Jiashi continued in April with four more destructive earthquakes: magnitude-5.9 on April 5 and April 6 (23 injured, some 3,000 buildings damaged), magnitude-6.1 on April 11 (at least 9 killed and 100,000 more homeless), and magnitude-5.7 on April 15. The April 11 quake was the largest in the swarm to that date.

A magnitude-6.7 earthquake struck the southern Windward Islands on April 22, causing injuries and extensive damage on Tobago. On May 10 a devastating magnitude-7.1 earthquake struck northeastern Iran, killing some 1,560 people, injuring several thousand, and destroying more than 10,000 houses. Most of the damage was concentrated along the Iran-Afghanistan border between Birjand and Qayen, an area of subsistence agriculture where buildings of brick and mud construction could not withstand seismic shaking. The earthquake was caused by left-lateral strike-slip faulting on the Abiz fault in an area of complex, very active tectonics related to collision between the Eurasian and Arabian

AFP Photo

The collapse of the ceiling of the church of St. Francis in Assisi, Italy, caused by one of a pair of earthquakes on Sept. 26, 1997, is captured on Italian television.

tectonic plates. It occurred near the location of the magnitude-7.3 Dasht-e-Bayez earthquake, which killed 12,000–20,000 people in 1968. On May 13 a magnitude-6.5 earthquake centered in the Hindu Kush region of Afghanistan killed one person. A magnitude-5.8 earthquake on May 21 killed at least 38 people and caused extensive damage near Jabalpur in central India. On July 9 a magnitude-7.0 earthquake centered off the coast of Venezuela near Cumana killed some 80 people, injured more than 500, and left more than 3,000 homeless. Much of the damage was caused by earthquake-generated landslides. The main shock was followed three weeks later by a destructive magnitude-4.3 aftershock. On July 21 a magnitude-5.0 earthquake killed at least 15 people at the Avgold Hartebeesfontein mine near Stilfontein, S.Af.

A pair of destructive earthquakes struck the Marche and Umbria regions of central Italy on September 26, killing 11 people, injuring more than 100, destroying or damaging about 80,000 houses, and damaging many historic structures. The church of St. Francis in Assisi and several important early Renaissance frescoes by Cimabue and Giotto di Bondone were extensively damaged. The magnitude-5.6 first main shock occurred at 2:33 AM local time. The magnitude-6.0 second main shock struck approximately nine hours later, killing four people who were inside the church assessing damage from the first quake. The second main shock was felt as far south as Rome and as far north as Slovenia and Austria. Hundreds of aftershocks followed, including destructive quakes on October 3, 6, and 14.

On September 28 a magnitude-5.9 earthquake killed at least 17 people and caused extensive damage in the Parepare area, Sulawesi, Indon. A magnitude-7.1 earthquake near Pueblo Nuevo on the central coast of Chile on October 15 killed at least seven people, injured close to 100 and destroyed or damaged about 1,000 houses. Much of the damage in the epicentral area was caused by landslides. Felt in parts of Argentina, Bolivia, and Peru, this quake was followed by a damaging magnitude-6.3 aftershock on November 3. A magnitude-5.2 earthquake in southern Quebec on November 6 was also felt in parts of Ontario and New Brunswick in Canada, as well as in Maine, northern Vermont and New Hampshire, and northeastern New York in the United States. On November 21 a magnitude-6.1 earthquake near Chittagong, Bangladesh, in the India-Bangladesh border region killed 23 people and caused extensive damage.

The sequence of devastating eruptions of the Soufrière Hills volcano continued in 1997. Ash and rock flows from an eruption in June killed 19 people and damaged several villages. In September a flow struck Montserrat's abandoned airport, burying a runway and destroying the main terminal building. Other noteworthy volcanic activity occurred at Kilauea volcano in Hawaii, Rabaul caldera in Papua New Guinea, Okmok volcano in Alaska, Mt. Hili Aludo and Mt. Karangetang in Indonesia, Popocatépetl in Mexico, San Cristóbal volcano in Nicaragua, Mt. Ruapehu in New Zealand, and Hakkoda volcano in Japan, where volcanic gases killed three Japanese soldiers in July.

In late 1997 geophysicists continued to monitor thousands of small earthquakes at Long Valley in California's Sierra Nevada, 320 km (200 mi) east of San Francisco.

The seismic swarm was accompanied by the expansion of a dome near the center of the Long Valley caldera at rates as high as 25 cm (10 in) per year, evidence that magma was rising toward the surface. The caldera is part of a chain of volcanic features along the east side of the Sierra that have been very active during the past three million years. A major explosive eruption 700,000 years ago formed the caldera and scattered ash over much of the western United States. The nearby Mono-Inyo Craters erupted as recently as 500–600 years ago. A strong seismic swarm in May 1980 (just one week after the explosive eruption of Mt. St. Helens) included four magnitude-6 earthquakes. Likely scenarios for the late-1997 stage of activity at Long Valley included magnitude-5–6 earthquakes and/or a small eruption. Scientists felt that the probability of a damaging or cataclysmic eruption was very small.

Convection in the Earth's mantle

One of the important unanswered questions in geophysics since the development of plate tectonics has been the nature of convection within the Earth's mantle. The mantle extends from the bottom of the Earth's crust, which is 5–50 km (3–30 mi) thick, down to the mantle-core boundary at a depth of approximately 2,900 km (1,800 mi). Laboratory studies have revealed that a rock will flow like a fluid at the high pressures and temperatures found in the mantle. Scientists have also determined that the mantle is heated from below at the core boundary and internally by radioactive decay and that heated fluids generally convect (move from one place to another). First postulated in the 1920s, the idea of mantle convection was by 1998 a widely accepted part of plate tectonics theory; motions within the mantle are thought to provide the forces that move the tectonic plates. Questions about the details of these motions remained, however.

As a result of studies of the travel times of seismic waves from distant earthquakes and explosions, seismologists have long recognized a worldwide seismic-velocity discontinuity at a depth of 660 km (410 mi). Coincidentally, this is near the depth of the deepest earthquakes, which are typically associated with subducted lithospheric plates. If the 660-km reflector marks the boundary between chemically distinct upper and lower mantles, then the boundary must present a barrier to subducting slabs, which would then be recycled completely within the upper mantle, and the upper and lower mantle must have separate convection systems. Alternatively, if the 660-km reflector represents a phase change in a chemically mixed mantle, then subducted slabs can go much deeper (but cannot support the high stresses necessary to cause earthquakes at great depth), and convection can involve the whole mantle.

In two recent independent studies, traces of subducting slabs have been found at depths much greater than 660 km, which favors the whole-mantle convection hypothesis. (There is geochemical evidence for isolated upper and lower mantles, however, that must still be reconciled with the seismic data). Stephen Grand of the University of Texas and Rob van der Hilst of the Massachusetts Institute of Technology and his colleagues computed a three-dimensional image of the Earth's velocity structure from large new data sets of global seismic travel times. Subducting slabs are colder and therefore transmit seismic waves faster than does the surrounding mantle. Using similar methods, seismologists were also discovering that the mantle-core boundary is one of the most active and heterogenous regions in the Earth's interior. According to one hypothesis, dead slabs of subducted oceanic crust fall all the way down to the mantle-core boundary and pile up there. The resulting lateral variations in thermal conductivity along the boundary may then control convection patterns within the mantle. Possible fluid instabilities associated with heterogeneity along the mantle-core boundary could generate so-called superplumes of upwelling hot rock, which might account for enigmatic episodes of massive volcanism that are preserved in the geologic record.

Eugene Shoemaker

A remarkable career in Earth science ended with the death in July 1997 of Eugene Shoemaker at age 69. When he began his career with the United States Geological Survey, the prevailing wisdom held that craterlike structures observable on the Earth and the Moon all had to be volcanic in origin, but Shoemaker's pioneering studies of the shapes and mineralogy of these structures led to the discovery that some of them on the Earth and most of them on the Moon were in fact caused by meteorite impacts. He discovered that coesite, an exotic high-temperature, high-pressure form of silica, was a diagnostic trait of impact structures. His work led directly to subsequent theories about catastrophic meteorite impacts and dinosaur extinctions on the Earth. Shoemaker later persuaded the Geological Survey to create a branch of astrogeology and helped convince NASA that scientific exploration should play a large part in space exploration.

Shoemaker, who was self-taught as an astronomer, and his wife, Carolyn, together or separately discovered 32 comets and

U.S. Geological Survey

Eugene Shoemaker, one of the chief founders of planetary geology and considered by many scientists to be the consummate sky gazer of the 20th century, died on July 18, 1997.

1,125 asteroids. Crowning his many achievements, he co-discovered Comet Shoemaker-Levy 9 and observed its spectacular impact on Jupiter in 1994.

(*See* SCIENTISTS OF THE YEAR: *Obituaries.*)

—Charles S. Mueller

HYDROLOGY

During the past year significant advances were reported in characterizing the hydrologic response of steep, forested slopes to rainfall events, determining the sources of water that inundate floodplains adjacent to major river channels, assessing the role of dry-lake playas in semiarid regions as sites of enhanced recharge for groundwater systems, and identifying mechanisms that control the movement of contaminants in the subsurface.

David Montgomery of the University of Washington led a research team that reported new observations on runoff generation and shallow subsurface flow on a steep, extensively instrumented hillside in Oregon's Coast Range. Ground cover on forested mountain slopes is generally described by three layers: colluvium (soil), weathered or disintegrated rock, and massive bedrock. Shallow landsliding is the dominant mechanism of sediment transport in this type of terrain. Timber harvesting and the construction of logging roads dramatically increased the frequency of slope failures (the downward and outward movements of masses of soil beneath natural slopes). When planning timber harvesting, steps to minimize the environmental impacts must be based on a sound understanding of the relationships between rainfall, runoff, and slope failure. Hydrologists had long questioned the role of water flow through shallow bedrock in both the generation of surface-water runoff during rainfall events and the development of fluid pressures within the colluvium. Higher fluid pressures contribute to the destabilization of the sediment cover on mountain slopes.

The instrumentation used in the experiments included weirs in several channels to measure surface-water flow during rainfall events, a large number of wells to record water pressures in the colluvium and underlying bedrock, and rain gauges. A sprinkler system built above the hillside

to simulate rainfall events permitted the scientists to augment the number of experiments that could be carried out to examine the storm-flow response.

Data collected by the research team indicated that a significant component of the storm flow moved through the near-surface bedrock. It had initially been thought that this component of the flow would have been minimal. The researchers concluded, however, that the weathered bedrock must have contained a network of conductive fractures that permitted a rapid hydrologic response during intense rainfall events. Hydraulic conductivity is a parameter that measures the ease with which water flows through a porous medium. Montgomery and his team concluded that an important link may exist between spatial variations in the hydraulic conductivity of the shallow bedrock and local regions on the hillside where water pressures build up in the colluvium during storms. They proposed that a local downslope decrease in hydraulic conductivity within the bedrock could drive water upward into the colluvium. Local changes in the intensity of fracturing may control the location on a slope where shallow landslides in the colluvium are initiated. Because it would be extremely difficult to characterize these variations in hydraulic conductivity on the scale of an entire hillside, this mechanism of subsurface storm flow introduced considerable uncertainty into conventional methods used to assess landslide potential on forested mountain slopes. These observations were relevant to mountainous areas beyond the Pacific Northwest and required hydrologists who worked in other areas of the world to reconsider the implications of rapid storm flow within shallow bedrock.

Leal Mertes of the University of California, Santa Barbara, provided new insight into the character of floodwaters that inundate floodplains along major river channels. She considered two sources of water on floodplains: overbank flow from the main river channel, and local water derived from direct rainfall onto the floodplain, melting of snow and ice, groundwater saturation, runoff from surrounding slopes, and/or flooding of local tributaries prior to the onset of overbank flooding from the main channel. Researchers previously had emphasized the importance of overbank flow from the main channel. Mertes used field data and optical remote sensing data from Landsat satellite images to study floods on six large rivers (the Missouri, Mississippi, and Altamaha rivers in the United States, the Amazon and Taquari rivers in Brazil, and the Ob-Irtysh River in Russia). Floodwaters that originated from the main channel had a chemistry and sediment content that differed from that of local water. Mertes found that of the floods that were examined, only the Missouri River in the 1993 flood had its entire valley covered with sediment-rich river water. All the other rivers had extensive zones of mixing between overbank flow and local waters. Mertes concluded that it is important to recognize the presence of zones where overbank flows and local waters mix and that these observations have significant implications for the interpretation of geomorphological features and the analysis of the biogeochemistry, productivity, and vegetation cover on a floodplain.

Dry-lake playas are a common feature of the landscape in arid and semiarid regions. For example, the southern High

A truck stands loaded with logs on a dirt road in a forest in Oregon. Timber harvesting and the construction of logging roads often contribute to the environmentally harmful movements of masses of soil beneath natural mountain slopes.

Gary B. Braasch—Allstock/PNI

Plains of Texas and New Mexico drain internally to about 25,000 playas. Each playa is generally less than 1.5 sq km (0.6 sq mi) in area and is underlain by clay-rich lake sediments. Upland settings between the playas are called interplayas. After periods of significant rainfall, water drains from the interplayas and ponds on the playas and creates temporary lakes. The presence of thick deposits of clay on the surface of the playas caused some hydrologists to argue that playas act primarily as evaporation sites; no water infiltrates downward to recharge underlying aquifers. Other hydrologists suggested that recharge occurs only when the water level on the playa is high enough to cover more permeable sediments found in an annular region around the playa. Yet others have claimed that root holes and cracks that form when a playa dries provide pathways for surface-water flow through the thick clay deposits. In the latter case, playas would be focused recharge sites to underlying aquifers.

Bridget Scanlon, Richard Goldsmith, and W.F. Mullican III of the Texas Bureau of Economic Geology reported the results

of the first comprehensive investigation of the hydrologic behavior of playas and interplayas. Studying seven playas near Amarillo, Texas, they collected physical measurements such as subsurface water content and chemical data such as the chloride content of the soil profile and also carried out several dye-tracing experiments to visually characterize the infiltration of water. Scanlon and her colleagues concluded that the floor of the playa acted to focus recharge, with infiltration rates estimated to range from 6 to 12 cm (2.4 to 4.7 in) per year. The volume of water recharging the subsurface was estimated by multiplying the recharge rate by the surface area of the playa. They concluded that recharge rates in the interplayas during the past 2,000 to 5,000 years were negligible. The data they collected also showed that recharge was not limited to the annular region around the playas. Flow through cracks and root holes in the clay-rich playa surface was observed in dye-tracing experiments, which pointed to the importance of preferential flow as the recharge mechanism. The researchers also cautioned that

the transport of contaminants through the floor of the playa was potentially quite rapid if water was channeled into preferential pathways that bypassed much of the buffering capacity of clay-rich sediments. This behavior increased the risk that the groundwater quality in the underlying aquifers could be degraded if the surface runoff was itself contaminated.

Robert Schincariol of the University of Western Ontario, working with Frank Schwartz of Ohio State University and Carl Mendoza of the University of Alberta, reported significant advances in the understanding of how dense plumes of dissolved contaminants spread within the subsurface. Trace concentrations of contaminants do not influence the natural rates or directions of groundwater flow. Groundwater that contains moderately high concentrations of metals or salts, however, has a higher density than the surrounding water. In these circumstances instabilities may form along the lower boundary of the contaminant plume. These instabilities (which initially appear like small fingers of contaminated water dangling from the bottom of the plume) can eventually cause contaminants to spread over a much greater vertical distance than is the case when the plume is stable. The plume is stable if the fingerlike instabilities decay after they form rather than grow in magnitude. Understanding this process, which had been largely ignored by most hydrologists, is important in the design of groundwater monitoring programs to detect subsurface contamination and in the prediction of plume migration at a contaminated site.

Marc Parlange of Johns Hopkins University, Baltimore, Md., received the Macelwane Medal of the American Geophysical Union, given for significant contributions to the geophysical sciences by a young scientist of outstanding ability. Parlange made important advances in the description of daily precipitation variations and in the understanding of factors that control the evaporation and infiltration of water through cracked soil horizons. John Bredehoeft, recently retired from the U.S. Geological Survey, received the Horton Medal of the American Geophysical Union and the Penrose Medal of the Geological Society of America. He was honored for pioneering studies in the use of computer models for the analysis of groundwater flow and contaminant transport, the development of methods for estimating hydrogeologic properties of a porous medium, experiments that revealed the link between fluid pressures in groundwater systems and seismicity, and studies that documented the hydrodynamics of deep sedimentary basins.

—Leslie Smith

OCEANOGRAPHY

A strong El Niño developed in the central Pacific Ocean during 1997 and early 1998, upsetting typical weather patterns throughout the world and threatening millions of people with flooding, droughts, forest fires, intense storms, and outbreaks of disease. El Niño is a natural warming of equatorial surface waters in the central and eastern Pacific. Generated by broad waves that slosh back and forth across the Pacific basin, El Niño appears irregularly about once every two to seven years. During these events warmth normally confined to the western Pacific around Indonesia spreads eastward toward the South American coast. The oceanic warming is accompanied by a shift in atmospheric pressure called the Southern Oscillation, and the combined effect is known as the El Niño/Southern Oscillation, or ENSO.

The recent El Niño began in early 1997 as sea-surface temperatures started to rise in the central Pacific. By November a vast pool of warm water had spread across the equatorial Pacific with temperatures more than 2° C (3.6° F) above average from latitude 170° W to the coast of South America. Between 115° and 90° W, temperatures reached 5° C (9° F) above average. These values broke records going back to 1950, when detailed measurements began.

As the warmth spread across the central and eastern Pacific, it spawned towering thunderheads and intense rainstorms that shifted the typical pattern of atmospheric jet streams. The redirected storms contributed to the worst drought in five decades in Southeast Asia. Lack of rain exacerbated forest fires in Indonesia, casting a pall of smoke that spread over an area more than half the size of the continental United States. Excessive rains in equatorial eastern Africa, ranging between 400 and 600 mm (15.75 and 23.6 in) above normal in parts of Kenya, caused extensive flooding in that region. Record precipitation fell in Peru during mid-1997, and heavy rains struck the coast of California in early 1998.

The 1997–98 El Niño represented a coming-of-age for computer models used to predict ocean conditions. Several models predicted the arrival of the warming several months to a half-year in advance. Because these models are still subject to errors, however, oceanographers and meteorologists waited until signs of El Niño developed before they alerted the world.

The recent El Niño rivaled, and in some ways surpassed, the 1982–83 El Niño, formerly considered the strongest of this century. That earlier event caused an estimated $8 billion in damages worldwide. This time, however, scientists provided advance warning to governments, enabling them to take defensive steps. Zimbabwe, for example, purchased more than $100 million in grain in expectation of drought and poor harvests. Australian farmers altered their planting patterns to accommodate lower-than-average rainfall. World health experts prepared for potential outbreaks of cholera and malaria in South America and of dengue fever in New Zealand, as well as other diseases around the world.

George Mulala—Reuters

Family members push their car along a flooded street south of Nairobi, Kenya, in January 1998. Triggered by El Niño, excessive rains in equatorial eastern Africa, ranging between 400 and 600 mm (15.75 and 23.6 in) above normal in Kenya, caused extensive flooding in that region.

The El Niño virtually shut down the production of hurricanes in the Atlantic during the summer of 1997 but enhanced the hurricane activity in parts of the eastern Pacific. In addition, the shift in winds caused by El Niño was strong enough to slow down Earth's rotation by a small but noticeable amount and thereby lengthened the day by four-tenths of a millisecond.

Ocean reefs

In an effort to increase understanding and awareness of ocean reefs, researchers declared 1997 the International Year of the Reef. This special focus was initiated because of widespread signs that the health of coral reefs was declining, in some cases precipitously.

In international meetings and in scientific journals, scientists discussed the plight of reefs, which are subjected to pol-

lution, overfishing, competition from seaweed, and other threats. The dwindling reefs in Florida, the Caribbean, and Southeast Asia had attracted widespread attention over the last several years, but more remote reefs in the Pacific were, in many cases, in good health. Lacking even fundamental data about the extent of reefs in the world, ocean researchers launched several programs to collect information on reefs and to monitor their health. (*See* Feature Article: WHAT IS KILLING THE REEFS?)

Sea ice

A dramatic decline in Antarctic sea ice between the 1950s and the 1970s was detected by an Australian oceanographer who studied whaling records going back to the 1930s. The controversial study, which garnered substantial press coverage, appeared to support other observations of climatic

warming across much of the globe during the century. Sea ice surrounding Antarctica covers an area about twice the size of the U.S., waxing and waning with the seasons. Because the formation of polar ice depends critically on ocean temperatures and other climatic variables, researchers regard changes in the extent of sea ice as a possible early warning sign of global greenhouse warming.

Satellites began measuring sea ice in the 1970s, and there has been little change since that time. Information on earlier decades, however, was gleaned from records of whale captures. These provided clues about the position of sea ice because some species of whales congregate near the edge of the ice, where nutrients and fish are plentiful. The whaling records indicated a decline of some 25% in the area of sea ice around Antarctica, a decrease that equals about 5,650,000 sq km (2,180,000 sq mi). Other researchers, however, questioned the methods of the study.

Seafloor map

Researchers during the year exploited a set of formerly secret satellite measurements to produce the best available map of ocean depth throughout the world. The map fills in huge holes in existing charts and provides more than twice the resolution of the previous best global seafloor map.

The new information came from satellites that bounce microwaves off the ocean surface to measure its height. Ocean height provides clues about seafloor depth because the gravitational force of submerged mountains causes the ocean surface to bulge by several meters. Oceanographers combined these gravity data with actual ship measurements of seafloor depth to create the global map.

Seabed mining

An Australian-backed company during the year obtained rights to mine bountiful deposits of gold, silver, and other metals located on the ocean bottom off the coast of Papua New Guinea. This move marked the first time that miners would attempt to extract wealth from the 65,000-km (40,000-mi)-long system of submerged volcanic ridges that wind around the globe.

The claim was located about 1.5 km (0.9 mi) below the sea surface and covered nearly 5,000 sq km (1,930 sq mi). Samples of the ore suggested that it contained up to 26% zinc, 15% copper, and significant quantities of silver and gold. These metal deposits lay at a site where volcanically heated brine erupts from the crust and mixes with nearly freezing ocean-bottom water. As the brine emerges, its load of dissolved metals precipitates out onto the ocean floor. The Australian miners planned to start by pulling up 10,000 tons of ore each year during the next two years. It remained unclear whether the value of the ore would exceed the cost of hauling it up from the depths. Environmentalists raised concern that such mining activity would damage the rich array of ocean life surrounding the hydrothermal deep-sea vents. Mining experts, however, hailed the Australian action as opening a new frontier in the recovery of metals.

Ocean current collapse

Oceanographers warned that global warming could eventually shut down important currents that transport heat around the globe—an effect that would trigger a sudden change in climate and drastically cool Europe. Resembling a conveyor belt, the system of currents shuttles heat from the tropics to the polar regions. Known as the thermohaline circulation, it is driven by cold, salty water in the North Atlantic that is dense enough to sink to the ocean bottom. This North Atlantic Deep Water current has a volume 16 times greater than all the world's rivers combined. It flows southward through the Atlantic and then circles Antarctica. The current eventually heads northward into the Pacific and Indian oceans, where it slowly warms and rises to the surface.

The North Atlantic is one of the few places on Earth where water is cold enough and salty enough to sink to the ocean floor to form such a deep current. Recent research, however, revealed that this conveyor-belt system is sensitive to changing climate and that it has turned off abruptly in the past. During those times vast armadas of icebergs have flowed south into the North Atlantic, and the temperature of Europe has plummeted. Global warming could shut down the conveyor by raising the water temperature of the North Atlantic and reducing the water's saltiness (a by-product of melting glaciers or increases in precipitation falling on the ocean). If this were to happen, winter temperatures in the North Atlantic would fall by 10° C (18° F) in a decade.

Ice age theory

Two researchers proposed a new hypothesis in order to explain why Earth has slipped in and out of 10 ice ages over the last million years—one of the great puzzles of oceanographic research. According to the researchers' hypothesis, this natural cycle of long-term global cooling and warming results from the Earth's periodically passing through a cloud of extraterrestrial dust.

During the last few decades, scientific studies of seafloor sediments have revealed that ice ages have repeatedly gripped the planet for the last 2.5 million years. Prior to one million years ago, the ice ages occurred every 40,000 years—a frequency that matches characteristic wobbles in the Earth's axis of rotation. For that reason oceanographers regard the orbital variations as the cause of the ice ages—an idea known as the Milankovitch hypothesis, after a Serbian scientist.

The Milankovitch hypothesis, however, has trouble explaining the ice ages of the last million years, which have occurred with a frequency of 100,000 years. Two scientists during the past year suggested that this most recent set of ice ages resulted from subtle shifts in the plane of Earth's orbit, which tilts above and below the plane of the other planets every 100,000 years. They hypothesized that the slow teetering of the orbital plane may cause Earth to pass periodically through a cloud of extraterrestrial dust, which upsets climate in a way that would trigger the initiation of an ice age. This theory drew some support from an analysis of ocean sediments suggesting that the amount of extraterrestrial dust reaching Earth rises and falls every 100,000 years. Many climate researchers were regarding this new hypothesis with skepticism, however. Critics charged that there was no clear explanation for how extraterrestrial dust would cool climate enough to send Earth into a deep freeze.

Other developments

New clues emerged in the quest to understand why the Earth warmed mysteriously a little more than 55 million years ago, near the end of the Paleocene Epoch. This dramatic climate change caused massive extinctions in the deep sea and supported the evolution of many land mammals, which have dominated the continents ever since. The answer to the Paleocene warming may lie beneath the ocean floor in deposits of solidified natural gas called methane hydrates. These icelike deposits are buried under seafloor sediments around most continents, but they are unstable and can melt if temperatures in the deep sea rise.

One group of scientists proposed that the melting of such methane hydrates may have produced much of the Paleocene warming. When methane reaches the atmosphere, it becomes a greenhouse gas and helps heat the Earth's surface. The researchers performed a computer simulation to test their hypothesis. If 1,120,000,000,000 tons of methane hydrates had melted—an amount equivalent to 10% of the currently existing deposits—the planet's temperature would have risen 1.7° to 1.9° C (3.1° to 3.4° F), they found. The hydrate hypothesis would also help explain a distinctive shift in the carbon chemistry of the ocean at that time.

Another team of scientists found evidence of gigantic volcanic eruptions in the Caribbean that coincided with the Paleocene warming. They suggested that these eruptions may have reoriented ocean currents in a way that caused the release of methane hydrates and thus triggered the climate change.

Chemists discovered evidence that life may have originated at the bottom of the sea, near the blistering volcanic vents known as black smokers, which spew out chemically laden fluids. Two German researchers explored the chemistry of the deep-sea vents by mixing together four compounds present in those fluids: methyl thiol, carbon monoxide, nickel sulfide, and ferrous sulfide. The metallic sulfides acted as a catalyst for a reaction that produced a compound resembling activated acetic acid, which plays an important role in the metabolism of all known life. Their work raised the possibility that reactions between exotic vent chemicals may have been among the first steps leading toward the development of life on Earth.

Japan in 1997 launched the world's largest oceanographic research vessel, providing a potent symbol of the country's drive to become an important participant in marine research. With a length of 130 m (426 ft) and a weight of 8,600 tons, the ship provided space for a crew of 80 people. Among other activities, it was to be used to set out buoys that can track ocean temperatures and currents at various sites around the world. Japan was also planning to work with the international research community to build a ship designed to drill 3,500 m (11,500 ft) into the ocean floor in order to probe the deep ocean crust.

—Richard Monastersky

PALEONTOLOGY

The controversy over the role of an asteroid impact in the extinction of the dinosaurs and other animals and plants continued with no loss of vigor during the past year and showed no sign of early resolution. William A. Clemens and L. Gayle Nelms of the University of California, Berkeley, reported the discovery on Alaska's North Slope of the remains of a small, lightly built hypsilophodont dinosaur that lived in Late Cretaceous time about 70 million years ago. The fossils were found in association with plant remains, which suggested that the climate at the time of burial was similar to that of present-day Anchorage, Alaska. Clemens—who has long been an opponent of those who believe that an impact of an asteroid with the Earth was wholly responsible for the great extinction in Late Cretaceous–Early Tertiary time—and Nelms argued that the finding of these remains at that northern latitude suggests that some dinosaurs were capable of surviving a long, dark winter. The onset of a prolonged period of dark and cold following an asteroid impact has been invoked as the cause of the extinction of the dinosaurs as well as the extinction of many other terrestrial and marine animals. That there was a collision between the Earth and an asteroid at the end of the Cretaceous appears to have been firmly established, nor is there much doubt in the paleontological community that this event coincided with a major extinction. As Clemens and Nelms pointed out, however, many species survived the event at the end of the Cretaceous, and any satisfactory hypothesis must take this fact into account.

Some planetary scientists agree that a prolonged period of darkness and low temperatures might not have been sufficient to account for the extinction of so many different kinds of animals. H. Jay Melosh of the University of Arizona suggested, for example, that a lethal concentration of acid rain may have developed as a consequence of a major asteroid collision. In addition, planetary scientists have countered the view of many paleontologists that the energy released by an impact of an asteroid of a size believed to have formed the Chicxulub crater on the Yucatan Peninsula was insufficient to have wrought such devastation. Virgil Sharpton of the Lunar and Planetary Institute, Houston, Texas, and his colleagues reported that surface traces indicate that the crater may be 300 km (185 mi) in diameter, nearly twice that of previous estimates, which suggests an impact eight times more powerful. Sharpton and his colleagues believe that this event may have been the most devastating since the origin of complex life on Earth, 650 million years ago. No matter how devastating the collision, however, Clemens's question remained unanswered. By what mechanism was the agent of extinction so selective?

The debate over the origin of birds continued undiminished in 1997, with those opposing the view that they arose from small, light-boned theropod dinosaurs some 150 million years ago seeming to gain some ground. Many reptiles, birds, and mammals have fewer than the five digits on each limb found in primitive tetrapods, which are generally accepted as their ancestors. This departure from the ancestral condition has occurred through reduction in the course of evolution. One similarity between theropod dinosaurs and birds is that in each, two of the five digits have disappeared or remain only in a rudimentary state, a fact that is consistent with the view that one may be the ancestor of the other. Ann Burke and Alan Feduccia of the University of North Carolina at Chapel Hill, however, reported on research that strongly suggests that the theropods and the birds, although they have the same number of digits, have not lost the same digits. Investigations of the developing embryos of domestic chickens, ostriches, and cormorants reveal that it is the middle three digits that have been retained. Fossil evidence, on the other hand, points to a loss of the fourth and the fifth digits in the theropods. The authors maintain that because of this fundamental difference, theropod dinosaurs could not have been the ancestors of the birds. The authors go on to point out that the two groups may have an ancestor in common whose remains have not yet been found. (*See* Feature Article: FEATHERS: AN ANCIENT PERFECTION.)

Mark A. Norell of the American Museum of Natural History in New York City and his colleagues have struck a blow for the other side. It has long been maintained that dinosaurs could not have been the ancestors of the birds because they lacked a furcula, the bone formed by the fusion of the clavicles, called in the vernacular the wishbone. A furcula has, however, now been found in several theropod dinosaurs. Norell and his colleagues describe a theropod skeleton recovered in 1991 by a joint expedition of the Mongolian Academy of Sciences and the American Museum of Natural History. On this specimen the furcula is well preserved, and, what is more important, it is fully articulated with the scapular bones. The authors do not suggest that the furcula in dinosaurs served the same function that it does in birds, but rather suggest that whatever its function in

The largest and most complete skeleton of *Tyrannosaurus* known to date, "Sue" (head shown below) was bought at auction by Chicago's Field Museum of Natural History in October 1997.

dinosaurs, it was adapted to the requirements of flight in their bird descendants, much as the small bones near the articulation of the jaw of reptiles became, during the course of evolution, the ossicles of the inner ear of mammals.

Though cataclysmic extinctions and the origin of the birds captured the lion's share of public and media attention, many paleontologists throughout the world engaged during the year in significant work devoted to other subjects. For example, at the 1997 meeting of the Society of Vertebrate Paleontology, held in Chicago in October, John Bolt of the Field Museum of Natural History in Chicago and his fellow paleontologist R. Eric Lombard of the University of Chicago reported on the remains of a microsaur recovered from rocks of the Mississippian Period (320 million–360 million years ago) by researchers from the University of Kansas. Microsaurs were small reptiles ranging in length between 12 and 15 cm (4.7 and 5.9 in). They are particularly significant because they were among the first vertebrates to take the revolutionary step from an aquatic to a terrestrial environment. The new specimen, having been recovered from rocks formed 330 million years ago, represents the earliest recorded occurrence of a microsaur.

A remarkable group of 20 fossilized dinosaur and tortoise eggs was

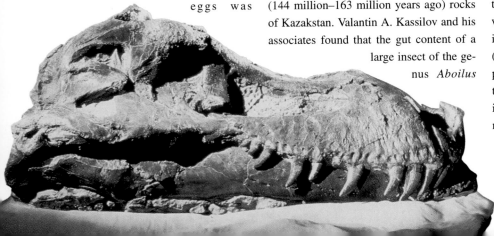

found in sediments of Late Cretaceous age (65 million–100 million years ago) in Mongolia in 1992. Meticulous preparation revealed the skeletons of embryos in some of the eggs. The exhibit of these specimens at the University Museum of Zoology at the University of Cambridge aroused widespread interest and excitement. The fossils were not the property of the museum but belonged to a consortium of fossil collectors who had exported them from China. Paleontologists were eager that these important fossils eventually find their way into an academic setting where they could receive the scientific attention that they deserved. Members of the consortium hoped to find a buyer for the fossils who would donate them to an academic institution.

Ownership of the largest and most complete skeleton of *Tyrannosaurus* known to date, which was discovered in 1990 in South Dakota and nicknamed "Sue," had been a subject of controversy for several years. The courts finally resolved the issue, which cleared the way for the designated owner to auction off the skeleton to the highest bidder. Sue was bought by Chicago's Field Museum of Natural History in October 1997 for $8,360,000.

Three Russian scientists writing in the *Journal of Paleontology,* reported a remarkable discovery in the Upper Jurassic (144 million–163 million years ago) rocks of Kazakstan. Valantin A. Kassilov and his associates found that the gut content of a large insect of the genus *Aboilus*

contained pollen belonging to the genus *Classopolis.* So concentrated was the pollen in the gut of those insects that the authors concluded that they must have fed almost exclusively on *Classopolis.* At other locations *Classopolis* is usually found in rocks that are plainly of littoral (coastal) origin. From this it appears that these large grasshopper-like insects must have lived near a shoreline that supplied an abundant source of pollen.

Jack A. Wolfe of the University of Arizona and his colleagues succeeded in estimating the elevation of the Basin and Range province of western Nevada between 15 million and 16 million years ago. The assumption that certain kinds of plants are adapted to a range of environmental conditions like those of their nearest living relatives has long served as a foundation for inferences about past climates. The researchers took into account the further fact that plants may manifest structural characters that vary in response to changing conditions, as, for example, in the stunting of some species of trees at high altitudes. It is possible to infer past climatic conditions by comparing the structures of the fossil leaves with those of present-day species that vary when subjected to different climatic conditions. Taking this added information into account, Wolfe and his colleagues were able to infer that 15 million–16 million years ago the western part of the Basin and Range province stood at an elevation of about 3 km (9,800 ft), about two times higher than at present. The authors attributed the change to crustal thinning and consequent faulting in the region during the last 40 million–50 million years.

—David B. Kitts

ELECTRONICS AND INFORMATION SCIENCES

In 1997 computers and other high-end electronics systems manifested themselves in a variety of consumer products, including portable data-storage and automotive devices. In the field of photonics, advances in semiconductor-laser research showed promise in new military and space systems as well as scientific, industrial, and consumer applications. The growing use of the Internet, particularly in its incorporation of innovations such as the Java programming language, paved the way for increased availability of on-line research and telecommunications.

ELECTRONICS

Consumer products

Consumer-electronics manufacturers in 1997 hoped that digital versatile (or video) disc (DVD) technology would whet consumers' purchasing appetites, and the computer industry envisioned DVD as its best opportunity to expand personal computer (PC) usage. Computers equipped with DVDs having read-only memory (DVD-ROMs) were expected to become more important as consumers made greater use of multimedia data streams. A typical single-sided DVD's 4.7-gigabyte capacity made it a superior medium for storing data, yet it functioned much the same as the more familiar compact-disc-based CD-ROM.

Many observers believed that DVD technology would play an integral part in next-generation digital consumer products. Leading silicon-chip vendors, in cooperation with consumer-electronics vendors, had plans for integrating support for DVD-based products into their chips. Even

Microsoft Corp. was planning to add a range of application program interfaces (APIs) and other features to the next upgrade of the company's ubiquitous Windows operating system to make the Windows-based PC platform truly DVD-friendly.

In another area of consumer electronics, the smart phone—which could integrate a cellular telephone, a pocket organizer, and a portable computer—became the most demanding consumer-electronics device ever attempted. It coupled multiple-computer, communications, and silicon-integration technologies to provide personal computing functions as well as portable World Wide Web access in one package. Limited battery life, however, had hampered the development of the smart phone. Whereas pocket-organizer fans expected weeks to months of use from a pair of dry-cell batteries, cellular-telephone users needed to plug their phones into a battery charger every night, and notebook-computer users had to carry extra battery packs for long airplane flights. It was, therefore, a challenge for the industry to produce a smart phone that could run for a full day or more on a set of batteries.

The year heralded a breakthrough for personal digital assistants (PDAs), including units with built-in wireless capabilities. Nokia OY's Nokia 9000 combined a GSM (Global System for Mobile Communications, a popular digital system for cellular telephony developed in Europe) cellular phone and an organizer. In Japan mobile assistants appeared as part of the Personal Handy-Phone System (PHS). These could link to closely spaced base stations several hundred meters apart while consuming only about 10% of the power of cellular

phones. Matsushita Electric Industrial Co., Ltd., tested a prototype of its Pinocchio mobile communicator, which was memo-pad-sized and slightly smaller than the Nokia 9000. Its lithium-ion rechargeable battery provided the Pinocchio with enough power for an eight-hour phone call, 200 hours of call waiting, or more than four hours of on-line use with a built-in modem.

Digital still cameras saw major advances in the past year. These devices stored photographic images in digital form on a miniature flash-memory card, which, when inserted in a special reader, allowed users to see the photos on a Web-ready television set. The user could manipulate the images digitally by means of techniques that professional custom photo labs used on traditional 35-mm photographic negatives. The images could also be stored on a server, posted on a Web site, or printed with near-photographic quality on a personal color printer or at a local photofinisher.

A Toshiba employee demonstrates Allegretto, billed as the world's smallest and lightest digital still camera, at the unveiling of the device in Tokyo in June 1997. The business-card-sized Allegretto weighs only 130 g (4.6 oz) and employs a complex complementary metal-oxide-semiconductor sensor.

Reuters

289

It was also a year of breakthroughs in technologies needed to get digital cameras clicking en masse. One technology, the imaging chips that were a central feature of these cameras, became the subject of tremendous debate. The issue was whether to use charge-coupled devices (CCDs) or complementary metal-oxide-semiconductor (CMOS) technology for the imaging-chip sensors. (CMOS was the most widespread electronics technology being used in integrated circuits.) Kodak stayed with CCDs for its next digital still-camera products, whereas Toshiba brought out a camera that employed a complex CMOS sensor. The underlying technology of digital photography opened the market not only to traditional camera and film manufacturers but also to electronics companies. Toshiba, Hewlett-Packard, and Epson were among the early entrants into the market.

Expanding applications of smart cards were demanding new ways to access all

A representative at an automobile show sits in front of a car dashboard that includes a voice-operated personal computer designed by Microsoft Corp. By 1997 the dashboard was primed to incorporate a variety of electronic gadgetry—from DVD players to wireless Internet-access devices.

Reuters

the digitized information to be recorded in the cards, and a new generation of minidisplays were expected to provide that capability. The tiny flat-panel displays also met the needs of mobile-communications equipment and data-delivery services for a convenient means of viewing data. Electronic projectors were expected to move more minidisplays into the conference room and, perhaps, into the home, and digital cameras and visual-display headgear for PC game players would further increase the demand. In 1997 as many as 25 companies were developing minidisplays. The first low-cost color minidisplay to reach the market was the CyberDisplay from the Kopin Corp. Kopin had established development partnerships with firms representing a wide range of application areas, including cellular telephones and pagers, smart-card readers, and digital cameras. The CyberDisplay, which measured only 6.1-mm (0.24-in) diagonally and had a backlight and lens, could make a 51-cm (20-in) virtual image look like it was 1.5 m (5 ft) away.

GPS applications

Portable global positioning system (GPS) devices were also showing up on the market. Consumer devices had been available since 1995, but in 1997 many innovations were being introduced that were expected to lower the price. For example, the American Technology Corp. (ATC) designed a prototype portable device to simplify the locational tracking of a person or object. This system employed GPS technology, but, unlike most portable GPS devices, it did not require complicated longitude-latitude readouts, mapping software, or

stored information based on previously recorded locations. In December 1997 ATC received the first of several patents that it had filed on its GPS approach, which it called Tracker technology.

GPS was designed to replace or complement other forms of electronic navigation and position data systems. It offered major advantages in accuracy with worldwide coverage in three dimensions (in addition to providing time and velocity data) using global positioning satellites around the Earth. In 1997 the global positioning system comprised 24 orbiting satellites. GPS positioning was based on a triangulation technique that measured distances to three or more satellites, which continuously broadcast radio signals that were precisely timed with atomic clocks. A GPS receiver ascertained its position—longitude, latitude, and altitude—by determining the time required for the signals from those satellites in view to reach it, calculating the distances from the satellites, and using those distances to triangulate its position. A stand-alone GPS receiver could calculate its position at any point on Earth, in the atmosphere, or in a lower Earth orbit to within 25 m (82 ft). Differential GPS, which involved two or more GPS receivers, improved the accuracy to some 2–5 m (6.5–16 ft). When coupled with a known, precise reference position, a single GPS receiver could achieve accuracy of less than one centimeter (0.4 in).

ATC's new Tracker technology used a small handheld device with a screen display that indicated the direction to a miniature device (called a node) attached to a target person or object and provided readouts for distance and differential altitude with respect to the node in simple units of

The "father" of the computer mouse, Douglas C. Engelbart, poses with his invention after being awarded the 1997 $500,000 Lemelson-MIT Prize. Engelbart is also the inventor of hypermedia, multiple-window computer screens, groupware, on-line publishing, and E-mail systems.

measure (feet, yards, meters, or miles). Tracker was designed to operate in two modes. In the tracking mode, it could track a remote target (with a node attached) to within 0.3–0.6 m (1–2 ft) and functioned with greater accuracy than differential GPS. In locating mode, it was designed to find either a preset location or an entered location with the accuracy of other portable GPS devices but without their added complexity.

Automotive electronics

By 1997 the automobile dashboard was primed to incorporate a variety of electronic gadgetry—from radios, DVD players, and car phones to GPS-based navigation units and wireless Internet-access devices. One of the hottest debates in the industry was over whether the architecture for the "edutainment" system in the car would ultimately look like a PC, a consumer-electronics product, or some new device unique to the automobile. The Society of Automotive Engineers (SAE) was moving to define a standard data bus on which information and control signals could travel back and forth between devices. This would aid product acceptance and create demand, much like the huge consumer aftermarket for automotive stereo systems and car alarms. The U.S. Department of Transportation helped fund the SAE's effort to develop the Intelligent Transportation System (ITS) Data Bus.

The ITS Data Bus was intended to be an open, nonproprietary serial-communications protocol for linking items inside the vehicle's passenger compartment into a network. It would function independently of automotive networks that link the en-

gine, brakes, air bags, and transmission and other body subsystems. Unlike other subsystem networking schemes, however, the ITS Data Bus avoided special microprocessors.

The ITS Data Bus project was advancing along two parallel paths. One bus had a 115-kilobit-per-second data-transfer rate, which was suitable for pagers and cell phones. A higher-speed version, intended to run at 100 megabits per second, would target DVD video and other multimedia devices. Carmakers, however, had remained silent about their possible adoption of the proposed SAE standard.

Microchip manufacturer Intel Corp. and software giant Microsoft maintained that they were already in possession of the necessary architecture for the auto electronics revolution. Pushing its Connected Car PC technology, Intel was designing an architecture to be used in a major automobile manufacturer's vehicles. In its current configurations, however, a PC might not be suitable for use in an automobile. The PC's reliability would have to be improved to withstand a harsh environment with extreme variations in temperature, humidity, and vibration. The user interface also would need to be redesigned for improved safety and ease of use.

Awards

Douglas C. Engelbart, who held some of the most fundamental patents in the computer industry, was awarded the 1997 $500,000 Lemelson-MIT Prize. The 72-year-old Engelbart—inventor of the computer mouse, hypermedia, multiple-window screens, groupware, on-line publishing, and E-mail systems—did much of the work while at the Stanford Research Institute (now SRI International) in Menlo Park, Calif., in the 1950s and '60s. His invention of the first fully integrated two-way computer/video teleconference led to the development of ARPANET, the precursor of the Internet. In 1988 Engelbart founded the Bootstrap Institute in Fremont, Calif., the goal of which was to dramatically improve society through the development of technologies that could effectively manage the increasing volume of useful information "to boost the Collective IQ."

The government of Australia granted the $A 300,000 Australia Prize, the country's highest science award, to three engineers for outstanding achievements in the field of telecommunications. Rodney Tucker, director of the University of Melbourne's Photonics Research Laboratory, was honored for "developing laser technology to increase the network's carrying capacity by tenfold." Gottfried Ungerboeck of IBM's Zürich (Switz.) Research Laboratory was cited for his development of trellis-coded modulation (TCM) in the 1970s. Originally used for coding data for transmission between computer modems, TCM enabled reliable data transmission over telephone lines and other transmission media at higher speeds than had been thought possible. By 1997 it was being used in numerous systems, including satellite and terrestrial wireless systems, digital audio and television broadcasting, and Internet-access systems. Allan Snyder, head of the Australian National University's Optical Sciences Center, was cited for "ground-breaking technology by providing the cornerstone research for the optical-fiber telecommunications network."

Women in Technology International inducted "the first programmers in the world" into their society's Hall of Fame. The women had worked on the development of the ENIAC computer in the mid-1940s. Acknowledged for their contributions as software pioneers were Kay Mauchly Antonelli, Jean Bartik, Betty Holberton, Marlyn Meltzer, Frances Spence, and Ruth Teitelbaum.

—Nicolas Mokhoff

PHOTONICS AND OPTICAL TECHNOLOGY

Advances in visible and mid-infrared semiconductor lasers in 1997 led the parade of developments in photonics and optical technology that promised to find significant scientific, industrial, and consumer applications in the near future. Researchers and manufacturers also devised ways to improve telecommunications, military and space systems, optical sensors, microscopy, and semiconductor manufacture, producing new solutions for problems in settings ranging from laboratory and factory to outer space.

Semiconductor lasers

Japan's Nichia Chemical Industries Inc. led the hot news in photonics with its announcement of the development of a violet-light-emitting semiconductor diode laser with an estimated lifetime of 15,000 hours at room temperature. Emitting with a wavelength of 403.7 nm (nanometers), the gallium nitride device would enable manufacturers of digital versatile (or video) discs (DVDs) and CD-ROMs to write considerably more information onto each disc. Whereas the red lasers in common use emit at 650 nm and can write 4.5–5 gigabytes of information on a DVD, the violet laser's considerably shorter wavelength would allow 15 gigabytes (equivalent to about seven hours of movies) to be written onto a disc. Earlier developmental blue and violet semiconductor lasers had been relatively short-lived because of heat buildup, but Nichia managed to overcome the problems. The company predicted that it would have commercial violet lasers by the end of 1998.

Nichia was not alone in the race for commercialization. The significant market potential attracted many companies to invest considerable time and money in research and development of visible and ultraviolet diode lasers. Several other groups announced visible semiconductor laser developments in 1997; Toshiba, Fujitsu, Sony, Cree Research, Hewlett-Packard, Xerox, Meijo University, and the University of California, Santa Barbara, all had research programs aimed at producing semiconductor lasers that emit in the blue or violet.

Exploring the mid-infrared range of the spectrum, researchers at Lucent Technologies' Bell Laboratories measured a peak power of 750 mw from a pulsed eight-micrometer (μm)-wavelength quantum cascade laser that was cooled to liquid-nitrogen temperatures (below about −196° C, or −320° F), the highest power on record for a semiconductor laser in the mid-infrared wavelength region (a micrometer is about 0.00004 in). At its highest operating temperature, −33° C (−27° F), the device produced 30 mw of power. The team also developed lasers that emit at about 5 and 11 μm.

Lasers in the mid-infrared range have significant potential applications in medical testing, military countermeasures, pollution monitoring, and industrial process control. The U.S. Naval Research Laboratory, Washington, D.C.; Hughes Research Laboratory, Malibu, Calif.; the University of Houston, Texas; Sandia National Laboratories, Albuquerque, N.M.; Northwestern University, Evanston, Ill.; the University of Illinois; and the University of Paris also made strides in 1997 in developing semiconductor lasers in the mid-infrared.

Telecommunications

Another significant market prompted advances from NEC's Optoelectronic Device Research Laboratory in Tokyo. The company developed a technique that produces diode lasers of many wavelengths on a single semiconductor wafer. Conventional diode laser manufacturing techniques produce many laser units of a single wavelength on a wafer. NEC's manufacturing technique also produces many laser units, but not at the same wavelength; lasers from one indium phosphide wafer emit at 40 different wavelengths from 1,518.2 to 1,593.2 nm. The lasers have uniform lasing characteristics and a threshold current (the current at which lasing action begins) stabilized at nine milliamperes, parameters that are key to stable system operation.

Photographs, Air Force Research Laboratory/Propulsion Directorate, Edwards AFB; Rensselaer Polytech Institute, NASA

The technique is significant because new telecommunications systems will use a technique called wavelength division multiplexing (WDM). In WDM, communications companies can expand the capacity of their fiber-optic systems by putting many signal-carrying wavelengths of light into a single optical fiber.

Members of the Multiwavelength Optical Networking (MONET) Consortium announced major advances toward the development of an all-optical telecommunications network that incorporates multiplexed signals using WDM that can operate across both local and long-distance networks. The consortium demonstrated three interconnected test beds for novel optical telecommunications technologies: a 2,000-km (1,240-mi)-long test bed with a data-transmission rate of 2.5 billion bits per second on each of eight channels, a multiwavelength ring that is self-healing (if one signal route fails, another is found automatically) and constitutes the first part of a local-exchange test bed, and a cross-connect system for switch testing. A fourth test bed will link consortium members— including the U.S. National Security Agency and Naval Research Laboratory— in the Washington, D.C., area. The goal of the consortium—a cooperative of U.S. government and industrial research institutions—is to develop multiwavelength optical networking on a national scale that would serve both government and commercial applications.

Military and space systems

Researchers with NASA's Advanced Space Transportation Program used a 10-kw car-

Propelled by pulses of light from a carbon dioxide laser, a miniature test rocket rises several meters off the ground (above) at the White Sands Missile Range in New Mexico. The spike-shaped reflector in the rear of the craft (top) concentrates the light, which heats the air under it into a luminous plasma.

bon dioxide laser to launch a miniature rocket and propel it several meters off the ground at the White Sands Missile Range in New Mexico. (A meter is about 3.3 ft.) A reflector in the rear of the miniature craft concentrated the laser beam, heating the air under it. The heated air then blasted out of a nozzle, propelling the craft. Beamed-energy propulsion was being explored as a potential method of moving satellites and other spacecraft, and the earthly success cheered proponents of that technique.

In October U.S. Air Force investigators fired a high-power chemical laser from White Sands at a satellite that was orbiting Earth. They used the Mid-Infrared Advanced Chemical Laser (MIRACL), a megawatt-class deuterium fluoride laser, to hit an air force satellite twice. The two test hits simulated two events. One used a low-power setting and a duration of less than a second to provide data showing how a satellite might react to the inadvertent illumination by a ground-based laser. The second used higher power and several illuminations of less than five seconds each, simulating a deliberate firing. The tests provided information that would improve computer models used in developing protective measures for U.S. spacecraft.

Optics technology

Researchers at the Massachusetts Institute of Technology (MIT) successfully simulated on a computer a "photonic crystal" that bends light sharply with near-perfect transmission. Photonic crystals are semiconductor materials provided with a geometry—typically a regular latticelike pattern comprising regions of semiconductor separated by gaps—that allows them to control light waves similar to the way that conventional semiconductor devices control electrons. The team found in computer simulations that a photonic crystal made of gallium arsenide could act as a waveguide, steering light around a slightly rounded corner at 100% transmission and through a right angle at 98% transmission. The previous best means of controlling light, total internal reflection, provides only 30% efficiency for a similar corner. The discovery is important because it could significantly reduce the size of optoelectronic modules such as those used in telecommunications, sensing, and optical computing. MIT's "virtual" photonic crystal comprised a series of evenly spaced dielectric rods. The spacing and size of the rods determined the crystal's opacity. The researchers hoped to demonstrate the physical photonic crystal itself by the year 2000.

Carl Zeiss GmbH of Germany built the world's largest ring-laser gyroscope for installation in a subterranean cave on the Banks Peninsula in New Zealand. The gyroscope comprised a 1.2 × 1.2-m (3.9 × 3.9-ft) block of Zerodur (a glass-ceramic material with exceptional thermal stability) that had four longitudinal bores, each one meter (3.28 ft) long with deflecting mirrors at the intersections, forming a closed square pathway for the laser beam. The gyroscope's sensitivity to changes in position—its rotational resolution was one part in 10 million over long time spans—permitted highly accurate detection of fluctuations in the Earth's rotation. The sensing of those fluctuations could help in the detection of small changes in the Earth itself for research related to relativity theory. The German project was commissioned by the Institute of Applied Geodesy, Frankfurt, and the Technical University of Munich.

Biological applications

Short pulses of an infrared laser offered a new, less-damaging fluorescence method of imaging living biological specimens. Researchers at Cornell University, Ithaca, N.Y., used brief, intense pulses of infrared light from a titanium-doped sapphire laser to induce fluorescence from molecules in living cell specimens by means of a technique called multiphoton excitation. The laser pulses are so short that groups of photons strike the target area over a time span brief enough to be considered simultaneous for the purposes of satisfying quantum theory. Select biological molecules whose excitation energy is normally

Rebecca Williams and Warren Zipfel, School of Applied Physics & Engineering, Cornell University

Bombarded by brief, intense laser pulses, granules containing serotonin molecules fluoresce brightly in living cells from a rat. The fluorescence technique used, called multiphoton excitation, offers a less-damaging method for imaging and measuring molecular concentrations in living specimens.

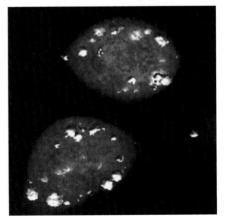

three or even six times higher than the energy of the infrared photons thus can become excited by absorbing several of the lower-energy photons together. The excited molecules then emit their extra energy in the form of energetic fluorescence photons, which are detected and imaged under the microscope.

The use of lower-energy infrared photons avoids the damage to specimens, especially living samples, that would occur if single higher-energy photons—for example, from an ultraviolet laser—were used to induce fluorescence. Another benefit of infrared light is that it penetrates tissue better than other wavelengths do.

In Japan researchers at Kyushu University developed a technique that they called optical chromatography to watch antibody-antigen interactions as they occur. In the technique a laser beam is focused onto a capillary filled with water that flows toward the beam. Particles of interest are then released into the capillary so that they flow toward the laser. If the force exerted on the particles by the incoming laser light exceeds that of the water flow, the particle is pushed upstream. When the forces balance, the particle stops and remains trapped at a particular site along the capillary. If two different kinds of particles flow into the beam, they will stop in different places according to their size and refractive index.

The Kyushu scientists applied their approach to immunoassay, a method of identifying proteins and measuring their amounts. They placed tiny polystyrene beads that had been coated with an antibody into a solution of the specific protein (the antigen) to which the antibody binds and allowed the beads and antigen to react immunologically. Beads that bound to the protein antigen also became bound to each other, whereas unreacted beads stayed unbound. The researchers then used optical chromatography to separate the bound and free beads. By aiming a magnifying camera at the trapping site within the capillary, they could see the beads as they combined. Determining the ratio of bound and free beads allowed the researchers to measure the concentration of antigen present.

Semiconductor manufacturing

Semiconductor manufacturers have used lasers and other methods to create tiny features on integrated circuits. Nevertheless, as they have tried to squeeze more features onto a single chip, the features have necessarily shrunk, which has pushed manufacturing technology to its limits. Current-generation semiconductor manufacturing uses krypton fluoride excimer lasers with a wavelength of 248 nm to produce features that are 0.18–0.25 μm wide. To shrink features further, manufacturers must move to a new laser, the 193-nm argon fluoride laser, which can create features that are only 0.13 μm wide. Farther in the future, 157-nm lasers could produce features as small as 0.07 μm.

These latter two wavelengths, however, do not interact well with conventional photoresists, the wafer coating material onto which lasers "write" the patterns that will be physically created in the wafer during subsequent processing. Bell Laboratories announced the development of a photoresist that is compatible with 193-nm lasers. The material consists of a class of matrix resins based on cyclo-olefin-maleic anhydride alternating copolymers.

Lightning protection

Japanese researchers at Osaka University and the Kansai Electric Power Co. used a laser beam to trigger a lightning discharge to a specific target. Employing an electron-beam-controlled carbon dioxide laser and two large-aperture Cassegrain telescopes, they created a plasma channel—a pathway of electrically charged atoms and molecules—from the top of a metal "lightning tower" toward a thundercloud. Electronic equipment timed the firing of two one-kilojoule, 50-nanosecond laser pulses just as the thundercloud was about to discharge. Lightning strikes damage power transmission lines thousands of times each year. Power companies hope the laser research will enable them to divert lightning bolts to less-damaging locations.

—Stephanie A. Weiss

COMPUTERS AND COMPUTER SCIENCE

As the millennium approached, computer science continued to become ever more closely intertwined with the real world. By 1997 the Internet had become integral to millions of computer users, and Java—a hot new programming language designed specifically for the Internet—was increasingly taking center stage in software development. Semiconductor giant Intel Corp. was spending large sums to promote its new MMX multimedia technology via expensive television commercials. The ongoing search for solutions to the millennium bug, or the Y2K (industry jargon for the year 2000) problem, loomed large in 1997, with businesses in many industries fearing widespread computer crashes and other problems at the start of 2000, which many

computers could not distinguish from 1900. The computing community also witnessed its share of legal battles as the U.S. Department of Justice (DOJ) relaunched its antitrust investigation of the Microsoft Corp., the world's largest software company.

Java

After decades of a "Tower of Babel" approach toward developing software, using many different programming languages, in 1997 the computer industry rallied around a language with the potential to become its first lingua franca—Java. Launched less than three years earlier by Sun Microsystems, Inc., Java had progressed rapidly from its initial role as the subject of unprecedented hype to its position as a widely used tool for creating software for the World Wide Web, the graphical component of the Internet.

Java's role was expected to expand to encompass mainstream computing applications in the business world. The IBM Corp. was developing a rich line of Java middleware (software that enables disparate computers to work together) and tools intended to carry Java into the business software arena. IBM's lineup included VisualAge, a Java development environment, and Lotus BeanMachine, a tool for creating downsized Web-based programs called Java applets.

Even more interesting was Java's potential move into consumers' homes. Hongkong Telecom, the largest telecommunications provider in Asia and the ninth largest in the world, was preparing to use Java as the programming language at the heart of its interactive cable-television network. Hongkong Telecom, which operated a fully digital network, planned to offer a range of interactive services, including home shopping, home banking, Internet access, and, most notably, video-on-demand.

Nevertheless, Java was not without its detractors. The biggest criticism was the charge that Java software did not perform as well as older, more mainstream programming languages such as C and C++. To blunt such criticism, Sun released a code called HotSpot, which optimized Java programs to make them run as quickly as possible. In addition, Symantec Corp. in 1997 introduced a new compiler that converted Java software directly into x86 machine code—Intel microprocessor instructions—which ran on personal computers equipped with Microsoft's Windows 95 operating system.

In mid-1997 Sun and Microsoft began an acrimonious legal battle that involved Java. Sun alleged that Microsoft had violated its Java license by altering parts of the technology in Microsoft's Internet Explorer Web browser. In an early courtroom round, a judge ordered Microsoft to remove the trademarked Java logo from the browser.

In addition, Sun's supporters publicly complained that they believed Microsoft was attempting to subvert the intent of Java's inventors, who envisioned a programming language that could run on all types of computers. The focus of their ire was a pair of new Java programming commands that Microsoft included in its Visual J++ software-development tool. Microsoft's changes, the critics charged, would limit some Java software to computers equipped with Windows 95.

By early 1998, however, the consensus in the computer industry was that Microsoft's actions would neither halt nor derail the Java juggernaut.

Network computers

On the computer-hardware front, the network computer—a low-cost computer that lacks a hard disk and is used primarily to browse the Internet and to exchange E-mail—appeared to gain renewed momentum in 1997. The devices were originally announced by Oracle Corp. and IBM in 1996, but a dearth of hardware and a consumer community enamored of personal computers had made the systems nonstarters. Network computers debuted to a huge amount of fanfare and the promise of a very low price, but a real market for the machines had been slow to materialize.

In 1997, however, network computers rebounded somewhat, thanks to a new offering from Sun and a loss-leader marketing thrust from the British Acorn Group PLC, which offered to provide free hardware to computer manufacturers that planned to use its design. Still, the major impediment to the success of the network computer—a paucity of end-user software applications—remained. This lack of software grew worse in 1997 after Corel Corp. canceled plans for a Java-based suite of word-processing, spreadsheet, and related office applications.

The year 2000

By 1997 concern was rising in government and industry around the world about the possibility that many computer applications, most notably financial applications

such as banking and payroll software, would freeze up at the turn of the century because of the Y2K problem. The fear was that data-processing systems using older dating systems that represented the year by using only two digits would not be able to tell whether "00" stood for the year 2000 or for 1900, which would thereby cause massive dislocations of data.

According to the consultants at Gartner Group Inc., the global cost of correcting the situation would be some $300 billion to $600 billion. Led by consulting firms such as Cap Gemini, information-technology managers planned to attack the problem full tilt in 1998. In the U.S. Congress the Subcommittee on Government Management, Information, and Technology of the House Committee on Government Reform and Oversight held hearings in 1997 to determine how prepared government agencies were to deal with the Y2K issue. The general consensus: many of them were not as prepared as they should have been.

Technically savvy observers, however, were worried that the problem might have even greater implications for computers used in so-called embedded applications—that is, in software used to run everyday hardware found in systems such as elevators, factories, and even nuclear power plants. These applications were typically controlled not by a PC-based operating system such as Windows 95 but instead by real-time operating systems—tightly wound "kernels" of code that interacted directly with valves and sensors. While it would be relatively simple to determine if the problem plagued a PC's software, it would be far trickier to find out whether an embedded system with hidden computer code had the potentially fatal bug.

Industry developments

Legal issues continued to be a thorn in the side of Microsoft as the software giant and the DOJ tussled over antitrust issues. In December 1997 U.S. District Court Judge Thomas Jackson issued a preliminary injunction that required Microsoft to "cease and desist" from requiring that PC vendors include the company's Internet Explorer Web browser on machines equipped with Windows 95. The court ruling was an outgrowth of a DOJ investigation to determine whether, in its judgment, Microsoft had monopolistic control of the computer-software industry.

Microsoft's lawyers and company chairman Bill Gates vigorously disputed those charges. As 1998 commenced, however, Gates and other industry leaders were called to testify before the Senate Judiciary Committee, and the legal donnybrook showed no signs of abating.

On the technology front, Microsoft's Windows 98, the much-anticipated upgrade of Windows 95, was scheduled to be released in mid-1998, and company software developers were hard at work preparing Windows NT 5.0, a mature release of the operating system designed to run on heavy-duty computer servers and workstations. NT was aimed at corporate customers, for whom it was positioned as an alternative to the well-established Unix operating system. Microsoft also appeared intent on establishing itself in the nascent realm of interactive television, wherein graphical Web pages and other Internet-based services were delivered to consumers via a cable-TV set-top box. To that end Microsoft purchased the interactive-television company WebTV Networks in 1997 for $425 million and took a $1 billion

As Microsoft chairman and CEO Bill Gates (left) looks on, Sun Microsystems chief Scott McNealy speaks before the U.S. Senate Judiciary Committee in early 1998. McNealy urged the Department of Justice to pursue its investigation to determine whether Microsoft had monopolistic control of the software industry.

interest in cable-television operator Comcast Corp.

Intel Corp. achieved some new highs in 1997, releasing new microprocessors and seeing company chairman Andrew S. Grove anointed *Time* magazine's Man of the Year. In the marketplace Intel thrust its MMX multimedia technology into the mainstream, unveiling new microprocessors equipped with the feature and launching an unprecedented high-budget consumer-marketing campaign and media blitz. Industry experts said that Intel orchestrated its marketing efforts so carefully because it had so much riding on MMX, characterized as the company's most important initiative since the debut of the Pentium chip in 1993. Intel kicked its MMX marketing effort into high gear in January 1997, when it launched its first Pentium-class microprocessors incorporating MMX. In May the company unveiled

the Pentium II, a high-powered chip designed to bring MMX features to computer workstations, used mainly by engineers and scientists.

Some observers characterized MMX as an incremental, rather than a revolutionary, technological advancement. Others dubbed it a "secret sauce" that Intel was using to entice consumers into buying new computers to replace their existing Pentium-equipped machines. Technically, MMX added 57 new instructions to Intel's microprocessor instruction set. The extensions boosted performance by using a technique called single instruction, multiple data (SIMD) to process many chunks of data simultaneously with just one instruction.

For any real benefit to be gained from MMX, however, software that used the new instructions had to be written. Applications that exploited MMX began to hit the market in 1997, in the form of programs, such as Adobe Systems Inc.'s PhotoDeluxe 2.0, and systems software, such as Microsoft's DirectX. CD-ROM makers were among the quickest to board the bandwagon. DK Multimedia released a special MMX-optimized version of its educational title *The Ultimate Human Body,* and Byron Preiss Multimedia Co., Inc., targeted its new *The Timetables of Technology* disc specifically at MMX users. Nevertheless, industry experts said that it would be a while before MMX-specific code was pervasive.

During the year Intel was also shaken by reports of bugs in its Pentium-class microprocessors. The first, which struck in May, involved the Pentium II and Pentium Pro chips. Known as the flag erratum, the obscure glitch could cause problems, Intel admitted, under certain conditions when two very large floating-point numbers were added together. Intel quickly released a software fix for the bug and said that it would rectify the problem in future versions of its chips. The second bug, which became known in November, involved a sequence of illegal opcodes—low-level microprocessor instructions not normally intended for use with the Intel chips. When such opcodes were used, the chip was supposed to alert the programmer that something was wrong. Instead, the illegal sequence sent the processor into an endless loop and thereby caused it to lock up. Although the two glitches were minor issues for Intel, the news about new chip bugs harkened back to November 1994, when a Pentium floating-point-division bug mushroomed into a public-relations disaster for Intel that resulted in its first-ever chip recall and an eventual $475 million charge against company earnings.

Looking forward

As the 1990s drew to a close, computer software technologies that were heretofore thought too advanced for the commercial market began moving out of the research lab. A good case in point was the development of software "agents"—automated computer programs that ply the Internet like robots in search of data and information.

Some of the first effective agents were beginning to hit the market by way of Firefly Network Inc., a Cambridge, Mass., start-up company cofounded by a professor at the Massachusetts Institute of Technology (MIT), Pattie Maes. (In early 1998 Microsoft acquired Firefly.) The company unveiled several commercial products based on Firefly, an agent that was originally designed to create lists of CD recordings that a specific consumer might like, on the basis of a query of that customer's musical tastes.

Agents like Firefly were often touted by experts as a potential driving force for electronic commerce on the Internet. Such agents were envisioned as helping consumers search through the vastness of cyberspace and settle on goods and services they might wish to buy.

Firefly, however, was only the simplest incarnation of what was already becoming a hotbed of activity in helping consumers navigate the Internet. Oren Etzioni of the University of Washington was working on a more sophisticated agent that functioned as an intelligent assistant for Internet users; Michael Genesereth of Stanford University was investigating programming languages that could be used to control agents; and MIT's Media Lab was conducting research on SodaBot, a development environment

that had the potential to help programmers devise their own agents.

—Alexander Wolfe

COMPUTER SYSTEMS AND SERVICES

As the information systems community approached the year 2000, the computer world faced increasing pressure concerning the so-called Y2K problem, which resulted from the formerly standard method of recording a date by using only two digits to represent the year. This problem had arisen because of design decisions made many years earlier on the basis of such factors as cost, the need to save digital storage space (*i.e.,* memory), and a desire to reduce the number of key strokes used to enter a date. Beginning in the year 2000, the use of a two-digit designation for the year would create problems in many circumstances, including numerical calculations and sorting dates. For example, the sequence 1904, 1954, 1985, 1990, 2015 would be recorded incorrectly as 04, 15, 54, 85, 90. The crisis facing the computer industry was very real and very costly to correct, particularly in the identification and correction of embedded software. Some companies reported soaring wages and shortages of skilled programmers and consultants to handle the problem. (See *Computers and Computer Science,* above.)

U.S. systems and services

The ninth annual National Library Survey, the most recent and most comprehensive survey of electronic reference materials in U.S. libraries, revealed a very large increase in the number of public and academic libraries that allowed patrons access to electronic information databases. More surprising was the fact that nearly half of all libraries in the United States offered computer users remote access to their catalogs of books and other holdings and that this percentage was expected to increase in the future. The survey concluded that libraries were striving to reach out and improve services by transforming themselves into electronic centers for community information.

The National Information Standards Organization began developing a new standard that would define minimum performance requirements and optional features for a digital talking book to be used by blind and other physically handicapped individuals. The new digitally based system would replace the older analog cassette tapes but would not be restricted to any particular distribution media. In addition to the visually impaired patron, producers of talking books and magazines, equipment manufacturers, and software developers would all be affected by the new standard.

The National Library of Medicine (NLM) had until recently required users to register and pay a fee to search MED-LINE, a large database of medical information prepared by the NLM, as well as several other NLM databases (http://www.ncbi.nlm.nih.gov/PubMed). In 1997, however, the service was made available for free to everyone. As Donald A.B. Lindberg, NLM's director stated, "The health care delivery landscape is changing. Citizens are increasingly turning to the Web as a source of information to improve their daily lives, including their health." It was believed that free access would provide consumers with the current and creditable medical information they needed.

Chemical Abstracts (CA) Student Edition, a database containing more than 1.5 million records along with abstracts and bibliographic information, was designed and customized to serve the information needs of undergraduate chemistry students. The subjects covered were applied chemistry and chemical engineering, plus general, organic, physical, and analytic chemistry. New records were being added to the database each week. The CA Student Edition was provided to libraries on an annual subscription basis from the Online Computer Library Center FirstSearch service.

The Federal Emergency Management Agency (FEMA) unveiled a Web site designed to deliver a serious message about disaster preparedness to children and their parents. As FEMA director James Lee Witt explained, "Children are an important part of the disaster recovery process." The FEMA for Kids Web site (http://www.fema.gov/kids) used stories, colorful graphics, fun facts, and other features to make youngsters and their parents aware of actions that could be taken to protect themselves and reduce their risk of loss from natural disasters.

The Federal Electronic Research and Review Extraction Tool (FERRET) was developed by the U.S. Census Bureau and the Bureau of Labor Statistics to present statistics from the Current Population Survey (CPS) and the Survey of Income and Program Participation (SIPP). The CPS surveyed about 50,000 households on a range of topics, such as income and poverty, health insurance coverage, and school enrollment, whereas the SIPP collected data from about 37,000 households concerning sources of income and participation in government assistance programs. FERRET could be used to quickly locate current and historical information from these sources and make comparisons between different data sets.

IBM opened a free Internet Web service (http://www.patents.ibm.com) to enable users to search for and view more than two million patents issued by the U.S. Patent and Trademark Office beginning Jan. 5, 1971. Information and images of newly

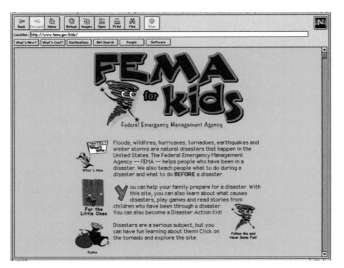

The FEMA for Kids Web site uses stories, colorful graphics, fun facts, and other features to make youngsters and their parents aware of ways they can protect themselves and reduce their risk of loss from natural disasters.

Federal Emergency Management Agency

The Britannica CD 98 Multimedia Edition offers a host of new graphics-rich features, including Timeline overviews of various aspects of human history, an Analyst function that allows world statistical data to be manipulated in numerous ways, and thousands of relevant Internet links.

issued patents would be added regularly to this database. Patent searching could be done by keywords, phrases, or patent numbers, as well as by more advanced techniques. Free access to patent information was expected to hasten the pace of innovation because inventors could easily find and improve upon existing inventions or create new patentable inventions.

The Library of Congress (LOC) placed more than 4,000 photographs and approximately 90 documents spanning the 15th to the mid-20th centuries on American Memory, the library's database of materials relating to American history. These and related collections could be viewed on the library's Web site (http://www.loc.gov).

In cooperation with the LOC, Scott, Foresman & Co. published *AuthorWorks,* a series of CD-ROMs for use in public school grades 6 through 12. The discs contained in-depth information about the lives, times, and works of classic American, British, and world authors. The Life section emphasized the personal history of the author, his family, friends, and fellow writers; the Time section explored the history, technology, art, and music of the period; and the Work section focused on each author's writing style, along with critiques and influences. Various media, including historical documents, interviews, slides, and oral readings, were used to present this information.

Encyclopædia Britannica, Inc., released two significant electronic products. *Britannica CD 97,* an updated version of its CD-ROM, contained the entire 44 million-word *Encyclopædia Britannica* plus *Merriam-Webster's Collegiate Dictionary* and *Nations of the World,* including articles, maps, and flags of 191 nations. The new

CD-ROM had the depth and accuracy of the printed versions, as well as easy-to-use electronic search functions that made looking for information easier and more rewarding. Also released was the *Britannica CD 98 Multimedia Edition,* a greatly expanded two-disc version of its electronic reference package accessed through a thoroughly redesigned, more versatile interface. Its host of new graphics-rich features included Spotlight multimedia tours of entire subjects, Timeline overviews of various aspects of human history, an Analyst function that allowed world statistical data to be manipulated and displayed in numerous ways, and thousands of relevant Internet links.

Picasso: The Man, His Works, The Legend, a CD-ROM released by Grolier Interactive, Inc., contained the images of hundreds of paintings, drawings, sculptures, and ceramics gathered from more than 70 museums, galleries, and private collections, plus many photographs of Picasso taken in his various studios. A measuring scale and zoom capabilities for examining the works were included on the disc, as were a glossary and a time line for showing the relationship between major historical events and Picasso's artistic periods.

NASA, in collaboration with the National Technology Transfer Center, produced a CD-ROM titled *NASA Solutions: Sharing Aerospace Technology with America.* Included on the CD-ROM were 19,500 technologies, 3,500 patents, 11,500 technical briefs, 15,000 contracts, and information about the NASA field and regional technology transfer centers. According to NASA administrator Daniel S. Goldin, the content and organization of the disc were designed to enable users to browse for NASA technologies that matched their needs and to make these technologies available to U.S. industry quickly and easily.

International systems and services

A major European survey of the on-line information industry was conducted over a three-month period in the U.K., France, and Germany to ascertain the size and worth of the industry, its trends, and the strategic issues that would govern growth into the 21st century. The survey revealed that the main growth areas would be in the end-user markets, especially in pharmaceuticals, food, travel, and advertising. Major companies were expected to grow in size and services through the use of the Internet and local information networks.

The German state of Bavaria entered into an agreement with BIOSIS to provide the life sciences database BIOSIS Previews to a consortium of five universities in Bavaria. The disciplines covered included agriculture, biochemistry, biology, ecology, genetics, medicine, pharmacology, and public health. Approximately one-half million records, including references to international scientific journals and worldwide meetings, were being added to the file every year.

The Royal Society of Chemistry, headquartered in Cambridge, Eng., had a worldwide membership of about 46,000. Its main objectives were to advance the science of chemistry and its applications. The large international database Chemical Business NewsBase, which was marketed by the society, contained information about companies, products, markets, and environmental issues of concern to the industry. It was updated twice weekly.

An electronic version of the newspaper *International Herald Tribune* was placed on the Web (http://www.iht.com). In addition to a summary of the daily print edition, the site's archive stored editions from previous weeks. All articles were categorized as news, dispatches, features, funds, and markets, and all began with an introduction for quick browsing, followed by a hyperlink to the full story. Access to the site was free.

Chadwyck-Healey released a CD-ROM of *Early English Prose Fiction* that contained more than 200 complete works by British authors for the years from 1500 to 1700. Each work was reproduced in full, including all prefatory matter, annotations by the original authors, and relevant illustrations. The database was also available by subscription on the company's Web site (http://www.chadwyck.com/lion) so that many rare books scattered in libraries throughout the world could be searched quickly and conveniently.

Research and development

To study the question of whether the importance of the printed book was being displaced by the use of computer-based sources, the Lawyers Cooperative Publishing Co. investigated how New York City law librarians conducted their research. The survey indicated that for the period 1994–96 the percentage of research performed by using printed law books dropped below 50%, whereas the use of computer-assisted research increased. The reasons were fairly obvious: users had increased familiarity with computer technology; machine interfaces had become more sophisticated and user-friendly; the amount of information available electronically had increased tremendously; and, perhaps most significant, computer-assisted research had become more encompassing, faster, and cheaper than research performed through the use of printed materials. Although the use of printed works in research was likely to continue to decline, it was not expected to disappear. Books are efficient packages of information. They are portable, transportable, and inexpensive; they require no outside source of equipment; and, for a large portion of the population, they are a source of tactile pleasure.

The libraries of Emory University and the Georgia Institute of Technology, both in Atlanta, received a $1.5 million grant from the Woodruff Foundation to create a multimedia "virtual archive." The three-year collaborative effort, Selected Archives of Georgia Tech and Emory (SAGE), was designed to serve as a pilot project for technological innovation and the development of new ways to index, store, and display library materials on the computer. The project was especially challenging because there was no established way of putting multimedia archival sources into computer format. When available, project findings would be shared with other institutions through conferences and reports posted on the SAGE Web site.

A research project conducted by the Center for Technology in Government, located at the University of Albany, N.Y., prepared guidelines designed to help state and local government agencies develop Internet Web sites. Citizens, especially those unable to get to a government office during normal business hours, would be able to visit the agency's "virtual office" Web site and obtain information at a more convenient time and with less effort. The center staff worked with seven state and local agencies and helped them deal with the policies and organizational issues involved in providing services on a Web site.

—Harold Borko

TELECOMMUNICATIONS SYSTEMS
Implementing the Telecommunications Act

In the late 1990s the world continued to rush into the information age, stimulated in part by advances in technology. In the U.S. the "taking hold" of the Telecommunications Act of 1996, and a rash of corporate mergers and acquisitions, had an equivalent effect. This act, signed into law by Pres. Bill Clinton in February 1996, was a rewrite—and an expansion—of the Communications Act of 1934. Its declared purpose was "to accelerate rapidly private sector deployment of advanced telecommunications and information technologies and services to all Americans by opening all telecommunications markets to competition"—*i.e.*, to promote competition and preserve universal service.

The Federal Communications Commission (FCC), which was given the job of implementing the act, took steps to aggressively introduce competition. These steps included means by which erstwhile competitors of the local telephone companies could easily enter the business. To the incumbent telephone companies, many of these means seemed not only inappropriate but also illegal, and they filed suit. In July 1997 the U.S. Court of Appeals for the 8th Circuit ruled that the claims presented in the suit were essentially correct and blocked the FCC's attempts at implementation. An appeal was filed with the U.S. Supreme Court, and it was apparent that a final disposition of the matter was unlikely for some time.

The Telecommunications Act also made special note of "advanced" services and specifically dealt with schools, libraries, and health care facilities. It committed $2,250,000,000 per year to schools and libraries, as well as several hundred thousand dollars to health care facilities, to expand services. (Such support, for example, could allow more schools to be connected to the Internet or permit medical specialists to review X-rays and other findings on patients in remote hospitals and clinics through systems of networked medical facilities.)

These funds were to be recovered through discounts, and the discounts were to be collected by the various contractors—a not-insignificant task facing those entering the telecommunications industry. In any case, 1998 would undoubtedly see many new entrants to the local exchange telephone business, as well as significant technological expansion in schools, libraries, and health care facilities.

Mergers and acquisitions

The avowed mission of the Telecommunications Act was to encourage competition. Thus, one would expect 1998 to see many more participants, but as rapidly as new, small companies entered the business, large, established companies merged and formed joint ventures. The most obvious example was the changing status of the "Baby Bells"—the seven regional telephone operating companies that were formed in 1984 by the breakup of AT&T. In 1997 the seven shrank to five, with Bell Atlantic merging with NYNEX and SBC Communications (formerly Southwestern Bell) acquiring Pacific Telesis Group. For a time in mid-1997, there was talk about SBC combining with AT&T, but that came to naught.

Beyond the ranks of the Bell operating companies, Century Telephone Enterprises acquired Pacific Telecom, and WorldCom acquired MFS Communications. British Telecommunications agreed to acquire MCI Communications (the second largest long-distance carrier in the U.S.) but was surprised when WorldCom and then GTE came forward with bids.

Although WorldCom emerged as the winner, antitrust regulators representing the European Union initiated an investigation that could derail WorldCom's takeover of MCI or force structural changes in the deal.

Wireless communications

Competition in the field of wireless telephony continued unabated as people signed on for cellular services at a rate greater than 30,000 subscribers per day. Because the demand for wireless communications was so great, the FCC auctioned off several frequency bands for use in similar services. Originally these frequency slots were intended for personal communications services (PCS)—*i.e.,* for short-range and pedestrian, rather than vehicular, services. The winners of the auctions had other ideas, however, and opened what amounted to additional cellular companies in a particular area.

Although all of these new services employed cellular principles, they were not designed to be compatible. For example, within a particular system's service area a subscriber could move about freely, with a signal handoff from one cell to another taking place as needed to maintain consistent service. If that subscriber moved outside that service area, however, there was no assurance that the adjacent service area would employ the same system.

One possible solution was to sell cellular phones that were compatible with more than one system. The "standard" system (and the least technically advanced) was the analog advanced mobile phone system (AMPS). It was the original system and operated at a frequency dedicated to "cellular" phones (rather than PCS). Thus, many of the cell phones being sold by new entrants had the capability of switching to older frequencies should a phone be carried to a city where the system was not identical to that in its home territory.

Newer systems employed digital techniques. As a result, they produced higher-quality voice transmission, were almost immune to eavesdropping, and could accommodate more subscribers per cell. The three digital techniques most commonly employed in 1997 were time-division multiple access (TDMA); global system for mobile communications, which was quite similar to the TDMA systems and was accepted as the standard outside the U.S.; and code-division multiple access (CDMA). CDMA was a technologically advanced system that permitted even more subscribers per cell site than did TDMA—which, in turn, had greater capacity than AMPS. CDMA was the system of choice for many of the new PCS systems.

Another wireless system—far different from cellular radio or PCS—was satellite communications. Synchronous satellites, located in geostationary equatorial orbits at an altitude of 35,900 km (22,300 mi), were used extensively for data transmission, but the time delay in transmission (voice requires ⅛ second to go up and ⅛ second to come down) made their use for voice transmission less than satisfactory. Low-Earth-orbit (LEO) satellites would be generally better suited for voice transmission, but they are not synchronous. Because LEOs rise and set as the Earth revolves, many such satellites would be required in order to handle a smooth transfer of the transmission as each satellite handed off a call to a different satellite when it moved out of range of the subscriber. In 1997 several such systems were being planned and one (Iridium) already had several satellites in place, but full operation was still more than a year away.

The Internet

The most exciting segment of the telecommunications field in 1997 was the growing use of the Internet. The Internet is, in effect, a network of networks connected and essentially serving as an overlay network to the public switched telephone network. The major distinction between the two is that the Internet is a packet network that transmits data in electronic bundles.

A packet network first digitizes that which is being transmitted. In the case of an E-mail message, for example, it converts the letters and numbers of the message into a series of 1s and 0s. Several hundred of these 1s and 0s are stored in a computer, packaged together in what is known as a packet, and transmitted (accompanied by an electronic address and

error-checking bits) to a distant subscriber. At the distant station the 1s and 0s are reconverted into the characters of the original message and transmitted to the computer of the user. The speed of the channel being used for this transmission can be upgraded to accommodate increased traffic. Thus, a packet of information from an E-mail message can be transmitted in a matter of microseconds, and then the channel can be used to transmit a packet from a different user. The beauty of such an operation, of course, is its efficiency. A channel is seized—and used—only when information is stored and ready for trans-

mission. At other times the channel is available for use by others.

For most people, connection to the Internet (as opposed to communications within the Internet) has been done on an analog basis through a computer connected to a modem and has required full-time use of the local telephone line during the period that the modem is sending and receiving data. This, of course, has precluded use of the line for normal voice operation. As a result, in 1997 energized local telephone

Perched atop a computer monitor (left) at a California elementary school is Rattie, a trained albino rat that helped wire the school for the Internet by dragging a string attached to cables through walls and crawlways (below).

companies scrambled to install additional lines to both residences and businesses.

One other potential loomed on the horizon in the late 1990s: voice transmission over the Internet. Sound can be digitized as easily as data, and a digitized stream of 1s and 0s can be packetized for transmission. Packets, however, often travel by different routes and at different speeds; in fact, it is possible for later packets of a transmission to arrive ahead of other, earlier packets. For the proper transmission of data, it is necessary for the equipment to receive these packets in the proper order and reconvert them to the analog sound in an almost real-time manner. It would be particularly important in voice transmission that the listener hear the voice within a few milliseconds of the words' being spoken and be able to respond as if it were a face-to-face conversation. Some progress in sound transmission was being made, and it was likely that greater progress would be made in voice transmission before the end of the 20th century.

Digital subscriber lines

The public switched telephone network was designed to transmit voice, a design that set the upper frequency limit at about four kilohertz. As more and more data were introduced to the network, however, efforts were made to increase the transmission capability. In 1948 the American engineer Claude Shannon provided a concise mathematical understanding of channel capacity. His formula included parameters involving bandwidth and signal-to-noise ratio, but it was many years before anyone came close to achieving such speeds.

As late as the 1960s, speeds of 1,200 and 2,400 bps (bits per second) were considered technological breakthroughs, and there was little hope of achieving speeds 10 times higher. It became obvious that sophisticated error-checking codes would be needed before such speeds were achieved. It was in the late 1980s that real progress was made. Speeds by then were

as high as 28.8 kbps (kilobits per second). By the 1990s sophisticated techniques had been developed that permitted data-transmission speeds approaching 56.6 kbps. In fact, by using very sophisticated techniques, it could be possible to transmit at speeds as high as six megabits per second (Mbps) over distances as long as 3.2 km (2 mi).

The ability to transmit at such speeds over a telephone channel had profound effects on the telecommunications industry. Might it not be possible, went the argument, to transmit television signals over twisted copper pair and hence avoid the cost of installing fiber-optic or coaxial cable? Indeed, it was possible, and the resultant solution was one of a class of coding techniques called digital subscriber lines, or xDSLs, which allowed high-speed transmission over copper pairs.

In the late 1990s a number of such schemes existed, including high-bit-rate digital subscriber line (HDSL), which permitted the transmission of 1.5 Mbps signals over copper (identified as T1 in the U.S. and E1 in Europe); single-line DSL, which accomplished the same thing—but over a shorter distance—with a single copper pair; and asymmetric DSL (ADSL), which transmitted the signal streams with much more bandwidth devoted to the downstream leg than to the upstream leg. Many companies were testing ADSL systems for both Internet access and cable TV.

—Robert E. Stoffels

ENERGY

Nations throughout the world began to look carefully at their energy supplies during the past year as the demand for energy,

electricity in particular, continued to expand, especially in less-developed countries such as China and India. In the United States total energy consumption grew from 90.86 quadrillion BTU (British thermal units) to 94.01 quadrillion BTU from 1995 to 1996, an increase of 3.5%. This increased worldwide demand, which was predicted to increase by 50% by 2015, prompted action in many countries to diversify energy production and patterns of use. This trend was coupled with a growing global awareness of the adverse environmental legacies from energy production and consumption, which were addressed in a global conference on energy and the environment held in Kyoto, Japan, in 1997.

Environmental challenges

Worldwide energy use and climate change are inextricably related topics. Recognition of the possible adverse effects of climate change led to international negotiations in February 1991 and the signing, 16 months later, of the Framework Convention on Climate Change by 155 countries at the 1992 United Nations Conference on Environment and Development, sometimes called the Earth Summit. In December 1997 parties to that agreement met in Kyoto to negotiate binding commitments for reducing future emissions of greenhouse gases. (*See* Year in Review: ENVIRONMENT.)

The Kyoto conference sharpened the debate on the role that energy plays in a nation's economic development, and it highlighted the fact that energy usage had become the major driver of environmental problems—both locally, as the principal source of pollution in urban environments, and globally, as the major source of green-

house gases. The U.S. in particular was criticized for generating a quarter of such emissions with only 5% of the world's population, and it was pointed out that the U.S. produces twice as much greenhouse gas per capita as any European country. For example, carbon emissions from energy use in the U.S. increased roughly 1.2% in 1997 and were expected to continue to do so. This was contrasted with the fact that the less-developed countries of Asia, Africa, and Latin America, with 80% of the world's population, generated only a third of such gases.

A protocol developed at the Kyoto conference required industrialized countries to reduce emissions of six greenhouse gases by an average of 5.2% from 1990 levels by 2008–12. The U.S. must reduce emissions by 7%; European countries agreed to an 8% reduction. Less-developed countries were not included. The six greenhouse gases included in the agreement were carbon dioxide, methane, nitrous oxide, and three synthetic gases—hydrofluorocarbons, perfluorocarbons, and sulfur hexafluoride. In order to achieve reductions in the least costly manner, the protocol embraced the concept of an international emission-permit trading system. The protocol was not to enter into force until 55 countries that accounted for 55% of the 1990 emissions of carbon dioxide from the Annex 1 nations (developed nations, plus nations in the former Soviet Union and Eastern Europe with economies in transition to market economies) had ratified the agreement. If fully implemented, the protocol would require significant changes in the way energy is produced worldwide and could lead to increased markets for energy sources that do not emit carbon products. Nations could earn emission credits by protecting or planting woodlands (which absorb carbon dioxide from the atmosphere).

The difficulty of achieving the changes expected as a result of the Kyoto agreement should not be minimized. For example, the protocol faced serious opposition in the U.S. Senate, where it would be sent for ratification, owing to its anticipated economic consequences for six major American industries that were energy-intensive—chemicals, steel, aluminum, oil refining, paper products, and cement—and to the fact that less-developed countries were not yet included in required emission reductions. Other industrialized nations struggled with similar problems. The relationships between cheap, available energy and expanding economies and between expensive hard-to-find energy and economic stagnation promised to keep these issues at the top of international agendas.

Energy efficiency

After the oil embargoes of the early 1970s brought home to the economies of developed countries the importance of using energy more efficiently, numerous efforts were made to increase the efficiency of industrial and home equipment and processes. In the U.S. from 1973 to 1986, energy consumption remained nearly flat, whereas the gross national product grew by more than 40%. This was accomplished primarily by replacing old and inefficient designs and processes with new technologies. From 1986 a primary strategy to address the environmental problems of carbon emissions was to develop and introduce equipment that produced significantly lower residues than had previous models. For example, significant gains were being made in increasing the efficiency of compressors and refrigeration systems.

An excellent example of an effort to increase efficiency and reduce pollution was the development of oxy-fuel firing, initially for manufacturing glass but later deployed in the steel, aluminum, and metal-casting industries. Rather than using furnaces that burn fuel in air, which is about 80% nitrogen, the new process burned fuel in pure oxygen. By eliminating the nitrogen, which in the past carried away much of the process heat in the nitrogen exhaust, oxy-fuel combustion reduced emissions of the nitrogen oxides by 90% and of carbon monoxide by 96%. The process produced energy savings of 15% to 45%, depending on the furnace size.

The most important areas of research were those addressing the problem of oil usage in the transportation sector, which in 1997 was 97% oil-dependent. As the world price of oil declined, the economic motive for introducing more efficient engines also lessened. Though fundamental research and development programs to understand and better exploit combustion in both stationary and moving engines made only slow progress in increasing efficiencies, lean-burn engines with a variety of new exhaust catalysts were successful in greatly reducing pollution, particularly the nitrogen oxides.

The increasing use of microcomputer-based process controllers also resulted in improvements in overall engine efficiencies, tailoring conditions to be closer to optimum for the entire range of transportation operations.

The frontier for major improvements was considered by many to be electric vehicles, equipped with either onboard batteries or fuel cells. Microturbine systems were expected to achieve 40% efficiencies in converting fuel to power, whereas fuel cell–gas turbine combined systems held the promise of 70% efficiencies.

Oil and gas

During the past year oil and natural gas accounted for just over 50% of the world's energy supply and 65% of that within the U.S. Improved technology for oil and gas exploration, extraction, and distribution resulted in rather steady development and production costs.

Proven oil reserves were known to exceed a 50-year supply, and natural gas reserves exceeded a 60-year supply. The world energy usage of both was expected to increase, with oil consumption rising substantially as economic growth in less-developed countries drove up the demand for oil for transportation fuels and for a wide range of industrial, residential, and commercial uses. The world price of oil continued to decline, and at the same time, and likely determined by that fact, the gas mileage of American cars and trucks worsened.

Natural gas experienced the highest growth rate of all major fuels worldwide as demand continued to increase in almost every end-use sector. The fact that coal produces 80% more carbon emission per calorie than does natural gas increased the attractiveness of the latter for both electricity generation and industrial energy supplies. In fact, natural gas was used for approximately 10% of the production of electricity in the U.S. in 1997, and its use as a fuel for automobiles and trucks also increased.

Several exciting new ventures emerged, either funded by or operated by major energy conglomerates, such as Exxon Corp., Shell Oil Co., Texaco Inc., and Syntroleum Corp., to convert natural gas to a synthetic liquid fuel. One of the key breakthrough developments was the production of new catalysts for use in conventional fixed-bed or slurry reactors. Conversion of gas to paraffinic hydrocarbons (at costs of $15–$20 per barrel) provided a new strategy for dealing with possible oil disruptions in the Persian Gulf region by providing an alternative source of hydrocarbon fuels for gasoline, diesel, and jet fuel. Because current crude oil prices were $15–$17 per barrel, the synthetic fuels would be competitive.

These developments offered the potential to improve the worth of otherwise "stranded reserves" of natural gas, those that are too distant from markets to be exploited economically because of the lack of transmission pipelines. Similarly, some gas fields that relied on conversion to liquid natural gas for efficient transport were likely to increase in value because their gas could be converted to synthetic fuels to compete with oil.

These new processes were also thought capable of increasing the value of low-quality oil fields by means of blending the petroleum with synthetic fuels produced from gas. By 1998 these technologies already were being used at plants of substantial size but had not yet reached world-scale production.

Coal

The use of coal for energy was increasingly becoming limited to the generation of electricity—providing roughly half of the worldwide output—and to the production of steel, cement, and certain chemicals. Coal supplied 22% of the energy used worldwide, but other than in China, its use was rapidly decreasing for all but electricity generation and in the industries mentioned. Coal use overall was expected to continue to grow, however, with the decline in industrialized countries being offset by strong growth in China and other Asian countries.

Coal, which is composed mainly of carbon, received increased attention from an environmental standpoint as nations throughout the world attempted to cope with both domestic air pollution and greenhouse gas emissions. Some effort was given to mixing coal with other fuels in order to reduce the emissions of sulfur dioxide and other pollutants.

Interest in cofiring coal with biomass was rising. In a cofired system of the future, up to 25% by weight of biomass might be fired with coal in a coal facility. Such a scheme would allow the use of biomass to benefit from the specialized staff and sophisticated equipment available for large-scale coal combustion while providing some relief from the global warming effects of coal. Biomass also generally produces lower gas-pollutant emissions than coal.

Railroad cars are parked along a huge mound of coal at a loading station in Shanxi province, China. Coal supplied 22% of the energy used worldwide, but other than in China its use was rapidly decreasing for all but electricity generation and the production of steel, cement, and certain chemicals.

Nuclear power

In 1997–98 there were 441 nuclear power reactors operating throughout the world, producing 17% of the world's electrical energy. Another 38 plants were under construction.

Fifteen countries obtained more than 30% of their electricity from nuclear power. The U.S., with the largest number of operating nuclear reactors of any nation (109), obtained about 20% of its electricity from nuclear power but did not plan to build any new nuclear plants for at least two decades.

The primary reason seemed to be economic; large initial capital costs and strict regulation of plant construction (and oper-

ation) resulted in construction times of more than 10 years; consequently, contractors were vulnerable to changes due to inflation during that period. These factors combined to make it unlikely that industrialized nations, which would have the same costs and regulations as the U.S., would choose nuclear power when adding new generation capacity.

The outlook for new construction of nuclear-energy facilities in less-developed countries, particularly in Asia, however, was considerably different. Many nuclear power plants were planned, and construction began; their use in those countries was expected to increase threefold by 2015.

An attractive feature of nuclear energy is that it produces little or no carbon emis-

sions, which led the Japanese to devote 75% of their energy research and development budgets to the nuclear option. Despite this commitment to nuclear modernization on the part of such an economic giant as Japan, in many ways the nuclear industry found itself at a crossroads in 1998; in industrialized nations some plants had been operating for more than 20 years, whereas in less-developed countries the nuclear-power infrastructure was just being created. Older plants required new technologies in order to remain safe; newer plants had to implement technologies to be even safer than current designs in order to gain public confidence. In the future, new technologies that decrease the cost of construction and operations are expected to make nuclear power plants more economically competitive with conventional power sources.

A growing problem that remained unsolved by all nations was the disposal of radioactive wastes. Many countries sought to develop geologic repositories for permanent disposal, and the U.S. had a major goal in 1998 to complete an assessment of a site at Yucca Mountain in Nevada to determine its suitability in that regard.

The development of the science and technology required for producing energy from nuclear fusion was increasingly becoming a collective international program rather than a national go-it-alone strategy. Principal collaborators were the European Union, the U.S., Japan, and Russia. In the United States the Tokamak Fusion Test Reactor at the Princeton (N.J.) Plasma Physics Laboratory completed its successful experimental series and its decommissioning activities, which had begun in 1997.

The Joint European Torus (JET) researchers proceeded in their quest to achieve the amount of plasma required for a reactor to become viable. After the 1996 decision to extend the project to the end of 1999, JET achieved many new records during the past year: 21 megajoules of fusion energy, 16 MW of peak power, an energy gain (fusion power divided by heating power) of 0.65, and significant demonstrations of tritium technology.

The International Thermonuclear Experimental Reactor (ITER), a large magnetically confined toroidal (doughnut-shaped) plasma reactor for heating hydrogen isotopes to fusion temperatures, had been targeted for a July 1998 completion of its engineering design process, but the international parties involved in the project agreed to an additional three-year period to evaluate prototype components, determine possible locations, and examine possible cost reductions that might be achievable before a decision was made on construction.

In addition to the work on magnetic confinement, which had been making steady progress to achieve fusion reaction temperatures of 100,000,000° C, the U.S. and France were placing increasing emphasis on inertial confinement fusion approaches, in which ions, lasers, and X-ray sources are used to rapidly compress and heat deuterium-tritium plasmas, which have been shown (in experiments using thermonuclear explosives) to produce fusion at lower temperatures. The applications of these methods, as well as the harnessing of magnetic fusion reactors, would require considerable technological developments over many years before they could be seriously considered for commercial energy production.

Renewable energy sources

Technologies that exploit renewable energy sources continued to contribute to the supply of energy throughout the world, with interest in new technologies and fuels spurred by a rising global concern about the environmental impact of the use of fossil fuels. Total grid-connected electricity generation from renewable sources increased only slightly, as a 34% increase in generation from other renewables was off-

An employee of Sandia National Laboratories performs work at Solar Two, the world's largest central receiver solar thermal electric generating plant. Solar Two uses a field of 1,926 mirrors to focus sunlight on a tower-mounted energy receiver, which subsequently drives a turbine generator to produce energy.

set by a decline in hydroelectricity. The generation of electricity from renewable sources other than hydroelectric was expected to provide about 2.5% of the American grid-connected supply by 2020. Biomass and wind were expected to account for the majority of this growth.

Advances in renewable energy technologies were steady, most of them having the goal of reducing cost and increasing efficiency. For example, in solar energy the world's largest central receiver solar thermal electric generating plant, Solar Two, near Barstow, Calif., was operational during the past year after its 1996 plant retrofitting. The plant used a field of flat tracking mirrors to focus sunlight on a tower-mounted energy receiver, which subsequently drove a turbine generator for producing electricity.

The principal change was the replacement of water as the working fluid with molten salt, a mixture of sodium and potassium nitrate. Solar Two's 1,926 mirrors, which collect the Sun's rays and focus them onto a receiver atop a 90-m (300-ft) tower, produced temperatures greater than 535° C (1,000° F) and a power generation of 10 MW of electrical energy without creating any pollution. The reconfigured plant allowed sufficient capacity to operate for two hours after sundown and an hour before sunrise, which helped to match its output to urban power needs. This technology held promise for utility-scale production of electricity in sunbelt regions.

Another solar thermal technology that emerged as a serious contender for producing electricity economically used a parabolic dish concentrator to focus solar energy onto a Stirling engine (a type of external-combustion engine) to produce electricity. This system held the world's record of 30% efficiency in converting solar energy to electricity. Enthusiastic about this success, researchers sought to achieve further gains.

Nonpolluting photovoltaic systems are especially effective where no electrical distribution systems exist. Worldwide the market for these systems grew 42% in 1997, from 89 to 126 MW.

Solar photovoltaic energy utilizes the photovoltaic effect (the generation of a voltage from radiant energy striking the boundary between two dissimilar materials) to convert solar energy directly into electricity. A record efficiency of 19.1% (conversion from sunlight to electricity) was measured when using crystalline silicon cells made via rapid thermal processing. (Rapid thermal processing heats only the silicon wafer, which has low mass, and thus reduces processing time from 30 minutes to about 5 minutes. This, in turn, results in faster manufacturing and lower costs.)

Improvements to the nonsolar components of photovoltaic systems included a new 97% efficient grid-tied inverter (the component that converts the direct-current power produced by the photovoltaic system into alternating current).

Electricity from geothermal energy, produced by tapping into the heat that is stored in the Earth, accounted for about 18 billion kw-hr in the U.S. during the past year. Projected expansion due to new technology was expected to be offset by the decline at the Geysers Power Plant in California, where reservoir water was being depleted. In 1997 total installed geothermal generating capacity in the U.S. was about 2.85 GW (gigawatts; 2.85 billion watts); worldwide the figure was about 8.3 GW.

The major goal for the new technology was to reduce the cost of drilling geothermal wells. Such improvements in field technology were important because drilling can account for as much as half of a power plant's total cost. This continued to be the focus of major research efforts, such as the development of rock bits with new cutting mechanisms to improve the life of bits and the drilling rates.

By 1998 wind energy had become a clear leader among the renewable sources. The worldwide installed capacity of more than 7,000 MW represented tens of thousands of individual wind turbines, enough to supply electricity to millions of homes. More significantly, these turbines were installed in diverse locations, ranging from less-developed nations like India to such developed countries as Germany and Denmark.

From a technological perspective, this growth was fueled by continued improvements to develop a next generation of larger wind turbines, each of which would produce 500 kw–1 MW. Already significant strides have been made in the design and energy output of wind-based systems. Over the years wind turbines had evolved from small, rigid configurations that produced electricity for tens of cents per kilowatt-hour to larger, more flexible units that could be as cheap as five cents per kilowatt-hour. Scientists stood to better this record with advanced designs that offered the potential of achieving rates of less than three cents per kilowatt-hour.

—C. Paul Robinson and Joan B. Woodard

See also Feature Articles: THE FORCE IS WITH US; GOING WITH THE FLOW.

ENVIRONMENT

Two new studies in 1997 assessed the cash value of products and services that natural ecosystems provide to people free of charge, such as food, drugs, and water purification. Declaring 1997 the International Year of the Reef, governments and international organizations participated in activities designed to raise the visibility of the Earth's troubled coral reefs. Disastrous forest fires in the Amazon and Indonesia focused the world's attention on the mismanagement of rain forests that has imperiled these extraordinary ecosystems and threatened human health. Issues related to global warming also dominated many environmental agendas as representatives from 159 countries met in Kyoto, Japan, to negotiate a reduction in the emissions of greenhouse gases.

ISSUES AND POLICY

Putting a price tag on nature

Two separate studies estimated the value of ecosystem services—benefits to humans

that are provided free of charge by the Earth's natural systems. Reporting in the Ecological Society of America's series *Issues in Ecology,* a team of 11 American scientists pointed out that the Earth's biological diversity has served as a free storehouse of useful substances and services. In 1997, for example, the world's oceans, lakes, and streams yielded an estimated 100 million metric tons of fish for human consumption, a natural boon valued at between $50 billion and $100 billion. One of the beneficial characteristics of soil—its ability to hold and nurse young plants— was estimated to be worth $55,000 per hectare. (A hectare is 2.47 ac.) As many as 100,000 species of bats, bees, beetles, birds, flies, and butterflies pollinated crops, orchards, garden plants, commercial forests, and rangeland. One-third of all food items consumed by people were derived from plants that depended on these free pollination services. (*See* Feature Article: THE BIRDS AND THE BEES, THE FLOWERS AND THE TREES.) The scientists argued that people could not afford to replace these and other natural ecological services

Two 1997 studies assigned price tags to nature's services. Wetlands were particularly valuable for providing flood mitigation, water purification, and wildlife habitat. The reports urged a full-cost accounting of the loss of these free services to development, such as the construction of housing.

Raymond Gehman—Corbis

with technology, even if the technology were possible and available.

In May 1997 Robert Costanza, director of the Institute for Ecological Economics, University of Maryland at Solomons, and 12 colleagues also released a study that placed a dollar value on nature's services. Costanza's group estimated these services to be worth $33 trillion per year, nearly double the value of the world's combined gross national products. According to the scientists, the estimate was conservative, since the group was unable to collect complete information for some regions such as deserts and tundras. On the basis of available information, the researchers found, coastal ecosystems provided the most valuable services to humans—roughly $20,000–$22,000 per hectare. The report

Children holding a silk-covered representation of the planet celebrate an international conference on global climate change that opened in Kyoto, Japan, in December.

was intended to provide information to policy makers in an effort to curb actions that would further erode ecosystems and put humans at risk. (*See also* Year in Review: LIFE SCIENCES: *Ecology*.)

Global climate change

According to global climatologists, 1997 was the warmest year of the 20th century. Furthermore, 9 of the past 11 years were the warmest since record keeping began in 1880. Few scientists disputed that the Earth was warming and that human-produced greenhouse gases were partly responsible. In 1995 the Intergovernmental Panel on Climate Change, a group of more than 2,000 scientists established by the United Nations, estimated that if greenhouse gases were not controlled, the average temperature of the Earth would increase by a minimum of 0.3° C (0.5° F) by 2020 and about 1°–3.5° C (1.8°–6.3° F) by 2100.

Armed with these and other findings, negotiators from 159 countries met in December 1997 in Kyoto to draft an international climate-control treaty, an outgrowth of the 1992 United Nations Conference on Environment and Development in Rio de Janeiro. Industrialized nations agreed to reduce emissions of carbon dioxide and five other greenhouse gases by an average of 5.2% below 1990 levels. The U.S. committed to a 7% reduction of emissions below 1990 levels; Japan agreed to a 6% cut. The European Union sought to cut emissions of greenhouse gases to 8% below 1990 levels. Target dates for the reductions of these gases were set between 2008 and 2012. China and other less-developed nations, however, refused to abide by re-

ductions proposed by the industrialized countries, arguing that the nations producing most of the greenhouse gases—including the U.S., which contained 5% of the world's population and produced roughly 25% of the world's greenhouse gases—first had to show improvement in reducing emissions. Some members of the U.S. Congress declared publicly that they would not approve the treaty in its present form. Negotiators were hopeful, however, that the impasse could be broken before the treaty was ratified in March 1999.

In a surprise move at the year's end, American manufacturers announced plans to develop affordable cars with a fuel efficiency of 80 mi per gal (34 km per liter), which reversed decades of assertions that these cars were not economical to build.

Population and consumption

Citing evidence that the rate of worldwide population growth was declining, the United Nations Population Division estimated that the Earth's population would climb from its current estimate of nearly 6 billion people to 8 billion people in 2025 and around 9.4 billion in 2050. Under this medium-growth scenario, the world's population was expected to stabilize at just under 11 billion people by 2200. In 1997 approximately two-fifths of all people lived in countries that were experiencing below-replacement birthrates—*i.e.,* populations that would decline in the next generation. Many of these below-replacement birthrates occurred in developed nations, where women had better access to education and birth control, or in countries that had suffered economic dislocations, including the former Soviet Union.

Despite the decline in the rate of population growth, agricultural scientists expressed concern about the challenge of feeding 3.5 billion more people in the next 50 years as well as meeting the increased demand for meat in newly affluent countries. With cereal stockpiles dangerously low—an estimated 281 million tons in 1997, down from 383 million in 1992—agriculturalists felt pressured to perform miracles like those brought about by the Green Revolution in the 1960s and '70s, in which world grain yields were dramatically increased through seed-breeding programs and intensive crop management.

A report by an international team of scientists in the July 25, 1997, issue of *Science,* however, warned that agricultural intensification had potential adverse ecological consequences for farmed fields as well as the larger environment. The researchers pointed out that organic matter in the soil, for example, is often severely depleted in intensively farmed soils. Without this organic matter, the soil loses its fertility and water-holding capacity, which are both key ingredients of healthy crop yields. The authors suggested that better management of soil fertility, fertilizers, and pesticides was key to a more sustainable and environmentally benign agriculture.

Deforestation

Forest fires in the Amazon and Indonesia destroyed vast areas of the world's tropical rain forests in 1997. According to the World Wide Fund for Nature, in the Amazon scattered fires burned more than 20,000 sq km (1 sq km=0.386 sq mi) of

forest—an increase of 50–70% from 1996. In Borneo and Sumatra fires smoldered for months, casting a smoke pall over seven nations from July to November. In both regions many small fires were fanned to conflagration by an especially strong El Niño weather pattern that lowered the humidity and dried the forests. Most of the fires were set by ranchers, timber companies, settlers, and subsistence farmers.

The rate of tropical deforestation due to other factors also increased between 1995 and 1997 after having dropped by half since the 1980s. Interpreting satellite images recorded by Brazil's National Institute for Space Research, researchers found that loggers, ranchers, and farmers annually destroyed some 15,000 sq km. A separate study by a Brazilian congressional committee arrived at a higher figure—50,000–60,000 sq km yearly—after factoring into their calculations logged areas smaller than

0.065 sq km, which satellite photos cannot detect. The same study estimated that 12% (about 600,000 sq km) of the Amazon's forests had now been destroyed. According to a study published in the July 25, 1997, issue of *Science,* each year between 1980 and 1995, farmers cleared more than 130,000 sq km of forest worldwide. During the same period, only some 13,000 sq km of new trees were planted annually.

Extinctions and recoveries

A report issued by the Nature Conservancy, an international environmental organization, estimated that nearly one-third of the 20,329 species of animals and plants in the U.S. were at risk of extinction. These included birds, mammals, freshwater fish, and flowering plants and totaled one-fifth of all American species. Using information derived from 20 years of ob-

Schoolchildren in Jambi, Sumatra, wear makeshift masks as protection against smoke from burning rain forests. Pollution from the fires cast a pall throughout Indonesia from July to November.

servations by researchers, the authors stated that at least 110 species of plants and animals were already extinct, 416 had not been seen in years, and 6,275 were in trouble. Animals living in rivers, streams, lakes, and wetlands were especially threatened, as were plants in general.

In a dramatic reversal of scientific opinion, researchers established that forest songbird populations remained stable overall across the U.S. between 1966 and 1996. Scott Robinson of the University of Illinois at Champaign-Urbana drew these conclusions after analyzing data from the North American Breeding Bird Survey, an annual roadside census of birds in the continental U.S. and southern Canada. Robinson cautioned, however, that birds in some locations, such as the Adirondacks and Great Smoky Mountains, were not doing as well as expected and that some species, such as the wood thrush and cerulean warbler, were declining in all surveyed locations. Robinson credited the conservation of large, intact forested habitats for the continued health of bird populations.

In another sign of improved conditions, the International Whaling Commission granted permission to members of the Makah Indian tribe in Washington state to harvest four gray whales annually. The tribe, which had hunted whales for 1,500 years, was guaranteed the right to continue hunting them under an 1855 treaty with the U.S. government. The Makahs, however, had not harvested a whale since the 1920s. Gray whales were listed as an endangered species in 1972 and removed from the list in 1994 after their population rebounded.

In 1997 biologists documented the continued existence of several species thought to be extinct, among them two species not seen since the late 1800s. Fishermen in the Kinabatangan River of Borneo, for example, captured several young Borneo river sharks, previously known only from a specimen taken from a river in Borneo more than 100 years ago. A species of wild pig (*Sus bucculentus*) was identified from the dense forests of the Annamite Range, located at the Laos-Vietnam border.

Land and water conservation

The 1997 International Year of the Reef closed to mixed reviews on the state of coral reefs worldwide. Even as some scientists documented outbreaks of new coral diseases in the Caribbean, other researchers offered evidence that many reefs located in waters away from population centers were improving and even thriving. Among the healthiest were reefs in the Pacific and Indian oceans, including those around the Maldives, Australia's Great Barrier Reef, and the Chagos Archipelago, southwest of India. (*See* Feature Article: WHAT IS KILLING THE REEFS?)

To help replenish locally declining fish stocks and to provide greater protection for Florida's coral reefs, a no-take fishing zone was declared in the Florida Keys following similar regulations implemented in places such as Bermuda and Palau in recent years. The experimental management in Florida's Western Sambos Ecological Reserve was established after a tumultuous six-year public debate.

In March the San Diego (Calif.) City Council approved the first step in a plan to set aside 68,800 ha (690 sq km; more than 30% of a larger study area comprising 233,000 ha) in San Diego county for the preservation of some 17 federally endangered species of plants and animals and dozens of others considered at risk. The experimental approach, hailed as a cooperative model for administering the Federal Endangered Species Act in the future, involved the participation of municipal, county, state, and federal governments and agencies; developers and private landowners; and environmental organizations. Under the plan, large habitat blocks for endangered species were created in San Diego county in exchange for the opening of other tracts to development regardless of the presence of endangered species. The San Diego plan was just one of 12 such plans involving 15,600 sq km throughout southern California. Conservation biologists, however, cautioned that the reserve network may not provide adequate protection for plants and animals in the event of natural disturbances or catastrophes in the core preserves.

Environment and human health

In 1996 researchers in New Orleans reported that two estrogen-mimicking pollutants could act in concert to magnify by 1,600 times the estrogenic effects of just one of the agents in the human body. Public reaction to the news was so strong that it influenced the outcome of U.S. legislation. In the July 25, 1997, issue of *Science,* however, John McLachlan of Tulane University, New Orleans, and Xavier University, Cincinnati, Ohio, a scientist from the group that conducted the initial study, withdrew the paper after his team and other independent researchers could not reproduce the results. Meanwhile, endocrinologists at the Vanderbilt University School of Medicine, Nashville, Tenn., discovered that some pollutants mimic androgens, the male sex hormones that, like estrogen, control reproductive functions and the development of embryos.

Other pollutants, such as polychlorinated biphenyls (PCBs), were shown to pose serious threats to animal and human health, particularly in the most northerly reaches of the globe. Studies of polar bears in Hudson Bay, for example, revealed that the weight of bears of all ages had declined since the early 1980s. During the same period, the survival of first-year cubs also dropped—from 75% to 50%. Researchers implicated high concentrations of PCBs that were found in the fat of bears and the seals that they eat. A major report by scientists from eight Arctic nations found that a majority of the Inuit living in northern Canada and Greenland also had high concentrations of PCBs and other chemicals in their bodies.

Using computer models of the atmosphere, Frank Wania and Donald Mackay of the University of Toronto demonstrated how these pollutants may have contaminated northern reaches far from their source point in more southerly regions. They showed that once some toxic materials entered the atmosphere, they moved quickly—some in just five days—from the Equator to the poles. At the poles the cold air condensed the pollutants, which dropped to the ground as snow or rain and then entered the food chain.

Environmental awards

Five scientists received the 1997 Right Livelihood Awards, considered the alternative Nobel Prizes, for their "outstanding work in upholding human values," said the Stockholm-based Right Livelihood Award Foundation, which administered the prizes. The awards went to Jinzaburo Takagi, founder of the Citizens Nuclear Information Center, Tokyo; Mycle Schneider, director of the Paris office of the World Information Service on Energy; Joseph Ki-Zerbo, a historian and social scientist in Burkina Faso; Cindy Duehring, an American environmental activist and creator of an international network on chemical-related injuries; and Michael Succow, a conservationist noted for his environmental achievements in the former East Germany.

—Kim Alan Chapman

ENVIRONMENTAL TECHNOLOGY

An article in the Nov. 10, 1997, issue of *Business Week* reported that environmental concerns continued to shape the agendas of companies around the world. According to the authors, corporate executives increasingly subscribed to the view that "sustainable businesses—those built on renewable materials and fuels—present a tremendous opportunity as the world copes with the environmental problems that are the 20th century's legacy."

Whether stimulated by economic, societal, or regulatory forces, the developers of environmental technology in 1997 responded to this sustainability challenge by expanding markets for existing pollution technologies as well as pushing new green technologies in unprecedented directions.

Cleaner, greener automobiles

To the average person the most significant advances in environmental technology probably were most obvious in the family car. In a Jan. 5, 1998, front-page article in *The Wall Street Journal,* Rebecca Blumenstein reported, "The auto industry sees a growing business case for making multi-billion-dollar investments in new technologies." With gasoline costs in many parts of the world far higher than in the U.S., she wrote, "alternative technologies may be necessary simply to make driving a car affordable for millions of new consumers" in countries where per capita vehicle ownership historically has been low. Blumenstein also observed that "in Europe, clean technology is becoming the price of admission....Technology could be a significant force in sorting out the next century's winners and losers."

In 1997, for instance, the auto industry's hallmark trade expositions in Tokyo and Detroit showcased important technological innovations from nearly all the world's major automakers. At the forefront the Toyota Motor Corp. announced the introduction in Japan of the Prius, a four-seat sedan that travels more than 65 mi on a gallon of gasoline (about 28 km per liter) and emits half as much carbon dioxide, a key greenhouse gas, as standard cars. The Prius, a "hybrid" vehicle, *i.e.,* a car that alternately uses electric power and gas, also exemplified the growing trend in cleaner automobile technology.

Most significant, however, were not individual innovations like the Prius but the breadth and depth of the overall changes in the automobile industry. According to Blumenstein, "Time is starting to run out for the internal-combustion engine." Although the "pistons and crankshafts that have powered automobiles and the auto industry for more than a century" will not disappear overnight, she added, "auto mak-

ers from Tokyo to Stuttgart to Detroit have reached a surprising consensus on an idea deemed heretical not long ago: A fundamental shift in engine technology is needed."

Carmakers were clamoring to announce their green breakthroughs, and examples abounded of the innovations under way. The Ford Motor Co., for example, announced that it would join with Germany's Daimler-Benz AG and with Canada's Ballard Power Systems Inc. to begin producing as many as 100,000 fuel-cell-powered cars (whose systems convert hydrogen to electricity and produce harmless water vapor as a by-product) by 2004. The General Motors Corp. (GM) announced that it would introduce by that same year or sooner an electric vehicle powered by a fuel cell, and the company said that by 2001 it would introduce a hybrid car that got up to 80 mi per gal (34 km per liter). Noting that consumers in Arizona and California were slow to buy its EV1 two-passenger coupe, an electric car introduced in 1996, GM was preparing to come out with a new nickel-metal-hydride battery

that would increase the car's driving range to 255 km (160 mi) without a charge and expand its seating to four passengers. The Chrysler Corp. announced efforts to produce a hybrid known as the Dodge Intrepid ESX2. The company aimed to produce a car that was powered by a diesel engine and an electric motor and that got 70 mi per gal (30 km per liter).

Innovations in automaking did not stop with the development of alternative-energy systems. To make green auto technologies practical and affordable, manufacturers were developing new materials and designs for automobile components. To reduce the weight of the new high-mileage cars, for example, engineers created designs that used high-strength steel, aluminum, and polymer composites. They also conducted extensive research into the increased use of recycled materials and ceramics, low-resistance tires, technologies for mitigating traffic congestion, reformulation of fuels, and strategies for the easy disassembly of auto bodies and parts.

The trends among American auto buyers made for an interesting irony at the Tokyo

In 1997 the Toyota Motor Corp. introduced the Prius in Japan. The four-seat sedan travels more than 65 mi on a gallon of gasoline (about 28 km per liter) and emits half as much carbon dioxide, a key greenhouse gas, as standard cars.

and Detroit auto shows, where hybrid cars and zero-emission "concept" cars were sandwiched among the gasoline-hungry sport utility vehicles and muscle cars that had become so popular with American drivers in recent years. That contrast prompted *Washington Post* reporters Warren Brown and Frank Swoboda to write in a Jan. 7, 1998, article: "On the one hand, auto makers are being pressed by regulators, environmentalists, and the emerging demands created by global warming to develop vehicles that use less fuel and produce fewer pollutants. But they also are struggling to satisfy consumer preferences in the United States—the world's single largest and most lucrative auto market, where electric vehicles are statistically invisible and where demand for gas-thirsty trucks and mega-horsepower cars overrides calls for fuel economy."

Green manufacturing

In December representatives from 159 different nations met in Kyoto to reach an agreement on reducing emissions of carbon dioxide and other gases that contribute to global warming. Even though the resulting Kyoto protocol was criticized by both supporters and opponents, its focus on carbon dioxide, in particular, began to drive long-range thinking in a wide variety of manufacturing sectors. Steel manufacturers, for example, expressed a commitment to reducing levels of carbon dioxide emissions below those called for by the Kyoto agreement. U.S. appliance manufacturers stepped up their production of more energy-efficient machines in response to guidelines issued by the U.S. Department of Energy and the Environmental Protection Agency.

Other regulatory initiatives in the U.S. and Europe—such as restrictions on the use of certain toxic raw materials in manufacturing and laws mandating that manufacturers assume responsibility for the goods they produce by taking products back for recycling at the end of their life cycles—gave further impetus to a movement within the manufacturing sector known as Design for Environment (DFE). A term newly popular among environmental professionals, DFE stresses the importance of preventing pollution, a measure that often is far more effective, and less costly, for maintaining a clean environment than cleaning up contamination after the fact. This new manufacturing philosophy takes a life-cycle, or "cradle-to-grave," approach to the management of resources. It reflects a commitment to considering environmental cleanup and waste-management implications not at the end of

a product's life or of a manufacturing process but rather at the very beginning stages of a product's conceptualization and design. It entails, for example, creating products whose components can be easily disassembled (known as demanufacturing) for reuse or recycling once the product has reached the end of its life cycle, reducing the size of products to eliminate or conserve materials, and using more environmentally benign paints and other finishes.

New applications of existing technologies also prodded other innovations. In the wake of a ban on the manufacture of ozone-depleting chlorofluorocarbons (CFCs), for example, manufacturers of semiconductors and other electronics in the early 1990s turned to a variety of CFC substitutes, including potentially toxic solvents, to clean component surfaces. Scientists at Motorola, Inc.'s corporate-research laboratory in Tempe, Ariz., tested laser technologies to remove contaminants from semiconductor surfaces, which had the potential to provide manufacturers with a safer cleaning method.

Conventional pollution-control technologies

The expanding economies of China and the countries of the former Soviet Union and socialist Eastern European nations presented enormous emerging markets for the kinds of pollution-control technologies that had become standard equipment in the automobiles and industries of more developed Western nations. These technologies included catalytic converters on vehicles, electrostatic precipitators used for removing particles from industrial-waster gases,

and flue-gas scrubbers used to reduce emissions of sulfur dioxide and nitrogen oxides from coal-fired electric-utility stations. Unleaded gasoline and catalytic converters increasingly became standard in cars not only throughout much of South America but also in Central Europe, China, and Asia.

Consumer products

Impressive changes in environmental technologies also reshaped other aspects of society. Among numerous examples were the manufacture of longer-lived batteries that used less-toxic components and the substitution of more environmentally benign raw materials in everything from paper products to furniture.

Some advances in green technology in 1997 offered indirect environmental benefits. Emerging electronic services—such as movie-on-demand home-video options, for example, which allow viewers to order videos from an electronic library—conserved fossil fuels and prevented pollution by reducing the need for trips to video-rental outlets and the manufacture of videotapes. In the 1997 book *Thinking Ecologically: The Next Generation of Environmental Policy,* businessman John Preston observed that "even technologies that seem entirely unrelated to the environment, like the availability of information over the Internet, offer the potential for significant environmental gains. In fact, a more technologically and information-intensive society offers the promise of becoming less dependent on the consumption of physical materials and less reliant on polluting activities."

—Bud Ward

FOOD AND AGRICULTURE

The impact of El Niño on food production could not be fully assessed before mid-1998, but Australia and parts of South America and Southeast Asia were expected to be seriously affected by this abnormal tropical weather phenomenon. Around the world, buyers increased their acquisition of commodities in anticipation of production problems.

Although many scientists felt it was impossible, researchers in Scotland reported the creation of the first clone of an adult mammal, a lamb they named Dolly. Two other cloned lambs were later produced from fetal cells bearing a human gene. These achievements represented significant steps toward the creation of genetically engineered farm animals.

A new set of rules regarding the production of organically grown foods in the U.S. was finalized during the past year. New dietary recommendations also appeared, as did a number of studies focusing on the role of nutrition in the prevention of chronic diseases.

AGRICULTURE

The 1997 return of El Niño, a weather phenomenon centered in the tropical Pacific that results in increased water temperature and a change in wind directions, could significantly influence agriculture around much of the world. (*See* Year in Review: EARTH SCIENCES.) A drought in Australia, floods in Peru, Bolivia, and Ecuador, and a severe drought and damaging frosts in Indonesia and Papua New Guinea were attributed to it. The previous major episode caused by an El Niño event had been in 1982–83. Weather scientists meeting in Geneva in 1997 warned that condi-

tions would not return to normal until at least the summer of 1998. In anticipation of production problems, commodities buyers were increasing their acquisitions. For example, as worldwide markets responded to anticipated effects of El Niño, Japanese soybean buyers stepped up their purchases.

Although Australian authorities, anticipating heavy drought damage, reduced production forecasts substantially during the spring of 1997, rains in the eastern part of the country were enough to improve crop prospects there. In early 1998 there were still clear indications of reduced output in Southeast Asia, especially in Indonesia. Some analysts interpreted a widespread drought in China as evidence of El Niño's impact, but correlations were weak. There was concern about India, where crops are historically subject to El Niño-related drought damage, but the amount of rainfall during the summer of 1997 was enough to forestall serious crop reductions.

Authorities in southern Africa were preparing for the worst, though the effects of El Niño on corn production would not be known until the early months of 1998. Corn is the region's food staple. Typically South Africa, Zimbabwe, and other countries in southern Africa experience intense drought during El Niño.

As the effects of El Niño were being assessed, analysts noted that since the early 1980s international trading in beef has increased substantially. Rising incomes in a number of key regions in the world and the advent of a more liberalized trading environment have contributed to the increase. Beef exports among major traders were projected at 4.8 million tons in 1997, a 45% increase from 1980. Total production for 1998 was expected to reach

55 million tons, most of it not slated for international trading. Trading barriers have included sanitation requirements, cultural differences, quality requirements, and issues related to new technologies such as biotechnology. Trade also has been affected by changing production, marketing, and political conditions.

Although beef is produced and consumed worldwide, only a few countries engage in large-scale beef trade. Beef production tends to be concentrated among the six top producers: the U.S., the European Union (EU), Brazil, China, Argentina, and Russia. The major importers are Japan, Canada, Mexico, Russia, South Korea, and the U.S., and the major exporters are the U.S., Australia, the EU, New Zealand, and Argentina. Beef constitutes 11% of the world's total food consumption, an increase of 4% since 1980.

The birth of Dolly

Scottish embryologist Ian Wilmut and his colleagues at the Roslin Institute, near Edinburgh, electrified the scientific community and the general public in February 1997 when they announced the birth of Dolly the lamb, the first clone of an adult mammal. Dolly, then seven months old, was cloned from a cell taken from the udder of a six-year-old Finn Dorset ewe. Because scientists had all but ruled out the possibility that a cell from a mature animal could be manipulated to generate an exact replica of the donor, the achievement by Wilmut and his team was regarded as a major scientific breakthrough.

A normal sheep, Dolly was the result of the transplantation of the nucleus of a cell from one adult sheep into an egg produced

How a Sheep Was Cloned

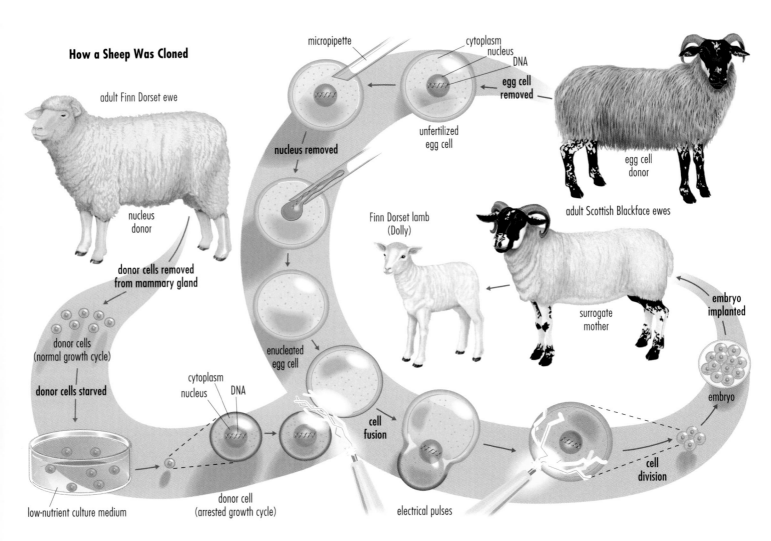

adult Finn Dorset ewe

nucleus donor

donor cells removed from mammary gland

donor cells (normal growth cycle)

donor cells starved

low-nutrient culture medium

cytoplasm
nucleus
DNA

donor cell (arrested growth cycle)

micropipette

nucleus removed

cytoplasm
nucleus
DNA

egg cell removed

unfertilized egg cell

enucleated egg cell

cell fusion

electrical pulses

cell division

Finn Dorset lamb (Dolly)

surrogate mother

adult Scottish Blackface ewes

egg cell donor

embryo implanted

embryo

The first clone of an adult mammal, Dolly the lamb was born in July 1996. Because scientists had all but ruled out the possibility that a cell from a mature animal could be manipulated to generate an exact replica of the donor, the creation of Dolly was regarded as a major scientific breakthrough.

by another. Although experiments had indicated that eggs would reject nuclei of the differentiated, or specialized, cells found in mature animals, members of the Roslin team theorized that an egg might bond with a differentiated cell and accept its nucleus if they could induce the cell to abandon its normal cycle of growth and division and enter a quiescent stage. To do this, the researchers deliberately withheld nutrients from cells extracted from the udder of the ewe they planned to clone. Unfertilized egg cells then were removed from a second sheep, a Scottish Blackface ewe, and their own nuclei were removed. Electrical charges were used to fuse the egg cells and the differentiated cells into 277 separate two-celled units. Of the embryos that developed from these fused pairs, only one survived. It was transferred to the uterus of yet another Scottish Blackface, and five months later, in July 1996, Dolly was born. Dolly has since been mated and gave birth to a healthy lamb in April 1998.

Although news of a successful attempt at cloning a sheep immediately prompted speculation about the possibility—and potential pitfalls—of cloning human beings,

Wilmut emphasized in interviews that finding a way to clone humans was not the impetus behind his group's research. Their eventual goal is, rather, to perfect a method for developing genetically engineered farm animals that will, among other things, produce therapeutic proteins in their milk and provide organs—especially hearts and kidneys—for human patients in need of transplants. By late 1997 the Roslin researchers had announced the cloning of two more lambs, Molly and Polly, who were produced from cells bearing a human gene. (Unlike Dolly, Molly and Polly were derived from the nuclei of fetal sheep cells, whose use in cloning experiments has had a much higher success rate.) The researchers hope that once the lambs mature, their milk will contain useful quantities of factor IX, a human protein that helps blood to clot. Once extracted, the protein would be valuable to patients who lacked it, such as people with hemophilia. This new work could pave the way for the creation of herds of cattle or flocks of sheep that would act as drug-making factories. (For additional information on recent cloning research and its implications, *see* Year in Review: LIFE SCIENCES: *Molecular Biology and Genetics;* MEDICAL SCIENCES: *General Medicine.*)

Food-recovery efforts

Held on September 15–16 in Washington, D.C., the first-ever National Summit on Gleaning and Food Recovery highlighted efforts to recover excess edible food and distribute it to the hungry. The summit was sponsored by the U.S. Department of Agriculture (USDA) and four leading antihunger organizations: Second Harvest, the Congressional Hunger Center, Foodchain, and the Chef and the Child Foundation. A USDA study released during the summit indicated that 12% of the 100 million American households experienced some "food insecurity," defined as the limited or uncertain access to food due to low or fluctuating incomes. A previous USDA study had found that some 43.5 billion kg (96 billion lb) of food are wasted in the U.S. each year. A new public service announcement on food recovery and large-scale donations of food to states from the Department of Defense were among a number of recent efforts to recover previously wasted food. To aid in the distribution of excess food, Congress also passed the Bill Emerson Good Samaritan Food Donation Act of 1996, which exempts donors and food banks from lawsuits over ill effects from food donated in good faith.

Rules developed for organic foods

The USDA has prepared a set of rules regarding organically grown foods. Consumer demand for organic foods has increased 20% per year since 1990, with more than $3.5 billion worth of organic foods sold in the U.S. during 1996. Such demand has meant that consumers also have wanted to be sure of what they were buying.

In preparation for seven years, the rules were scheduled to go into effect in late 1998. Consolidating guidelines used by various state, federal, and private certification agencies, they define exactly which products, either raw or processed, may be labeled as organic. In order to carry the USDA organic seal, raw foods, for example, must be grown without the use of hormones, pesticides, or synthetic fertilizers, and processed foods must contain 95% organic ingredients. Processed foods with 50–95% organic ingredients may be labeled "made with certain organic ingredients," whereas products containing less than 50% will be allowed to use the word *organic* only in the list of ingredients. The rules also establish standards for the handling of organically grown livestock. For example, the rules prohibit giving antibiotics to livestock except to treat illnesses.

The penalty for violating the rules was a fine of up to $10,000. States will be able to issue stricter standards with the approval of the secretary of agriculture.

A pest of a problem

From Florida to California, the southern tier of the U.S. was battling the devasting effects of *Coptotermes formosanus* Shiraki, the Formosan subterranean termite (FST), believed to have been introduced into the U.S from ships returning from East Asia after World War II. Traditional termite-control products and practices failed to provide significant control of this pest, which was costing consumers about $1 billion per year.

Recently Congress approved a $5 million program to combat the FST. Plans called for the development of new termite-control strategies and for demonstrations in affected areas of how citizens can use fumigants, physical barriers, soil treatments, and baits. The initial focus will be in Louisiana and subsequently in other Southern states and Hawaii.

Researchers at USDA laboratories in Gainesville, Fla., were in the final stages of developing an evaluation and monitoring approach using acoustic instruments that detect and quantify this specific termite population. USDA researchers as well as those at several universities and chemical companies were also investigating environmentally safe toxins or biological control agents that will help control FST. In addition, the USDA launched an effort to find natural predators in East Asia. If an otherwise environmentally safe predator can be found, it will be tested in restricted environments in USDA laboratories. Other studies focused on fungi whose toxins kill termites but are safe for humans.

Unmasking a fish killer

Scientists identified the microorganism that killed tens of thousands of fish in

Richard Ellis—Sygma

During the past year scientists determined that a unicellular microbe, *Pfiesteria piscicida*, killed tens of thousands of fish in Chesapeake Bay on the eastern coast of the U.S. Toxins produced by the microorganism cause lesions in fish (below) and are implicated in a variety of human health problems.

Chesapeake Bay on the eastern coast of the U.S. in June 1997. The culprit, *Pfiesteria piscicida,* is a unicellular microbe that can change its shape, release a strong toxin, and kill large fish. At the end of the year, *Pfiesteria* was still causing problems along the coast as far south as Florida.

Pfiesteria, a dinoflagellate, has long whiplike tails, or flagella, and is toxic to both fish and humans. It is more threatening than any other dinoflagellate because it dumps its toxin into the water to stun prey before attacking. Other dinoflagellates release toxin only when their cells are broken open.

Investigators believed that *Pfiesteria* proliferates when phosphorus in agricultural fertilizers and feed additives accumulates from water runoff. USDA and university laboratories were studying phytase, an enzyme that, if applied to animal feeds, may improve their nutritional quality. The application of phytase to animal feeds would reduce the need to add phosphorus to animal diets and thereby reduce the amount of phosphorus available for runoff. Other methods of combating *Pfiesteria*

were also being considered, including a number of alternatives in manure management and the use of phytase composts.

Environmentally friendly telephone cards

Researchers at the Industrial Agricultural Products Center of the University of Nebraska at Lincoln were working with CornCard International, Inc., to develop a cornstarch-based plastic substitute to be used in prepaid telephone cards and other single-application cards. The plastic substitute is made with polyactic acid (PLA), a water-resistant resin derived from cornstarch. A special additive makes PLA flexible but allows it to retain the desired ink adhesion. Unlike conventional plastics, PLA is biodegradable. As environmental concerns regarding waste management continued to mount, the cornstarch-based cards offered an environmentally friendly alternative to a nonbiodegradable product and provided an additional use for corn.

—John Patrick Jordan
and Patricia Brazeel Lewis

NUTRITION

During the past year researchers continued to explore the role of nutrition in the prevention of chronic illnesses. Studies focused on the relationships between specific foods or nutrients and cardiovascular disease, HIV, cancer, coronary heart disease, and obesity. A number of lifestyle changes, including reducing dietary fat and increasing physical activity, were endorsed by medical and nutrition experts. In addition, dietary recommendations were issued to promote health and prevent diseases.

Functional foods

Previously unrecognized health benefits of various foods or food components were recently reported. For example, Ian Record and Ivor Dreosti of the Commonwealth Scientific and Industrial Research Organisation's Division of Human Nutrition, Adelaide, Australia, showed that black tea protected mice against the development of skin tumors caused by overexposure to ultraviolet radiation. The high polyphenol content in black tea was believed to provide antioxidant protection from free oxygen radicals generated by the ultraviolet rays. Research conducted by Bo Lonnerdal of the University of California, Davis, focused on the benefits of lactoferrin, a bioactive component in mammalian milk. Lactoferrin is an iron-binding protein that may be added to foods as an iron fortifier, antimicrobial agent, or human growth catalyst. B.S. Reddy of the American Health Foundation, Valhalla, N.Y., also determined that live bacteria used to ferment milk products may be used to enhance intestinal immunity and reduce the risk of colon cancer.

Scientists continued their work to develop a document that outlines the scientific base for functional food applications. This work was part of an ongoing three-year project coordinated by the International Life Sciences Institute Europe in Brussels. The document will address six areas where functional foods could modify physiological targets through nutrition: growth and differentiation; substrate metabolism; defense against reactive oxidation products; the cardiovascular system; the gastrointestinal system; and behavioral and psychological functions.

Micronutrients

The professional literature regarding micronutrients—vitamins, minerals, and trace elements—and their relationship to disease prevention was expanded in 1997. Paul Jacques of Tufts University, Boston, and colleagues found that elderly women who had used vitamin C supplements for at least 10 years had a 77% lower prevalence of early lens opacities. The increasing loss of lens transparency as a person ages can result in cataracts in the eye. Intake of vitamin C may be a crucial factor in the eye's ability to deal with oxidative stress (cellular damage caused by oxygen radicals). Oxidative stress has been implicated in the development of age-related cataract formation. Lowering the risk of early lens opacities could make a substantial impact on public health costs.

Research on HIV-positive homosexual and bisexual men showed that low vitamin B_{12} levels in samples of their blood were linked to a nearly twofold increase in the risk of progression to full-blown AIDS in a given period of time. Alice Tang of the Johns Hopkins University School of Hygiene and Public Health, Baltimore, Md., together with other researchers, studied the effects of vitamin B_{12} levels on the progression of the AIDS virus. The median AIDS-free time in HIV-positive men with low vitamin B_{12} levels was found to be four years shorter than in those HIV-positive men with adequate levels of vitamin B_{12}. The researchers suggested further study to determine whether the correction of low vitamin B_{12} levels in cases of early HIV infection would influence the natural course of the disease.

At the University of Grenoble (France), I. Hininger and colleagues studied two groups, one of smokers and one of non-smokers. Both groups, each made up of healthy volunteers, were placed on diets with enough fruits and vegetables so that their total carotenoid (beta-carotene, lutein, lycopene, and alpha-tocopherol) intake increased to 30 mg per day. Before starting the diet, the smokers had lower carotenoid levels in their blood samples. After two weeks on the diet, the smokers' carotene levels increased by 23%, as opposed to an increase of 11% in the nonsmokers. The resistance of low-density lipoproteins (LDLs) to oxidation also increased in both smokers (14%) and nonsmokers (28%). These results suggest that increased intake of fruits and vegetables may be helpful to both smokers and nonsmokers in reducing the risk of atherosclerosis, which may be related to LDL oxidation.

Micronutrients were also in the news in 1997 as researchers sought ways to meet the goal of eliminating micronutrient deficiencies worldwide by the year 2000. This goal had been announced at an international workshop held in Salt Lake City,

Utah, in 1995. Inadequate intake of micronutrients, especially vitamin A, iron, and iodine, continued to be a major problem, affecting more than one-third of the world's population. Micronutrient deficiencies impair growth, intellectual development, and the chance of survival, particularly among women, infants, and children in less-developed countries. Food fortification to eliminate micronutrient deficiencies has been a viable strategy in more industrialized countries. A recent study conducted by Jesse Gregory and colleagues at the University of Florida showed that the addition of folic acid to cereal grain products effectively increases folic acid intake in adults. Adding folic acid to the cereal products consumed by subjects in the study increased the blood-serum and red-blood-cell concentrations of folate in the subjects, which indicated that the folic acid in cereal-grain products is readily available to the body. In the U.S., food-consumption data revealed that the average daily folate intake for women of childbearing age is 180–200 micrograms per day. This is well below the recommended level of 400 micrograms per day to reduce the chances of having a baby with a congenital defect involving the brain and spinal cord.

Lifestyle changes to improve health

Results from a study involving patients with coronary heart disease (CHD) showed that reduction of blood-vessel narrowing in the right carotid artery may be brought about by lifestyle changes such as reducing weight, lowering cholesterol, and stopping smoking. Over a two-year period, Howard Hodis and colleagues of the University of Southern California School of Medicine

measured the thickness of the inner wall of the right carotid artery in men and women with CHD. The thickness of the artery wall is a measure of the early stages of atherosclerosis, a disease characterized by the buildup of fatty deposits in the inner layer of the arteries. The researchers also tracked each subject's diet, body weight, and smoking habits. Results showed that changes in body weight, cholesterol levels, and number of cigarettes smoked determined the amount of progression or regression in the rate of thickening of the right carotid artery. Subjects who lowered their weight and cholesterol intake and stopped smoking experienced a decrease in the annual rate of progression of atherosclerosis.

Although the protective effects of fish oil against heart disease were identified

Tony Freeman—Photo Edit/PNI

The incidence of childhood obesity has increased significantly not only in the U.S. but in countries around the world. Increasing physical activity and eliminating high-calorie foods, such as fat-containing snacks, are recommended as ways for obese youngsters to lose weight.

about 10–15 years ago, new research continued to examine the mechanisms involved and implications for dietary management. Daniel Hwang and associates at Louisiana State University at Baton Rouge found that the protective effects against heart disease were present if subjects consumed 6–15 g (0.2–0.5 oz) of n-3 polyunsaturated fatty acids from fish oil for four weeks. They concluded, however, that it is unrealistic to expect most people to eat enough fish to obtain that amount of n-3 polyunsaturated fatty acids; consequently, people would have to consume fish-oil supplements to obtain the desirable effects.

Reports that the incidence of obesity in American youth has significantly increased in the past 20 years attracted much attention in the past year. A recent study, however, indicated that childhood obesity is in fact a worldwide epidemic. Using four representative surveys of Russian, Brazilian, South African, and Chinese children, Barry Popkin of the University of North Carolina at Chapel Hill and colleagues showed that the prevalence of obesity in the study's subjects ranged from 10.5% to 25.6%. Since obesity in childhood is associated with heart disease and diabetes in adulthood, this finding should be of concern to public health professionals.

Lack of physical activity is a major factor in childhood obesity. A nationwide telephone survey conducted recently in the U.S. by James O. Hill of the University of Colorado Health Sciences Center, Denver, showed that parents are a powerful influence on the total weekly physical activity of children. Hill also found that more than half of all children who say that they do not get enough physical activity cite lack of time or homework demands, although two out of three parents blame competition from TV, video games, and computers or lack of interest.

In addition to increasing physical activity, reducing the intake of calories is recommended as a way to lose or maintain weight. Many adults have eagerly tried popular weight-loss drugs prescribed by their physicians in the past several years. In 1997, however, two common diet drugs, fenfluramine (Pondimin) and dexfenfluramine (Redux) were withdrawn from the market after heart-valve abnormalities occurred in a number of patients using these medications. (*See* Year in Review: MEDICAL SCIENCES: *General Medicine.*)

Even without weight-loss drugs, some dieters have been very successful in changing their eating habits to lose weight. In a recent study, Mary Klem of the University of Pittsburgh (Pa.) School of Medicine and colleagues reported that the majority of formerly obese men and women who had been successful at significant long-term weight loss reported a trigger event or incident that prompted them to intensify their dietary and exercise strategies. Some of the subjects described a medical trigger, such as sleep apnea, low back pain, constant fatigue, aching legs, or varicose veins. Others described an emotional trigger, such as a change in marital status.

Dietary guidance

Dietary guidance is provided through many public health organizations around the world to help individuals make food choices that promote health and prevent disease. In 1997 the American Institute for Cancer Research issued a report with dietary recommendations for preventing cancer. A panel of international experts prepared the report, entitled "Food, Nutrition and the Prevention of Cancer: A Global Perspective," on the basis of scientific literature on the worldwide causes of cancer. The report concluded that the evidence of dietary protection against cancer is strongest and most consistent for diets high in fruits and vegetables. The report also concluded that the evidence is convincing that physical activity protects against colon cancer; alcohol increases the risk of cancers of the mouth, pharynx, larynx, esophagus, and liver; high body mass increases the risk of cancer of the endometrial lining of the uterus; and refrigeration of food protects against stomach cancer. The report suggested that appropriate food patterns need to be preserved and people need to be encouraged to change their diets before disease occurs.

To make it easier to interpret dietary guidance, it has been suggested that individual countries create dietary guidelines based on foods—rather than on individual nutrients—suitable for the unique populations of those respective countries. Upcoming revisions of the Dietary Guidelines for Americans will incorporate food-based dietary guidelines (FBDG). During the past year the rationale for using the FBDG approach was shared at an international symposium in Tokyo. Participants indicated they would consider information on the FBDG when revising their guidelines.

Awards

Alfred Sommer, dean of the Johns Hopkins University School of Hygiene and Public Health, was recognized for having demonstrated that low-dose vitamin A supplementation in children can help prevent death from infectious diseases, as well as helping prevent blindness. Sommer received a Lasker award from the Albert and Mary Lasker Foundation. Sommer estimates that 5 million–10 million cases of corneal ulceration and a half million cases of blindness could be prevented and more than a million lives saved with the alleviation of vitamin A deficiencies in children worldwide.

Stanley N. Gershoff received the Conrad A. Elvehjem Award for Public Service in Nutrition, given in recognition of specific and distinguished service to the public through the science of nutrition. Gershoff, dean emeritus of the School of Nutrition Science and Policy at Tufts University, made significant contributions to nutrition around the world. He carried out training and research activities in more than a dozen countries in Asia, Africa, and Latin America. He was involved in vitamin A fortification programs and grain fortification policy development in several Southeast Asian countries.

John M. Scott was recognized for his recent contributions to the basic understanding of human nutrition. Scott, a professor of biochemistry at University College Dublin, received the Lederle Award in Human Nutrition, given by Lederle Laboratories. He was honored for research focusing on the metabolic relationship between vitamin B_{12} and folate; the turnover, catabolism, and excretion of folate under various physiological states; and the role of folate and vitamin B_{12} in children with neural-tube defects.

—Marla Reicks

See also Feature Article: THE BIRDS AND THE BEES, THE FLOWERS AND THE TREES.

LIFE SCIENCES

In the past year scientists made startling discoveries that advanced understanding of some of life's fundamental processes. Botanists gained new insights into plant growth and reproduction, including double pollination, a process that produces the world's most important food crops. Ecologists intensified their focus on rivers, only recently recognized as one of the Earth's most biologically productive ecosystems. Two important studies assessed the economic value that ecosystems provide free of charge to humans.

Scientists also gained new knowledge of animal behavior, evolution, and genetics. Ornithologists released the results of studies on the behavior of colonial-nesting birds. Their findings had important implications for preserving endangered birds in the wild. Zoologists presented new data on the evolutionary relationship between domesticated dogs and wolves. Researchers concluded a 15-year project to map the genome of the bacterium *Escherichia coli,* one of science's most thoroughly studied organisms. The most publicized news of the past year in biology was Dolly, the sheep reported to have been cloned from a differentiated cell of an adult animal. Nevertheless, as of early 1998 that achievement had yet to be successfully repeated, and it appeared to be at odds with recent findings about the way cells grow old and die, which suggested a different origin for Dolly.

BOTANY

Fertilization in flowering plants

Many of the most important food staples consumed by humans—rice, wheat, corn (maize), numerous fruits, and all types of nuts—are the products of a remarkable process of plant sexual reproduction known as double fertilization; that is, two sperm are necessary for the formation of a seed.

Surprisingly, this function—so essential to human sustenance—was discovered only 100 years ago. In 1884 the German plant cytologist Eduard Adolf Strasburger noted that in some plants the pollen tube carries two sperm. (The pollen tube is a reproductive passageway that forms after the pollen germinates, allowing the transport of sperm to the plant's egg-containing ovules.) One sperm fuses with the egg to form the zygote, and the second fuses with the central cell's two nuclei, known as the polar nuclei, to form a triploid nucleus, the primary endosperm nucleus. The zygote nucleus divides to form the embryo, whereas the primary endosperm nucleus divides to form a tissue of reserve food, known as the endosperm, around the embryo. As they develop within the seed, the embryos of many plants consume the endosperm so that none of it remains in the mature seed. The seeds of plants such as wheat, rice, and corn, however, contain massive amounts of endosperm. One of the most spectacular examples is coconut, whose edible portions are composed of pure endosperm.

Since its discovery, scientists have settled many questions about double pollination. Many more, however, remain unanswered. Perhaps the most important is: how does one sperm come to fuse with the egg and the other with the polar nuclei? This is not an easy process to observe, since the tissues of the flower obscure these important reproductive events. One theory proposed by researchers is that the two sperm are biologically earmarked for their separate tasks. Using scanning electron microscopes, two groups of researchers from Canada and the U.S. recently examined sperm from several species and could detect no differences in their membranes, the place where dissimilarities might have been expected.

In 1997 plant researchers also yielded other important insights into pollination. The sperm of higher plants, for example, are not independently motile; that is, they must be carried to the egg and the central cell. The pollen tube, the transport device for the sperm cells, does a remarkable job of getting the sperm to the ovule. New research by a group of Italian researchers led by Alessendra Moscatelli of the University of Siena, Italy, identified various components of motor proteins in pollen tubes that promoted the rapid growth of the pollen tube, which enables the sperm to quickly drop to the ovule.

In order to reach the egg, the pollen tube must grow through the tissues of the flower (the stigma, style, ovary, and ovule). Research by Alice Y. Cheung of Yale University revealed the complex series of molecular and biochemical guidance mechanisms that keep the pollen tube growing in the right direction. Additional research by Scott Russell at the University of Oklahoma identified some of the various agents that direct the pollen tube into the ovule and guide the discharge of sperm into the egg and central cell.

Other researchers perfected fertilization techniques outside the flower, using in vitro methods—*i.e.,* isolating the eggs and sperm and achieving fusion of the cells outside the ovule. This extremely difficult

(Below) Adapted from information obtained from William Smith, University of Wyoming; (bottom) Darrell Gulin—Allstock/PNI

Although the cellular structure of leaves varies according to different light conditions (bottom), researchers recently discovered that in most leaves the upper epidermal and palisade cells magnify the intensity of surface sunlight by focusing it into the mesophyllic cell layer, where photosynthesis takes place (below). As sunlight penetrates the leaf, it is reflected back into the mesophyll by the lighter-colored lower epidermal cells.

work was carried out by two teams of researchers from France and Germany. The scientists used a variety of methods to fuse the cells, including electrical pulses and low levels of calcium in the media surrounding the egg. A group of international researchers led by Nathalie Leduc of École Normale Supérieure de Lyon, France, succeeded in removing zygotes from the ovules of corn and developing their embryos in cultures. This achievement opened the possibility of injecting plant embryos with genes at a very early developmental stage. (For further information on pollination, *see* Feature Article: THE BIRDS AND THE BEES, THE FLOWERS AND THE TREES.)

Leaves and light

Through a process known as photosynthesis—a series of biochemical reactions that convert atmospheric carbon dioxide into carbohydrates—the majority of plants are able to capture from sunlight the energy they need to survive. Most forests, however, contain a range of light conditions, from shade to full sun. Too much sunlight can cause the breakdown of chlorophyll necessary for the photosynthetic process. On the other hand, too little sunlight may not allow the plant to photosynthesize enough food to survive. Since all animals and plants on Earth consume the products of photosynthesis, scientists are very interested in the ways in which plants solve the problem of extreme variations in light.

How plants are able to carry out photosynthesis in different light conditions was the subject of a recent survey by a team of American researchers led by William Smith and Tom Vogelmann of the University of Wyoming. The scientists reviewed

Photosynthesis and Leaf Structure

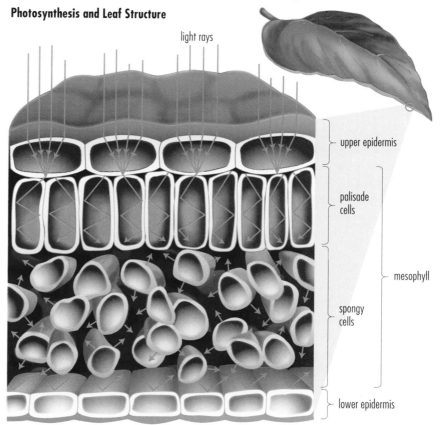

light rays

upper epidermis

palisade cells

mesophyll

spongy cells

lower epidermis

studies of the relationship between leaf structure and light intensity and its effect on photosynthesis. Their results revealed remarkable complexities in the structure of leaves that only now are becoming fully appreciated.

The structure of most leaves is composed of a tiered arrangement of cells. Each leaf has an upper and a lower epidermis that form, respectively, the upper and lower leaf surface. Each epidermal layer usually is only a single cell thick. Because they lack chloroplasts, these epidermal cells do not carry on photosynthesis. Embedded in the epidermis (most commonly on the lower epidermal layer) are special cells, known as guard cells, that regulate the size of the openings (known as stomates) in the leaf, allowing carbon dioxide to enter and water to leave.

Sandwiched between the two epidermal layers are the mesophyll cells, which carry on the leaf's photosynthesis. There are two types of mesophyll cells: the palisade and the spongy. As their name implies, the palisade mesophyll cells are long and narrow and are arranged like logs in a palisade, or wall. They are frequently found immediately below the upper epidermis in a layer ranging from one to several cells deep. Between the palisade layer and the lower epidermis is a layer of loosely packed, irregularly arranged spongy mesophyll cells.

In their comparisons of many different kinds of leaves, Smith and his collaborators found numerous variations in this basic pattern. The team also reported intriguing connections between leaf structure and the photosynthetic process. They discovered, for example, that the epidermal cells, which are frequently overlooked in photosynthesis studies because they lack chloroplasts, nonetheless play an important role in the photosynthetic process. The upper epidermal layer of lens-shaped cells on the leaves of *Begonia erythrophylla* focuses sunlight into the mesophyllic layers of cells with up to 12 times the intensity of the sunlight on the leaves' surface. The palisade cells also serve as conduits for light, their elongated shapes piping light to the spongy mesophyll cells below them.

Smith's team also demonstrated that leaves use color to trap light. The underside of a leaf, for example, is lighter than the surface facing the Sun. The researchers showed that as light penetrates the leaf's cellular layers, it is reflected back into the leaf by the lighter-colored lower epidermis. This mechanism allows leaves to maximize light retention for use in photosynthesis.

In addition, the researchers reported that leaf morphology changes in order to protect or enhance a plant's photosynthesizing abilities. Leaves that develop in sunlight, for example, are usually smaller and thicker than leaves that form in shade. The thick leaf helps protect the chloroplasts in plants exposed to sunlight. Leaves in the shade, on the other hand, tend to be larger and thinner, adaptations that allow the plant to maximize its light-collection ability.

Plant growth regulation

The factors and chemicals that control growth in plants continued to be of interest to scientists in 1997. Recent research by Andrew Fleming, Therese Mandel, and Cris Kuhlemeier of the University of Bern, Switz., and Simon McQueen-Mason of the University of York, Eng., identified the mechanism that controls the formation of new leaves.

All leaves emerge near the apex of the shoot tip, known as the apical meristem. There tiny leaf primordia are induced that will grow into the new leaves. These primordia are formed in a very precise manner that results in the particular arrangement of leaves found in a given species. The researchers applied tiny droplets mixed with purified expansin, an extracellular protein that increases the capability of plant-cell walls to expand in vitro, to the apical meristems of tomato plants. They were able to induce growths in the meristem that underwent morphogenesis to produce leaflike structures. According to the researchers, their results showed that the protein expansin can induce tissue expansion normally and that localized control of tissue expansion may induce leaf formation. Furthermore, they maintained that their data suggested a role for biophysical forces in plant development.

Scientists have identified five well-known plant-growth hormones: auxin, gibberellin, cytokinin, abscisic acid, and ethylene. Work by Jenneth M. Sasse of the University of Melbourne, Australia, made a strong case for adding a group of compounds known as brassinosteroids (BRs) to this list. BRs have been found in low concentrations in all plants thus far tested for them. These compounds affect the expansion, division, reproduction, vascular development, and stress responses of plants. There is evidence that BRs promote tissue growth and the linking of microtubules with the plasma membrane of the cell, a process that is responsible for controlling cell elongation. Sasse also found dramatic changes in the appearance of mutant plants that were defective in BR synthesis or response. BRs also appeared to reduce stress responses in some plants to drought and temperature extremes. Experiments testing the usefulness of BRs for the setting and development of fruit in agriculture and horticulture have begun.

Researchers also shed light on one of the least-understood plant hormones—abscisic acid (ABA), whose primary function is to mediate a plant's responses to stress, such as cold, drought, and salinity. A group of scientists led by Yan Wu at Rockefeller University, New York City, studied the mechanisms of ABA action by using microinjection experiments on single tomato cells. In a series of highly ingenious experiments, they unraveled the ABA response in these cells and identified possible intermediates involved in ABA signal transfer, laying the foundation for a much clearer understanding of the action of ABA.

The plant cell

The cells of living organisms show marked similarities, whether they occur in plants or animals. One of the major characteristics, however, that distinguishes plant cells from animal cells is the rigid wall that surrounds plant cells. These cells are joined to one another by microscopic living bridges called plasmodesmata. These tiny units are responsible for moving materials from one cell to the next and interconnecting cells throughout the plant.

Each plasmodesma is sheathed in a plasma membrane, which forms a tiny tube that connects the cells. In the center of this tube is a smaller tube of endoplasmic reticulum (ER), part of a larger system of

membranes that runs throughout the cell. The ER is held in place by strands of protein that connect it to the wall of the plasma membrane. Cell-to-cell communication is made possible by linking the ER of one cell to that of an adjacent cell.

How did such a structure as the plasmodesma arise? Martha Cook and colleagues at the University of Wisconsin at Madison examined the plasmodesmata in green algae and mosses, the group of organisms from which higher plants evolved. Their studies revealed that the basic structure of the plasmodesmata was the same in all groups, although in algae it was more primitive than in mosses, which are similar to higher plants. Cook's team also determined that the plasmodesmata evolved early in time.

Plastids, the green, chlorophyll-containing chloroplasts in cells responsible for photosynthesis, have been widely studied, and much is known about their structure and function. Recently, however, a group at Cornell University, Ithaca, N.Y., led by Rainer Köhler made a spectacular discovery. Using a green fluorescent protein as a detection device, they discovered thin tubular projections on individual plastids. Some of these projections were connected to other plastids. The researchers witnessed a flow of material through the tubes, suggesting that they facilitate the exchange of molecules within a larger communication system and may play a role in coordinating plastid activities. This degree of connectivity and communication was completely unexpected and very exciting to researchers, since until now plastids have generally been regarded as autonomous cell parts.

—William A. Jensen

ECOLOGY

Ecology and human history

In 1532 Francisco Pizarro and a contingent of some 180 conquistadores engaged tens of thousands of Incan soldiers in battle near present-day Cajamarca, Peru. Although they were vastly outnumbered, the Spaniards, armed with artillery, defeated their sling- and club-wielding opponents within a few hours, establishing a pattern of conquest that would be followed throughout the Americas by other European groups. This is the stuff of history. The question, however, remains: why were Europeans able to conquer the New World—and Australia and Africa—and not the other way around?

University of California, Los Angeles, scientist Jared Diamond explored this question in his 1997 book *Guns, Germs, and Steel: The Fates of Human Societies.* Diamond became intrigued by these his-

Using a green fluorescent protein as a detection device, researchers identified tubular projections on plastids, some of which were connected to other plastids. By facilitating the exchange of molecules, the projections may play a role in coordinating plastid activities.

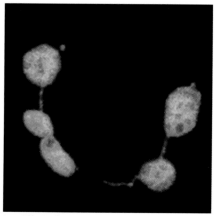

toric events 25 years ago after talking with Yali, a politician in New Guinea (now Papua New Guinea). Yali noted that the Dutch, German, and British colonialists who took control of New Guinea in the 19th century brought with them a startling array of material goods, what the indigenous people referred to as "cargo." "Why is it that you white people developed so much cargo and brought it to New Guinea," Yali asked, "but we black people had little cargo of our own?"

From the beginning, Diamond rejected the scientifically inaccurate and sometimes politically motivated explanation that genetic or racial superiority enabled some groups to become more technologically sophisticated than others. History followed different courses for different peoples not because one group was biologically superior to another, Diamond maintained, but because people in some places, particularly Europe and Asia, enjoyed certain ecological advantages.

One of these benefits was access to wild plants that were capable of being cultivated. Diamond pointed out that the growth of agriculture depended on the availability of wild plants with large seeds. Only a handful of wild grasses worldwide fit this criterion, and almost all of them eventually were domesticated. As a result, agriculture arose in just a few places, such as the Fertile Crescent of the Middle East (wheat), East Asia (rice), and Central America (maize). Diamond contended that the people who domesticated the wild ancestors of these grasses were not smarter than those in hunter-gatherer societies but just plain luckier. Eventually, food surpluses allowed agricultural societies to support full-time technological innovators as well as to form centralized bureaucracies that could exploit their inventions in warfare and exploration.

Eurasians benefited not only from the availability of plants that could be turned into crops but also from animals that could be domesticated. The ancestors of dogs, cows, horses, and sheep, Diamond observed, lived in social groups and therefore could readily be tamed. In contrast, sub-Saharan Africa possessed none of the important domesticated animals despite the continent's abundant wildlife. Even the zebra, although a member of the horse family, was not suitable for riding. The Americas had only the llamas and alpacas.

Furthermore, Diamond asserted, there were few ecological barriers to impede the spread of domesticated plants and animals across Europe and Asia. Wheat and horses, for example, were able to survive across the entire east-west spread of the two continents, from Ireland to Japan. In Africa and the Americas, on the other hand, ecosystem barriers isolated the few species that were domesticated. A plant or animal that thrived on the plains of North America would have had to survive a long journey across an inhospitable terrain of rain forest before it reached a compatible habitat on the pampas of Argentina. Species domesticated in the Mediterranean were separated from a similar environment in southern Africa by great tracts of jungle and desert.

Diamond argued that the domestication of animals also played a second—albeit less-obvious—role in the spread of European power. Domesticated animals were the source of many human diseases. Over

(Below) Shawn G. Henry/Material World; (opposite page) Peter Ginter—Peter Menzel/Material World

In his book *Guns, Germs, and Steel,* Jared Diamond argues that certain ecological advantages enabled some societies, such as the U.S. (opposite page), to develop greater technological sophistication and a wider array of material goods than others (below).

thousands of years, however, their keepers developed immunities as natural selection largely weeded out susceptible individuals. When Europeans encountered the people of the Americas, these diseases wreaked havoc on native populations who were exposed to them for the first time. Many more people died of Eurasian germs than of Eurasian steel, Diamond pointed out, adding that Hernán Cortés was able to conquer the mighty Aztec empire because its citizenry had been decimated by smallpox (originally contracted from cows).

Wild rivers

Changes on the land—the places where crops and pastures, for example, have replaced once-extensive forests—are fairly obvious. The human transformation of rivers, however, is less evident. In part, this is because there are so few wild rivers—waterways free of dams—left for comparison. In 1994 Mats Dynesius and Christer Nilsson of Umeå (Sweden) University assembled data about the largest rivers in the northern third of the world. They found that the Torne River, which forms part of the border between Finland and Sweden, is Europe's only big wild river outside Russia. Only a couple dozen major wild rivers remain in North America, all of which drain into the Arctic Ocean or the Bering Sea.

Little is known about the long-term environmental effects of dams on rivers and their adjoining ecosystems. Preliminary research, however, has shown that the damming of rivers has harmed river-bank vegetation that depends on periodic flooding and other seasonal disturbances for its vitality. Nilsson and colleagues Roland Jans-

son and Ursula Zinko surveyed the riparian vegetation along 88 reservoirs and river dams in central and northern Sweden. In the May 2, 1997, issue of *Science,* Nilsson and his colleagues reported a significant drop in the plant diversity of river margins after the rivers were dammed. In study areas around reservoirs, for example, the researchers recorded a 50% drop in the number of plant species. Around dams the diversity of plant species fell by 15%. These numbers documented a substantial loss in the species diversity of river-margin habitats, which have come to be recognized as some of the world's most diverse ecosystems. (For a detailed discussion on the environmental effects of dams, *see* Feature Article: GOING WITH THE FLOW.)

Pricing the planet's resources

In 1997 economists and ecologists joined forces to estimate the global value of ser-

vices that ecosystems provide free of charge to humans. The studies were conducted by two teams of researchers—one led by Robert Costanza, director of the University of Maryland's Institute for Ecological Economics, Solomons, and the other by Gretchen Daily of Stanford University—in an effort to provide a full accounting of the benefits of natural resources for use in guiding development and public-policy decisions by private citizens and governments.

Although the words *economics* and *ecology* share a common root, the dialogue between the experts in these two disciplines has been fraught with contention and controversy.

To ecologists, putting a price tag on nature is a woefully incomplete measure of its value. Indeed, economists, who have been accused of knowing the price of everything and the value of nothing, have been challenged by how to measure an

ecosystem's nonmarket values—such as aesthetic values, for example.

An even more difficult task for economists is predicting how these values might change in the future. The 18th-century social philosopher Adam Smith once said that diamonds trade for a higher price than water. Yet water is of infinitely greater value—no living thing could survive without it. As water becomes scarce, its cost may rise rapidly and unexpectedly, as it already has in many parts of the world.

In addition, ecologists have been very suspicious of applying economic models to natural resources, citing numerous ecological disasters in recent history that have resulted from applying bottom-line thinking to the management of living things. For example, very often it has been far more profitable to intensively harvest natural resources, even if it resulted in driving many species to extinction. The ecological history of whales provides a case in point. Calculations made by University of British Columbia mathematician Colin Clark in 1973 demonstrated how the economics of 19th-century whaling helped bring about the near extermination of such species as the right whale. The most lucrative strategy was to liquidate as many whales as possible into cash, since financial investments of the profits yielded extremely high returns. According to this model, maximizing profits demanded that the most easily accessible species, such as the slow-moving, inshore-feeding right whale, be harvested first before more elusive species that required a greater investment in more advanced technology were tackled.

Assigning a price tag to nature's services also is made difficult by the complexity of ecological interactions. Whales,

for example, are valuable for more than just meat. They play ecological roles in maintaining the abundance of other marine species. Forests do more than supply humans with wood. The clear-cutting of a forest may depress the price of adjacent homes. Nearby streams fill with sediment and lose their ability to support fish. As sediments flow into the sea, they may smother offshore coral reefs, destroying the fish that provide food or the invertebrates that someday might offer a cure for cancer. Gone also is the reef that provides mainlands with protection against storms. The loss of the forest, which serves as a carbon sink, also may accelerate global warming and sea-level rises.

To calculate these complex benefits, Costanza's group came up with a list of 17 different ecological services, including such benefits as food, flood protection, and medicine, that nature provides free of charge. Then they classified ecosystems into 16 different types and calculated the value per hectare of the services in each ecosystem, which resulted in calculations for a total of 272 combinations of services and ecosystems.

Costanza and his colleagues, for example, estimated the value of the world's plant and animal species as a source of medicines and genes for crop improvement. Quoting 1994 figures by David Pimentel of Cornell University, Ithaca, N.Y., Costanza's group put the current value of over-the-counter plant-based drugs at $84 billion. The cultural and recreational uses of biodiversity were even more valuable. Ecotourism, for example, was worth between $500 billion and $1 trillion each year. By comparing the higher costs of coastal real estate with the prices of inland

properties, the researchers arrived at a value of $76 per hectare for the cultural value of the world's oceans. Multiplied across the planet's oceans, this value adds up to roughly $2.8 trillion.

Another concern that the studies' ecologists expressed was that the pricing of nature's services often has not fully factored in the consequences of exponential human growth. The price of water may be cheaper than diamonds, but water is an essential resource. As a result, its price will rise sharply as it becomes more scarce. Humans currently use half the available global supply of freshwater. In some regions the situation already has become critical. Israel, for example, supplements its shortage of local water supplies by tapping aquifers under the occupied West Bank and off watersheds in the Golan Heights and southern Lebanon. As the region's population increases, the pressures on ecosystem services will have dramatic political as well as economic consequences.

Some ecologists questioned the premise of the studies, charging, for example, that meeting the bottom line is not the only valid reason for protecting nature. They cited moral and ethical grounds for preserving a sustainable environment for future generations. Costanza's group recommended that any cost accounting for nature's services encompass both moral and economic concerns. Regardless of the uncertainties and controversies, the value of ecosystems is clearly huge. All these services combined, according to Costanza's calculations, are worth $33 trillion—a sum about twice the global economy.

—Stuart L. Pimm

MICROBIOLOGY

Life underground

Bacteria are the most versatile organisms in the world when it comes to obtaining energy for growth and reproduction. In 1993 Texaco engineers drilling for oil in the Taylorsville Triassic Basin in northeastern Virginia discovered living subterranean bacteria. The microorganisms were located 2.8 km (1.7 mi) below the surface in sediments that have been buried since the dawn of the dinosaur age. How were they able to survive in the absence of sunlight, the principal source of energy for life forms on the Earth's surface?

To answer this question, it is important to first understand how nonphotosynthetic cells make energy. Cellular energy is produced through a process known as respiration, in which energy-rich electrons are removed from reduced compounds known as electron donors. As electrons are shuttled through a series of proteins in the electron-transport chain located in the cell membrane, energy is extracted from them. This extracted energy is used to make the cell's principal energy, adenosine triphosphate (ATP), which fuels the process of cell replication. In the final step of the energy-production process, oxygen is used as the terminal electron acceptor to remove the energy-depleted electrons so that the process can be repeated.

In mammals energy-rich organic molecules such as glucose serve as the electron donors. Without these organic compounds, cells cannot produce ATP, and they starve. Unlike mammalian cells, however, not all bacteria are dependent on organic molecules for their electrons, nor do they necessarily depend on oxygen as the terminal electron acceptor. They can therefore live in environments where glucose and oxygen are not abundant. The use of alternate electron donors and acceptors is the key to the versatility of bacteria and the principal reason that they inhabit places where other organisms cannot survive.

A research group led by Tommy Phelps of the Oak Ridge (Tenn.) National Laboratory recently reported that the bacteria from the Taylorsville Triassic Basin, which exist at temperatures of 65°–85° C (149°–185° F), use simple organic acids such as formate, acetate, and lactate as the electron donors and oxidized iron [iron(III)] as the terminal electron acceptor.

Phelps's group also found that the bacteria produce the magnetic minerals magnetite and maghemite as by-products of their respiration. The discovery that some bacteria, like those in the Taylorsville basin, are able to generate magnetic materials and live at extreme temperatures led some scientists to suggest that the banded-iron formations (iron-rich sedimentary rocks) of the early Precambrian Period (between 2.5 billion and more than 3.9 billion years ago), which formed at high temperatures of 55°–76° C (131°–169° F), may have been produced by these iron(III)-reducing bacteria rather than by geochemical processes.

Just how much life can scientists expect to find below the Earth's surface? Since temperatures rise as depths increase, heat tolerance places a significant constraint on the number of organisms that can live in subterranean environments. The most thermophilic organism known to science, an inhabitant of thermal vents on the ocean floor, lives at 113° C (235° F), which is the equivalent of temperatures found at about five kilometers (three miles) below the surface.

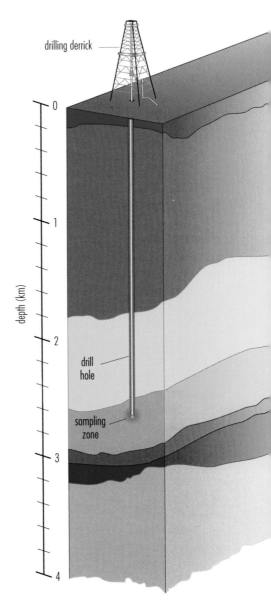

While drilling for oil in northeastern Virginia, Texaco engineers discovered microorganisms (above left) living at depths of 2.8 km (1.7 mi).

(Above left) David Boone, Oregon Graduate Institute, and Henry Aldrich, University of Florida

Frederick Blattner of the University of Wisconsin at Madison was part of an international team of scientists who in 1997 completed a 15-year project to sequence the genome of *Escherichia coli.*

The biggest limitation, however, may be the scarcity of nutrients, since microbes rapidly deplete organic matter from the groundwater. Tullis Onstott of Princeton University suggested that the Taylorsville Basin microbes have been eking out a living without a resupply of nutrients from surface groundwater for approximately 180 million years. He observed, however, that microbial populations decreased with depth. Agricultural fields, for example, contain one billion culturable cells per gram of soil, whereas the deep Taylorsville Basin contains only 1–10,000 culturable cells per gram of soil. These subterranean bacteria may compensate for the lack of nutrients by reducing their metabolism and rates of growth and reproduction. Scientists suspected that some microorganisms may reproduce only once every several hundred years. (For further information about organisms that live in environmental extremes, see *1998 Yearbook of Science and the Future* Feature Article: LIFE ON THE EDGE.)

The *Escherichia coli* blueprint

Escherichia coli, a common inhabitant of the human gastrointestinal tract, is one of science's most thoroughly studied organisms. Since the 1930s researchers have used the bacterium to develop seminal insights into the fundamental mechanisms of cellular machinery; they involve elucidating the major biosynthetic pathways, refining the concept of the gene, discovering the mechanisms of gene regulation, deciphering the genetic code, formulating the central dogma involving DNA replication, transcription, and translation, and discovering DNA repair and mutagenesis. The

organism has been so important to science that seven Nobel Prizes have been awarded to *E. coli*-based research. This work, in turn, has led to important advances in biotechnology and genetic engineering.

In 1997 researchers made yet another important advance in the understanding of *E. coli.* Frederick Blattner of the University of Wisconsin at Madison and a Japanese group led by Hirotada Mori of the Nara (Japan) Institute of Science and Technology and Takashi Horiuchi of the National Institute for Basic Biology, Okazaki, Japan, completed a 15-year project to sequence the bacterium's genome (the linear order of chemical subunits in all of an organism's genes).

The researchers determined that *E. coli* contains about 4,288 genes, nearly 40% of which have no known function. Deciphering these functions will be the next challenge. (*See* Year in Review: LIFE SCIENCES: *Molecular Biology and Genetics.*)

Alarm over antibiotic resistance

The alarming ability of dangerous disease-causing bacteria to develop a resistance to antibiotics has sent the medical profession and the biotechnology industry scrambling for new drugs. According to some scientific speculation, however, discontinuing the use of certain antibiotics for a period of time would reestablish susceptible populations of bacteria and thereby enable

older therapies to once again become effective in combating disease. Researchers have suggested that bacteria could lose their resistance to drugs in one of two ways. Some bacteria become resistant to antibiotics by acquiring a mutation in an existing gene. Because this mutation alters the normal functioning of organisms, scientists speculated that it would adversely affect the bacterium's fitness. In the absence of the antibiotic, the resistant strain might be outcompeted by bacteria lacking the mutation, in the long run establishing a population that is once again sensitive to the antibiotic.

In a proposed second scenario, bacteria acquire a resistance to drugs by importing genes for resistance from other bacterial species. Scientists theorized that in the absence of the antibiotic, cells that had eliminated this antibiotic-resistance gene would grow faster and eventually displace resistant strains.

In 1997 two independent teams of scientists reported the results of studies that tested these assumptions. Bruce Levin and Bassam Tomah of Emory University, Atlanta, Ga., sampled the bacterium *E. coli* from the diapers of 25 infants at an Atlanta day-care center. They found strains of *E. coli* that remained resistant to streptomycin, despite the fact that the antibiotic had rarely been used in the past 30 years. The scientists demonstrated that rather than losing the original mutation, the bacteria had acquired a compensatory mutation that improved their fitness without diminishing their resistance to streptomycin. In a second study Richard Lenski of Michigan State University selected an *E. coli* strain carrying the *rpsL* mutation—a mutation that confers streptomycin resistance and is known to reduce the bacterium's fitness—and grew it in an antibiotic-free environment for 10 years. Lenski found that the resistance trait was maintained. These results sent a clear and disturbing message that antibiotics may be losing their punch forever.

Lethal injection

Yersinia enterocolitica, a close relative of the bacterium responsible for outbreaks of bubonic plague in the past, is a food- and waterborne pathogen that causes gastroenteritis in humans. The immune system protects itself against *Yersinia* infections through defender cells known as macrophages, which engulf and digest the invading bacteria. To combat the macrophage, *Yersinia* injects into it a toxin through a specialized secretion channel. The toxic protein, known as YopE, paralyzes the defender cell, which allows the bacterium to escape and continue multiplying in the host.

The question of how the *Yersinia* bacterium selects the YopE protein to secrete through its molecular-injection system—given the presence of thousands of other proteins in the cell—was answered by Deborah Anderson and Olaf Schneewind of the University of California, Los Angeles. The researchers knew that proteins secreted by a different type of secretion system contain an amino-acid-targeting se-

quence, a kind of "zip code," that enables them to be recognized by the secretion apparatus.

The method that had been used to discover this targeting sequence involved fusing different bits of the gene that codes for the secreted protein to a gene that is not normally secreted—a reporter protein—and then looking for the secretion of the hybrid reporter protein and identifying the specific gene bit responsible. Performing this same experiment with *yopE,* the gene for the YopE protein, Anderson and Schneewind discovered that only the first 45 nucleotide building blocks of *yopE* are necessary to direct secretion of the reporter protein.

Since each amino acid in a protein is encoded by a three-base codon in the gene, there was the possibility that the YopE secretion apparatus is directed by a targeting sequence of 15 amino acids at the beginning of the protein. On the other hand, there was also the possibility that the apparatus is directed by the corresponding nucleotide sequence in the messenger RNA (mRNA) that takes the instructions for making the protein from the gene to the ribosome, the cell's protein-synthesis machinery. To test which possibility was true, Anderson and Schneewind modified that portion of the mRNA by adding or deleting single nucleotide subunits such that it was "read" differently by the ribosome. Although the modified mRNA sequence differed in a very small way from the unmodified version, it gave rise to a sequence of amino acids that was considerably different from the unmodified sequence. Remarkably, when the reporter protein experiment was performed with this modification, the protein was still se-

creted. This result conclusively demonstrated that the targeting sequence being recognized was that in the mRNA and not that in the protein product. The authors suggested that the mRNA folds into a structure that cannot be translated into protein unless it comes into contact with the YopE-injection apparatus, which unfolds it, translates it on nearby ribosomes, and secretes the YopE protein product.

The war against HIV

Clinical trials have demonstrated that AIDS therapies based on a combination of drugs—including inhibitors of HIV protease and of HIV reverse transcriptase—have dramatically reduced the number of viruses in the patients' blood as well as the number of AIDS-related diseases. As HIV-infected T cells slowly die off, anti-HIV therapies prevent the infection of new cells. So effective are these drug-cocktail therapies that in tests of blood taken from HIV-infected patients undergoing combination drug therapy, a research team led by Robert Siliciano of Johns Hopkins University, Baltimore, Md., measured no more than 16 infected cells per one million T cells.

Several independent research teams, however, found evidence that patients who rigorously adhered to the drug regimen still harbored latent viruses in a few of their memory T cells (immune-system cells that are the primary target of HIV), despite having undetectable blood levels of HIV. When HIV enters a T cell, the T cell's reverse-transcriptase enzyme changes the HIV's RNA genome into DNA, which then can be integrated into the host cell's DNA. When the infected T cell divides, both daughter cells can produce new HIV particles. Some HIV-infected T cells remain in a nongrowing state that is invulnerable to current anti-HIV drug therapies.

Researchers remained uncertain about the life span of these infected T cells. Angela McLean of the University of Oxford and Colin Michie of London's Ealing Hospital showed that the average memory T cell lives for about 200 days, but some individual cells could survive for many years. It is possible that patients who abandon drug therapy before this T-cell population is eliminated will begin producing new viruses as soon as the T cells become immunologically active. Researchers were investigating alternate strategies to hasten the demise of this T-cell population, including the development of new drugs against HIV enzymes called integrases, which allow the integration of the viral DNA into the host genome. This may reduce the formation of the hidden HIV reservoirs. Researchers also continued to pursue the development of an anti-HIV vaccine that could stimulate the immune system to destroy the infected cells.

—Lawrence J. Shimkets

MOLECULAR BIOLOGY AND GENETICS

The biggest news of the past year in molecular biology and genetics was necessarily Dolly, the sheep produced in a laboratory in Scotland by cloning from a single cell of an adult animal. (*See* Year in Review: FOOD AND AGRICULTURE: *Agriculture;* MEDICAL SCIENCES: *General Medicine.*) This achievement was remarkable in several ways, not least of which was its

contradiction of prevailing views of the molecular biology of cell senescence and aging. Those views, which were buttressed by some very recent experiments, had important implications for the true origin of Dolly.

Old cells and chromosome ends

Two sets of biochemical facts provide the necessary background for the topic. First, normal cells cultured from body tissue—from human skin, for example—have a finite lifetime. They may divide in culture 40–50 times or more, but then they abruptly senesce, or grow old, and die. Second, replication of the DNA in chromosomes requires rebuilding the ends of the chromosomes after every cell division. This rebuilding requires an enzyme that disappears as cells age. Consequently, one theory that has been advanced to explain the limited lifetime of cultured tissue cells is that these cells slowly lose their chromosome ends, eventually to the point that the chromosomes can no longer be replicated.

The special nature of chromosome ends in the cells of eukaryotes—humans, sheep, and all other organisms whose cells are nucleated—is due to the linear structure of the DNA in their chromosomes. By contrast, bacterial chromosomes and the chromosomes of viruses that use DNA as their genetic material generally consist of circular DNA molecules. The replication mechanism that copies the chromosomes during cell division or viral replication uses short RNA molecules to prime the synthesis of all the new DNA sequences that will constitute the chromosome copies. Although those short stretches of RNA become in-

corporated into the newly synthesized DNA, they eventually are removed by enzymatic activity. Because of chemical and topological constraints imposed by the replication mechanism, however, this removal can occur only if there is another DNA sequence that is being synthesized upstream.

For circular DNA molecules this condition poses no problem—on a circle there is always an upstream region regardless of the point of reference. On linear molecules, however, there is nothing upstream for one of the paired strands at each end of the chromosome. Therefore, any linear DNA molecule needs a special structure at its ends to provide a primer for replication of the terminal DNA sequences.

For the chromosomes of eukaryotes, the special structures are called telomeres. These stretches of nucleic acid have long been known to be different from the interior regions of chromosomes. Classical genetic studies have shown that genes located close to telomeres behave differently from genes elsewhere in the chromosomes. Since the late 1980s, much has been learned about the chemical nature of telomeres and their synthesis. This knowledge was applied in a dramatic way last year, leading to deep understanding of cell senescence and its prevention.

Telomeres consist of simple repeating DNA sequences. In human cells the sequence is TTAGGG repeated 2,500 times. (T is the base thymine, A is adenine, and G is guanine.) It is possible to imagine how a repeated sequence primes DNA replication, becoming partially used up in the process, and then is rebuilt at each cell division, either by the DNA replication machinery or by a novel mechanism.

The novel mechanism was discovered several years ago by Elizabeth Blackburn of the University of California, San Francisco, and by Thomas Cech of the University of Colorado at Boulder, in studies of very simple unicellular eukaryotes. They found that telomeres at the chromosome ends are rebuilt by an enzyme called telomerase, quite independently of the usual enzymes involved in DNA replication. Furthermore, telomerase has two components. One is a protein with reverse transcriptase activity, which means that it can copy the nucleotide sequence of an RNA template molecule into a DNA sequence. This activity alone, however, cannot rebuild a telomere—there has to be a template molecule. Sure enough, telomerase turns out to have an RNA component that fulfills this function.

As long as telomerase activity is present in human cells, the chromosome ends are rebuilt. As cells age, however, their telomeres shorten by about 100 base pairs at each cell division, and their telomerase activity declines concomitantly. Telomerase activity cannot be found in most adult (*i.e.,* nonembryonic) body tissues, the exceptions being a few stem cells of the blood-forming and immune systems. Another exception is found in cancer. When normal human cells are transformed into tumor cells, telomerase activity reappears and telomere ends are rebuilt.

These correlations were supported by dramatic, direct experiments carried out in the laboratories of Serge Lichtsteiner of the Geron Corp., Menlo Park, Calif., and Woodring Wright of the University of Texas Southwestern Medical Center at Dallas. Their work was based on the observation that the RNA component of

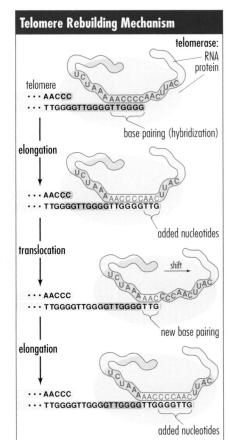

Telomere Rebuilding Mechanism

Telomerase is thought to rebuild telomere ends in a stepwise fashion. Part of its RNA base sequence binds to a sequence on the telomere end. Adjacent bases on the RNA then serve as a template for adding nucleotides to the telomere. As the telomere elongates, telomerase shifts to a new position.

telomerase is present in senescent cells; it is the protein activity that disappears with age. They constructed recombinant DNA molecules that specified the synthesis of human telomerase reverse transcriptase and then introduced these genes into normal human cells in culture. The cells were from retinal pigment epithelium or from foreskin fibroblasts; they normally have no telomerase activity and senesce after 50–60 cell divisions. Upon addition of the telomerase genes, the cells rebuilt their telomeres and continued to divide, still going after 100 divisions. They appeared youthful, the cellular equivalent of Ponce de León's mythical goal.

The implications of this work are vast. They shed new light on the mechanisms by which normal cells become tumor cells. The age- or development-specific loss of

telomerase ensures that cells do not continue dividing when they are supposed to fulfill a specialized function, such as a muscle or nerve cell must do. In tumor cells, telomerase is active, which permits the unchecked DNA replication and cell growth that is characteristic of cancer. New research will focus attention on the relation of well-known tumor suppressor genes (*Rb, p53*) to the activity of telomerase. Perhaps telomerase inhibitors will be determined to be new anticancer agents that can selectively stop the growth of tumor cells.

Implications for Dolly

These studies also are relevant to the cloning of Dolly. Numerous animals have been cloned successfully by removing the nucleus from a cell of a developing embryo and then placing that nucleus in an egg that has been treated so as to destroy the egg's own nucleus. Recall that a fertilized egg normally has two sets of chromosomes, one set from its own nucleus and one set from the sperm that fertilized the egg. In the animal cloning experiments, the sperm does not participate, and the egg's genetic material is removed. Instead, both sets of chromosomes are provided by the nucleus taken from a cell that already has two sets—that is, a diploid cell. In such a case, if the egg carrying the nucleus from a diploid cell survives and differentiates into an embryo and then a full-term individual, the newborn should have exactly the same genetic makeup as the animal from which (as an embryo) the nucleus came. There is a small caveat here because the egg cytoplasm contains mitochondria, cell organelles that have a few genes of their own; these mitochondrial genes are not from the donor cell but from the recipient egg. Nevertheless, they make up only a tiny fraction of the total genetic information in the cell.

It is an experimental fact that when the donor nucleus is taken from an embryonic cell, nuclear transplantation procedures succeed in producing viable embryos and, eventually, adult animals. The remarkable feature of Dolly, however, is that she was reported to have originated from a donor nucleus—specifically, a breast-cell nucleus—from an adult animal. The practical applications of animal cloning are obvious, as is the importance of this experiment. If one wishes to produce animals with a particular set of features, it is more expedient to take the donor nuclei from cells of an adult whose properties have already been measured than to take them from an embryo whose future is uncertain. The problem is that adult nuclei do not usually work in such experiments. In light of the recently gained knowledge of the role of telomerase and the shortening of telomeres in cell aging, it can be seen why this is so. Adult nuclei cannot replicate their chromosomes because their telomeres are too short, and they lack the ability to rebuild them.

What, then, can account for Dolly? First, it must be noted that she is the only animal to have emerged from 277 attempts at such cloning by her originators. Furthermore, as of early 1998 the experiment has not been repeated successfully. Indeed, others working with mice, in which embryonic nuclear transplants are routinely successful, have remained unable to clone an animal from an adult nucleus. Thus, Dolly must be considered a very rare event, one

that may not reappear in thousands of tries and is hardly the basis at present for a new kind of animal husbandry.

Nevertheless, explaining the existence of Dolly brings up two interesting possibilities. First, the cytoplasm of the recipient egg somehow may have reactivated telomerase in the transplanted nucleus. If that was the case, it may be possible to discover the conditions under which reactivation occurred and so increase its frequency in future experiments. (Alternatively, it may be possible to introduce genes for telomerase reverse transcriptase at the proper stage of the transplant procedure so as to reactivate telomere rebuilding in the donor nucleus.) The second possibility is that Dolly originated from a nucleus that did not come from a true adult differentiated cell as reported but rather came from a stem cell, such as one that might escape from the bone marrow. Such stem cells should have telomerase activity and therefore might be capable of chromosome replication.

Developments in genome sequencing

The pace of sequencing the genomes—the entire genetic blueprints—of organisms accelerated in the past year. Very rapid methods for determining the nucleotide sequences of DNA molecules, coupled with the prospect of rewards to be gained from the discovery of drugs that target hitherto unknown proteins of disease-causing bacteria, fostered the formation of numerous companies devoted to such efforts. Much of their work was proprietary, which means that a drug manufacturer wishing to examine the genome of an infectious bacterium that such a company had sequenced

had to pay for the privilege. On the other hand, many bacterial genomes were in the public domain, thanks to very modest support from federal agencies. The sequence of the circular chromosome of *Escherichia coli,* started in the early 1980s by Frederick Blattner of the University of Wisconsin at Madison, was finally completed, with contributions from a competing Japanese team led by Hirotada Mori of the Nara Institute of Science and Technology and Takashi Horiuchi of the National Institute for Basic Biology, and in January 1997 it was made freely available on the Internet to scientists worldwide. The second most widely studied bacterium, *Bacillus subtilis,* was sequenced by an international consortium led by Japanese and European Union researchers.

The work on *B. subtilis* turned up two big surprises. First, the bacterium was found to have the ability to make all the enzymes it needed to grow in the absence of oxygen (anaerobically); previously it had been thought to require oxygen without exception. Armed with the genome information, researchers saw the possibility of reconstructing the metabolic pathways that would permit anaerobic growth and, therefore, of devising a suitable set of conditions for growing the bacterium anaerobically in the laboratory. Second, the sequencing revealed a suite of genes for the synthesis of secondary metabolites— *i.e.,* potential antibiotic drugs. This discovery was totally unexpected and may well lead to a new class of useful therapeutic agents.

Another genome completely sequenced recently was that of the cyanobacterium *Synechocystis,* done by an industrial group in Japan called the Kazusa DNA Research

Institute. They took on this organism to tune up their methods for a big push on human DNA, specifically in search of disease-related mutations. The exercise was extremely fruitful nonetheless. Cyanobacteria and plant chloroplasts, both of which are capable of photosynthesis, are believed to have a common evolutionary ancestor. (The original chloroplast is thought to have been a cyanobacterium engulfed by a colorless cell and maintained in its cytoplasm.) One striking feature of the *Synechocystis* sequence, in addition to providing the sequence of every protein required for photosynthesis in green plants, is that it contains genes for phytochromes.

Phytochromes previously had been thought to occur uniquely in plants. They are pigmented proteins that respond to day length (actually, the ratio of red to far-red light) and transmit signals to activate expression of other genes. Phytochromes control seed germination, flowering, ripening, and other fundamental plant processes. Proper genetic studies of phytochrome action hitherto had been very difficult to do in plants. Finding phytochrome genes in a much simpler, unicellular organism like a cyanobacterium meant that all the tools of molecular genetics could be brought to bear on the relationship between the structure of a phytochrome and the mechanism of its action.

In an early example of the fruits of such research, a group in Germany found that a cyanobacterial phytochrome adds a phosphate group to one of its histidine residues (one of the amino acid building blocks of the protein) and can transfer that phosphate to another protein, called a response regulator. The latter protein often serves to promote the transcription and thus expression of specific genes by binding to DNA. Although there are many such two-component signaling systems in bacteria, none were known in plants. However, among the genes that have been sequenced for the mustard plant *Arabidopsis thaliana,* the workhorse of plant genetic studies, there are several whose protein products are candidates for response regulators. Two of these proteins were found to accept a phosphate from an enzyme of the histidine kinase family. Thus, it seems likely that plants use signaling systems, particularly for responding to changes in light quality, that derive from ancient bacterial precursors.

—Robert Haselkorn

ZOOLOGY

Bird behavioral ecology

The colonial nesting of birds has long intrigued ornithologists. One hypothesis to explain group nesting is that it reduces the likelihood of predation. A colony of birds, for example, might spot predators sooner or, if attacked, could "mob" them and chase them away. Another theory—the "selfish herd" hypothesis—proposes that individuals might decrease their probability of being preyed upon by surrounding themselves with many other individuals. Those animals in the middle of the colony presumably would fare better than birds on the edge, fueling competition for the more central positions.

In order to test these hypotheses, Dianne Brunton of the University of Auckland, N.Z., examined the influence of predation on one of the world's largest breeding colonies of least terns (*Sterna antillarum*),

located on the Atlantic coast in West Haven, Conn. Brunton observed roughly 500 pairs during the nesting season (April to August) in 1987 and 1988.

Brunton's findings presented a more complicated picture of group nesting than was accommodated by either the group-defense or selfish-herd hypothesis. In the case of the least terns, colonial nesting reduced predation from daytime interlopers that approached from the perimeter, but it was not effective in fending off the far more threatening nighttime attacks from the air into the center of the nest. During the day, for example, the terns were extremely effective in driving off raids by formidable predators such as American crows, which approached the tern colony from the edge.

Dianne Brunton, University of Auckland

Tracks near the broken egg of a least tern were identified as those of a black-crowned night heron, the major predator of least tern eggs and chicks.

Far more dangerous, however, were black-crowned night herons. Her study revealed that predation by herons was the major cause of nest loss and chick mortality. In fact, in the 1988 nesting season, 74% of the 378 failed nests were due to heron raids. Interestingly, contrary to the selfish-herd hypothesis, most heron predation was concentrated in the center of the colony. Brunton found that the black-crowned night herons, as their name suggests, were active at night and always landed in the center of the colony to feed on eggs and chicks. The least terns, which are active during the day, showed no defensive behavior toward the herons.

Brunton's findings could have important conservation implications. Owing to habitat loss from human activities, the number of least tern colonies has declined, whereas the number of individuals in the remaining colonies has increased. This concentration could expose greater numbers of birds to the efficient, uncontested predation of herons and eventually result in a long-term reduction of the species.

Evolution of gastropods

Gastropod mollusks, which include snails, slugs, abalones, sea hares, limpets, and nudibranchs, are one of the most diverse groups of animals in the world. With estimates ranging from 40,000 to 100,000 living species, gastropods have figured prominently in biological research, including ecological, paleontological, behavioral, and physiological studies.

Despite their appeal to biologists, however, little work has been done on the evolutionary relationships of this diverse group for most of the 20th century. Sys-tematics, the study of evolutionary relationships, is an extremely important discipline, since knowledge of kinships among species allows for better-informed conservation strategies and provides basic data to help determine a more sustainable use of biological resources.

Winston Ponder of the Australian Museum, Sydney, and David Lindberg of the University of California, Berkeley, recently compiled an impressive database to support their hypothesis of the evolutionary relationships of gastropods. To "root" the evolutionary tree, they examined circulatory, reproductive, and nervous systems, shells, muscles, guts, larvae, and a variety of other anatomic characteristics across 35 groups of gastropods and several other representative mollusk classes (*e.g.,* bivalves, cephalopods, and chitons). Using computer programs that grouped species on the basis of shared derived characteristics, the investigators presented a fairly well-resolved evolutionary hypothesis. Certain divergent groups of gastropods—such as abalones, limpets, nerites, and species living along hot thermal vents at the bottom of the ocean—occupied the more basal, or "primitive," part of the tree, whereas various freshwater families, terrestrial snails and slugs, and several marine groups such as sea hares and whelks occupied the more derived, or "advanced," branches of the tree.

Origin of dogs

From the diminutive pug to the imposing Great Dane, few groups of domesticated animals display a more striking variation than dogs. Despite their extreme differences, however, it is thought that dogs are most closely related to a single species—the wolf. Given that humans and wolves coexisted over a wide geographic range during most of the Late Pleistocene (roughly 400,000 to 1,000,000 years ago), some scientists have suggested that the domestication of dogs may have occurred independently in a variety of places and over several periods of time.

To test this intriguing hypothesis, Robert K. Wayne of the University of California, Los Angeles, and his colleagues collected blood or hair samples from 162 wolves at 27 locales throughout Europe, Asia, and North America as well as from 140 domestic dogs representing 67 breeds and 5 mixed breeds. In addition, the scientists collected samples from coyote and golden, blackbacked, and Simien jackals, which, as members of the genus *Canis*, also may have served as potential ancestors of the dog. They extracted DNA, the genetic blueprint of cells, and sequenced a portion of the samples' control region (*i.e.,* a stretch of mitochondrial DNA that, because it exhibits a high mutation rate, would likely reveal any genetic differences among the canids). The genetic data showed that dog DNA sequences differed from those of coyotes and jackals by at least 20 nucleotide positions. (DNA is a polymer chain of four different kinds of building-block molecules called nucleotides. If a dog has one kind of nucleotide and a coyote has a second kind at corresponding positions in their DNA sequences, this amounts to a difference of one nucleotide.) The dog DNA sequences differed from those of the wolf, however, by no more than 12 nucleotide substitutions. Furthermore, using phylogenetic methodology, a technique used to deter-

Scientists measured *Anolis* lizards in different Caribbean habitats to determine the physical differences they developed in response to the particular circumstances of their environment.

mine relationships on the basis of shared derived DNA attributes, the scientists obtained results that revealed four distinct groups of dog DNA sequences nested within different wolf lineages. Thus, not only did dogs evolve from wolves, but it also appeared that they were domesticated more than once. Amazingly, the results also showed that many modern dog breeds actually may have more than one evolutionary lineage. The five differing DNA sequences found in German shepherds, for example, appeared in three genetically distinct dog groups, which suggests that pure breeds may not be so pure.

Wayne and his colleagues also estimated that the first domestication of dogs occurred roughly 135,000 years ago. Although scientists were excited by the investigators' findings, many were dubious about this proposed dating, since the DNA technique that the researchers used can be subject to a huge margin of error. Furthermore, archaeological data supported a date of only 14,000 years ago. Wayne and his colleagues nonetheless argued that dogs may not have been morphologically differentiated from wolves earlier than 14,000 years ago and, therefore, not skeletally distinguishable in fossil remains.

Adaptive differentiation of *Anolis* lizards

The islands of the Caribbean are home to about 150 species of *Anolis* lizards (commonly referred to as anoles or, inappropriately, chameleons). Zoologists have noticed for many years that anoles living on islands of the Greater Antilles exhibited visible differences depending on circumstances of their environments, adaptations

known as phenotypes. Some species, for example, prefer to live on the trunk of a tree, whereas others opt for shorter, thinner vegetation. Each "ecomorph" has a limb length and toe size adapted to its given habitat. Anoles that perch on narrow branches and twigs are smaller and have shorter hind limbs and wider toes than those that perch on wider branches or tree trunks. Longer limbs result in greater running speeds, which presumably is more important to an anole living on the trunk of a tree than to one in a bush, where shorter limbs provide greater agility.

Jonathon Losos of Washington University, St. Louis, Mo., Thomas Schoener of the University of California, Davis, and

others have been studying anole populations for many years. In 1977 and 1981 scientists collected lizards from Staniel Cay, a small island in the Bahamas covered with a variety of vegetation ranging from brush to a moderately tall forest, and introduced them to 14 islands that lacked lizard populations. These islands all were smaller than Staniel Cay and were covered mostly with narrow-stalked vegetation and few, if any, trees. Researchers stocked each island with individuals from both forest and bush environments and then followed the colonization success of the two lizard types over a five-year period.

In 1991 Losos and others have returned to the islands to collect data on how the lizards have adapted to their new surroundings. The researchers observed the lizards' behavior and also correlated behavior with habitat by recording the height and diameter of the animals' perches. They also captured the lizards and measured a variety of physical features, including snout-to-vent length, fore- and hind-limb length, and width of one of the toe pads. Statistical analysis of the raw data—including measurements taken from lizards captured from the original source area, Staniel Cay—showed that the lizards had indeed adapted to their new environment. In other words, the lizards had evolved wider toe pads and relatively shorter limbs than the initial source population from Staniel Cay, physical characteristics that were better suited to the thinner-stalked vegetation. Whether these changes were genetic or caused by nongenetic environmental effects on morphology remained to be determined by future experiments.

Bon appétit for fireflies

A firefly's luminescent flashing is a familiar part of a summer evening. As might be expected, flashing fireflies are just as conspicuous to potential predators as they are to humans.

Biologists have shown, however, that species of the genus *Photinus* possess novel substances whose noxious taste makes the insect unpalatable to birds and other enemies. The chemicals belong to a newly discovered class of steroidlike toxins whose structure resembles that of the cardiotonic steroids found in the venom of Chinese toads (*Bufo* species). In recognition of this similarity, a group of biologists led by Thomas Eisner of Cornell Univer-

sity, Ithaca, N.Y., named the new substances lucibufagins (LBG).

Further investigations of the distribution of LBG in other firefly species revealed that the members of the genus *Photuris* also possessed LBG, but they did not manufacture the chemicals themselves, obtaining it instead through deadly subterfuge. Fireflies communicate by using a species-specific light-flashing pattern. Mating *Photuris* females, known as firefly "femmes fatales," can match the pattern flashed by *Photuris* males or, if they are hungry, they also can flash like *Photinus.* Unsuspecting *Photinus* males, drawn to what they think is a prospective mate, are devoured instead, which impregnates the body of the *Photuris* female with LBG.

Eisner and colleagues showed that eating *Photinus* males not only provided *Photuris* females with a snack but also afforded them protection from some predators. LBG-tainted *Photuris* females that were caught by *Phidippus* jumping spiders, for example, were rejected. Furthermore, the researchers found a direct correlation between the level of protection afforded *Photuris* females and the concentrations of LBG in their bodies.

A future for Florida manatees?

The federally protected Florida manatee (*Trichechus manatus latirostris*) has been adopted by the state of Florida as a mascot of sorts. One of four living species in the order Sirenia, this herbivorous aquatic mammal seems as vulnerable to humans as many of its relatives, including the Steller's sea cow, which became extinct 27 years after its discovery by Europeans in 1741. Despite the warm reception manatees have

received from native Floridians and non-natives alike, proponents of development, tourism, and the boating industry have consistently opposed legislation to restrict boating activity in manatee-populated waters, the primary cause of human-related manatee deaths.

Another major obstacle to the better management of manatee populations has been a lack of knowledge of population demography (age structure). Thomas J. O'Shea of the U.S. Geological Survey and his colleagues recently compiled data on the reproductive age and age at death of Florida manatees, using a sample of 1,212 manatee carcasses found in Florida waters from 1976 to 1991. An analysis of the carcasses revealed that the age of sexual maturation for manatees is three to four years and that 33% of mature females become pregnant each year and give birth to one calf on average. Although the oldest individual was 59 years old, half of the carcasses were under 3 years of age.

The researchers used the data to conduct a population viability analysis (PVA). By providing population estimates for a range of conditions that the manatees were likely to encounter—such as cold weather, hurricanes, disease, and boating accidents—the biologists were able to predict population size and the probability of manatee survival.

Based on estimates of current mortality rates, the PVA showed that manatee populations would decline such that the species had only a 44% probability of surviving over the next 1,000 years. A mere 10% increase in adult mortality—which, according to the researchers, was an accurate prediction of long-term trends, given Florida's high rate of human population growth and the concomitant increase in recreational boating—would be enough to drive the manatee population to extinction in 1,000 years. Interestingly, a 10% decrease in adult mortality yielded slow population growth and a high probability (nearly 100%) of persistence over 1,000 years. The biologists concluded that if boating regulations were implemented and enforced, manatees and humans could coexist indefinitely. Without intervention, the Florida manatee's long-term outlook was bleak.

Conserving threatened mussels

Although they are found nearly worldwide, freshwater bivalves, or mussels, of the family Unionidae reach their greatest diversity in North American waters. Once used by Native Americans for food, tools, and ornaments, today their shells provide seeds for cultured-pearl production in marine pearl oysters. They also serve as a valuable food resource for many different kinds of animals.

During the 20th century, however, many mussel species have become extinct, endangered, or threatened owing to habitat destruction and the pollution of rivers and streams. Indeed, unionid mussels currently are considered one of North America's most threatened groups of animals. Numerous conservation efforts are under way to protect remaining mussels in the wild and to propagate captive populations for future reintroductions and relocations.

These efforts, however, require comprehensive knowledge of the biology of mussels, since unionids have a highly unusual life history. Their larvae, known as glochidia, are brooded in the gills of fe-

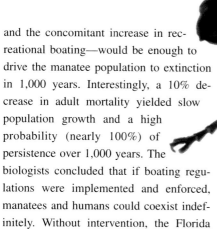

male mussels until they mature. They are then released to infest a suitable host fish, undergoing a brief period as a parasite on the fish's external parts, such as gills or fins. This interim parasitism is so important to their survival that some mussels have evolved amazing structures to lure their prospective hosts. While encysting on the host fish, the glochidia eventually metamorphose into juvenile mussels. The juveniles then drop off the surface of the fish to adhere to a more stable substrate, where they spend the rest of their lives. Fish host specificity differs widely among mussel species. Some are able to parasitize a wide range of fish species, whereas others rely on only one or a few closely related species. Knowledge of fish hosts is critical for reestablishing lost populations and understanding the distribution of mussel species.

A study by Wendell Haag and Melvin Warren, Jr., of the U.S. Forest Service's Forest Hydrology Laboratory, Oxford, Miss., provided useful life-history data for developing long-term conservation strategies for freshwater mussels. The researchers identified the host fish for six mussel species that are considered endangered, threatened, or of special concern. The zo-

Using deadly subterfuge, a female *Photuris* firefly has lured a male from the genus *Photinus* to his death. By consuming the male firefly, the female *Photuris* not only secures a nutritious meal but also ingests substances, known as lucibufagins, that afford her protection from some predators.

Thomas Eisner, Cornell University

ologists collected gravid mussels and potential host fish from their native habitats in Alabama. They were able to match mussels to their preferred hosts by inducing glochidial infestations in laboratory trials and monitoring the rejection of glochidia or production of juvenile mussels. The researchers found that species such as the southern creekmussel use a taxonomically wide range of fish host species, including minnows, suckers, sunfish, and darters, whereas mussels such as the orange-nacre mucket and Alabama rainbow prefer bass. They also determined the methods of glochidial release and gravid periods for each of the six mussel species.

—Charles Lydeard

See also Feature Articles: ENCHANTING THE EARTH; FEATHERS: AN ANCIENT PERFECTION; IZANAGI'S INHERITORS: THE SEARCH FOR JAPANESE ORIGINS; WHAT IS KILLING THE REEFS?

MATERIALS SCIENCE AND ENGINEERING

Major advances in the science and engineering of materials during the past year included the development of durable lightweight ceramic composites for use in brakes, the creation of polymer gels that change volume or shape in response to environmental stimuli, and the use of iron carbide as a source of iron for minimills that produce steel.

CERAMICS

Significant progress was made during the past year on the development and application of fiber-reinforced ceramic-matrix composites for brakes. These materials hold significant potential for use in land and air transportation. Emphasis during recent months was on the optimization of properties for automotive vehicles and high-speed trains.

When a vehicle brakes, its energy of motion is converted into heat by friction, and the heat is absorbed primarily by the braking assembly. Brake performance is controlled by the friction characteristics of the braking material and its ability to absorb and dissipate the heat. Good brakes exhibit high and stable friction, excellent wear resistance, and suitable thermomechanical behavior. The most commonly used materials for brake rotors are cast iron and steel. Carbon-carbon composites (very-lightweight materials in which carbon fiber reinforces a carbon matrix) are used where high performance and low weight are important considerations, such as in racing cars and aircraft. Wear rate and heat dissipation for carbon-carbon composites are excellent. More widespread use of these composites is limited, however, by their high production cost, degraded braking performance when wet, and reduced life because of oxidation.

The German Aerospace Research Establishment (DLR), together with MAN-Technology of Germany, sought to develop a lightweight braking material without the deficiencies of carbon-carbon (C/C). Carbon composites are costly because of the lengthy production times required for obtaining matrix densification. DLR's approach was to infiltrate an undensified carbon-carbon preform with liquid silicon metal. The silicon quickly filled the open spaces in the composite and reacted to form silicon carbide (SiC). The resulting dense C/C-SiC material (about two-thirds C/C and one-third SiC by weight) consisted of load-carrying carbon-fiber bundles protected from oxidation by the SiC. It could be rapidly fabricated and was less susceptible to absorption of water than carbon-carbon. It was stronger than carbon-composite braking materials, and its thermal properties made the material suitable as a heat sink for braking applications. Further testing revealed extremely low abrasive and oxidative wear. Sufficiently high friction was obtained over a range of temperatures and test speeds. During 1998 such materials were being optimized for a variety of applications by varying fiber orientation and conductivity, by changing the respective content of C/C and SiC, and by using wear-resistant surface coatings. For example, brake manufacturer Knorr-Bremse AG of Germany worked on high-speed trains, for which stopping capability and brake wear are critical. During the past year C/C-SiC was being tested for this application.

Taking a different materials approach, Northrop Grumman's Advanced Systems and Technology unit in the U.S. developed a family of lightweight ceramic friction materials with the trade name TEMROK. These composites were based on a silicon oxycarbide matrix trade-named Blackglas by developer AlliedSignal Corp. and containing Nextel 312, a trade name for a boroaluminosilicate fiber produced in the U.S. by the 3M Corp. The fiber is first nitrided (treated at high temperature in a nitrogen-containing atmosphere) to form a boron nitride surface layer in situ. This layer acts as an engineered interface with the Blackglas matrix, serving to deflect matrix cracks initiated during service and so provide toughening for the otherwise brittle ceramic.

TEMROK components can be fabricated at costs less than those for carbon-carbon. Brake rotors are made by dipping layers of the treated Nextel fabric into a resin developed by AlliedSignal that serves as a precursor to the Blackglas matrix. The resin wicks into the layers, which are then stacked in a die and shaped with the application of modest heat and pressure in a molding press. The resultant rotor is machined before being heated to high temperature (pyrolysis) so that the resin is converted to the ceramic state. To increase matrix density, the rotor is reinfiltrated with resin and repyrolyzed a number of times. Brake pads are made by compression molding a mix of chopped fiber and particulate with a fiber-reinforced backing plate. This preform is then resin-infiltrated and pyrolyzed as for the rotors. Friction behavior can be tailored by the choice of particulate in the pad as well as surface treatments. The ceramic rotors can also be mated with conventional brake-pad materials as appropriate for the application.

New lightweight ceramic friction materials, known under the trade name TEMROK, have found applications in brake rotors (right). In tests conducted on Triumph racing motorcycles, not only were TEMROK rotors more efficient at radiating heat from hard braking (seen below as an orange glow on the bike's front wheel) than carbon-carbon rotors, but they also weighed less and provided a more powerful and predictable performance.

Photographs, Northrop Grumman Corp.

TEMROK appears unique in the manner in which heat is dissipated upon stopping. Its thermal conductivity is much lower than carbon-carbon, but its capability to radiate heat (emissivity) is considerably higher. Consequently, only 50% of the energy of motion absorbed during a stop is retained in the rotor as heat, the balance being expended primarily by radiation away from the open rotor surface.

TEMROK was evaluated during the past year in Europe for use on motorcycles. The friction products group of Ferodo of the United Kingdom tested TEMROK brakes on Triumph racing bikes. Results were very promising, with stopping distances far shorter than were achieved with other brake materials. The ceramic rotors are half the weight of conventional steel rotors, an important consideration in a racing motorcycle, in which reduced weight improves control in turns and enhances stopping efficiency. Also, the TEMROK brake does not fade (lose stopping capability) as it heats during use. Compared with carbon-carbon composite brakes, the ceramic provided superior performance when cold and when wet. Overall, the TEMROK brakes were more powerful and more predictable over a range of operating conditions. Combined with their light weight and excellent wear performance, they offered significant advantages for the racing bike. For the consumer motorcycle market, Ferodo developed an organic pad for use with the TEMROK rotor.

During 1998 the TEMROK rotor was in preliminary evaluation for use on Formula One racing cars and heavy-duty trucks. New Formula One regulations required a downsizing of the brakes, and the commonly used carbon-carbon rotors may wear too fast on tracks where heavy braking is required. Using steel brakes would add too much weight to the cars. TEMROK may provide a viable lightweight alternate. For heavy-duty trucks that use steel rotors and sintered metal pads, the issue is durability.

It is expected that using ceramic-composite rotors with appropriate pads will extend brake life significantly.

—Allan P. Katz

METALS

In recent years there has been a growing concern among steelmakers about the increasing demand for and cost of high-quality feedstocks. This concern has been particularly strong at the minimills, most of which rely on scrap steel as their primary or only source of iron for electric-arc furnaces (EAFs), which melt and mix iron with alloying elements to make steel. (This is in contrast to larger, integrated mills, which use scrap only as a supplement to iron that has been reduced from ore in a blast furnace.) Using recycled steel has been cheaper than reducing iron from ore, but quality control has been a problem because of the difficulty in controlling the chemical content of the incoming scrap. One solution for the minimills has been to buy carefully sorted scrap and thereby ensure that there is only a small residue of unwanted elements, but this effort adds to the cost. Also, as more minimills are built (eight in the U.S. in 1997), and as they strive to improve quality by using more of this material, the cost of high-quality scrap seems certain to rise. Because of these developments, along with the inherent volatility of scrap prices, the minimills have moved vigorously to develop alternative sources of iron.

One such source is iron carbide (Fe_3C), material that has been reduced from hematite iron ore (Fe_2O_3) to free iron and then carburized. The reduction/carburizing process uses ore fines, pieces of hematite that are much smaller (0.1–1 mm [0.004–0.04 in]) than the pelletized ore used in most ironmaking techniques. Because of their small size, the fines react more quickly with the process gas and are also roughly half the price of the pellets. Another ad-

vantage of making Fe_3C is that its carbon content, 6–7% by weight, is combusted with oxygen in the EAF to produce significant heat, which thus saves electricity at that stage and shortens the time needed to melt and mix a single heat (batch) of liquid steel. Of course, heat must be added during the production of Fe_3C, but that is done with natural gas, which is much cheaper than using electricity.

In fact, it is this quality that makes iron carbide most attractive to some steelmakers, as opposed to a common alternative, direct-reduced iron (DRI). DRI has a much smaller carbon content than Fe_3C and, consequently, a smaller energy release in the furnace; it can easily burn when wet and generally is made from the more expensive pelletized ore. In 1998, however, the technology for producing high-quality iron carbide was still being tested, whereas at least a half dozen German, American, and British companies built or expanded DRI facilities in the U.S. and in Trinidad.

The first, and at the beginning of 1998 the only, commercial iron carbide plant in the world was operated by Nucor Iron Carbide, Inc. (NICI), in Trinidad. The plant approached economic viability in 1997 as production rates rose and quality improved after more than two years of debugging the process. The purpose of this venture was to supply the Nucor Corp.'s minimills with a supplement to scrap steel and also to provide feedstock for a revolutionary new process to be developed jointly with U.S. Steel and Praxair to make steel completely from iron carbide.

NICI's process for making iron carbide begins by using hot air from a gas heater to preheat Fe_2O_3 fines to 570° C (1,060° F). The fines then enter a fluidized-bed

reactor, where they are mixed with a gas stream consisting of methane, hydrogen, and cleaned and recycled process gas. A fluidized bed is a device in which the solid ore fines are suspended and mixed by a strong gas flow from below. The fines travel slowly through the bed as they react. The suspension of solids in the gas flow allows better contact between solids and gas than if the solid was agglomerated, and the reaction rate between the two phases is thereby increased. The chemical reactions in the reactor reduce the hematite to magnetite (Fe_3O_4), a partially reduced iron oxide, and finally to free iron. This iron then reacts with the carbon from the natural gas to form Fe_3C, and the freed oxygen and hydrogen form water. The net reaction is endothermic (heat-absorbing), with heat supplied by the incoming process gas.

During the first tests of the new process, the reaction was not complete, and the product was reported to be about 70% Fe_3C, with most of the remaining 30% unreduced magnetite. The low percentage of iron carbide and high amount of magnetite in the final product threatened the economic viability of the process. Because one of the driving forces behind using iron carbide was the energy released by the additional carbon combustion in the EAFs, a low percentage that was produced was a concern. Another problem was that either the unreduced magnetite would be reduced in the EAF, which required more energy input, or its iron content would be lost in the slag, which increased the total amount of material needed to make a ton of steel. These increases in cost were important, as steel was sold with a small profit margin.

Nucor used the product of the Trinidad plant in the EAFs in its Crawfordsville,

Ind., minimill and reported no significant difference, compared with processes that used only scrap steel, in either the time required for making a heat of steel or the energy input. The lack of difference, in spite of the extra carbon available for combustion, suggests an energy sink in the process, possibly caused by the reduction of magnetite. Nonetheless, there was enough confidence in the concept that Nucor planned to expand production in Trinidad and a competitor, Qualitech, was building a similar facility in Texas.

—Matthew John M. Krane

POLYMERS

Polymer gels that respond to environmental stimuli by changing volume or shape sparked considerable interest among materials scientists during the past year. These stimuli-responsive substances, called hydrogels, or "smart" gels, are cross-linked polymer networks that can undergo volume changes spanning several orders of magnitude. Hydrogels (water-retaining polymer networks) respond to a variety of stimuli such as ion and solvent concentrations, electric fields, level of acidity, pressure, temperature, and light intensity. This phenomenon spurred efforts to develop gels for applications ranging from drug-delivery systems to toys. Advances during the year in hydrogel technology came in the form of gel performance, pulsating gels, chemical sensors, and shape-forming gels.

Improvements in the response time and the magnitude of volume expansion of the gels were particularly geared toward biomedical applications. Artificial muscles and organs are potential applications for hydrogels because induced changes in gel volume convert chemical and electrical energy into mechanical work. One problem researchers faced was that the response time of the gels was too slow for them to be used as contractile agents for artificial muscles. Sonja Krause and Katherine Bohon at the Rensselaer Polytechnic Institute, Troy, N.Y., developed a gel that will respond to electric stimuli in the same time frame as do human skeletal muscles after they receive electrical signals from the brain. The gel is a combination of polydimethylsiloxane, commonly known as silicone, and an electrorheological fluid, which changes viscosity in response to an electric field. Under an application of a one-hertz alternating-current electric field, the resulting gel compressed into a stiff, elastic solid within 100 milliseconds and stretched when the current was reversed.

Advances were also made in the magnitude of expansion. Yukio Nagasaki and Kazunori Kataoka at the Science University of Tokyo synthesized polysilamine gels that can swell more than 20 times original size when exposed to methanol and more than 160 times original size when exposed to acidic water solutions.

Researchers at the National Institute of Materials and Chemical Research in Tsukuba, Japan, developed a "self-oscillating" gel that alternately expands and contracts because of an internal, autocatalytic reaction, a reaction catalyzed by its products. Their gel is a copolymer of temperature-responsive N-isopropylacrylamide (NIPA) and a polymerizable ruthenium-based catalyst (Ru[bpy]$_3$), that is used to catalyze oscillating reactions in which reactant, intermediate, and product concentrations vary periodically (*see* Figure). Their study showed that submersion of the transparent gel in an aqueous solution of the reagents used in an oscillating reaction (malonic acid, sodium bromate, and nitric acid) allowed the reagents to permeate the gel. The Ru(bpy)$_3$ catalyzed the reaction such that ruthenium oscillated between the 2+ (reduced) state and the 3+ (oxidized) state. The researchers found that in the oxidized state the gel accommodated more water because of the increased positive charge. The additional hydration in-

Photographs, Zhibing Hu, University of North Texas

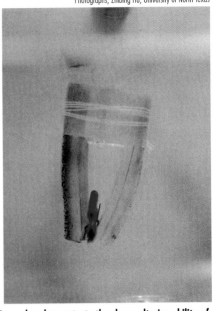

A two-fingered "hand" made of opposing bigel strips is used to demonstrate the shape-altering ability of the material in response to temperature changes. In room-temperature water the fingers are open (left). When the water is heated near body temperature, the fingers close on and grasp the test object (right).

creased the phase transition temperature, the temperature above which the gel collapses. Therefore, at a constant temperature the gel expanded in the oxidized state and contracted in the reduced state. The dimensional changes depended greatly on the shape and dimensions of the gel sample. For example, a $1\times1\times20$-mm strip of the material fluctuated in length by several tens of micrometers (millionths of a meter) in a rhythmic motion that was likened to the wavelike motion observed in earthworms. Small spheres, in contrast, expanded and contracted uniformly, similar to a beating heart. Aside from applications such as molecular pumps, one application of considerable interest is periodic or rhythmic drug-delivery systems that could be synchronized with biological cycles such as the secretion of hormones.

Investigating simple and inexpensive methods of detecting minute quantities of chemicals, several researchers at the University of Pittsburgh, Pa., devised chemical sensors that change color in the presence of metal ions and glucose. These sensors are ordered, three-dimensional arrays of polystyrene spheres 100 nanometers (billionths of a meter) in diameter set in an acrylamide gel modified with functional groups that react with specific chemical species—*i.e.*, the chemicals to be detected. Prior to exposure to the species, the spheres are spaced closely together in a hydrogel matrix. As the chemical species reacts with the hydrogel's functional groups, the matrix expands owing to increased osmotic pressure and increases the average distance between the spheres. Consequently, light is diffracted from the ordered arrangement at longer wavelengths. Color changes can be observed

because the resulting shifts in wavelength take place in the visible spectrum. The process can be reversed by soaking the sensor in deionized water to flush out the species being tested, which thus collapses the matrix.

For hydrogel sensors modified with functional groups (crown ethers) that react specifically with lead ions (Pb^{2+}), color changes visible to the naked eye were observed for lead concentrations as low as four parts per million. This type of sensor would be applicable for indicating lead-toxicity levels in tap water. Glucose sensors, modified with the enzyme glucose oxidase, responded to glucose concentrations as low as one part per trillion. The lack of response by the glucose sensor to concentrations of sucrose or mannose validated the sensor's selectivity. In this context the Pittsburgh researchers envisioned sensors based on gels modified with HIV antibodies to detect low concentrations of the human AIDS virus.

Researchers at the Kimberly-Clark Corp. and the University of North Texas designed gradient gel structures that can form various predetermined shapes and can curve over $180°$ when exposed to appropriate stimuli. These structures consist of two gels of different sensitivities that are

polymerized so that portions of one diffuse into the other to form an interpenetrating polymer network. The researchers demonstrated this technique by producing bigel strips of NIPA and polyacryamide (PAAM). The NIPA contracted significantly when exposed to temperatures above $37°$ C ($98.6°$ F), whereas PAAM was insensitive to the temperature change. In contrast, PAAM contracted much more than the NIPA gel when exposed to acetone-water mixtures (greater than 34% acetone by weight). The study demonstrated that NIPA-PAAM bigel strips at temperatures above $37°$ C curved toward the NIPA as that gel contracted, whereas bigel strips submerged in the appropriate acetone-water mixtures curved in the opposite direction.

More complex bigel structures were engineered by forming the interpenetrating network of NIPA into PAAM at specific locations. These designs yielded bigels that bend at specific sites to form predetermined geometries under the appropriate conditions. As the temperature increased from room temperature, various geometries such as spirals, pentagons, and letters of the alphabet were obtained from previously straight bigel strips.

—David E. Collins

MATHEMATICS

Mathematics in 1997 was marked by the celebration of achievements and the contemplation of philosophical questions and computational results. The Nobel Prize for economics was awarded for a mathematical model formulated in the 1970s that is crucial to today's securities markets. As one mathematician received a famous long-standing prize for proving Fermat's last theorem, others began to attack a related problem that, like the Fermat conjecture, is easy to formulate but may prove very difficult to solve. New results in mathematical logic emphasized that some facts in mathematics cannot be proved and, hence, must be true for no good reason whatsoever. Statisticians debunked alleged statistical support for claims that the Bible encodes predictions of future events, and they reconsidered what it means for an event to be called random. A college student found a new prime number while participating in an organized search by people with spare personal computer time.

A prize for pricing

The 1997 Nobel Memorial Prize in Economic Science was awarded to Robert C. Merton of Harvard University and Myron S. Scholes of Stanford University for their method of determining the value of financial derivatives, such as stock options. Together with the late Fischer Black in the 1970s, Scholes formulated a mathematical model with appropriate assumptions and solved the resulting equation, deriving a pricing formula known as the Black-Scholes formula. Merton built on the formula, showing that with modifications it has many risk-management applications beyond options. For example, it can be used to evaluate guarantees, as found in insurance and annuity contracts, and the flexibility of capital equipment. A major feature of the formula is its demonstration that in valuing an option one need not separately formulate the risk involved in the uncertainty of the market; that risk is already incorporated into the current stock price and volatility used in the formula.

Fundamental to the success of Merton, Scholes, and Black was their use of stochastic differential equations, as developed by mathematician Kiyosi Ito in Japan in the 1940s. A stochastic differential equation is an equation in which the unknown sought is a random process—that is, an evolving statistical phenomenon, like the length of a queue or the price of a stock, that is governed by probabilistic laws. The value of an option is a function of both time and the price of the stock; Ito developed the "chain rule" necessary to calculate the rate of change of the option value as a function of these two variables. Using this rule, Black and Scholes were able to work backward from their model for the rate of change of the option value to calculate the value itself.

A new prize for a new conjecture

Andrew Wiles of Princeton University received the Wolfskehl Prize, established in 1908 by the will of physician Paul Wolfskehl for the first person to prove Fermat's last theorem, which Wiles accomplished with a paper published in 1995. Debunking a myth that inflation had wiped out the prize fund, Wiles received $50,000.

Shortly after Wiles's award, Andrew Beal, a Texas banker, offered a prize of $50,000 for resolution of what has hence become known as Beal's conjecture: the equation $x^p + y^q = z^r$ has no solutions when p, q, and r are integers greater than 2 and x, y, and z are positive integers and

Texas banker Andrew Beal (below) has posted a $50,000 prize for the resolution of a problem that has become known as Beal's conjecture. The problem is a more general version of Fermat's last theorem, which finally succumbed to a proof published in 1995 after more than 300 years of challenges.

coprime (no pair of them has a common factor greater than 1). In other words, apart from the case of squares—$3^2 + 4^2 = 5^2$ and other integer triples that satisfy the Pythagorean relation—no two powers of integers sum to another power unless at least two of the integers have a common factor—e.g., $2^3 + 2^3 = 2^4$ or $3^3 + 6^3 = 3^5$. Wiles's accomplishment was to show that Beal's conjecture is true when $p = q = r$, which is Fermat's last theorem.

In 1995 Henri Darmon of McGill University, Montreal, and Andrew Granville of the University of Georgia had shown that for any specific triple of exponents p, q, and r, the equation $x^p + y^q = z^r$ has only finitely many solutions. (A related conjecture, dubbed the ABC conjecture, implies that $1/p + 1/q + 1/r$ is greater than $\frac{1}{2}$ and, hence, that there are no solutions for exponents p, q, and r sufficiently large—e.g., if all of them are greater than 6.) Darmon and Granville had also investigated related open (unresolved) problems and formulated what they called the Fermat-Catalan conjecture: $x^p + y^q = z^r$ has only finitely many solutions when x, y, and z are coprime and $1/p + 1/q + 1/r$ is less than 1.

Whether Beal's conjecture and its relations will survive challenges for more than 300 years, attract the attention of generations of leading mathematicians, and lead to the development of major fields of mathematics—as Fermat's conjecture did—remains to be seen.

Unprovable facts

Although Wiles succeeded in giving a mathematical proof of Fermat's last theorem, other conjectures in number theory that are, in fact, true may not be suscepti-

ble to mathematical proof. In 1931 the Austrian-born American mathematician Kurt Gödel showed that the consistency of arithmetic cannot be established in the ordinary logic commonly used in mathematics, even though such consistency—i.e., that arithmetic is free from contradictory results—is not disputed, and can be proved, in a wider logical framework.

In 1997 Gregory Chaitin of the IBM Thomas J. Watson Research Center, Yorktown Heights, N.Y., popularized such ideas in the context of computer programs. In one example Chaitin began by defining a computer program as "elegant" if no smaller-size program in the same programming language has the identical output and then reasoning that there exist infinitely many elegant programs, each producing one of the infinitely many possible outputs. Next, he embedded into the computer programming language LISP a formal axiomatic system for reasoning about computer programs, much as Gödel had embedded into arithmetic a statement that says of itself that it is unprovable. He then showed that such a system cannot prove the elegance of programs much larger than itself—in other words, that it can prove the elegance of at most finitely many programs. Hence, there will always be some elegant programs for which there is no demonstration of their elegance within the system of reasoning.

Although most people believe that anything that is true must be true for some reason—i.e., that there exists a proof of the fact even though no proof may be known—Chaitin's results demonstrate that some things are true "accidentally, or at random," because there is, and can be, no proof. The nature of the demonstrations by

Gödel and Chaitin, however, precludes identifying exactly which results are true "at random." Hence, mathematicians must continue their struggles toward finding proofs or counterexamples without the comfort of knowing that either one or the other must exist.

What is "random"?

The nature of randomness was a major topic that occupied statisticians in 1997. A popular book published that year, *The Bible Code* by Michael Drosnin, claimed that encoded within the Hebrew Old Testament are references to later historical events and predictions about contemporary ones. Supporting the book was a statistical article claiming that the appearance in Genesis of the names and birth dates or death dates (or both) of several dozen rabbis who lived after the writing of Genesis was extremely unlikely to have occurred at random. Statisticians were overwhelmingly skeptical of these claims, even as they considered how popular ideas about randomness differ from scientific ones.

The result of a coin toss—heads or tails—is regarded as random because it is not predictable (provided that the coin rotates many times), even though it is determined by physical laws. Similarly, numbers from a computer random-number generator are accepted as random, even though they derive from a purely mechanistic process of computer arithmetic. Statisticians regard a sequence of outcomes as random if each outcome is independent of (unaffected by) the previous ones. The belief that after a long sequence of heads, tails is more likely on the next toss is known as the "gambler's fallacy."

Many people feel that a truly random sequence should have no "obvious" patterns, such as a sequence of consecutive heads in coin tosses. In the 1960s a team of mathematicians suggested measuring randomness by how short a computer program needs to be to reproduce the sequence. For a sequence of consecutive heads, the program's job is simple—just write H repeatedly. A sequence with no discernible pattern requires a longer program, which enumerates each outcome of the sequence. Requiring a long program is equivalent to having the sequence pass certain statistical tests for randomness.

According to this measure, however, the first million decimal digits of pi (the number expressing the ratio of the circumference of a circle to its diameter and beginning 3.14159265...) are not random, since very short computer programs exist that can reproduce them. That contradicts mathematicians' sense that the digits of pi have no discernible pattern. Nevertheless, the spirit of the approach does correspond to human intuition; people assess the randomness of a sequence by how hard it is to memorize or copy.

In 1997 freelance mathematician Steve Pincus of Guilford, Conn., Burton Singer of Princeton University, and Rudolf E. Kalman of the Swiss Federal Institute of Technology, Zürich, proposed assessing randomness of a sequence in terms of its "approximate entropy," or disorder. To be random in this sense, a sequence of coin tosses must contain (as far as possible given its length) equal numbers of heads and tails, equal numbers of each of the possible adjacent pairs (HH, HT, TH, and TT), equal numbers of each of the eight kinds of adjacent triples, and so forth. This

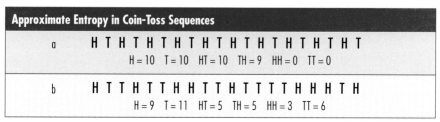

Approximate Entropy in Coin-Toss Sequences

a   H T H T H T H T H T H T H T H T H T H T
    H = 10   T = 10   HT = 10   TH = 9   HH = 0   TT = 0

b   H T T H T T H H T T H T T T T H H H T H
    H = 9   T = 11   HT = 5   TH = 5   HH = 3   TT = 6

Although both sequences of 20 coin tosses (a and b) have nearly equal numbers of heads and tails, the more irregular-appearing sequence (b) is more random because it also contains roughly equal numbers of each of the possible adjacent pairs. The regular-appearing sequence (a) contains no HH or TT pairs.

must hold for all "short" sequences of adjacent outcomes within the original sequence—ones that are significantly shorter than the original sequence (in technical terms, for all sequences of length less than $\log_2 \log_2 n + 1$, in which n is the length of the original sequence and logarithms are taken to base 2).

When this definition is applied to the 32 possible sequences of H and T having a length of five, the sequence HHHHH is not random; only HHTTH, HTTHH, TTHHT, and THHTT are. Furthermore, when considered in this sense, the decimal digits of pi do form a random sequence. In the case of a nonrandom sequence, the approximate entropy measures how much the sequence deviates from the "ideal."

Other investigators have used the concept of approximate entropy to investigate the possibility that symptoms anecdotally ascribed to "male menopause" may be sufficiently nonrandom to indicate the existence of such a condition and to assess how randomly the prices of financial stocks fluctuate.

Cooperating computers

Several cooperative search efforts involving large numbers of personal computers produced mathematical fruit in 1997. The Great Internet Mersenne Prime Search (GIMPS) used spare time on the computers of over 4,000 volunteers to discover several new Mersenne prime numbers, including the largest prime known. (Mersenne primes are of the form $2^p - 1$, in which p is a prime. They are named after Marin Mersenne, a 17th-century French priest and amateur mathematician.) Each computer in the GIMPS effort tries a different set of candidates. The most recent successful candidate, the 37th known Mersenne prime, was verified on the personal computer of a college student. Mersenne primes are used in testing computer hardware and in an encryption system based on elliptic curves; the GIMPS program itself is used by the computer chip maker Intel to test its Pentium chips before they ship.

Another joint effort, by 14,000 computers, decoded a message rendered in the American commercial 56-bit Data Encryption Standard code, a system used by banks in transferring funds. A brute-force attack of trying all 72 quadrillion possible keys succeeded partway through the project. This success did not immediately imperil banks but demonstrated that longer keys would be needed soon.

—Paul J. Campbell

MEDICAL SCIENCES

New technology in the medical sciences received considerable attention in 1997. The announcement in February of the birth of Dolly the sheep, the first clone of an adult mammal, marked the culmination of a decade of painstaking research by Scottish scientists and immediately prompted speculation about the possibility—and potential pitfalls—of cloning human beings. In the field of dentistry, a new laser that painlessly removes tooth decay promised to end the days of whining drills and numb gums. Technological advances were also made in veterinary medicine as researchers developed an ultrasonic technique for the treatment of prostatic abscesses in dogs. A new vaccine for people allergic to cats was in the final stages of testing.

GENERAL MEDICINE

Medical science often glides sedately forward, creating scarcely a ripple in the pub-lic consciousness. That was not the case in 1997, a year filled with sensational, and often controversial, medical developments that sent shock waves throughout society.

From the creation of a cloned sheep in Scotland to the birth of septuplets in Iowa, from a massive recall of tainted hamburger in the U.S. to the outbreak of the A(H5N1) "bird flu" virus in Hong Kong, medical news stirred hope and fear among people around the globe. Ethics panels were convened. New regulations were put in place. Yet for many complex issues it would be years before the final chapter was written.

With all the hoopla over septuplets and carbon-copy lambs, it was easy to lose sight of less-photogenic stories with significant—and perhaps more immediate—implications for public health. Some popular diet pills were linked to serious heart-valve problems. New estimates showed the AIDS epidemic to be far worse than previously thought. Evidence continued to mount that common drugs and vitamins may slow or even prevent the onset of Alzheimer's disease. Moreover, after years of skepticism, practitioners of conventional Western medicine began to acknowledge some of the powers of acupuncture and other alternative therapies.

Reproduction

Even the best science-fiction writer would be hard pressed to come up with more dramatic story lines than those generated by real-life reproductive science researchers in 1997.

The action began in February with the announcement that Scottish embryologist Ian Wilmut and his colleagues at the Roslin Institute near Edinburgh had created the first genetic clone of an adult mammal, a lamb they named Dolly. The achievement touched off a storm of controversy because of concerns that the same technology might be used to replicate humans. A number of nations took prompt action to bar human-cloning experiments. In the U.S., Pres. Bill Clinton banned the use of federal money for such research. Worries about the abuse of cloning technology resurfaced, however, when physicist Richard Seed of Chicago announced plans in December 1997 to set up a privately funded clinic to create clones for infertile couples.

While condemning human cloning, many researchers held out hope that cloning technology could be used for positive purposes. Ten months after the birth of Dolly was made public, Roslin Institute scientists announced the creation of a second sheep, Polly, that possessed a human gene. The gene was added to the nucleus of a fetal sheep cell in hopes that it would

A sign in a storefront in Carlisle, Iowa, announces the birth of septuplets to residents Kenny and Bobbi McCaughey. The septuplets, four boys and three girls, who were born in nearby Des Moines on Nov. 19, 1997, were the first known case of seven live human births.

cause a human protein to be produced in the offspring animal's milk. Once extracted, the protein in question would be valuable to patients who lacked it, such as people with hemophilia. (For additional information on recent cloning research and its implications, *see* Year in Review: LIFE SCIENCES: *Molecular Biology and Genetics;* Year in Review: FOOD AND AGRICULTURE: *Agriculture.*)

The spotlight in the field of reproductive science shifted from sheep to people when it was revealed in April that in vitro, or test-tube, fertilization had enabled a 63-year-old woman to have a baby. She was the oldest known woman to have given birth. Doctors at the University of Southern California said that the woman, who was well past menopause, became pregnant by using an egg donated by a younger woman. The birth sparked debate over whether there should be an age limit for test-tube pregnancies and renewed calls for more uniform regulation of fertility clinics.

Additional pressure to rethink the regulation of reproductive technologies came in October when doctors at Reproductive Biology Associates in Atlanta, Ga., announced that a 39-year-old woman had given birth to twin boys created from donor eggs that were frozen—and then thawed—before they were fertilized. The case, along with similar successes reported by researchers in Australia, Germany, and Italy, sent younger women rushing to "bank" their eggs as insurance against the day when they wanted a child but their ovaries could no longer provide an egg. Nevertheless, the technology remained highly experimental, with the Atlanta team reporting only two pregnancies in 23 attempts using frozen eggs.

In August 1997 millions of kilograms of ground beef produced at the Hudson Foods plant in Columbus, Neb., were pulled from supermarkets and fast-food restaurants across the U.S. after tests showed that some of the beef was contaminated by a potentially deadly strain of bacteria.

There may have been more significant scientific advances in reproductive health in 1997, but for sheer drama the birth of the McCaughey septuplets—the world's first known living set—was unprecedented. Although the sight of the seven healthy babies born on November 19 to Bobbi and Kenny McCaughey of Carlisle, Iowa, warmed the hearts of people around the world, it also sparked heated debate about fertility drugs like those used to conceive "the magnificent seven." Noting that such drugs often lead to more than one fetus, critics warned that multiple births beyond triplets pose a health risk to the mother and often produce children with serious physical or mental disabilities. Two months after delivery, however, all appeared to be going well for the McCaughey babies, whose birth weights ranged from 1.1 kg (2 lb 5 oz) to 1.5 kg (3 lb 4 oz). Fertility drugs were also credited for the birth of the world's second living set of septuplets, born on Jan. 14, 1998, to 40-year-old Hasna Mohammed Humair in Saudi Arabia.

Food safety

While getting pregnant at retirement age or figuring out how to care for septuplets was far removed from most people's daily lives, another health issue was not—food safety.

In August the U.S. government ordered the largest recall of beef in the nation's history after the discovery of a potentially deadly strain of bacteria, *Escherichia coli* 0157:H7, in frozen hamburger patties produced at a Hudson Foods plant in Columbus, Neb. Some 11.3 million kg (25 million lb) of ground beef were pulled from supermarkets and fast-food restaurants across the country. The threat of foodborne illness was not limited to meat. Frozen strawberries imported from Mexico were blamed for an outbreak of hepatitis A in

Scott Sady—AP/Wide World

Two children suffering from malnutrition linger in front of their home in a slum in Port-au-Prince, Haiti. A recent UNICEF report indicated that malnutrition contributes to the deaths of nearly seven million children each year—more than any infectious disease, war, or natural disaster.

March that struck more than 200 people in the U.S.

Concerned by estimates showing that as many as 33 million cases of foodborne illness occur in the U.S. each year, the government stepped up efforts to improve food safety in 1997. Under regulations unveiled by the U.S. Food and Drug Administration (FDA) in December, red-meat processors would be allowed to use nuclear irradiation to combat germs, exposing meat to bacteria-killing gamma rays. According to most health experts, the irradiation process is safe and leaves no radioactivity behind in meat.

Obesity and diet

Another health risk posed by food—or, more precisely, by too much of the wrong kinds of food—is obesity. Despite hopes that a new breed of diet drugs that suppresses appetite by altering brain chemicals would make it easier for obese people to lose weight, doctors at the Mayo Clinic in Rochester, Minn., reported severe heart-valve problems among women taking fenfluramine and phentermine, the popular diet-pill combination known as fen-phen. Spurred by this and a number of similar reports, drug manufacturers recalled fenfluramine (Pondimin) and dexfenfluramine (Redux) in September. (Phentermine was not determined to cause adverse side effects.)

In November the FDA approved sibutramine (Meridia), another antiobesity drug. Like fenfluramine and dexfenfluramine, sibutramine raised levels of the appetite-suppressing brain chemical serotonin, but in safety tests it did not appear to cause heart-valve problems. Because it can raise blood pressure, however, sibutramine was far from being the "magic" weight-loss pill that so many dieters eagerly awaited.

In bleak contrast to the obsession with weight loss in the U.S., malnutrition continued to pose a major problem in other countries around the world. UNICEF issued a report in December showing that malnutrition contributes to the deaths of nearly seven million children each year—more than any infectious disease, war, or natural disaster.

Menopause and osteoporosis

In 1997 women received more guidance in making the difficult decision of whether to take hormone drugs after menopause. In a study published in *The New England Journal of Medicine* in June, Harvard University researchers found that women who received hormone replacement therapy had a 37% lower risk of death than women who did not; results were even better for those at high risk for heart disease. There was, however, a major caveat: the benefits seemed to diminish when women took hormones for a decade or more. Researchers attributed the decline to a higher rate of breast cancer among the long-term hormone users.

One reason that postmenopausal women take replacement doses of the hormone estrogen is to prevent osteoporosis. In December the FDA approved raloxifene (Evista), a custom-designed drug that mimics some of estrogen's activities, for the treatment of osteoporosis. In clinical trials raloxifene acted like estrogen by increasing bone density and protecting against heart disease; unlike estrogen, however, it did not boost the risk of breast cancer in the safety tests.

Diet is also an important factor when it comes to protecting against weak bones and fractures. In August new dietary guidelines issued by the U.S. National Academy of Sciences urged people older than age 50 to boost their intake of bone-building calcium. The new recommendation of 1,200 mg per day was 50% higher than the previous recommended dosage.

Cancer

As it was in so many other areas of medicine, debate was the name of the game when it came to cancer in 1997. In January an expert panel convened by the U.S. National Cancer Institute (NCI) came under fire from doctors and patients alike when it concluded there was not enough evidence to justify regular mammography screening for women in their 40s. The NCI later reversed its position, recommending that women in their 40s at average risk undergo mammograms to check for breast cancer every one to two years.

Another controversy centered on the causes of breast cancer, specifically whether exposure to chemical pollutants that mimic estrogen, such as DDT and polychlorinated biphenyls (PCBs), increases a woman's chance of developing the disease. In October a study conducted by the Harvard School of Public Health found that women with high levels of DDE (an organochlorine produced by the metabolic breakdown of DDT) and PCBs in their bloodstream were no more likely to get breast cancer than those with lower levels. Yet just two months later, research-

ers from the Barbara Ann Karmanos Cancer Institute in Detroit reported that DDT and PCBs promoted the growth of some precancerous and cancerous human breast cells in the test tube.

During the year women were also furnished with a few more clues about what they can do to protect against breast cancer. One study, released in May, found that women who exercise at least four hours a week have a substantially lower risk of developing breast cancer than those who do not exercise. Other research showed that women who put on extra weight as they age are more likely to develop breast cancer than those who keep their weight stable.

Progress was also made in understanding the risk factors for the most common kind of childhood leukemia, acute lymphoblastic leukemia (ALL). In July the NCI researchers reported that contrary to the fears of many parents and environmental activists, they could find no evidence that living near power lines increases a child's risk for ALL.

Cancer genetics research continued to move forward. In August researchers at Johns Hopkins Medical Institutions, Baltimore, Md., announced the discovery of a genetic mutation that causes familial colorectal cancer. The researchers estimated that the mutation is present in more than 500,000 Ashkenazi Jews. The Johns Hopkins team used its findings to create a simple, inexpensive blood test for colon-cancer mutation, but some of the researchers revealed in a report published in *The New England Journal of Medicine* (March 20, 1997) that doctors who tested patients for a gene mutation that causes a less-common form of colon cancer than that

found in Ashkenazi Jews often performed the test improperly and gave patients flawed results.

Heart disease

Gene therapy was a major focus of heart disease research in 1997. At a meeting of the American Heart Association in November, a team lead by doctors from St. Elizabeth's Medical Center in Boston reported the first use of gene therapy to grow new blood vessels. The therapy involved injecting a gene that promotes the growth of new arteries into the legs of patients whose original arteries had been clogged by severe disease. According to researchers, the gene treatment created functional new blood vessels in 16 of 20 patients, healing or improving both ulcers and gangrene caused by poor circulation. Researchers hoped ultimately to be able to inject the treatment gene directly into the hearts of people with clogged heart arteries in order to avert the need for coronary bypass surgery.

Gene therapy was far from the only innovative strategy to emerge for the treatment of heart disease. A study of 162 people, led by heart surgeons at St. Vincent Hospital in Indianapolis, Ind., found that using a laser to drill tiny channels in the heart significantly reduces chest pain in people who are unable to undergo bypass surgery or angioplasty. Researchers speculated that the procedure, called transmyocardial revascularization, helps to ease pain by increasing the amount of blood that reaches the heart muscle. Still to be determined was whether the procedure decreases the incidence of heart attacks or helps people live longer.

Despite the promise of such technological wizardry, prevention, as always, continued to be the best weapon against heart disease. A study published in *The New England Journal of Medicine* in April showed that a simple lifestyle change can have a major impact on one of the biggest risk factors for cardiovascular disease—high blood pressure. The study found that a low-fat diet rich in fruits, vegetables, and low-fat dairy foods can reduce blood pressure as much as some drugs commonly used to control hypertension. The diet that produced such benefits featured 8 to 10 daily servings of fruits and vegetables and 3 daily servings of predominantly low-fat dairy products—twice the average American's intake of both types of foods.

If health-conscious people did not know what homocysteine was when 1997 began, they probably did when it ended. The year saw the publication of two major studies showing that levels of homocysteine, an amino acid found in the bloodstream, may influence the risk of heart disease. The first study, published in July in the journal *Circulation,* found that women who had high blood levels of homocysteine had a risk of heart attack that was double the risk of women who had normal levels. A study of Norwegian men published the same month in *The New England Journal of Medicine* found a strong relationship between homocysteine levels and death from heart disease. In contrast to cholesterol, homocysteine levels can be easily lowered through dietary measures, specifically by increasing the intake of foods rich in folic acid, vitamin B_6, and vitamin B_{12}.

Most people know that smoking is a risk factor for heart disease, but unsettling new evidence suggested that exposure to secondhand smoke may be more dangerous than previously thought. A 10-year study of 32,045 nonsmoking women found that those who were regularly exposed to cigarette smoke at home or work had twice the risk of developing coronary heart disease than women who were not exposed.

Transplants

More uses—and potential pitfalls—of transplantation technology came into focus during 1997. In October researchers at the University of Florida reported encouraging early results from an experimental nerve tissue transplant to slow the progression of spinal-cord damage. In findings presented to the Society for Neuroscience, doctors said that they injected human embryonic spinal-cord tissue into the spinal cord of a 43-year-old man with a severe spinal-cord injury. The injection was made in an attempt to "fill" an expanding cavity, called a cyst, which can cause severe pain and progressive loss of movement in some people with spinal injuries. According to doctors, the patient's condition remained stable 3½ months after the transplant, but they cautioned that it may take up to a year before the final outcome of the procedure can be determined.

The fact that transplantation is not without risk was underscored in September by the unusual case of a man who developed a severe peanut allergy after undergoing a liver and kidney transplant. Reporting in *The New England Journal of Medicine,* doctors said the 35-year-old man, who had had no previous reactions to peanuts, developed a skin rash and swelling of the throat after eating peanuts three months after receiving his new organs. A review of medical records found that the organ donor had a long history of allergic reactions to peanuts, which led doctors to speculate that immune cells transferred along with the donated liver were to blame for the recipient's "new" allergy. Needless to say, the transplant recipient was advised to give up peanuts permanently.

Alzheimer's disease

Although a cure for Alzheimer's disease remained a distant dream, there were encouraging signs that some common medications and nutritional supplements may help to delay, and possibly even prevent, symptoms of the progressive neurological disorder.

Evidence that both vitamin E and selegiline, a drug used to treat Parkinson's disease, may slow Alzheimer's destructive course came in April. Scientists from the U.S. National Institute on Aging (NIA) reported that high doses of vitamin E and normal doses of selegiline delayed the onset of disabling symptoms by about seven months among people with moderately severe Alzheimer's.

A study published in *Neurology* in June lent strong support to the idea that estrogen may protect against Alzheimer's. Researchers from the NIA and Johns Hopkins Medical Institutions found that estrogen replacement therapy cut the risk of Alzheimer's by more than 50% among postmenopausal women.

The flashiest headlines, however, were reserved for a study that showed that ginkgo herbal extract may help Alzheimer's patients retain their mental functions longer. The study, published in *The Journal of the American Medical Association* in October, showed that an extract from the leaves of *Ginkgo biloba* appeared to slow the decline of people with mild to moderately severe Alzheimer's for at least six months. Although ginkgo extract has been used by the Chinese for more than 5,000 years and is considered generally safe, the researchers were quick to caution that ginkgo is definitely not the wonder drug so desperately desired by Alzheimer's sufferers and their families.

AIDS and other infectious diseases

In the battle against AIDS and other infectious diseases, 1997 was a disheartening year, one in which epidemics grew, treatment hopes were dashed, and formidable new foes emerged.

Armed with staggering statistics, UN health experts in November dramatically hiked their estimates of the extent of the global AIDS epidemic. The experts calculated that each day about 16,000 people around the world are infected with HIV, which causes AIDS—double their previous projections. The UN also raised its estimate of the number of people living with HIV to more than 30 million, or about one in 100 adults between the ages of 15 and 49.

The mortality figures were equally grim, with 2.3 million people expected to die of AIDS in 1997—up 50% from 1996. The UN estimated that AIDS had claimed the lives of more than 11.7 million people worldwide since the disease emerged in the early 1980s.

Although new drugs called protease inhibitors were credited with having slowed the rates of AIDS deaths in the U.S. for the first time since the epidemic began, it became clear as the year progressed that such drugs were far from a miracle cure. Late in the year a series of studies by several different research teams showed that even patients who had taken the most potent cocktail of AIDS drugs up to 30 months still had potentially infectious HIV hiding in their immune cells.

Faced with the growing threat of antibiotic-resistant microbes, scientists scrambled to find new drugs to combat infections. In 1996 doctors in Japan reported an unsettling first: a case of a patient infected with a strain of *Staphylococcus aureus* that was resistant to vancomycin, an antibiotic used to treat severe infections not responding to other drugs. In 1997 the bacteria appeared for the first time in the U.S.

Another worrisome development in infectious diseases popped up in Hong Kong—the A(H5N1) "bird flu" virus. Although the problem did not attract wide-

Tony Aw—AFP

More than one million chickens and other poultry in Hong Kong were infected with a virus that was transmitted directly from birds to people. The virus, which killed at least five persons in an outbreak of influenza known as the bird flu, was common in chickens but had never before been seen in humans.

spread publicity until December, the outbreak actually began in May when a three-year-old boy died of the virus, which was common in chickens but had never before been seen in humans. In the ensuing months the bird virus infected at least 16 more people, killing 4 of them. To quell public anxiety and reduce the risk of a possible epidemic, Hong Kong health officials in December ordered the extermination of over one million chickens and other poultry.

Alternative therapies

For decades most Western doctors looked askance at treatments that traced their roots to sources other than conventional medical science. Patients either had to go along with the conventional therapy that their doctor ordered or turn to an alternative practitioner to guide them into the exotic world of herbs, acupuncture, and massage.

In 1997 practitioners of both conventional medicine and alternative medicine finally began to find some middle ground. The shift began in February when a panel of experts convened by the U.S. National Institutes of Health (NIH) recommended that more studies be conducted on the potential medical benefits of marijuana. The recommendation followed a hearing at which patients with glaucoma, multiple sclerosis, and AIDS testified how marijuana had helped relieve symptoms such as pain and nausea.

The most ringing endorsement of an alternative therapy came from a consensus panel on acupuncture sponsored by the NIH. Whereas acupuncture was hardly "alternative" to the Chinese, who have used it for 2,500 years, Western doctors have been slow to steer their patients toward the therapy, in which fine metal needles are inserted into the skin and manipulated with the intention of changing the flow of energy throughout the body. The panel concluded that acupuncture is effective in reducing nausea resulting from chemotherapy or anesthesia and in combating pain after dental procedures. According to the experts, acupuncture can also be teamed up with traditional therapies or used as an alternative treatment for a variety of conditions ranging from arthritis to migraine headaches to low back pain.

Awards

In 1997 the choice for the Nobel Prize for Physiology or Medicine raised some eyebrows. The award went to Stanley Prusiner of the University of California, San Francisco, for his contributions toward identifying the infectious agent behind a mysterious class of fatal brain disorders. Called transmissible spongiform encephalopathies, the disorders include Creutzfeldt-Jakob disease in humans, "mad cow" disease in cattle, and scrapie in sheep. Most in the scientific community concurred with Prusiner that such diseases are probably caused by a completely new type of infectious agent, but support was less than widespread for Prusiner's unproved hypothesis that the new infectious agents are small, twisted proteins, which he named prions. In any event, both supporters and critics of Prusiner's "prion hypothesis" had to agree that this Nobel Prize winner had

In Springfield, Md., a physician inserts acupuncture needles into a patient's back in order to relieve back pain. In 1997 the National Institutes of Health concluded that acupuncture, which has been used by Chinese medical practitioners for 2,500 years, is effective as an alternative treatment for a variety of conditions.

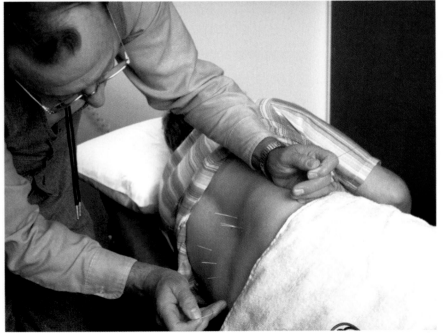

Dan McCoy—Rainbow/PNI

done what few scientists ever do: galvanized the biomedical research world to look at a perplexing problem from a new perspective. (*See* SCIENTISTS OF THE YEAR: *Nobel Prizes.*)

The 1997 Albert Lasker Medical Research Awards highlighted achievements in the fields of nutrition and genetics. The clinical research award honored Alfred Sommer of the Johns Hopkins University School of Hygiene and Public Health for his discovery that vitamin A supplementation can protect children from blindness as well as life-threatening infections. Sommer's conclusions stemmed from his study of 4,600 children in rural Indonesia in the mid-1970s. In that work he found that giving children vitamin A not only could save their sight but also could save their lives by strengthening their immune systems. The basic medical research award honored Mark Ptashne of Memorial Sloan-Kettering Cancer Center in New York City for his work on gene regulation. Among Ptashne's accomplishments over three decades of research were his discoveries of the basic mechanisms that turn genes on and off. A special achievement award honored Victor McKusick of Johns Hopkins University for his pioneering work in the field of medical genetics. McKusick was instrumental in establishing medical genetics as a distinct branch of medicine in the late 1950s. He also played a pivotal role in early efforts to map the human genome.

—Rebecca Kolberg

DENTISTRY

Research and technology were in the forefront of the field of dentistry in 1997. New uses of glass ionomer cements in combination with resin components helped to change the way in which dentists performed restorative dental work. These cements were composed of aluminosilicate glass powder, a very durable filling material. Computer-assisted design and manufacturing were used to create overlays, veneer laminates, and single full crowns. New surgical techniques focused on guided tissue regeneration (GTR), a periodontal (gum) technique in which synthetic or collagen membranes were used to rebuild gum tissue. GTR allowed patients to keep teeth that might otherwise be considered beyond saving. The advantage of GTR was that it could bring about bone regeneration around the root of a tooth, producing new bone as strong as the original. Gold-based dental restorations, once considered very costly, were not much more costly in 1997 than base-metal restorations and could cause fewer tissue reactions.

There was more good news for dental patients. The erbium:yttrium-aluminum-garnet (Er:YAG) laser appeared to be as effective in removing decayed tooth material as a high-speed drill and, in some cases, eliminated the need for an anesthetic. Researchers compared the effectiveness of the Er:YAG laser with that of the drill in 167 patients. Patients treated with the laser were offered an anesthetic only if they requested one. The laser treatment was as effective as the drill, and fewer than 2% of the patients in the laser group requested an anesthetic. In May the FDA approved the near-painless dental laser to remove tooth decay, prepare cavities for fillings, and roughen enamel to improve bonding of restorations. Previous dental lasers had been cleared for use only on soft tissue like the gums, for curing restorations, and as a heat source in some bleaching systems.

Tooth gene studied

The investigation of a new gene by a research group headed by Anne George of the Northwestern University Dental School, Chicago, Ill., offered insight into how teeth and bones normally harden. The gene, called Dmp1 (for dentin matrix protein 1), was discovered in 1993 during a study of how the mineralization of bones and teeth is controlled. Mineralization, the process whereby bones and teeth are hardened, is important for the proper function of these tissues. Poor and deficient mineralization leads to bones and teeth that fracture easily. Dmp1, the first gene associated specifically with a tooth protein to be localized at the chromosomal level, was mapped to a specific region of human chromosome 4, the locus of the hereditary mineralization disorder dentinogenesis imperfecta type II, which affects one in every 10,000 people.

Amalgam research

The U.S. National Institute of Dental Research announced that it would award more than $9 million in grants over five years to fund clinical trials to examine the health effects of mercury-containing amalgam (silver) fillings in children. A number of studies had suggested that various ailments, ranging from mild skin conditions to neuromuscular diseases, may be caused by mercury-containing amalgam fillings. In a report issued in 1993, however, the Public Health Service (PHS) found no evidence suggesting harmful effects of amalgam fillings. The PHS continued to encourage research of amalgam safety as well as the development of alternative filling materials.

A joint study of amalgam safety was begun by the University of Washington School of Dentistry and the University of Lisbon and involved a group of school-age children who needed substantial dental care. A similar study was being conducted as a cooperative effort by the Forsyth Dental Center in Boston, the New England Research Institutes, Harvard Children's Hospital, and the University of Rochester, N.Y. Although the two studies were being conducted independently, both used the same overall design and a common set of clinical procedures, dividing the children into groups treated with traditional restorative materials and with alternative materials. To determine any possible health effects, teams of experts in dentistry and other medical fields planned to administer behavioral, renal, and neurological tests before and after the children received dental treatment.

Gum disease treatment and prevention

The incidence of periodontal (gum) disease was on the rise in 1997. Over 60% of adults in the U.S. aged 46–54 had experienced moderate periodontal attachment loss, and 80% of persons over the age of 65 had experienced such loss. A study presented at the March 1997 meeting of the International Association for Dental Research in New Orleans showed that dry brushing reduced gum bleeding by 50% and reduced tartar buildup by 60%. The recommended brushing technique involved

using toothpaste and a soft-bristled toothbrush, starting to brush on the inner surfaces of the teeth, and then moving to the outer surfaces, followed by a good rinse. The dry technique disrupted bacterial buildup and was not harmful to the gums.

The best way to avoid gum disease was to have regular checkups to remove plaque and tartar that allow the disease to take hold and spread.

New treatments that were being studied during the year included the use of antibiotics, the introduction of bacteria harmless to gums but destructive of disease-causing bacteria, the use of substances that prevent bacteria from binding with the teeth as well as substances that break down the structure of plaque, and the use of anti-inflammatory agents that reduce immune response to bacteria and thus the gum-destructive effects of the immune system. Among the leaders in preventative drug

Patsy Lynch—AP/Wide World

At the annual meeting of the American Dental Association, a dentist applies a DentiPatch, a new form of anesthesia, to the gums of a patient. A small adhesive bandage, DentiPatch lessens the pain of shots administered by dentists by numbing gums at the site of an injection.

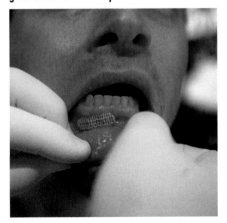

therapies were dental immunologists Martin Taubman and Daniel Smith of the Forsyth Dental Center who developed a vaccine that induced the body to develop antibodies against enzymes produced in dental decay. Researchers Roy Page of the University of Washington School of Dentistry and Marilyn Lantz at Indiana University-Purdue University Indianapolis worked on a vaccine against periodontal disease.

Fighting tooth decay

According to an article published in the April 1997 issue of *The Journal of the American Dental Association* (*JADA*), dental sealants should be covered by dental insurance, as sealants were very effective in combating tooth decay. A recent survey found that only 19% of children had one or more teeth sealed; another study, conducted by the U.S. Department of Health and Human Services, suggested that most childhood tooth decay was preventable with a combination of fluoride and dental sealants. Maria Lopez Howell of the University of Texas Health Science Center at San Antonio Dental School suggested that all children have their permanent molars sealed. Other dentists also recommended sealing the first set of baby molars.

Progress was made in other areas of research. Studies indicated that sport drinks as well as carbonated beverages and fruit juices can promote tooth erosion when they are overconsumed. Researchers suggested rinsing the mouth with water after drinking these types of beverages. A new form of anesthesia, called DentiPatch, lessened the pain of shots given by dentists. DentiPatch was a small adhesive bandage applied on the skin or gums at the site of the injection of a local anesthetic.

Controversy over dental practice variations

The image of the dentist received a blow from the press early in 1997. In the February issue of *Reader's Digest,* journalist William Ecenbarger cited variations in dental practice as evidence that dentists were not being honest with the public. In response, Lawrence H. Meskin, editor of *JADA,* noted that dentists often based their treatment recommendations on their success with various procedures and that, as a result, recommendations among dentists may differ. He also pointed out the generally positive view of dentistry held by the public. Studies indeed had shown that a majority of people respected and trusted the dental profession and were confident in the performance of their dentists.

Dentistry's shifting focus

Improvements in dental health may change the focus and future of the dental profession. Studies indicated significant decreases in the cases of tooth decay and the frequency of tooth removal among adult insured patients. Moreover, visits to the dentist continued to increase. These trends reflected a shift in focus from dental disease treatment to dental health maintenance and control. Use of computers was growing among dentists, with the highest usage (80%) among dentists aged 35–39. Computers were primarily used for business management purposes; however, other applications were being developed for use in dental exams and procedures.

Tooth bleaching and other aesthetic treatments continued to gain popularity among patients. The ADA supported tooth bleaching but warned dentists as well as the general public to use approved preparations. Tooth bleaching was a relatively simple procedure, using carbamide peroxide in most cases. Most tooth stains and discoloration were removable with bleaching agents, although tougher stains could require laser treatment.

—Ron Sims

VETERINARY MEDICINE

Recent revisions to the U.S. Federal Food, Drug, and Cosmetic Act began to have an impact on veterinary medicine in 1997. One of them, the Animal Drug Availability Act of 1996, which was signed into law by Pres. Bill Clinton on Oct. 9, 1996, sought to promote the availability of new animal drugs by making the approval process more efficient and cost-effective and to establish a new class of drugs called veterinary feed directive (VFD) drugs. The VFD category provided an alternative to prescription status for certain medicated-feed drugs that were previously available over the counter. The act required issuance of a VFD form by a licensed veterinarian based on his or her professional judgment on drug and dosage requirements for control of a particular health problem. This procedure would provide greater control over the use of drugs in food-producing animals. In December 1996 the FDA announced the approval of the first VFD drug, an antimicrobial for use in medicated feed to control respiratory disease in pigs.

New prescription drugs recently approved by the FDA for dogs included a

treatment for Cushing's disease (hyperadrenocorticism); a nonsteroidal anti-inflammatory drug (carprofen) for relief of pain, especially that associated with osteoarthritis; a short-duration general anesthetic (propofol); and an antifreeze-poisoning antidote (4-methylpyrazole). A survey of veterinarians indicated that approximately 91,000 household pets died of antifreeze poisoning in 1996. The key ingredient in antifreeze, ethylene glycol, has a sweet taste and smell that attracts pets, wildlife, and even children.

Vaccines for pets and people

The Advisory Panel on Feline Vaccines, which was established in early 1997 by the American Association of Feline Practitioners and the Academy of Feline Medicine, reviewed evidence and conducted extensive interviews with scientists pertaining to the frequency of vaccinating cats against several diseases. The panel concluded that ample evidence existed to support vaccinating cats every three years, rather than annually, for feline panleukopenia (feline distemper), feline calicivirus infection, and feline viral rhinotracheitis. The increased interval for vaccinations did not appear to compromise protection against these viral diseases. Evidence supporting lengthened vaccination intervals for other feline vaccines was lacking.

Canine distemper is a highly contagious viral disease that is endemic in most parts of the world. Low levels of vaccination of dogs against the disease were leading to problems in certain regions. In Finland, for example, distemper had been absent from 1976 to 1990. Near the end of that period, an import restriction on dogs was lifted;

the resulting influx, estimated at 100,000 during 1992–94, represented a 25% increase in the Finnish dog population. Between July 1994 and August 1995, a distemper outbreak occurred, and an estimated 5,000 cases were diagnosed. Analysis of the outbreak by a Finnish veterinary team was described in a 1997 report, which noted that only about half the dog population had been vaccinated annually during the 1992–94 period. The investigators concluded that the outbreak resulted from a marked decrease in the immunity of the dog population in Finland to distemper. Improvements in distemper vaccines beginning in early 1995 and an increase in their use helped terminate the outbreak. In Kotzebue in northwestern Alaska, nearly 300 dogs died during a distemper outbreak in 1997. It had been a number of years since a dog had died of distemper in this community of 3,000 people. Many dogs in Kotzebue had not been vaccinated, which resulted in a population with a high susceptibility to the disease.

A new vaccine for people allergic to cats was in the final stages of testing in 1997. Loren Will, director of the Association of Animal Allergic Veterinarians, noted that the vaccine was an important medical breakthrough that would enable veterinarians who were allergic to cats to continue or return to their practice of feline medicine. The new vaccine was much less hazardous and less complex to administer than the conventional injection series.

Vaccination-site tumors in cats

In 1988 Mattie J. Hendrick, a pathologist at the University of Pennsylvania School of Veterinary Medicine, noted an increase in cats of malignant tumors called sarcomas that appeared to be associated with vaccination sites. This association subsequently was confirmed, with the incidence being estimated, on the basis of a survey of vaccinations given in 1992, at 3.6 cases per 10,000 vaccinated cats. The problem was not restricted to a specific kind or brand of vaccine, and its occurrence was not noted in other species. Although the risk of injection-site sarcomas was usually outweighed by the disease protection provided by the vaccines, the tumors were of special concern because they could spread to other parts of the body, such as the lungs, and many were resistant to treatment. To gain a better understanding of the cause and to prepare recommendations for dealing with the problem, the Vaccine-Associated Feline Sarcoma Task Force was formed in 1996 through the combined efforts of the American Veterinary Medical Association, American Animal Hospital Association, American Association of Feline Practitioners, and Veterinary Cancer Society. Its objectives were to define the true scope and incidence of the tumor problem, determine causal and prognostic factors, and educate and inform veterinarians and the public. Some of these objectives were addressed through establishment of a research grants program in 1997.

Surgical advances

Prostatic disease in dogs is commonly associated with prostate enlargement caused by cysts and abscesses, which can lead to life-threatening infections and toxic shock. Antibiotics usually have not been effective because adequate concentrations cannot be attained in the diseased prostatic tissue.

Conventional surgical treatment involving removal of the prostate has often been accompanied by side effects such as incontinence. A surgical team at the University of Georgia College of Veterinary Medicine developed a new technique for treatment of prostatic abscesses and cysts. The technique, termed intracapsular partial prostatectomy, involved the use of an ultrasonic surgical aspirator. Ultrasonic waves transmitted through a tube fragmented the diseased tissue, which allowed it to be removed by suction. Fewer side effects were noted after postoperative recovery with the new technique.

Three organizations—the Colorado State University College of Veterinary Medicine and Biomedical Sciences, the Steadman Hawkins Sports Medicine Foundation in Vail, Colo., and the National Football League—established a collaborative program to develop new methods for treating human and equine knee injuries. The initial project applied to horses a microfracture technique used on people. This technique involved punching small holes in the subchondral bone near the site of injury to a joint surface in the knee. It was developed by Richard Steadman, an internationally known human orthopedic surgeon and the director of Steadman Hawkins. The results of the microfracture operations were significantly better than those associated with other surgical methods. This research was expected to benefit injured horses and human athletes suffering from osteoarthritis.

Canine diseases

Researchers from the School of Medicine, University of California, San Diego, and the School of Veterinary Medicine, University of California, Davis, studied risk factors for acquired myasthenia gravis in dogs. The disease, which causes generalized weakness in people and dogs and esophageal dilatation in dogs, appeared to be triggered by a spontaneous pathogenic autoimmunity (an attack on the body's tissues by components of its own immune system).

The study included 1,154 dogs in the U.S. having a confirmed diagnosis for the disease during 1991–95. Confirmation of diagnosis included such criteria as demonstration of a specific titer of antibody against the acetylcholine receptor, which is an essential component of the neuromuscular system.

Compared with mixed-breed dogs, the highest risk of breed disposition to the disease was noted in akitas, Scottish terriers, German shorthaired pointers, and chihuahuas. Low relative risk was noted in rottweilers, doberman pinschers, dalmatians, and Jack Russell terriers.

Veterinarians from the Ontario Veterinary College in Canada and the Faculty of Veterinary Medicine in Sweden reported the results of a study of the rates and causes of death in over 222,000 Swedish dogs. The dogs included in the study were enrolled in a life insurance program of a Swedish insurance company in 1992–93 and represented about one-third of all Swedish dogs, of which approximately 80% were purebred. The overall mortality rate for the dogs in the study was 260 deaths per 10,000 dog years at risk. For breed-specific calculations, the analyses were limited to 70 breeds, each with at least 500 dogs at risk in either 1992 or 1993.

Reproductive physiologist Ralph L. Brinster, who developed gene-regulation techniques that enabled the introduction of foreign genes into germ lines, won the Bower Award and Prize in Science in 1997. Brinster was able to produce "super" mice by introducing the rat growth-hormone gene into the germ line of mice.

The four breeds at highest risk were Irish wolfhounds, Bernese mountain dogs, Great Danes, and St. Bernards, and the five breeds with the lowest risk were the standard poodle, toy and miniature poodles, Finnish spitz, and Irish soft-coated wheaten terrier. Mixed-breed dogs, on the other hand, were uniformly located in the low-risk category.

Awards to veterinarians

The Franklin Institute in Philadelphia awarded its Bower Award and Prize in Science to Ralph L. Brinster, Richard King Mellon professor of reproductive physiology at the University of Pennsylvania School of Veterinary Medicine. Brinster developed gene-regulation techniques that enabled the introduction of foreign genes into germ lines and passage of these genes to offspring. He was able to produce "super" mice by introducing the rat growth-hormone gene into the germ line of mice.

Thomas J. Lane, an extension veterinarian at the University of Florida, received the 1997 Bustad Companion Animal Veterinarian-of-the-Year Award. The award recognized veterinarians who had made major contributions to the human-animal bond. One of Lane's contributions was establishing a pet assistance program for people with AIDS or other life-threatening illnesses.

The British Small Animal Veterinary Association Bourgelat Award was presented to Kirk Gelatt, professor of comparative ophthalmology and former dean of the University of Florida College of Veterinary Medicine, for his contributions to veterinary ophthalmology.

—John M. Bowen

PHYSICS

Physicists during the past year demonstrated "quantum teleportation," a provocatively named strategy for instantaneously transferring certain properties of one particle to another. They also built the first-ever computer that uses the quantum properties of atoms to process calculations and announced their observation of the rarest decay of a subatomic particle yet seen. Nuclear scientists had their first glimpse of light emitted directly from an atomic nucleus, and researchers studying matter in the solid state demonstrated new electronic devices that manipulate single electrons and confirmed the existence of particle-like entities that carry only one-third of the electron's charge.

ATOMIC, MOLECULAR, AND OPTICAL PHYSICS

Measuring light from an atom

Physicists in Germany made the most precise measurement to date of the ultraviolet light radiated by a hydrogen atom. Their technique will allow scientists to perform increasingly demanding tests of quantum mechanics, the modern theory describing the behavior of the atom, and to better understand the properties of the light from state-of-the-art lasers.

Hydrogen consists of just two subatomic particles, a negatively charged electron bound to a much heavier, positively charged proton. In the simplest picture, the electron can be thought to orbit the proton, similar to the way in which the Earth revolves around the Sun. The higher the electron's orbit, the greater is its energy.

When the electron drops from a higher energy level to a lower one, it releases an electromagnetic wave to get rid of the excess energy. The wave has a precise frequency, and a determination of that frequency yields the energy difference between the two orbital levels. Measuring the frequency of electromagnetic waves, therefore, can yield a blueprint of the electron's energy levels in the atom.

A wave's frequency is determined by the number of wave fronts passing a given point per second; the more closely spaced the wave fronts, the higher is the frequency. For electromagnetic waves in the microwave part of the spectrum, for example, the frequency is on the order of a billion wave fronts, or a billion complete wave cycles, per second. Whereas electronic circuits can be used to measure microwave frequencies, no electronic equipment devised to date can make similar measurements of electromagnetic waves in the infrared, visible, or ultraviolet region of the spectrum; their frequencies are just too high.

Theodor Hänsch and his colleagues at the Max Planck Institute for Quantum Optics, Garching, Ger., solved this problem by taking advantage of a wave phenomenon known as a beat. On a piano, for example, a beat is heard when two keys corresponding to notes of slightly different frequencies are struck at the same time. The resulting note has a frequency that is the average of the two, but the listener also hears the intensity of the sound wavering up and down at a lower "beat frequency," which is equal to the difference between the two original frequencies.

With their technique the researchers were able to measure precisely the frequency of ultraviolet light needed to boost a hydrogen atom's electron from its lowest-energy level (named $1s$) to a higher level ($2s$). They first shone a dye-laser beam on a gas of hydrogen atoms and tuned the beam frequency until the sample's electrons underwent the $1s$–$2s$ energy transition at a maximum rate. This told them that their laser was tuned to one-half of the energy difference between levels. (The $1s$–$2s$ transition is a special "two-photon" transition in which the electron must absorb two packets of light energy, or photons, to make the energy jump.)

Next, the researchers turned on a reference laser having a well-known frequency. Then a series of lasers were used to produce light at frequencies between those of the dye and reference lasers. The first laser in the series produced light at the exact midpoint of the dye- and reference-laser frequencies, the second laser generated light halfway between this midpoint and the dye-laser frequency, and so on, until the final laser in the series produced light at a frequency sufficiently close to that of the dye laser. Mixing this light with the dye laser light produced a beat frequency in the microwave range, which could then be measured with standard electronic equipment. Combined with the knowledge of the reference laser's frequency, the measured beat signal was used to reconstruct the precise frequency of the $1s$–$2s$ transition.

The researchers obtained a frequency value of $2.46606141318734 \times 10^{15}$ Hz (cycles per second) for the $1s$–$2s$ transition, with an uncertainty of only 0.3 parts in a trillion, exceeding the accuracy of previous measurements by almost 100 times. This technique can be applied to any infrared, visible, or ultraviolet light radiated by the hydrogen atom or any other object.

Quantum teleportation

In a development that captured the imaginations of Star Trek fans and others worldwide, two groups of physicists based in Austria and Italy independently demonstrated a scheme known as quantum teleportation. Originally proposed in 1993 by Charles Bennett of the IBM Thomas J. Watson Research Center, Yorktown Heights, N.Y., and his colleagues, quantum teleportation allowed the researchers to transfer the properties of a photon—namely, its polarization, the direction in which its electric field vibrates—to another photon even though the particles were isolated from each other. What is important to note is that the photon's properties were teleported, not the photon itself.

In experiments performed at Innsbruck (Austria) University, Dik Bouwmeester and his colleagues first prepared a pair of photons that were quantum mechanically "entangled." According to quantum theory, a photon's polarization can exist in all of its possible states simultaneously and is not defined until a measurement is made on it. Nevertheless, if one photon of an entangled pair is later measured to have a particular polarization, say, a horizontal one (in which its electric field vibrates parallel to some horizontal plane), then the other photon is instantly defined as having the complementary state of vertical polarization (in which the electric field vibrates perpendicularly to the horizontal plane). In the Innsbruck experiment, one of the entangled photons (which can be called photon A to distinguish it from its partner, photon B) was sent to an optical device. It arrived at the same time as a third, distinct "message photon" (photon M), which carried the polarization value to be teleported.

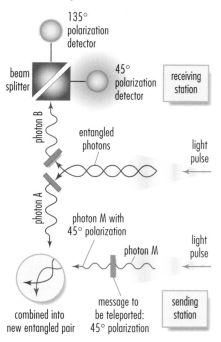

Quantum Teleportation

In quantum teleportation experiments, physicists in Austria polarized a photon, M, at a 45° angle. They also prepared a pair of entangled photons, A and B, and sent photon A to become entangled with photon M. Although photons M and B were not in contact, B took on M's polarization value.

AIP/Discovery Communications

The researchers had endowed photon M with a polarization value of 45° relative to the horizontal plane. At the device, photons M and A themselves became entangled. Since photon A's polarization now had to be complementary to that of photon M, photon B was forced to assume the same polarization value as photon M's. In other words, although M and B had never been in direct contact, B was branded with M's polarization value.

Another version of quantum teleportation was demonstrated by Francesco De Martini of the University of Rome and his colleagues in Italy and England. Whereas the Innsbruck experiment teleported the polarization value of a third, message photon to one of the entangled photons, this demonstration transferred the polarization value of one of the entangled photons to its partner.

The technique can work for any quantum-scale particles, such as electrons, atoms, or molecules. Although there is no physical law against it, researchers believed that it would be impractical or technologically infeasible to apply this strategy to large objects such as humans or even bacteria, since quantum properties such as entanglement break down quickly for large-scale objects. Furthermore, quantum teleportation cannot be used as the basis for faster-than-light information transfer because the parties at both ends of such a system must still compare notes by phone or some other conventional means of communication to verify that teleportation has occurred properly or make any adjustments to the particle at the receiving end to ensure success. Nonetheless, teleportation will have applications in transmitting information by the use of quantum-scale particles, such as in quantum computing, and in transferring short-lived or rare quantum states to other, more stable quantum systems for further study.

The first quantum computer

Physicists in the U.S. announced that they had built a primitive version of a quantum computer, a device that uses the properties of single quantum-scale particles (such as atoms) to perform calculations. The announcement followed on the heels of an earlier achievement in which researchers built a quantum-scale version of a logic gate. (See *1998 Yearbook of Science and the Future* Year in Review: PHYSICS: *Atomic, Molecular, and Optical Physics.*) The building blocks of computer processors, logic gates process the binary digits, or bits (0s and 1s), used to carry out calculations.

Constructed by Neil Gershenfeld of the Massachusetts Institute of Technology (MIT) and Isaac Chuang, currently at the IBM Almaden Research Center, San Jose, Calif., the quantum computer was limited to adding two small numbers and finding one of four items in a search. Nevertheless, more complex quantum computers have the potential to be exponentially faster than conventional computers in performing tasks such as searching astronomically huge databases and factoring the extremely large numbers used as the basis for top-secret codes.

The physicists demonstrated an unexpected way to make a quantum computer based on a cup of liquid, specifically one containing an organic molecule, the amino acid alanine. In the presence of a magnetic field, the molecule's atomic nuclei can act like tiny bar magnets. A quantum property called spin describes how a nucleus responds to an external magnetic field.

In the researchers' experiment, one in every million nuclei in the alanine liquid entered a spin state in which its internal magnet was aligned with that of the outside field. Subsequent radio pulses then carried out calculations by exploiting the fact that the spin of a particular nucleus could affect the spin of a different nucleus in the same molecule or in a neighboring one. In all, there were as many as four distinct spins in the molecule that the re-searchers could control with radio pulses of different frequencies. By using radio pulses to manipulate the spins of two carbon nuclei in the alanine molecule, the physicists carried out the arithmetic operation $1+1=2$. By choosing more complex molecules, the researchers believed that they could create quantum computing devices with 10 distinct spins, which would allow them to perform slightly more sophisticated tasks such as factoring the number 15.

Quantum computers are potentially much more powerful than these early successes might suggest because they have the ability to perform multiple mathematical calculations simultaneously. Whereas a bit in ordinary computers can exist only as a 0 or a 1, the spin of a nucleus can be put into a combination or "superposition" of multiple states that, for example, can represent a 0 and a 1 at the same time. Physicists caution, however, that such superpositions break down quickly, especially when they are disturbed by attempts to retrieve information from them. In addition, the uncertainty principle limits the amount of information that can be retrieved from quantum calculation. Despite these problems and others, such devices will bring about insights into how to process information at the level of quantum particles.

Exploding clusters

In recent years scientists have intensively studied the properties of clusters, aggregates of atoms or molecules held together by chemical forces. Because they are larger than individual atoms or molecules, but smaller than bulk solids, clusters have unique properties. Researchers in England discovered a new surprise in their properties when they trained light on a cluster.

Using an ultrashort burst of laser light, Todd Ditmire and his colleagues of Imperial College, London, heated up and exploded a cluster of about 2,500 xenon atoms. Their laser delivered a pulse of light lasting just 150 femtoseconds (quadril-lionths of a second). Such femtosecond lasers can produce extremely powerful bursts of light, since their energy is concentrated into a small spot over a short time span. The laser in the experiment delivered a burst of power comparable to focusing all the power that the Sun delivers to the Earth's surface onto the head of a pin.

To their surprise, the researchers discovered that the exploding cluster produced extremely high-velocity xenon ions possessing energies as high as one million electron volts in their motion. This energy was tens of thousands of times greater than that possessed by ions produced in similar femtosecond-laser explosions of molecules containing just 2–10 atoms, and it was thousands of times greater than the energy of ions ejected from bulk solids with femtosecond lasers.

Although it remains a mystery as to why the xenon ions emerged from the clusters at such high energies, further investigation may provide deep insights into how light interacts with clusters. Moreover, the current experiments have raised the possibility of carrying out tabletop nuclear-fusion experiments. Specifically, intense femtosecond light pulses would be shone on a cluster of deuterium and tritium atoms, the fuel of nuclear-fusion reactions. The ions produced in the resulting explosion may

Model of Elementary Particles

key: R = red, G = green, B = blue

electric charge / color charge / symbol / name / mass

	three generations of matter (fermions)			force carriers (gauge bosons)	
	I	**II**	**III**		
quarks	$+2/3$ R,G,B u up 2–8 MeV	$+2/3$ R,G,B c charm 1–1.6 GeV	$+2/3$ R,G,B t top/truth 176±6 GeV	0 0 γ photon 0	electromagnetism
	$-1/3$ R,G,B d down 5–15 MeV	$-1/3$ R,G,B s strange 100–300 MeV	$-1/3$ R,G,B b bottom/beauty 4.1–4.5 GeV	0 R,G,B g gluon 0	strong interaction
leptons	0 0 ν_e electron neutrino less than 7 eV	0 0 ν_μ muon neutrino less than 170 keV	0 0 ν_τ tau neutrino less than 31 MeV	± 1 0 $W^\pm$ W boson 80.400±0.075 GeV	weak interactions
	-1 0 e electron 0.511 MeV	-1 0 μ muon 105.658 MeV	-1 0 τ tau less than 24 MeV	0 0 Z^0 Z boson 91.187 GeV	

The known elementary particles can be grouped into a "periodic table" of quarks, leptons, and gauge bosons, the last of which mediate the basic forces, or interactions, between particles. Quarks and leptons form three generations, or families, each containing two quarks, a neutral lepton, and a charged lepton.

have sufficiently high energies and temperatures to bring about the conditions needed to initiate fusion reactions.

Awards

In addition to sharing the 1997 Nobel Prize for Physics (see SCIENTISTS OF THE YEAR: *Nobel Prizes*), William D. Phillips of the National Institute of Standards and Technology (NIST), Gaithersburg, Md., won the American Physical Society's 1998 Arthur L. Schawlow Prize for his pioneering efforts in cooling and trapping atoms with laser light. The 1997 King Faisal International Prize in Science and a $200,000 award went to Eric Cornell and Carl Weiman, both at JILA, a joint research institute of NIST and the University of Colorado at Boulder. They won the prize for having helped to create the first Bose-Einstein condensate, a new state of matter predicted from the work of Satyendra Nath Bose and Albert Einstein in the 1920s.

—Ben P. Stein

ELEMENTARY-PARTICLE PHYSICS

Elementary-particle physics, the study of the basic building blocks of matter and the forces by which they interact, involves the use of particle accelerators and associated detectors to record the particle collisions achieved in the accelerators. These massive facilities can be viewed as specialized microscopes for examining the structure of matter at the shortest distance scales. In early 1998 the most powerful such microscope in the world remained the Tevatron, located at the Fermi National Accelerator Laboratory (Fermilab), Batavia, Ill. The

high-energy collisions of protons and antiprotons at the Tevatron can produce the heaviest, and shortest-lived, of all known elementary particles—the top quark and its antimatter counterpart, the antitop quark, which were discovered at Fermilab in 1995.

Brief history of the leptoquark

Early in 1997 considerable excitement occurred at the HERA collider, located at the DESY (German Electron Synchroton) laboratory, Hamburg. HERA, which collides electrons or positrons (antimatter electrons) with protons, has been used largely to explore the internal structure of the proton. A total of 12 rare scattering events were seen at HERA by two particle-detector collaborations (H1 and ZEUS), all in positron-proton collisions at the very highest energies (shortest distances) observable in the machine. The standard model, the central theoretical description of all the known particles and their interactions

(with the exception of gravity), predicts about one such event in the same energy range. This discrepancy indicated the possibility of the existence of a new kind of elementary particle, called a leptoquark.

Leptoquarks are particles that, like the constituent quarks of protons and neutrons, participate in strong interactions, but they also share some of the properties of electrons, positrons, and other leptons. Leptoquarks are anticipated in many theories that go beyond the standard model in trying to explain features of nature that the standard model cannot, such as the origin of the masses of the fundamental particles. In the 12 positron-proton collision events, it appeared as if the positron had combined with a quark in the proton to make a leptoquark having the properties of a bound state of the two particles. Technical problems, however, made insufficient positron-proton data available for further analysis.

The hint of a leptoquark at HERA was able to be checked quickly with Fermilab

Tevatron data. Leptoquarks, if they exist, would also be produced in the kind of high-energy proton-antiproton collisions available in the Tevatron. After its production a leptoquark would decay almost immediately into a quark and a lepton and could be identified by looking for these decay products. The energetic "naked" quark produced in the decay would immediately "dress" itself by transforming into a jet of particles. Jets are very highly collimated or focused blasts of outgoing particles in a collision that indicate the motion of the original source particle. The lepton from the decay would be either an electron or a neutrino. An electron would be easily identified in the Tevatron's detector, and a neutrino would be identified by an amount of "missing" energy in the collision event—energy that could not be accounted for after a tally of all the detected particles, since neutrinos interact very rarely and almost always escape the detector, carrying their energy away. Both the CDF and D0 particle-detector collaborations at the Tevatron searched for decay-product signatures that would indicate the production of pairs of leptoquarks while taking care to eliminate other interactions that could "fake" leptoquark events by exhibiting the same final products. They saw no events that could be attributed to leptoquarks.

The likelihood of producing a pair of leptoquarks depends on their mass. The more massive a leptoquark is, the less likely it is that a pair of them will be produced in a collision. Theorists have performed calculations that predict the expected number of leptoquarks on the basis of mass; therefore, the number detected in an experiment can be used to determine a limit on the mass of the leptoquark. The

CDF and D0 groups established that if leptoquarks always decay into an electron and a quark, their lack of appearance in the Tevatron data indicates that they are more massive than about 225 GeV (billion electron volts), which was well above the mass associated with the events seen at HERA. By the end of 1997, with roughly twice as much data collected, no additional leptoquark candidates had emerged in HERA experiments. Hence, over the course of the past year, the tantalizing possibility of discovering a leptoquark stimulated a lot of activity but failed to become reality.

Rare processes and particles

A research collaboration at Brookhaven National Laboratory, Upton, N.Y., in 1997 observed the decay of the K^+ meson (kaon) into a π^+ meson (pion) and a neutrino and antineutrino. This is the rarest decay of a subatomic particle ever detected. The phenomenon is thought to happen only once or twice in every 10 billion decays of the K^+. Physicists had to sift through 100 times that number—that is, one trillion ordinary decays—to achieve the one-in-10 billion level of sensitivity required. Study of these rare decay processes provided detailed information about the standard model and had the potential to reveal signs of very-short-distance (high-energy) phenomena not expected in the model.

Usually a K^+ decays though the momentary creation of a charged W boson, which then decays into two pions or two leptons such as a muon and a neutrino. (Although the W boson is hundreds of times heavier than the kaon, this decay process can occur by the uncertainty principle of quantum mechanics.) Nevertheless, the standard

model also predicts a rare decay mode for the K^+ that involves the momentary creation of both a charged W boson and a neutral Z boson; the W boson decays into a π^+, and the Z boson decays into a neutrino-antineutrino pair. This process can also involve the momentary creation of the very massive top and antitop quarks.

The rare kaon decays were studied in the E787 experiment at Brookhaven's Alternating Gradient Synchrotron (AGS), which was capable of producing the world's most intense kaon beam. Just as important to such studies as an intense beam is a detector array sensitive enough to catch the decays of the kaons. Once produced, kaons last only about 12 billionths of a second before decaying via a large number of different modes, creating showers of particles that can be seen only with specialized equipment. The apparatus used in the E787 experiment was sensitive enough to examine one million decays per second. In thousands of gigabytes of data, E787 observed one event that could be explained no other way than in terms of the rare kaon decay being sought. However, the number of rare kaon decay events predicted by the standard model is only one-tenth of that seen in the experiment. Thus, the experiment may have uncovered evidence for a new physical process that enhances the rare kaon decay rate above the predicted level. On the other hand, it may simply have observed an upward statistical fluctuation. In any case, physicists were looking forward with great interest to more data from this experiment and others.

Fermilab also was capable of producing intense kaon beams, and dedicated experiments to search for other kaon decay processes—such as the decay of a neutral kaon into a neutral pion and two neutrinos—were under consideration at both Fermilab and Brookhaven. These processes provide a very detailed look into the mysterious CP-violating interactions (weak interactions that violate the combined conservation laws associated with charge conjugation and parity). CP-violating interactions, which are required for the formation of matter in the universe, are the only interactions in nature that depend upon the direction of the flow of time.

Brookhaven physicists also found evidence for an "exotic meson." The laboratory's experiment E852 studied collisions produced when an 18-GeV AGS proton beam hit a target of liquid hydrogen in the Multi-Particle Spectrometer. The physicists employed complicated statistical methods to analyze their data and observed evidence for an extremely short-lived bound state believed to be an exotic hybrid meson composed of a quark, an antiquark, and a single gluon (the particle that mediates the strong interaction between quarks in particles such as protons, neutrons, and mesons). Such states are predicted in the standard model but had never before been seen. E852 may have provided the first experimental evidence for their existence.

Future machines

In late 1997 the U.S. formally agreed to participate in the construction and operation of the Large Hadron Collider (LHC) at CERN (European Laboratory for Particle Physics) near Geneva. According to the official agreement, signed December 8 by U.S. Secretary of Energy Federico Peña and CERN Director General Christopher Llewellyn Smith, the U.S. will contribute

$531 million to the project (a figure that is capped regardless of cost overruns) and will actively participate in use of the machine. The LHC will be a proton-proton collider with an initial energy of 5 TeV (trillion electron volts) per beam, which will be raised eventually to 7 TeV per beam. This capability contrasts with that of the Fermilab Tevatron, which is a proton-antiproton collider with energy of 1 TeV per beam. The LHC is scheduled to begin operation in 2005, will use the existing 27-km (17-mi)-diameter tunnel that currently houses the Large Electron Positron (LEP) accelerator-collider facility, and will cost as much as $6 billion. A fourth of all U.S. high-energy experimental physicists will participate in its construction and use and will have an appropriate role in management decisions. (*See* Year in Review: SCIENCE POLICY.)

Among the various options under consideration for future machines in the U.S. were (1) a very-high-energy hadron collider with a total collision energy as high as 100 TeV, (2) a large electron-positron linear collider with a total collision energy as high as 1.5 TeV, and (3) a muon collider. The muon collider idea was so novel and so bizarre that many physicists refused to accept that it may be possible, some claiming that it would be as difficult to build as a "starship engine." Nonetheless, an increasingly large component of the particle-physics community was coming to believe that such a machine may be feasible and that it may offer the best future pathway for the U.S. high-energy physics program. The machine would take unstable muons (with lifetimes of a millionth of a second), which would be produced by an accelerator upgrade of Fermilab's Booster machine

or Brookhaven's AGS, and instantaneously accelerate them to high energies. A machine with muon beam energies of about 4 TeV would fit on the Fermilab or Brookhaven site yet offer the discovery potential of proton-proton colliders with beam energies several times higher. Moreover, unlike an electron-positron collider, a muon collider could directly produce the Higgs boson, a hypothetical particle associated with the origin of the masses of all particles. In 1998 the muon collider idea was undergoing feasibility studies, with several known technical hurdles to be overcome. Nonetheless, it would be a tragedy if politics somehow shaped the future of the science such that remarkable new avenues of research came to be closed off in favor of something much less effective and potentially much more expensive.

—Christopher T. Hill

NUCLEAR PHYSICS

New address for Gammasphere

The months of 1997 were both turbulent and full of expectations for a device called Gammasphere. Built at California's Lawrence Berkeley National Laboratory in the early 1990s, Gammasphere started full operation there in late 1995. After two years of exceptional science, Gammasphere was moved east to a new home at Argonne (Ill.) National Laboratory.

The nucleus of an atom is composed of protons and neutrons. Although the nucleus contains the majority of an atom's mass, it takes up only a tiny amount of the atom's total volume. An atom's radius is about 50,000 times larger than the radius of its nucleus—roughly analogous to a pea sitting in the center of a large gymnasium. Although scientists have been able to observe individual atoms with powerful new types of microscopes, because the nucleus is so much smaller than an atom, it still can be studied only indirectly. Nuclear physicists study a nucleus by watching what it ejects.

Gammasphere is one of the world's best machines for watching a nucleus give off radiation. It consists of a metal sphere 1.8 m (6 ft) across that is riddled with a honeycomb pattern of 110 holes. The holes house detectors containing large crystals of germanium that are very sensitive to high-energy photons called gamma rays. (Photons are the particle-like packets of energy that make up electromagnetic radiation.) When a gamma-ray photon hits a detector, it interacts with electrons in the crystal. The crystals are so efficient that they multiply the signal created by a single incoming photon hundreds of thousands or even millions of times. This signal, in the form of an electric charge pulse, carries information about the energy of the gamma ray.

With 110 germanium detectors working together, physicists have been able to follow very complex nuclear reactions that emit many gamma rays in an instant. Recording the number of gamma rays, their respective directions in three dimensions, and their respective energies is crucial to the work of explaining the details of what happens inside a nucleus. Gammasphere is about 100 times more efficient at those tasks than previous detection tools.

Many experiments that make use of Gammasphere involve bombarding a very thin piece of target material with a high-energy beam of ions (atoms missing some of their electrons). At sufficiently high en-

Many of the 110 radially arranged germanium detectors are visible in this image of the partially assembled Gammasphere. At the center of the detectors is a chamber where energetic, gamma-ray-emitting nuclei are produced by bombardment of a target material with an ion beam.

ergy the nuclei in the target and the beam fuse to form new nuclei. The new nuclei are highly energetic; they lose that extra energy by giving off many gamma rays all at once. The properties of the gamma rays tell scientists the shape of the nucleus. Stable nuclei are often nearly spherical. Under special, high-energy conditions, however, they can become shaped like a rugby ball (known as superdeformation), a pear, or even a diamond.

Between September and December 1997, scientists disassembled Gammasphere in California and reassembled it, one detector at a time, at Argonne National Laboratory, where it resumed full operation in early January 1998. At its former Lawrence Berkeley location, it had enjoyed great success (see *A new type of nuclear excitation,* below), and scientists working with the device fully expect this to continue at Argonne.

Nuclear physicists plan to use Gammasphere in conjunction with Argonne's Fragment Mass Analyzer, a device that precisely tracks and identifies the debris of nuclear collisions and reactions. After excited nuclei are created, the Fragment Mass Analyzer will watch for the most interesting collision fragments and signal Gammasphere that they are on the way.

Teaming Gammasphere with the large particle accelerators available at Lawrence Berkeley and Argonne makes it possible to create and study some of the heaviest known nuclei. Typically these nuclei do not exist in nature. Because only a few nuclei are produced in an experiment, Gammasphere's unmatched efficiency should help scientists learn much more about them. (For a discussion of the synthesis of very heavy elements, see *1998 Yearbook of Science and the Future* Year in Review: PHYSICS: *Nuclear Physics.*)

Furthermore, scientists expect to use Gammasphere to study nuclei that occupy a highly unstable and short-lived region "over the $N=Z$ line." The phrase is in reference to a map of all the atomic nuclei on which the number of neutrons (N, the horizontal coordinate) for a given nucleus is plotted against the number of protons (Z, the vertical coordinate). (*See* the Figure on the opposite page.)

All nuclei prefer to have at least as many neutrons as protons, and the larger nuclei, those containing more than about 40 protons and neutrons in all, prefer to have more neutrons than protons. For example, the most prevalent isotope of the stable element iron is iron-56, which contains 26 protons and 30 neutrons. Every element has a number of different isotopes, each containing the same number of protons but

Map of the Nuclei

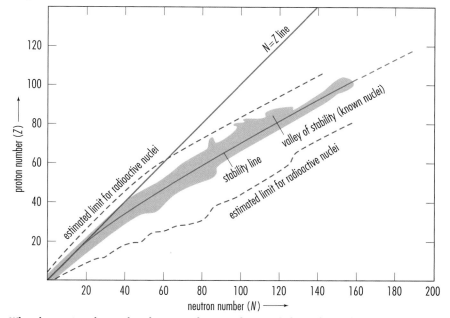

When the atomic nuclei are plotted on a two-dimensional map with the number of their neutrons (**N**) and protons (**Z**) as coordinates, their positions form a "peninsula" of stable nuclei bordered by outlying "reefs" of radioactive nuclei. The **N=Z** line defines nuclei that have equal numbers of protons and neutrons.

different numbers of neutrons. The more massive the nucleus, the greater is the preferred ratio of neutrons to protons.

Nuclei with too many protons either split apart into two smaller nuclei (fission) or emit alpha particles (particles containing two protons and two neutrons), losing mass until they become stable. A nucleus that has just as many neutrons as protons is said to be on the $N=Z$ line of the nuclear map. Larger nuclei that are on the $N=Z$ line have proved to be unstable. In the rare cases that a nucleus has fewer neutrons than protons, its position on the nuclear map is said to be "over the $N=Z$ line." A very unstable and largely unexplored realm of physics exists on that side of the line, and scientists expect experiments with Gammasphere to shed light on this realm.

A new type of nuclear excitation

Before it was moved, Gammasphere helped open a new window to understanding nuclei. The nuclei formed in the collision between a target and an ion beam are generally spinning very fast. After studying energetic lead nuclei that were formed this way, however, researchers found that they were not spinning as expected.

The laws of quantum mechanics say that a spherical nucleus cannot store excess energy by spinning, since it is impossible to know if such a nucleus is spinning. By analogy, a perfect glass sphere has no unique reference points; it would look the same from all directions whether spinning or not. Because excited lead nuclei are spherical, researchers were shocked to see that the gamma rays that they emitted appeared to be coming from a rugby-ball–shaped, superdeformed nucleus. To recon-

cile this with quantum mechanics, it was suggested that there must be something about these spherical nuclei that made it possible to tell that they were rotating. Again, by analogy, if the glass sphere had a tiny bubble near the surface, it would now be possible to tell that it was spinning. Similarly, because the nucleus comprises protons and neutrons, it can have an internal structure that appears different from different directions. Several protons and neutrons near the surface of the nucleus might move in such a way as to produce current loops that could help show which way the nucleus is pointing at a given instant. These currents would produce a magnetic dipole that rotates with the nucleus and causes it to radiate gamma rays rather like an antenna. This proposed phenomenon was dubbed magnetic rotation.

The recent Gammasphere experiments confirmed this model through precise measurements of gamma-ray emission at high excitation energies. In general, nuclear structure research has focused on highly excited nuclei, since under extreme duress they tend to reveal more about their inner workings than they do in a quiescent state. In addition, these energetic, deformed nu-

clei give scientists an opportunity to study matter in the extreme conditions that might exist in particle accelerators or in intriguing astronomical objects like neutron stars and white dwarfs.

Light from a nucleus

On the opposite end of the nuclear energy scale, researchers exploring the lowest energy level of all known nuclei got their first glimpse of visible green light from a nucleus. Most electromagnetic radiation emitted by nuclei is so energetic that it takes in the form of gamma rays, well out of the range of visible light. The lowest excited energy state of the nucleus of thorium-229, however, is so close to the unexcited, or ground, state that when the excited nucleus relaxes, it emits ultraviolet light. The ultraviolet light, in turn, excites some of the electrons around the nucleus, which then give off green light. The phenomenon is especially interesting because it suggested the rare possibility of a nucleus directly exchanging energy with an atom or molecule. Atoms commonly emit radiation in the visible-light range of the electromagnetic spectrum. For example, when something burns, excited atoms give off light corresponding to their characteristic energies—natural gas burns with a bluish light, whereas a wooden matchstick burns with an orange-colored flame. That light, however, comes not from the nucleus but from the electrons that orbit the nucleus.

Though convincing and successful, the experiments were difficult to perform. The researchers started with samples of uranium-233, whose nuclei decayed to ^{229}Th by giving off an alpha particle. Unfortunately, uranium is luminescent and, like a watch hand coated with radium paint, uranium atoms give off a greenish glow. This glow complicated the task of confidently measuring light from the nuclei of ^{229}Th.

Solar neutrinos

Scientists from Aarhus University, Århus, Den., teamed with scientists from the U.S. to make crucial contributions to nuclear astrophysics in 1997. An ongoing quandary in physics concerns a conspicuous lack of neutrinos coming from the Sun. (See 1998 Yearbook of Science and the Future Year in Review: PHYSICS: Nuclear Physics.) Neutrinos are elusive, supposedly massless subatomic particles that interact only infrequently with matter. They are the by-products of many nuclear reactions.

Physicists have considered two explanations to account for the puzzling measured deficit of neutrinos originating in the Sun's nuclear reactions. Either they do not correctly understand the nuclear reactions inside the Sun, in which case their theoretical models erroneously predict more neutrinos than the Sun actually generates, or they do not correctly understand neu-

trino behavior. The latter case has been the subject of much speculation because it would significantly change the accepted standard model of particle physics, the central theory that describes the fundamental particles and most of their interactions.

In 1997 scientists carefully studied recent astronomical data from the Sun, hoping to either confirm or overturn accepted beliefs about the Sun's nuclear reactions. The data came from a group of experiments in a field known as helioseismology. Much like terrestrial seismologists study the interior of the Earth, astrophysicists studied the density and temperature of the Sun's interior by measuring the speed of sound waves moving through it. Determining the temperature at different depths of the solar interior helped them estimate the number of neutrinos that the Sun should be emitting.

The researchers found that the accepted models of the Sun described the experimental data almost perfectly. The largest difference between the quantities measured by helioseismology and those predicted by leading solar models was only 0.2%, or one part in 500. This finding, however, did not explain the measured deficit of solar neutrinos. In fact, it placed the onus clearly on the community of particle physicists, who apparently now must adjust their ideas about neutrino properties and behavior.

By the end of 1997, many physicists believed that solar neutrinos "oscillated" on their trip to Earth. This means that they changed from one of the three types of neutrino to another type while in transit. Physicists believe that such a metamorphosis could happen only if neutrinos have mass.

Allowing one tiny particle to gain a little mass might sound like a small adjustment to a broad theory like the standard model. Nevertheless, such a change would be as problematic as it would be exciting. For example, physicists believe that neutrinos are very numerous in the universe. According to the big bang theory, about 100 million neutrinos inhabit every cubic meter (1.3 cu yd) of the universe. Discovering that these particles have even a very tiny mass could affect accepted models of the cosmos.

Prizes

Joel Moss of Los Alamos (N.M.) National Laboratory won the 1998 Tom W. Bonner Prize for experimental nuclear physics. The prize committee cited Moss for his leading role in a series of experiments that shed light on the nature of the "glue" that holds neutrons and protons together in the nucleus. In their experiments Moss and his colleagues guided highly energetic beams of protons at nuclear targets. In many of the subsequent collisions, pairs of particles called muons were created. By sensitively measuring the properties of these muons, Moss and his colleagues were able to probe the laws that govern the behavior of the nuclear constituents.

John Bahcall of the Institute for Advanced Study, Princeton, N.J., won the 1998 Hans Bethe Prize for Nuclear Astrophysics. The prize committee cited Bahcall's contributions to the ongoing investigation of solar neutrinos. Bahcall was one of the physicists who showed that the lack of observed solar neutrinos cannot be blamed on the Sun's inner workings.

—Brandon R. Brown

CONDENSED-MATTER PHYSICS

Single-electron devices

The year 1997 marked the centennial of the British physicist J.J. Thomson's discovery of the electron, made at the Cavendish Laboratory of the University of Cambridge. Fittingly, the year brought important progress in single-electron devices, including a breakthrough in controlling electric current at the one-electron level.

All methods aimed at producing such "quantized currents" use an oscillator to control a device that puts out one electron per oscillation. Devices that couple radio-frequency oscillators to electron-tunneling devices have been developed, but their output currents have been very small (about a trillionth of an ampere), which limits their application. In the past year a group led by Michael Pepper of the Cavendish Laboratory reported that quantized currents can be produced by the use of sound waves to sweep electrons along the surface of a semiconductor. Currents so produced were nearly 1,000 times larger than those previously available from any quantized-current source.

The Cambridge device achieves single-electron control in a particularly elegant manner. A sound wave is set up on the surface of a gallium arsenide crystal, and electrons are swept along in the troughs of the wave. In addition to being confined to the surface of the material, the trough-riding electrons are guided along a very narrow channel. In this extreme (*i.e.,* one-dimensional) geometry, their mutual repulsion plays a crucial role, ensuring that they are spread out uniformly along the wave. By adjusting a superimposed electric field, the number of electrons per wave trough can be reduced to just one. Under those circumstances, as the wave passes over a collection point, electrons are deposited one at a time. The output current, which depends on the number of troughs that pass the collection point each second, is then simply the sound frequency multiplied by the charge on an electron. The sound frequency lies in the microwave region, 1,000 times higher than the radio frequencies used in tunneling devices. Hence, the output current is 1,000 times larger. Among other uses, current sources of this type are contenders for providing a practical standard for electric current.

The past year was also the 50th anniversary of the invention of the transistor, widely acknowledged to be the most useful contribution of 20th-century physics to daily life. In response to the unflagging demand for increased computer speed and power, transistor size has been steadily whittled down over the years. Nonetheless, storage of a single bit of information still requires the movement of about a million electrons onto a tiny plate, or gate, inside the device. To store a bit of information with a single electron, the width of this already microscopic gate must be scaled down to the order of a millionth of a centimeter. A number of laboratory devices have achieved such single-electron storage, but none has proved to be well suited to large-scale integration. Important progress toward this goal was announced early in 1997 when a silicon single-electron transistor memory device operating at room temperature was demonstrated by a group of investigators at the University of Minnesota led by Stephen Chou (currently of Princeton University). The silicon gate of the device is less than a millionth of a centimeter wide, and the development represents a significant step toward the goal of building ultrahigh-density computer memories. At present the chief remaining obstacle to implementation is the high cost of techniques for forming the required structures.

Steven Y. Chou, Lingjie Guo, and Effendi Leobandung (Princeton University/University of Minnesota)

A silicon single-electron transistor memory device is shown in this highly magnified image. The thicker line is a silicon channel; where it crosses the thinner line is a gate on which a single electron, representing one bit of information, is stored.

Fractional charge

The charge on the electron, commonly represented as *e,* appears to establish an insuperable limit on the ability to control location and flow of electric charge. However, coming hard on the heels of the single-electron devices discussed above, experiments demonstrated the existence of particle-like entities carrying a charge only one-third that of the electron, or $e/3$.

The idea of a fractionally charged object is not easy to digest. A firmly established feature of the physical world is that all isolated elementary particles carry electric charge in quantized units of *e.* (Quarks carry fractional charge but are permanently sequestered inside nuclear particles and are never observed in isolation.) Both of the single-electron devices discussed above depend on the charge on the electron being precisely its established value. In some situations, however, the interaction between electrons can lead to qualitatively new properties, not of the electrons themselves but of the whole electron assembly. For example, all superconductors, from pure mercury to the new so-called high-temperature compounds, respond to external stimuli as if they were inhabited by particle-like entities carrying twice the electron's charge. Called Cooper pairs, these entities can form only if the material environment is conducive to superconductivity. Nonetheless, inside a superconductor their behavior mimics that of ordinary particles, and they are referred to as quasiparticles.

In the early 1980s Robert Laughlin, then at the Lawrence Livermore National Laboratory, Livermore, Calif., suggested that novel quasiparticles should be formed in a thin (two-dimensional) layer of electrons placed in a strong magnetic field. In this way he was able to account for certain

striking variations that had been observed in the conductivity of the electron layer as the field was increased. Nonetheless, in the intervening years direct experimental evidence for the most remarkable feature of his quasiparticles—a charge of only $e/3$—remained elusive. In the past year independent groups in Israel and France reported experimental evidence for the existence of these fractionally charged objects. The Israeli group consisted of Mordehai Heiblum, Michael Reznikov, Rafael de-Picciotto, Vladimir Umansky, Diana Mihalu, and Gregori Bunin, all of the Weizmann Institute of Science, Rehovot. The group in France was a collaboration between D. Christian Glattli and Laurent Saminadayar of the Commission of Atomic Energy, Saclay, and Yong Jin and Bernard Etienne of the CNRS (National Center for Scientific Research) Laboratory of Microstructures and Microelectronics, Bagneux.

In both sets of experiments, a thin electron layer was confined at the interface between two gallium arsenide crystals. The temperature was lowered to less than a

tenth of a degree above absolute zero, and a large magnetic field (several tens of teslas) applied perpendicular to the interface. Although the quasiparticles are thought to be formed everywhere inside the electron layer, it turns out that they are able to move freely only in a narrow, essentially one-dimensional channel around its perimeter. By constricting the electron layer in one place, the researchers brought two regions of the conducting channel close together. They observed current flowing between the nearby regions by means of the process of tunneling. Both experiments probed these resulting tunneling currents.

All electric currents, no matter what their microscopic origin, vary slightly from one instant to the next. Small variations are inevitable because charge is transported in discrete, albeit small, units. (Similar variations can be more readily observed in situations involving the flow of mass instead of charge. An example is the hourglass, which uses the smooth flow of sand grains through a constriction to mark the passage of time. Small grains are preferred over large ones, which would produce distracting variations in the flow.) In both of the quasiparticle experiments, the current between the channel regions was so smooth that it could not have originated from the motion of particles carrying the full electronic charge. The experimental verdict was unanimous: the underlying objects carried a charge of only $e/3$.

It is too early to predict what sort of useful devices might emerge from scientists' new ability to produce and monitor the flow of fractionally charged objects. Much remains to be explored; for example, by increasing the magnetic field, research-

Different geometries in a two-dimensional electron layer favor either conventional electron tunneling (left) or quasiparticle tunneling (right). Only electrons (e) can tunnel between conducting perimeter channels separated by an electron-depleted "isthmus," whereas fractionally charged quasiparticles ($e/3$) can tunnel between two channel regions brought close together by a constricted "strait" in the electron layer.

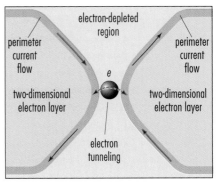
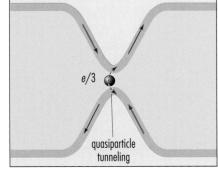

ers should be able to produce quasiparticles carrying an even smaller fractional charge. In addition, there are no clear theoretical predictions (and as yet no measurements) for the quasiparticle's mass. Nonetheless, the prediction and subsequent observation of fractionally charged objects represents a major milestone for condensed-matter physics.

The quantum leak

In sharp contrast to the exotic requirements for the production and movement of fractional charges, a leaking liquid is an everyday phenomenon, a generally unwelcome reminder of the distinction between liquids and solids. The simplest property of a water leak, as anyone with a punctured garden hose has observed, is that the leak rate increases when the water pressure is increased. Indeed, this property seems so obvious that it might be presumed to be a universal characteristic of all leaks.

Condensed-matter theorists have long insisted otherwise. At low temperatures both of helium's stable isotopes, helium-3 and helium-4, condense into special liquids called superfluids. In the superfluid state they display unusual properties that are a consequence of quantum physics. The behavior of a superfluid helium leak is predicted to be particularly odd if the hole is very small. In such a case the fluid should oscillate backward and forward through the hole, the oscillation frequency (rather than the leak rate) being proportional to the pressure.

The striking prediction that superfluid leaks must oscillate is implicit in a theory developed by the British physicist Brian Josephson in the early 1960s. His work actually describes the oscillation of superconducting quasiparticles (the Cooper pairs discussed above) across a thin insulator inserted between two superconductors. A leaky container of ^{3}He bears no obvious resemblance to a leaky superconductor. Nevertheless, it turns out that there is a deep physical analogy between them. In the liquid ^{3}He environment, quasiparticles are formed that consist of pairs of atoms, directly analogous to Cooper pairs of electrons in superconductors. The role of the thin insulator is played by the hole in the ^{3}He container. Because Cooper pairs carry electric charge, their oscillatory leakage is relatively easy to detect, as was done shortly after Josephson's prediction. By contrast, direct observation of the superfluid analogue has eluded experimentalists for more than 30 years.

In 1997 another hunt for the quantum leak was mounted, this time a collaboration between a research group led by Richard Packard and another led by Seamus Davis, both of the University of California, Berkeley. Their container held superfluid ^{3}He. This lighter isotope, whose superfluid behavior was not discovered until the 1970s, offered technical advantages over its heavier relative for the experiment. Nonetheless, the collaboration still faced formidable technical difficulties. Both the length and the diameter of the hole had to be less than a thousandth the thickness of a human hair. In an effort to raise the mass of the fluid oscillations above the inevitable background noise, an array of more than 4,000 such microholes were created in an ultrathin silicon nitride membrane. Even so, oscillations of only a few trillionths of a gram were anticipated, and a special microphone was installed to search for them. The microphone consisted of a membrane built directly into the container wall; the displacements of the membrane were monitored using ultrasensitive techniques developed for the detection of gravity waves.

The researchers found that they could best perform the experiment by first establishing a pressure difference between the two sides of the silicon nitride membrane and then allowing the pressure to slowly equilibrate. Since the oscillation frequency of a quantum leak should decrease as the pressure difference decreases, the researchers hoped that the hole array would produce an oscillation whose frequency gradually decreased. In musical terms, they hoped that the hole "ensemble" would perform a descending glissando, a rapid slide down the musical scale. Given the initial pressure difference, calculations indicted that the initial "note" should lie in the vicinity of top C on the piano. Headphones in place, the Berkeley audience was treated to a note-perfect world premier, the glissando ringing out clearly above the background noise.

The quest to observe the quantum leak was driven by curiosity, and its success promises no respite from the vagaries of domestic plumbing leaks. Nonetheless, an understanding of the way that current leaks between superconductors has led to sensitive electronic devices that can sense minute magnetic fields. With science's new ability to produce and monitor quantum leaks, fluid analogues of these devices—with potential applications as sensitive gyroscopes—become a realistic possibility.

—David E. Farrell

See also Feature Article: THE FORCE IS WITH US.

PSYCHOLOGY

Around the world many psychologists make culture a primary focus for theory and research, whereas others take advantage of new technologies to gain insight into the working of the human brain. These two thrusts are not incompatible because in both cases the ultimate concern is with basic psychological processes. During the past year psychologists made progress toward a better understanding of how these processes are influenced by culture on the one hand and biology on the other.

One legacy of Hans Eysenck, the brilliant and prolific German-born British psychologist who died in September, was the biopsychosocial model, an approach that highlights the importance of the interaction of biological processes with psychological mechanisms and social influences. Contemporary psychology has embraced this model, and the model has been productively applied to a wide array of normal and abnormal phenomena. Past generations of psychologists could be faulted for studying such processes as perception, learning, and memory out of context. A biopsychosocial approach does not move such topics off center stage but rather looks at the larger contexts in which these basic processes are most sensibly located.

It was no coincidence that the American Psychological Foundation 1997 Gold Medal Awards for Life Achievements went to psychologists who had employed broad and integrative approaches of the sort Eysenck advocated. Edward Zigler, whose work centered on economically disadvantaged children and their families, was honored for his contributions to the public interest. With the Head Start programs that Zigler had helped found a generation earlier, psychology had turned its attention

Martha Stewart

Philip Holzman, best known for his studies of the processes involved in schizophrenia, was honored for contributions to the application of psychology.

toward the child as a whole in his or her social context. Theodora Abel was cited for her contributions to the practice of psychology. Throughout her career as a researcher, teacher, therapist, and supervisor, Abel focused on the depth and expanse of human diversity. Raymond Cattell, an early rival of Eysenck, was selected as the recipient of the award for contributions to research in psychological science. Throughout his long career, Cattell applied the statistical technique of factor analysis to such diverse topics as personality, motivation, and abilities. He was concerned with heredity and the environment as well as with the interplay of the two, although his positive views on eugenics led some to protest his award. Owing to these protests, the presentation of the award was post-

poned, and in January 1998 Cattell requested that his name be withdrawn from consideration. He died on February 2. Finally, Philip Holzman was honored for contributions to the application of psychology. His best-known work involved studies of the physiological and psychological processes in schizophrenia.

The newest developments within psychology may be described as extending a biopsychosocial approach in several metaphoric directions—backward (to evolution), downward (to biology), outward (to culture), and inward (to psychological processes). The following is a description of some of the best recent work within each direction.

Backward to evolution

Psychologists have long participated in debates about nature versus nurture, but an important realization by contemporary psychologists is that an evolutionary perspective on behavior complements an environmental perspective. Like the nature of other animals, human nature was molded by evolution. A critical aspect of human nature involves the ability to adapt to a wide range of shifting survival demands. Evolutionary psychologists have therefore focused on these demands.

Recently David Buss of the University of Texas at Austin urged his fellow psychologists to specify and study what he termed evolved psychological mechanisms—*i.e.*, psychological processes shaped by evolution that allow the organism to respond selectively and adaptively to given environmental input. Examples of these mechanisms include the tendency to avoid tastes associated with nausea, to pre-

Evolutionary psychologist Karen Hollis designed and conducted experiments using blue gourami fish to demonstrate how conditioning can help animals increase their reproductive success.

fer fatty foods, to acquire and use language, and to fear snakes. Evolved psychological mechanisms were expected to be numerous and complex, to depend upon context, and to require environmental input (learning) for their development and activation. Each has provided a solution to a survival challenge faced by our species during evolution.

Evolutionary psychologists also have concerned themselves with nonhuman species. For example, Karen Hollis and her colleagues of Mount Holyoke College, South Hadley, Mass., studied blue gourami fish. Males of this species display strong territoriality, attacking other fish that ven-

ture too close to them. This aggressiveness not only keeps away rival males but also counterproductively repels potential mates. Hollis and her team demonstrated that male gourami can learn through classical conditioning to suspend aggressiveness in the presence of receptive females. In a series of training trials spanning 18 days, a bright light was turned on for 10 seconds, and then a female gourami was introduced to a male for 5 minutes. During subsequent test trials in which the light was turned on and a female introduced, male gourami that had experienced the light-female pairing responded less aggressively and spawned more quickly than males that had

not had this experience. This was a compelling illustration of how a psychological process (conditioning) provides an immediate reproductive edge.

Downward to biology

The increasing availability of neural imaging technologies, especially positron emission tomography (PET), has allowed cognitive psychologists to look—literally—into the human brain while people are engaged in complex activities and to draw increasingly precise conclusions about brain regions involved with specific psychological states. During the past year there were, for example, PET studies of verb conjugation, facial-expression recognition, phantom limbs, perceptual illusions, memory encoding and retrieval, stuttering, Braille reading, and schizophrenic hallucinations. As studies like these accumulated, they helped remake both cognitive psychology and neurology by uniting these traditionally separate fields. Some critics worried that the traditional concerns of cognitive psychology were being "reduced" to a neurological level, but the biopsychosocial rejoinder was that these concerns were at long last being placed in ecologically valid contexts.

Outward to culture

One of the important assumptions of the biopsychosocial approach is that social context—including the larger culture—moderates the psychological functioning of individuals, sometimes profoundly. That people from different cultures may exhibit startlingly different ways of thinking and acting has been demonstrated by cross-cultural comparisons of how people explain the causes of events. These causal attributions, whether strictly accurate or not, have widespread effects on how people think, feel, and behave. Studies of causal attribution began in the 1960s in the U.S., and several findings were so common that theorists elevated them to the status of universal psychological laws. More recently, however, when researchers investigated these "laws" among other cultural groups, they found limits to their universality.

One attributional law is the "fundamental attribution error," which holds that people tend to explain the causes of other people's actions in terms of inherent traits, ignoring the role played by situational pressures and demands. Another is "self-enhancement," which maintains that people, when explaining their own behavior, tend to attribute their successes to factors within themselves ("I did well on the test because I am smart") and their failures to factors outside themselves ("I did poorly because the teacher is harsh").

Later research revealed that although individuals in the U.S. display these attributional tendencies, individuals in East Asian cultures do not. Asians were found more likely to take into account situational factors, especially role demands, in explaining the behavior of others and to be modest in explaining the causes of their successes and failures. During the past year Shinobu Kitayama of Kyoto (Japan) University, Hazel Markus of Stanford University, Steven Heine of the University of Pennsylvania, and Darrin Lehman of the University of British Columbia explained these differences in terms of the requirements and values of the individualist culture of the

U.S., where individual achievement is emphasized, and the collectivist culture of Asian countries, where social harmony is paramount.

Another attributional difference noted between people in the U.S. and those in Asian countries is the tendency of Americans to explain academic achievement in terms of innate ability versus the tendency of Asians to emphasize effort. The educational consequences of these differing beliefs are provocative.

Richard Nisbett of the University of Michigan at Ann Arbor and Dov Cohen of the University of Illinois at Champaign-Urbana examined differences between Northern and Southern regional cultures in the U.S. and how these might explain some striking differences in homicide rates in the two regions. Both archival and laboratory data showed that Southern white males were more likely than Northern white males to respond to insults with violence. For example, the homicide rate was especially high in the South in cases of violence that involved persons who knew one another and in those that occurred in the wake of arguments. Nisbett and Cohen proposed that a "culture of honor," derived from economic considerations and an associated glorification of warriors, predominates in the South. More so than the North, the South was settled by people who practiced hunting and herding. Around the world, hunting and herding cultures are more violent than farming or artisan cultures. The culture of honor in the South appeared to be deeply rooted and could indeed be spreading to other regions of the U.S. Although Nisbett and Cohen's explanation was difficult to establish definitively, perhaps the more important point

was that it tried to make sense of violence in complex terms. Psychologists' previous explanations of violence had been simplistic at best, pointing to singular determinants (*e.g.*, frustration, poverty, or warm climate) with no reference to a cultural context.

Inward to psychological processes

One of the more notable recent occurrences in the field of psychology was the conclusion by experimental researchers that unconscious psychological processes indeed exist. To the uninitiated this conclusion may seem like old news. Although Sigmund Freud's ideas about the unconscious had been highly influential, convincing demonstrations of even the simplest versions of the unconscious were lacking—and not just because researchers did not try to provide them. The problem faced by researchers attempting to study the unconscious was that the probing of people about what was within or outside of their awareness affected their awareness and so contaminated the inquiry.

Among other psychologists, Anthony Greenwald of the University of Washington devised laboratory procedures that showed that complex psychological processes go on outside of awareness. The most compelling of his studies involved "priming"—presenting a word on a computer screen to research participants for a very brief moment, too quickly for them to become consciously aware of it—and then asking these individuals to perform some timed task that involved words similar or dissimilar to the word with which they had been primed. Greenwald speculated that if individuals were affected by a primed word, despite being unaware of it, their performances on the subsequent task would differ from those of individuals who had not had this experience or who had been primed with another word. He guessed that, for example, someone primed with the word *nurse* would respond faster to the word *doctor* than someone who had not been primed. His guess proved to be correct.

The view of the unconscious that emerged from these studies seems to differ greatly from Freud's account. Whereas Freud proposed that unconscious material could exert a strong effect on behavior over decades, contemporary research suggested that subliminal priming effects, though reliable, are highly transient. More important, Freud thought that unconscious processes were motivated, with repression defending the individual against anxiety. It is in this area that Freudian views have fallen on very hard times.

Modern-day Freudians maintain that painful memories from childhood can be repressed and that such repression can produce a variety of problems in adulthood. In this spirit some therapists have sought to uncover and work through such repressed memories in their patients in the hope of curing such adult disorders as multiple personality. When such memories—often of childhood sexual abuse—come to light, there is often doubt as to their authenticity. Because families are not infrequently broken up and the courts become involved when such memories surface, the truth of these memories is a matter of more than academic interest. Scientific and clinical skepticism has been growing about such therapy and about the underlying theory.

In the U.K. the Royal College of Psychiatrists (RCP) strongly advised clinicians against doing memory recovery therapy, urging professionals "to avoid engaging in any 'memory recovery techniques' which are based on the expectation of past sexual abuse of which the patient has no memory." The RCP further stated that there was "no evidence that the use of conscious-altering techniques, such as drug-mediated interviews or hypnosis, can reveal or accurately elaborate factual information about any past experiences, including childhood sexual abuse."

Psychology in the near future

Long-term predictions about psychology are hazardous at best, but some modest forecasting is possible. Applied research in psychology should continue to thrive in the near future, capturing both academic and general interest. Another trend that should persist is the strong presence of women in the field. By 1997 the majority of degrees granted in psychology in the U.S. at both the undergraduate and graduate levels were being awarded to women.

Clinical psychology as a profession will continue to serve the general public, but in the U.S., which has the largest number of clinical psychologists, concerns about profit-driven health care schemes may demand attention. Clinical psychologists were turning to research for evidence of the effectiveness of a variety of psychological therapies, which studies indeed continued to confirm. These studies usually have been carefully conducted efficacy trials, but a different sort of study was conducted by *Consumer Reports* magazine, which surveyed readers about their experiences in psychotherapy. More than 22,000 individuals responded to the survey, and their reports agreed with the conclusions from efficacy trials. Psychotherapy was determined to be highly effective, with 90% of respondents reporting improvement, but no specific type of therapy or medication appeared to be superior to any other for any disorder. Another important finding was a clear dose-response curve, which meant the more psychotherapy, the more improvement. This finding spoke to the trend in managed care to limit the number of therapy sessions covered by health insurance. Similarly, a recent cost-benefit review by David Antonuccio and his colleagues of the University of Nevada at Reno suggested that over a two-year period, Prozac treatment was 33% more expensive than cognitive-behavioral treatment for depression.

Finally, psychologists will continue learning how to prevent problems from occurring in the first place. In one recent study, for example, psychologists Karen Reivich, Jane Gillham, Lisa Jaycox, and Andrew Shatte of the University of Pennsylvania taught cognitive and social skills to children who had experienced parental conflict, displayed early signs of depressive symptoms, or experienced both situations. The children learned how to cope with negative life events by thinking about them in ways that enhanced mastery and competence. Later, as these children went through puberty, they showed far fewer depressive symptoms than children who had not been similarly instructed. Moreover, the effects of prevention became more pronounced over time.

—Christopher Peterson
and Martin E.P. Seligman

SCIENCE POLICY

The slowdown in research and development (R&D) expenditures by most of the world's major scientific nations, evident since the beginning of the decade, continued during 1997, with the United States and Japan the only exceptions. Faced with significant budget constraints, many national governments attempted to target basic research toward areas that promised economic reward. Another continuing trend, consistent with the globalization of science and technology, was the increase in research investments in American companies by foreign industrial firms and, reciprocally, in foreign industrial firms by American companies. The most unsettling developments were the series of problems that beset several Asian economies toward the end of the year and the questions these problems raised about the Japanese financial system. This financial turmoil suggested that the emergence of South Korea as a scientific nation would be delayed and that Japan's resolve to modernize its science system and take greater responsibility as a world scientific leader might erode.

INTERNATIONAL

Europe

R&D investments in Western Europe continued to decline in 1997. This reflected persisting sluggishness of national economies, which limited industrial investments, as well as constraints on expenditures as governments sought to reduce their budget deficits sufficiently by Dec. 31, 1998, to meet the criteria set by the Maastricht Treaty and thus qualify for the single European currency. In Germany the ratio of R&D expenditure to gross domestic prod-

AFP Photo

French Prime Minister Lionel Jospin addresses the National Assembly in Paris. During 1997 Jospin established a new Ministry of National Education, Research, and Technology. In addition, the French government announced a modest increase in basic research funding for the coming fiscal year.

uct (GDP) was estimated to be 2.2%, compared with a peak value of 2.9% at the beginning of the decade. In France and the U.K., that ratio declined from recent peak values of approximately 2.4% to the 2.1–2.3% range. Despite broad similarities in R&D expenditure trends, there were marked differences in the science policies of individual European countries—and in the attitudes of national scientific communities toward those policies.

By the end of 1997, the French research community was far more optimistic than it had been a year earlier, thanks to changes resulting from the June parliamentary elections that brought a Socialist prime minister to power. During the first months of the year, the country's scientists became increasingly vocal in their opposition to the policies of Prime Minister Alain Juppé's administration. In addition to constraining total research support, the government

froze previously allocated funds for basic research while announcing that it planned to increase the proportion of those funds earmarked for priority themes. Underlying much of the scientists' unhappiness was their conviction that Juppé's conservative government really cared little about science, a perception buttressed by the demotion of the research department to subministry level in 1995 under the leadership of a succession of three nonscientists. Among the first actions of the Socialist Party leader, Lionel Jospin, when he became prime minister in June was to establish a new Ministry of National Education, Research, and Technology, headed by Claude Allègre, a respected geochemist who had been close to Jospin since their student days. In August Allègre arranged to unfreeze the funds that had been withheld earlier and to create several hundred new research positions and doctoral fellowships. In October the government announced a modest increase in basic research funding for the coming fiscal year. Given the prospects of overall long-term government budget constraints, it appeared unlikely that research funding could increase dramatically in the near future. Additionally, there was a consensus that the overly centralized and bureaucratized French research system was badly in need of reform. One such reform could well be the introduction of more competition for research funds. No doubt the short-term pain likely to result from any effective set of reforms would be easier for French scientists to accept under a government they trusted than under one toward which they had become vocally hostile.

In Germany distress about reductions in research expenditures was expressed in a more systematic and, perhaps, more reasoned manner than in France. There was also more attention focused on expenditures by German industry and state governments than on those by the federal government, even though the budget of the Federal Ministry of Education, Science, Research, and Technology (BMBF) was cut by 3.7% from its 1996 level. In January the heads of five of the country's most prestigious scientific institutions issued a statement entitled "Priorities for the Future," declaring that Germany's R&D investments had to be increased to 3% of GDP if the country was to restore its once proud leadership role in science. Because industry has traditionally funded 60% or more of Germany's R&D, the decreasing level of its expenditures was seen as especially troubling—particularly since those decreases had led to the elimination of an estimated 40,000 R&D-related jobs. Significant cutbacks in state government budgets, which provided the bulk of baseline funding for universities, were regarded as a serious threat to the vitality of academic research.

One of the principal reasons for constraints on the overall German federal budget had been the unanticipated high cost of integrating the six new states (*Länder*) that had constituted the former East Germany. Ironically, the BMBF's 3.7% budget cut—part of a broader austerity budget designed to reduce the federal government's budget deficit to meet the impending single-currency deadline—might have a disproportionately greater impact on institutions in the new states. In the wake of reunification in 1990, immediate steps were taken to bring their science system up to the level of former West Germany. Following an

Claude Allègre (center), France's new education and science minister, signs the 1998 Intergovernmental Agreement on Space Station Cooperation with his German counterpart, Jürgen Rüttgers (left), and the Danish ambassador to the U.S., K. Erik Tygesen (right), at ceremonies in Washington, D.C., in early 1998.

evaluation of the 130 research institutions in the new states, the government decided to close approximately 40% of those institutions and to significantly reduce employment security for 50,000 of the 75,000 employees of the institutes of the former East German Academy of Sciences. At the same time, the federal government made a commitment to provide adequate resources to bring the remaining institutions up to par and integrate them into the federal system.

Because of reductions in German federal and state research budgets, the momentum evident during the first years after 1990 had largely abated. Whereas a small handful of scientific institutions in the six eastern states had become reasonably competitive with their western counterparts by 1997—as gauged, for example, by their success in obtaining competitive federal research grants—the large majority were

still under par. In the opinion of many observers, at least another decade might be necessary to bring most of these institutions up to the level of the west.

Unlike the situation in France, there were no reasons for optimism in Germany at the end of 1997. In the fall student demonstrations throughout the country protested cuts in university budgets—a boisterous counterpart to the reasoned, if somber, tone of the January leadership statement on "Priorities for the Future." In view of the strong position the German government had taken regarding the Maastricht criteria, it was unlikely that there would be much near-term relief from current constraints for either research or higher education.

If the condition of science in the leading Western European countries could be characterized as constrained, the situation in Central and Eastern Europe—particularly in Russia—remained disappointing at best and confounding at worst. Hungary and Poland each expended about 0.75% of their GDPs for R&D, and the comparable ratio for the Czech Republic was about 1%. Sharp reductions in government expenditures since the introduction of market economies after 1989, coupled with the lack of significant industrial investments, were the principal contributors to the decline of the R&D/GDP ratios for all three countries. Despite their disappointing research expenditures, however, the growing integration of these countries into the European system—signaled by decisions to admit them to NATO and, most probably, to the European Union—suggested that their long-term scientific prospects were positive.

The outlook for Russia was considerably less sanguine. In 1990 the R&D/GDP ratio for the Soviet Union was approximately 2%. By 1997 the ratio in Russia had declined to 0.7%, owing to sharp reductions in both the defense and the civilian government research budgets and the fact that industrial research expenditures were still negligible. In May the government announced a 55% reduction in the budget of the fledgling Russian Foundation for Basic Research—eliminating a substantial increase that it had granted a year earlier. This particular action had serious policy implications, since it called into question the government's commitment to nurture a scientific culture in which a competitive system for awarding research support would become the norm. Earlier in the year the Russian Cabinet approved a new draft code for the country that, according to *Science* magazine, would eliminate most of the tax exemptions enjoyed by the coun-

try's struggling research institutions. The government later promised to consider amending the draft code to ease the burden on science, but at the end of the year, the outcome remained unclear.

Despite constrained research budgets, many European countries continued to demonstrate that they were willing to pool resources to finance large-scale state-of-the-art scientific facilities. Negotiating details of cost-sharing agreements, however, had become more difficult than was the case during an earlier era when government funds for both national and international research activities were more abundant.

In December 1996 the council of the European Laboratory for Particle Physics (CERN) near Geneva agreed to a compressed construction schedule for the laboratory's Large Hadron Collider (LHC). Construction was expected to be completed in 2005 rather than in 2008, as envisioned when the project was approved in 1994. The LHC was designed to accelerate beams of protons circulating in opposite directions to unprecedented energies of 14 TeV (trillion electron volts) prior to their collisions at four predesignated regions along their paths. U.S. Department of Energy (DOE) officials estimated the cost of the facility, including collision-event detectors, at $5 billion–$6 billion.

The construction schedule originally envisioned called for completion of the first phase of the collider with less than the 14-TeV maximum design energy in 2004 and an upgrade to full energy by 2008. The council agreed to the compressed construction schedule because of contributions from countries that were not members of the European facility—primarily a contri-

bution of approximately $85 million from Japan and an anticipated $530 million from the U.S. (an amount that materialized near the end of the year), in addition to smaller pledges from Canada, India, Israel, and Russia. Nevertheless, there were concerns at the end of 1996 that dues paid to CERN by member countries might fall short of the amount required for the project. Germany, hard pressed to maintain the level of its domestic research activities, asked the council to agree to a substantial reduction in its dues, and the U.K. followed suit. Agreement was finally reached to reduce the dues of all members, though considerably less drastically than Germany had originally proposed. In order to accommodate to its diminishing income, CERN management proposed reductions in salaries, personnel, or both over the next 10 years as well as termination of several projects. This was the price that had to be paid to finance the LHC and thus maintain CERN's position as the world's premier particle-physics facility.

Japan

In 1997 Japan was estimated to have invested 2.9% of its GDP in R&D, the same ratio as in 1990 and up from 2.6% in 1994. Much of that increase was attributable to a 6.8% rise in government research support between 1996 and 1997, considered to be the first installment toward the stated objective of doubling 1992 public research expenditures by 2000. This fiscal objective was no doubt the most prominent feature of the government's July 1996 Science and Technology Basic Plan.

Several events that occurred during 1997 suggested that a sustained scientific as well as political consensus underlay the Basic Plan. In March plans were announced to create a new, well-endowed Brain Science Institute with an ambitious 20-year agenda at the Institute of Physical and Chemical Research (RIKEN) in suburban Tokyo. In October SPring-8, a third-generation synchrotron-radiation facility located near Himeji, was formally dedicated, and an active research program was under way by the end of the year. Construction of this facility, begun in 1991, had not been scheduled for completion before 1998, but supplementary funding for the past two years permitted an accelerated timetable. On university campuses throughout the country, recipients of highly competitive grants from new programs of the Ministry of Education, Science, Sports, and Culture (Monbusho), the Science and Technology Agency, and the Ministry of International Trade and Industry initiated a variety of research programs using state-of-the-art apparatuses housed in spacious facilities.

By mid-year, well before the onset of the Asian financial crisis, scientific and fiscal priorities had begun to collide. Alarmed by the continuing sluggishness of the economy and the growing public deficit, the government proposed an austerity budget for its next fiscal year, scheduled to begin on April 1, 1998. Although funding for science was proposed to increase by only 0.9%, the affected agencies fared better than many others, whose budgets were slated to be cut, in some cases substantially. The projected slowdown in research support meant that the proposed doubling of the budget, which according to the Basic Plan would be accomplished in five years, would now take six or seven years—or perhaps longer.

The overall goal of the Basic Plan was to streamline and modernize the Japanese science system, which both domestic and foreign observers had come to regard as overly regulated and centralized, and to integrate it more fully into the international system. To this end the plan included far-reaching organizational and institutional aspects in addition to its fiscal aspects. Thus, there were provisions to increase the mobility of both young and senior researchers by introducing a number of prestigious five-year contract appointments into the traditional system of guaranteed lifetime employment, to create larger numbers of postdoctoral appointments to encourage younger scientists and engineers to gain independent research experience in universities and public research laboratories and to facilitate more effective research cooperation between universities

and private industry. Although it was still too early to gauge the effects of these and other measures either individually or collectively, there seemed to be considerable optimism both in government agencies and among working scientists that trends were at least positive.

The problems besetting the Japanese financial system, which started to become apparent in November, were almost certain to shift political attention away from the rejuvenation of the country's science system, at least in the short term. At the end of 1997, it was impossible for anyone to know how many banks and other financial institutions were in danger of failing. Nevertheless, public confidence had eroded sufficiently to compel the government of Prime Minister Ryutaro Hashimoto to propose a substantial bailout for the beleaguered banks, in addition to a one-time tax

U.S. Secretary of Energy Federico Peña (left) and CERN Council president Luciano Maiani exchange papers on Dec. 8, 1997, after signing an agreement outlining U.S. participation in CERN's Large Hadron Collider, a particle accelerator under construction near Geneva. Construction was expected to be completed in 2005.

cut that was designed to increase consumption and stimulate the country's sluggish economy. These new measures ran counter to the government's earlier resolve to place a high priority on reducing the budget deficit. In this environment it seemed unlikely that government research expenditures would continue to increase, even modestly. If this was the case, then optimism about the long-term success of the Science and Technology Basic Plan might also erode.

Reuters

Upset by the Asian financial crisis, South Korean demonstrators burn effigies in Seoul in protest against the International Monetary Fund and Korean government and business leaders. The crisis posed a serious threat to South Korea's scientific community, which depended on public- and private-sector investments.

South Korea and East Asia

If the 1997 Asian financial crisis promised near-term disappointment for Japan's science system, for South Korea it held the prospect of a serious setback. One of the most stunning trends of the decade had been South Korea's emergence as a significant scientific nation. By 1996 it was investing 2.3% of its GDP in R&D—comparable to France, Germany, and the U.K.—with the stated goal of attaining a level of 3% by the end of the century. Although private industry accounted for up to 80% of R&D expenditures, the South Korean government reportedly was considering an increase in its investments in a bid to strengthen the research capabilities of universities and other public research facilities. There was little doubt that both public- and private-sector research investments would be severely curtailed as a result of the financial crisis that descended on the country in October. Although no details about plans for 1998 were available at the end of the year, the newly elected government of Pres. Kim Young Sam announced that it would increase research expenditures substantially during the next five years. It seemed certain, however, that South Korea's aspiration to become a significant scientific nation by the end of the century had been dealt at least a temporary setback.

For similar reasons the long-term scientific aspirations of Thailand, Malaysia, and Indonesia were also thwarted, although even before the onset of the financial crisis, the extent to which those aspirations would be realized was uncertain. China and India appeared largely insulated from the financial woes of their smaller neighbors, in part because their much larger economies were less integrated into the international system. Nevertheless, at least some portion of the scientific development in both countries was based on foreign investment, including investment from both Japan and South Korea. Thus, a slowdown in some sectors of their scientific effort might lie ahead.

UNITED STATES

Research funding

In 1997 total R&D expenditures in the United States were estimated to have reached an all-time high of $206 billion, or 2.6% of its GDP—up from the 1994 low of 2.4% but still less than the 1991 level of 2.7%. The decline in federal R&D investments relative to those of industry, apparent since the early 1990s, persisted. Of total national R&D expenditures, an estimated $133.3 billion (64.7%) came from private industry and an estimated $62.7 billion (30.4%) came from the federal government, with the balance attributed to a variety of other sources. Of American industrial expenditures, approximately 12% were invested abroad, and 12% of R&D investments in American companies were made by foreign firms.

At the end of 1997, the good news concerning federal expenditures was that the situation was not as bad as expected. The bad news—which the scientific community was organizing itself to forestall—was that worse might yet lie ahead. At the beginning of the year, Pres. Bill Clinton's Democratic administration and the Republican-controlled Congress had agreed, in principle, to balance the federal budget by fiscal year 2002, but they had yet to work

out details. Various scenarios suggested that substantial decreases in real (*i.e.,* inflation-adjusted) budgets were in store for the principal federal science and technology agencies. In March alarmed at the prospect of further erosion in funding for university research, an unprecedented coalition of 23 scientific societies called for a 7% increase in real support during fiscal year 1998, which began on Oct. 1, 1997. Although this increase did not materialize, neither did the anticipated reductions. Indeed, congressional nondefense R&D appropriations for fiscal year 1998 exceeded those in 1997, even in real terms, and in some cases the amounts appropriated were greater than the Clinton administration had requested.

The May 1997 balanced-budget agreement called for more drastic reductions in annual spending for discretionary programs as fiscal year 2002 approached. Both the administration's requests for R&D expenditures and congressional action on those requests might be conditioned by this feature of the agreement, with the result that the budgets of the principal science and technology agencies could experience significant declines starting in fiscal year 1999. In an attempt to forestall this dismal scenario, an expanded coalition of scientific societies representing more than three million members intensified efforts to bring about a substantial increase in federal research funding. Political support for an expansion in long-term funding gained considerable momentum during the year. In January Sen. Philip Gramm introduced a bill to authorize a doubling of that budget by the year 2007. Although the Senate did not consider Gramm's National Research Investment

Act during 1997, by the end of the year the bill had been endorsed by several influential members from both parties. By year's end, the continuing strength of the American economy suggested that the federal budget might actually be balanced in 1998, which would result in an almost unprecedented surplus. If so, there were bound to be many claimants to that unanticipated windfall, in addition to science.

Science and innovation

Solid evidence that public research support could appropriately be characterized as an investment was provided in a study released in May 1997 on the research basis of U.S. patents. The authors examined nonpatent references cited on the front pages of the almost 400,000 U.S. patents issued during 1987–88 and 1993–94. (References cited—the art upon which an issued patent is intended to improve—are a fundamental requirement of U.S. patent law.) Of the 430,000 references to documents other than previous patents, 175,000 were to papers published in leading scientific journals. The authors found that only 27% of these papers were written by industrial scientists, whereas 73% were based on research—most often very basic research—conducted in university and government laboratories and heavily supported by the National Institutes of Health, the National Science Foundation (NSF), and other government agencies. References from U.S. patents to U.S.-authored research papers tripled in the period from 1987 to 1994, which suggested that links between publicly funded basic science and commercializable technology had become increasingly important.

Strides were made in 1997 toward putting information at the fingertips of researchers. Grants were given to 35 U.S. academic institutions that allowed them to connect to the very-high-speed Backbone Network Service, which permitted electronic communication at speeds over 100 times that available on the Internet.

Research and information technology

In the same month that the patent study was released, the NSF demonstrated that the infrastructure requirements for cutting-edge science continued to grow in sophistication when it awarded $12.3 million in grants to 35 American academic institutions to allow them to connect to the NSF's pilot very-high-speed Backbone Network Service (vBNS). The vBNS permitted electronic communication at speeds over 100 times that available on the Internet. The Clinton administration regarded these NSF awards as the foundation of its Next Generation Internet (NGI) initiative, a $100 million-per-year, three-year project that involved several federal agencies in addition to the NSF and had been endorsed by leading information-technology companies. The NGI was designed to connect more than 100 research institutions and to support R&D for new networking technologies to achieve, among other objectives, transmission speeds 1,000 times faster than on the Internet. The administration's proposal encountered some congressional opposition, however. In hearings before the Senate Commerce Committee in June, Sen. Ted Stevens, according to *Science,* charged that on the evidence of the institutions that had received the vBNS awards from the NSF, the NGI would benefit the richer states at the expense of the poorer ones. "I think you should go back to the drawing board," he told a group of federal officials. "The institutions you're supporting, they don't need you—and we do."

Big Science

Despite continuing constraints in federal research support, the United States demonstrated its commitment to international cost sharing for large-scale facilities. The NSF's appropriations bill for fiscal year 1998 included funds to complete the Gemini 8-Meter Telescopes Project—a pair of identical 8-m (26.2-ft) optical telescopes located in the Northern (Hawaii) and Southern (Chile) hemispheres. The project was a unique international undertaking involving the U.S., the U.K., Canada, Brazil, Argentina, Chile, and Australia.

In December an agreement was reached with CERN whereby the U.S. promised to provide $450 million in hardware for the construction of the laboratory's LHC and an additional $80 million for its massive detectors. A notable feature of the negotiations that led to this agreement was the continuing personal involvement of Rep. James Sensenbrenner, who became chairman of the House Science Committee in January and almost immediately began to express skepticism about negotiations then in progress between the DOE and CERN on a U.S. contribution to the LHC. He and several other members of Congress remained openly bitter about the failure of any European country to offer contributions to the U.S. Superconducting Super Collider (SSC) project, a failure that was instrumental in leading Congress to terminate the project in 1993. Sensenbrenner, who traveled to Geneva at his own expense to meet with CERN officials, was ultimately convinced that U.S. participation in the LHC was important. Owing largely to his intervention, the DOE was able to re-negotiate its agreement to ensure that the U.S. would have an appropriate role in the LHC's management decisions and would not be liable for possible cost overruns on the facility.

Construction of an 8-m (26.2-ft) optical telescope is under way at this mountaintop site on Cerro Pachón, Chile. The telescope is one of an identical pair being built as part of the international Gemini 8-Meter Telescopes Project. The instruments will be used in a broad range of astronomical research programs.

With an outlook farther into the future, by the end of 1997 the Stanford Linear Accelerator Center (SLAC) had completed installation of its Next Linear Collider Test Accelerator, a 42-m (138-ft) prototype segment to conduct some of the R&D required for the design of what was called the Next Linear Collider. The latter collider was envisioned as two opposing 10-km (6.2-mi) linear accelerators, one of which would accelerate electrons and the other positrons at energies up to 1 TeV toward a collision region. Earlier in the year SLAC and the High Energy Research Organization (KEK), Japan's premier particle-physics facility, reached an informal agreement to cooperate in designing a possible Next Linear Collider. The site of the facility, if constructed, would be somewhere in the U.S., Japan, or possibly a third country in the Pacific region that

might agree to contribute to the project, with the assumption that it would be approved by the original partner governments.

Science and culture

Science continued to have important impacts on culture. Beginning in July 1997 and continuing into the autumn, countless individuals in the U.S. and throughout the world became engrossed by the exploits of the small Sojourner vehicle as it jolted over the Martian surface analyzing geologic specimens and returning striking photographs to Earth. (*See* Year in Review: ASTRONOMY; SPACE EXPLORATION: *Space Probes.*) The Mars Pathfinder mission, which had deployed Sojourner, proved that NASA could implement significant planetary missions with considerably more

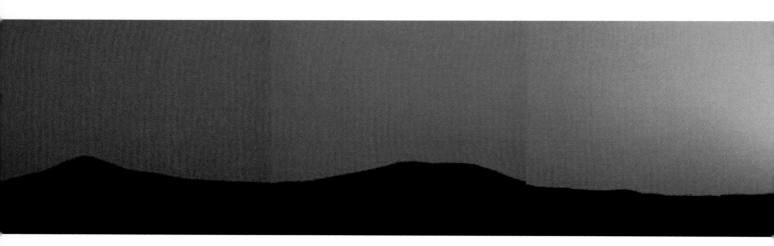

NASA's Mars Pathfinder captured this image of a Martian sunset during its mission. The Pathfinder vehicle, which remained on Mars after the mission ended in November 1997, was named the Carl Sagan Memorial Station in honor of the late planetary astronomer and popularizer.

modest funding than it had previously thought necessary and demonstrated the power of the Internet to make the dramatic images from Mars widely available. More important, the level of interest in the Pathfinder mission showed a widespread public desire to participate in scientific discovery.

The Pathfinder vehicle, which remained as a permanent feature of the Martian landscape, was named the Carl Sagan Memorial Station in honor of the planetary astronomer and popularizer who had died in December 1996. In an editorial obituary published in *Science* in January 1997, the paleontologist Stephen Jay Gould epitomized Sagan's "excellence and integrity" in terms of three points: "First, in an age characterized by the fusion of high and pop culture, Carl moved comfortably across the entire spectrum while never compromising scientific content....Second, for all his pizzazz and charisma, Carl always spoke for true science against the plethora of irrationalisms that surround us....Third, he bridged the gaps between our various cultures by showing the personal, humanistic, and artistic side of scientific activity."

—William A. Blanpied

SPACE EXPLORATION

Difficulties aboard Russia's *Mir* space station during the year and development problems that delayed the start of the International Space Station into 1998 highlighted the demands of building and operating a complex system that could support several people conducting research in space. In 1997 manned flights delivered astronauts to *Mir*, upgraded the Hubble Space Telescope, and performed various scientific experiments. In unmanned missions a constellation of communications satellites was launched, and a probe landed on and explored the surface of Mars.

MANNED SPACE MISSIONS

Of the 10 manned missions during 1997, half supported Russia's *Mir* space station—three by the U.S. space shuttle *Atlantis* and two by Russian Soyuz craft. The first shuttle visit (January 12–22) was flown by commander Michael A. Baker, pilot Brent W. Jett, and mission specialists John M. Grunsfeld, Marsha S. Ivins, Peter J.K. Wisoff, and Jerry M. Linenger. Linenger stayed aboard *Mir*, and John Blaha, launched in 1996, returned aboard the shuttle. The shuttle used the Spacehab double module (standard on most shuttle/*Mir* missions) to carry the supplies plus gear for experiments in advanced technology, Earth sciences, fundamental biology, human life sciences, microgravity, and space sciences.

On February 10 Soyuz TM-25 launched commander Vasily Tsibliyev, flight engineer Aleksandr Lazutkin, and German astronaut Reinhold Ewald to *Mir*. Ewald stayed on the space station for only a week, returning March 2 aboard TM-24 with Valery Korzun and Aleksandr Kalery, who had been aboard *Mir* since Aug. 17, 1996.

Following a series of emergencies aboard *Mir* (described below), *Atlantis* on its second visit (May 15–24) added a re-

JPL/NASA

placement "Elektron" oxygen-regeneration system to the planned load of supplies, including beetles and mustard plants, for space biology experiments. The mission was flown by commander Charles J. Precourt, pilot Eileen M. Collins, mission specialists C. Michael Foale, Carlos I. Noriega, Edward T. Lu, Jean-François Clervoy (European Space Agency), and Elena V. Kondakova (Russian Space Agency; RSA). Linenger returned aboard the shuttle, and Foale stayed aboard *Mir*.

On August 5 Soyuz TM-26 took Anatoly Solovyev and Pavel Vinogradov to relieve Tsibliyev and Lazutkin, who returned to Earth on Soyuz TM-25 on August 14. The last shuttle visit of 1997 (September 25–October 6) was flown by commander James D. Wetherbee, pilot Michael J. Bloomfield, and mission specialists Vladimar G. Titov (RSA), Scott E. Parazynski, Jean-Loup J.M. Chrétien

The *Mir* space station's Spektr science module shows damage to a solar panel, at right, and a nearby radiator. *Mir* suffered a near-fatal mishap on June 25, 1997, when an unmanned ferry being docked via remote control accidentally rammed into the module.

(French National Center for Space Studies; CNES), Wendy B. Lawrence, and David A. Wolf. Wolf stayed aboard *Mir,* replacing Foale, who returned to Earth.

Life aboard *Mir* was anything but dull during the past year as the crews fought to keep the aging station alive. Trouble started on Feb. 23, 1997, when an oxygen-generating canister (similar to aircraft emergency oxygen units) ignited and filled the cabin with smoke. The crew put out the fire with a wet towel and a fire extinguisher. The oxygen-regeneration system failed in March, and the crew had to use canisters like the one that burned in February. The crew repaired part of the system, but *Atlantis* had to deliver a replacement Elektron unit to restore the complete system. Then the cooling system leaked, which exposed the crew to hazardous fluids, allowed the temperature to soar to 30° C (86° F), and crippled the carbon dioxide removal system.

The worst damage occurred when Tsibilyev accidentally ran a Progress supply craft into *Mir*'s Spektr science module on June 25. Tsibliyev was practicing manual remote control, but the computer had not been adjusted for weight changes after the craft had been emptied and then re-

NASA

NASA

Space shuttle *Discovery* astronauts make repairs to the Earth-orbiting Hubble Space Telescope. In five space walks conducted in February 1997, astronauts replaced science instruments and operating equipment aboard Hubble and patched insulation blankets that were found to have eroded under conditions in orbit.

Deciding that a fresh team trained on the ground would have a better chance of success, Russia's mission control postponed the space walks until a new crew arrived on Soyuz TM-26. Other problems included repeated breakdowns of the oxygen system in late August and computer failures that required that a replacement unit be taken up by a shuttle.

Though *Mir* was brought back to life, the Spektr module remained disabled and uninhabitable. During a series of space walks, Solovyev, Vinogradov, Foale, and Wolf inspected and repaired various parts of the station. Two of these extravehicular activities were conducted inside the depressurized Spektr module. This was especially hazardous because there was less room to maneuver and there were more places to tear a spacesuit in the module. On August 22 Vinogradov went inside Spektr to connect power cables to a new hatch that sealed the module but provided airtight passageways for cables.

On September 6 Solovyev and Foale inspected the outside of Spektr. Although they documented extensive damage, they did not find the hole. They were able to reorient two solar arrays to face the Sun and retrieved a materials exposure experiment that Linenger had placed outside during a space walk in April. On October 1 Parazynski and Titov moved a 55-kg (120-lb) plug from the shuttle to *Mir*. The plug was designed to fill the suspected hole in Spektr. On a second internal space walk, on October 20, Solovyev and Vinogradov reconnected more cables inside Spektr and dodged debris that included a refrigerator door, but they were unable to make the last connection. In an especially busy week, they made more repairs, released a scale

loaded with trash. Progress went off course and punctured the Spektr module, which allowed its atmosphere to vent into space and forced the crew to disconnect power cables so that they could close the hatch. This left the station with about half its power supply. The stress of the problems took its toll on the crew. Doctors on the ground noticed a heart irregularity as they checked Tsibliyev's health in preparation for space walks to repair the station. On July 16 the crew accidentally disconnected the wrong power cable and plunged the station into darkness for almost 24 hours.

model of Sputnik 1 on November 3 (its 40th anniversary), and installed a new solar array that restored most of *Mir*'s power on November 6. Finally, on Jan. 14, 1998, Wolf and Solovyev made a space walk to document the effects of space exposure on experimental arrays outside the station. The work also secured Solovyev's record as the world's most experienced space walker, with more than 80 hours in 16 extravehicular journeys.

Meanwhile, American scientists on the Earth were reporting significant results from several experiments carried out aboard *Mir*, including a rotating bioreactor that grew large cultures of colon cancer cells and demonstrated tissue engineering with cartilage cells. The protein crystal growth program reported that a number of specimens were larger than crystals produced earlier in the program or had greater internal order, which thus enhanced the view provided by X-ray crystallography in studying the proteins' structures.

The other five missions by the space shuttle were occupied with upgrading the Hubble Space Telescope, microgravity materials research, and atmospheric studies. During *Discovery*'s first mission (February 11–21), two space-walk teams repaired and upgraded the Hubble Space Telescope in the second service call since it was launched in 1990. Mission specialists Gregory J. Harbaugh, Mark C. Lee, Steven L. Smith, and Joseph R. Tanner worked in

Pilot Susan L. Still (left) and other members of the *Columbia* crew utilize a planning session during the Microgravity Science Laboratory 1 mission. The mission was flown twice because a fuel cell problem cut the first flight short. All experiments were conducted as planned on the second try.

pairs through five space walks to replace science instruments and operating equipment aboard Hubble. They removed the Goddard High Resolution Spectrometer and the Faint Object Spectrograph, part of Hubble's original instrument complement, and installed the Space Telescope Imaging Spectrograph (STIS) and the Near Infrared Camera and Multi-Object Spectrometer. These provided improved spectral and spatial resolutions. In addition, NASA was helping industry transfer STIS technology to medical systems in order to guide physicians in using large-core needles rather than surgery to obtain breast tissue for biopsies. The astronauts replaced some operational gear and repaired several areas where Hubble's silverized Teflon coating was torn or frayed by space exposure.

During its second mission (August 7–19), *Discovery* carried Germany's Cryogenic Infrared Spectrometers and Telescopes for the Atmosphere-Shuttle Pallet Satellite-2 (CRISTA-SPAS-2) on its sec-

ond flight. CRISTA's three infrared telescopes and four spectrometers were designed to look at the Earth's atmosphere and measure the presence of trace gases. The SPAS satellite carrying CRISTA also carried an ultraviolet spectrograph to measure hydroxyl and nitric oxide in the atmosphere. CRISTA-SPAS was deployed by the shuttle's robot arm and allowed to operate independently of the shuttle for nine days, after which it was retrieved for the return to Earth. Among the preliminary findings was the discovery of a greater amount of water vapor in the middle atmosphere than scientists had previously believed was there. The crew also operated the Manipulator Flight Demonstration, forerunner of a new dexterous robot arm that was to be installed on the Japanese Experiment Module of the International Space Station (ISS).

Shuttle *Columbia* made three major microgravity science research flights, although two counted as one mission: the

389

On *Columbia*'s first-ever space walk, Takao Doi works with a crane device installed in a socket on the shuttle's cargo bay. During the space walk, Doi and fellow mission specialist Winston E. Scott demonstrated space station assembly techniques. Doi became the first Japanese to walk in space.

NASA

Microgravity Science Laboratory 1 (MSL-1) was flown twice (April 4–8 and July 1–17) because a fuel cell problem cut the first flight short. The unprecedented decision for a rapid reflight was driven by the value of the science to research planned aboard the ISS, the opportunity to demonstrate quick turnaround in case of an emergency aboard the station, and a gap in the flight schedule caused by delays in developing the Russian segment of the ISS.

On its second try, MSL-1 became a highly successful research mission. Japan's Large Isothermal Furnace melted and then cooled various alloys in an effort to understand the rates at which trace metals diffuse or migrate into a larger volume. Germany's Electromagnetic Containerless Processing Facility (TEMPUS) floated and melted samples of platinum, tungsten, and other metals that would easily react with a container. Instruments recorded viscosity, cooling rates, surface tension, and other fundamental aspects that could not be obtained on Earth. One set of experiments formed metallic glass, metal that forms an amorphous solid rather than crystallizing, by gently cooling it below its normal freezing point.

The greatest attention went to the Droplet Combustion Experiment and the Combustion Module-1 facility experiments. On Earth buoyancy drives combustion as warm exhaust products rise and are quickly replaced by fresh air. This forms the clas-

sic candle flame. It also drives combustion too fast for instruments to study it. In the weightlessness of space, however, diffusion drives combustion, which allows scientists to measure on a large scale what happens in the microscopic world. Their results were expected to contribute substantially to the design of more efficient internal combustion engines and gas space heaters.

Columbia's other microgravity science mission (November 19–December 5) carried the fourth U.S. Microgravity Payload (USMP-4) and the Spartan 201 solar observatory. During a space walk, mission specialists Winston E. Scott and Takao Doi demonstrated space station assembly techniques, an activity postponed from 1996 when the airlock jammed. Doi became the first Japanese to walk in space. Spartan 201, flown three times previously, carried a white-light coronagraph and an ultraviolet coronal spectrometer. The crew released the observatory on the third flight day but apparently skipped a step in the activation sequence, and so the craft did not become operational. The crew tried to

retrieve it by using the robot arm but were unable to do so. They backed away, and NASA rescheduled activities so that Scott and Doi grappled Spartan as part of their first space walk. A second walk took place near the end of the mission to complete the scheduled activities, including a test of a beachball-like remote-controlled spacecraft equipped with TV cameras to inspect space station exteriors.

The bulk of the work on USMP-4 was done by the four materials science facilities in the payload bay. NASA's Advanced Automated Directional Solidification Furnace processed samples of exotic alloys by moving a melt zone through the samples so that each refroze in the right direction. France's Material pour l'Étude des Phenomenes Interssant la Solidification sur Terre et en Orbite (MEPHISTO) experiment worked in a similar manner while using electrical resistance as a measure of the rate and quality of crystal formation. The Confined Helium Experiment (CHeX) used superfluid helium to model the ways in which electrons will behave in the ultra-thin microcircuits planned for the 21st century. Finally, the Isothermal Dendritic Growth Experiment used TV cameras to watch as a clear organic acid was repeatedly frozen and remelted at different rates. Measuring the length and tip radius of crystal dendrites was expected to help metallurgists understand and control better what happens inside similar—but opaque—metal alloys as they form on Earth.

In 1998 NASA planned to fly seven shuttle missions. *Endeavour* was expected to return from a major overhaul in time for the long-awaited start of assembly of the ISS in mid-1998. Russia was to launch the first element of the station, the Functional Cargo Block (FGB), a core module built from what would have been *Mir 2.* Subsequently, *Endeavour* would deliver the first U.S.-built element, a connecting node that would join the Russian modules in the rear with American, European, Japanese, and Canadian elements in the front. At the end of 1998 Russia would launch the Service Module, which had thrusters to maintain the station's orbit. (Delays in its preparation had forced NASA to postpone the start of ISS assembly from late 1997.) After the Service Module was in orbit, *Endeavour* would carry equipment to outfit the modules. Finally, in early 1999 *Atlantis* would attach a truss with a large solar array to power the station fully. It would then be ready for habitation.

The first crew to live aboard the ISS was to comprise an American commander, William M. Shepherd, and Russian cosmonauts Yury Gidzenko and Sergey Krikalev. They were scheduled to start a five-month stay when launched to the ISS on a Soyuz spacecraft in January 1999. Their replacements, a Russian commander and two

Robert Giroux—Reuters

American astronauts, would be transported up by the shuttle in the summer of 1999. More than 40 assembly missions would be required before the station was fully outfitted in 2003, at which time full-scale operations with a crew of six persons would begin.

In January 1998 NASA announced that it would fly U.S. Sen. John Glenn, the first American to orbit the Earth, on *Discovery* in October and teacher Barbara Morgan on a mission to be selected later. Glenn's mission was being justified as an effort to compare the parallels between aging—Glenn would be 77 at the time of his flight—and the effects of space travel on humans. Glenn's only trip into space was the three-orbit flight of *Friendship 7,* one of the Mercury spacecraft, on Feb. 20, 1962.

SPACE PROBES

The arrivals of Pathfinder and Mars Global Surveyor and the continued debate over possible signs of life inside the Allan Hills meteorite kept Mars at the center of space

NASA administrator Daniel Goldin (right) introduces U.S. Sen. John Glenn at a news conference held in January 1998 to announce Glenn's return to space aboard the space shuttle *Discovery* in October. Glenn, the first American to orbit the Earth, will be 77 at the time of the flight.

science during the past year, although the Moon, Jupiter, Saturn, and the cosmos received their share of attention. Mars Pathfinder, launched Dec. 4, 1996, bounced to a landing in Ares Vallis on July 4, 1997, more than 20 years after the Viking 1 and 2 landers became the first successful probes to the surface of Mars. In contrast to the controlled, helicopter-like landings of the Vikings, Pathfinder experienced a controlled crash as it inflated air bags to cushion the impact after it was dropped from a parachute that slowed its descent. A few hours later, when the Sun rose, solar panels deployed, and the craft started sending back images of the countryside. The site was named Carl Sagan Memorial Station in honor of the late Carl Sagan, who helped popularize science and planetary exploration.

After retracting and then reextending one petal to clear an air bag from the path, engineers sent the Sojourner rover onto the surface. Sojourner was equipped with a small television camera plus an alpha proton X-ray spectrometer that measured chemical content by means of the radiation that was scattered back from the target. To do this, Sojourner had to back up and "kiss" a rock.

Pathfinder itself returned more than 16,000 lander images from two color TV cameras mounted on a mast extending above the craft; the rover sent another 550 images. Weather instruments also were

EARTH SCIENCES: *Atmospheric Sciences*). The pictures were assembled into grand panoramas.

From the outset, however, the program was plagued with problems. Engineers found that the transmit and receive frequencies of the radio modems that linked the lander and rover would drift with temperature changes and thus require adjustments.

Nonetheless, contact did not become spotty until September 27, and the last contact with Mars Pathfinder was on October 7, almost three months after the landing and almost two months after it was

tical orbit around Mars on September 11. Controllers soon discovered that a solar panel had extended beyond its fully latched position and was flexing too much as the spacecraft dipped through the upper atmosphere to lower itself into an ideal mapping orbit (the technique, called aerobraking, reduces weight and costs). Aerobraking was suspended from October 12 to November 7 while engineers worked out a revised plan that would not tax the solar panel. In a series of three brief rocket firings, November 7–12, Surveyor started a new aerobraking profile that would place it in a mapping orbit that would descend across the Martian equator at 2 AM local time rather than 2 PM local time as originally planned. This would have no effect on mapping other than starting it one year late, in mid-March 1999, during the northern hemisphere summer. The spacecraft should still complete a full Martian year (23 Earth months) of mapping. While on its way to the mapping orbit, Surveyor used its cameras and laser altimeter. It obtained images of Vallis Marineris that revealed the possibility of active sand dunes and dried-up ponds.

Exploration of Mars was scheduled to continue at a brisk pace. Japan planned to launch its Planet B mission on Aug. 6, 1998, and the U.S. scheduled liftoff of the Mars Surveyor '98 orbiter on Dec. 10, 1998, and of the Mars Surveyor '98 lander on Jan. 3, 1999. The lander was to carry two Deep Space 2 probes that would be dropped onto the planet's surface as the craft descended. The probes were designed to drive a water-detection kit into the soil after striking the surface. Next on the schedule were the Mars Surveyor 2001 orbiter and the Mars Surveyor 2001 lander.

JPL/NASA

Mars Global Surveyor went into a preliminary elliptical orbit around Mars on Sept. 11, 1997. One of the early images the mapping spacecraft transmitted back to Earth was this view of Nirgal Vallis, a sinuous valley about 400 km (250 mi) long and about 5 km (3 mi) wide.

mounted on the boom. Images showed evidence of wind abrasion of rocks and dune-shaped deposits, that clouds, not ground fog, obscure the morning view (a distinction that Viking could not make), and that water flooding could be seen in the distribution of rock sizes and the identification of rounded pebbles and cobbles and of sockets and pebbles in some rocks. (*See*

thought it would cease to operate. Engineers believed that a battery that kept the spacecraft warm finally wore out and that the electronics became too cold to work effectively. The rover, designed to last only a week, was believed to be circling the lander, following its last instructions.

Meanwhile, Mars Global Surveyor, launched Nov. 7, 1996, arrived in an ellip-

The lander was to deploy the Athena rover to carry an advanced soil analysis package up to 100 km (60 mi) away from the lander.

The biggest planetary launch of the year was the Cassini/Huygens mission to place the Cassini spacecraft in orbit around Saturn and send the Huygens probe to the surface of Titan, Saturn's methane-shrouded moon. Controversy surrounded the October 15 launch as antinuclear activists sought a court injunction to block the mission because Cassini carried almost 33 kg (72 lb) of plutonium to provide electrical power. Like Galileo, Cassini/Huygens was to tour the inner solar system, using gravity assists to pump its orbit outward to its destination. This eliminated the expense of building energetic rockets that could send the craft directly to Saturn. Flybys were to include Venus (April 26, 1998, June 24, 1999), Earth (Aug. 18, 1999), and Jupiter (Dec. 30, 2000). The probe was scheduled to arrive at Saturn on July 1, 2004.

NASA returned to the Moon with the Jan. 6, 1998, launch of Lunar Prospector, the third of the Discovery missions. By January 11 Prospector had been inserted into polar orbit, where it was to survey the mineral and chemical composition of the surface by using an array of remote sensing instruments. Highest on the list of finds was water ice, which Clementine, a 1994 military mission, had indicated was hidden in the soil of craters at the lunar poles. Lunar Prospector carried five instruments to map surface chemistry and physical conditions: a magnetometer, an electron reflectometer, a neutron spectrometer, a gamma-ray spectrometer, and an alpha particle spectrometer. The latter three were to determine chemical composition by analyzing the radiation scattered back into space from minerals on the surface. The Moon's attitude is such that some regions in those craters are in perpetual shadow; consequently, water ice—deposited by comets—might remain undisturbed for eons.

Chemical assays were also the goal of the Near Earth Asteroid Rendezvous (NEAR) mission, which was scheduled to reach its objective, the asteroid 433 Eros, on Jan. 9, 1999. NEAR flew within 1,200 km (750 mi) of asteroid 253 Mathilde on June 27, 1997, and sent back images of a pocked boulder darker than charcoal. One of the surprises was that Mathilde had craters almost half as wide as the asteroid itself, which raised the question of how the rock stayed intact. NEAR also found that Mathilde reflects less than 4% of the light that strikes it, and thus is blacker than coal. NEAR also found no signs of outgassing, which might account for the fact that Mathilde rotates once every 17.5 days, almost 53 times slower than the average for asteroids its size.

On Jan. 19, 1998, NEAR test fired the laser that it planned to use as an altimeter to draw precise profiles of the surface of 433 Eros. NEAR aimed its laser at the Earth so that NASA engineers could determine its precise alignment on the spacecraft. NEAR then flew past Earth on January 23 for its last gravity assist to Eros. While orbiting Eros, NEAR was to take hundreds of images in order to help scientists understand the structure of asteroids. In turn, such knowledge would be used in determining whether an asteroid that might strike the Earth could be detoured or destroyed by human intervention.

Asteroids and comets were to be the objectives for Deep Space 1, the first New Millennium mission designed—like Pathfinder—to demonstrate new technologies for future space missions. The key element on Deep Space 1 was an ion engine that provided a gentle continual thrust as electric fields repelled ions and electrons from the craft. Deep Space 1 was scheduled to fly past an asteroid, Mars, and a comet after launch on July 1, 1998.

Deeper in space, Voyager 1 overtook Pioneer 10 on Feb. 17, 1998, and became the most distant manmade object. The mission of Pioneer 10, launched in 1972, formally ended on March 31, 1997, because its signal was growing too faint and its data stream too small to be useful. The Ulysses solar polar mission completed its arc over the solar system as it crossed through the orbit of Jupiter on April 17, 1997, and started back to repeat its crossing of the Sun's poles.

One of the most exciting discoveries in astronomy came from combined efforts by several telescopes led by the BeppoSAX X-ray astronomy satellite launched in 1996. On Feb. 28, 1997, BeppoSAX observed a burst of gamma radiation and was able to train its X-ray telescopes in the direction of the flash. Gamma-ray bursts had puzzled astronomers since the 1970s, when they were detected by satellites. The Burst and Transient Source Experiment (BATSE) placed aboard the Compton Gamma Ray Observatory (1991) was designed to observe the entire sky and, scientists expected, to confirm that the bursts came from neutron stars and black holes in our galaxy. Instead, in early 1997 the BATSE team announced that the burst locations were completely random, a strong

Rex Saffer, Villanova University; Dave Zurek, Space Telescope Science Institute; NASA

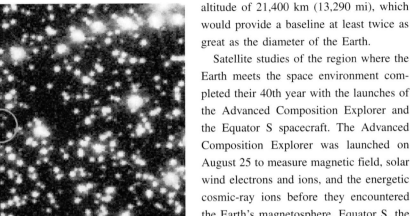

A region of globular cluster 47 Tucanae is shown in this image from the Hubble Space Telescope. Circles highlight "blue straggler" stars, which formed from stellar collisions or slow mergers within the crowded core of the globular cluster. Hubble found that one blue straggler is about 1.7 times the mass of the Sun but spins 75 times faster.

indicator that they are at extragalactic distances. BeppoSAX happened to be pointing in the right direction on February 28 and, in conjunction with monitors aboard other satellites, was able to provide a rough estimate of the location so that ground-based optical telescopes could capture the fading visible light component of one of the bursts. Images from the Hubble Space Telescope in March and again in September showed that the object continued to fade and had no proper motion, which thus established the bursts as extragalactic in origin and, because of their distance, as incredibly powerful. By the end of 1997, visible or radio components for four bursts had been identified.

The Hubble Space Telescope continued to provide a steady stream of discoveries as it resumed operations with two new instruments following its upgrade in February 1997. Images included the nearest known colliding galaxies, an event that offered the opportunity to observe star formation where gas clouds from the two bodies meet. Hubble also confirmed that "blue straggler" stars, which appear younger and more massive than their neighbors, are spinning much more rapidly than normal stars, evidence that they formed from collisions or slow mergers within the crowded cores of globular clusters where a million stars may be crammed into a region just 20 light-years across.

Japan's Highly Advanced Laboratory for Communications and Astronomy (HALCA; "far away") radio astronomy satellite, launched on Feb. 12, 1997, deployed an 8-m (26-ft)-wide dish antenna to be used in very-long-baseline interferometry with radio telescopes on the Earth. At apogee the spacecraft was to achieve an altitude of 21,400 km (13,290 mi), which would provide a baseline at least twice as great as the diameter of the Earth.

Satellite studies of the region where the Earth meets the space environment completed their 40th year with the launches of the Advanced Composition Explorer and the Equator S spacecraft. The Advanced Composition Explorer was launched on August 25 to measure magnetic field, solar wind electrons and ions, and the energetic cosmic-ray ions before they encountered the Earth's magnetosphere. Equator S, the last spacecraft in the International Solar-Terrestrial Physics program, was launched on December 2 into an orbit ranging in altitude from 212 km (132 mi) to 35,901 km (22,308 mi) and closely aligned to the geographic Equator. Carrying seven science instruments—including an electron and ion monitor, an ion emitter to reduce the satellite's own electrical charge, an electric field meter, and a magnetometer, Equator S was designed to complement measurements by spacecraft that orbit through the polar and extended tail regions of the Earth's magnetosphere and into the solar wind outside the magnetosphere.

Observations with the Solar and Heliospheric Observatory (SOHO) mission launched in 1995 revealed that magnetic fields transfer energy from the Sun's relatively cool surface (6,000° C; 10,800° F) to its superhot corona (1.7 million° C; 3 million° F). Other observations by SOHO of oscillations in the Sun's visible surface revealed the presence of jet streams of gas traveling within the Sun.

A mission to study the effects of long-duration weightlessness on animals ended in tragedy with the death of one of two monkeys it carried. Russia's Bion 11, a joint effort with U.S. and French investigators, was flown Dec. 24, 1996–Jan. 7, 1997, carrying two monkeys, rats, and various insects and plants. Although the flight itself went as planned, one monkey died during surgery for tissue biopsies a week after landing. The ensuing controversy effectively ended flight experiments with primates for the foreseeable future.

APPLICATIONS SATELLITES

The Tropical Rainfall Measurement Mission (TRMM) was launched November 28 with four instruments—a microwave imager, a visible-infrared sensor, a lightning imager, and a precipitation radar—for detailed measurements of the movement of rain in the tropics between latitudes 35° N and 35° S. By mid-December TRMM already had returned stunning images showing moisture patterns between those latitudes and radar cross-section images of a typhoon.

The Lewis Small Spacecraft Technology Initiative satellite was launched on August 22 but was lost a week later. Lewis apparently developed an attitude-control problem that pointed its solar arrays away from the Sun. By the time ground controllers were back on duty (a part of the low-cost plan was part-time control), it was too weak to recover. It reentered the atmosphere in September. A companion craft, Clark, was canceled.

Another loss was Japan's Advanced Earth Observing Satellite (ADEOS; also known as Midori), launched Aug. 17, 1996. On June 30, 1997, a solar panel was broken, and the craft lost power. Although a collision with space debris was initially suspected, investigators later blamed a de-

sign flaw. The loss was a blow to international efforts to build a flotilla of research satellites that would monitor different aspects of the environment. It prompted NASA to authorize the quick development of a satellite using backup parts for the winds scatterometer; QuickSCAT was scheduled to be launched in November 1998. The U.S. also planned to launch the first Earth Observing System satellite (EOS AM-1) on an Atlas IIAS rocket in June.

The major news in communications satellites was the launch of 49 spacecraft in the Iridium constellation of communications satellites. Iridium 1 through 44 were launched in 1997 and 45 through 49 in early 1998. As many as seven were placed in orbit at one time. The name Iridium came from the original plan to employ 77 satellites (iridium's atomic number is 77); the number was later reduced to 66.

On December 23 eight Orbcomm satellites, FM 5 through 12, were launched by a Pegasus rocket. The Orbcomm series relayed locations (determined by the Global Positioning System satellites) from trucks and trains and data from oil pipelines. Iridium, Orbcomm, and similar systems soon to be launched relied on sensitive, low-noise radio technology and advanced packet switching technology (similar to cell phones) to hand off transmissions from one satellite as it set below the horizon to another as it rose.

Spain's Minisat 1 was launched on April 21, 1997, to carry out automated microgravity fluids experiments. Russia's Foton 11 satellite (October 9–23) carried microgravity sciences experiments and then returned to Earth. It also deployed Germany's Mirka satellite. Two Global

Positioning System satellites, Navstars 43 (July 22) and 38 (November 5), were launched following the loss of Navstar 42 on January 17 when its Delta 2 booster rocket failed.

On Aug. 1, 1997, Orbital Sciences Corp. launched the SeaStar satellite carrying the new Sea-Viewing Wide Field-of-View Sensor (SeaWiFs). NASA contracted with the corporation to provide satellite operations for five years; the data were also available commercially. SeaWiFs observed ocean color in green through near infrared, with an emphasis on chlorophyll, as part of NASA efforts to study the environment's carbon cycle from space.

LAUNCH VEHICLES

The Ariane 5 vehicle was launched on October 30, carrying two dummy satellites, to demonstrate its flight worthiness after the failure of its first launch in 1996. Even with the guidance problem solved, vehicle rotation caused the last of the propellant to slosh away from the feed lines to the engines, which thus caused them to shut down earlier than planned and placed the two dummy satellites in low orbits.

The U.S. Air Force surprised the space industry with its decision in November to select both of the competitors for the Evolved Expendable Launch Vehicle program rather than the expected "winner take all" choice. Because the selected vehicle would also be marketed to commercial users, the competition for the contract was intense. Civil launch demand was expected to be high in the 21st century, and the Air Force believed it would save money in the long run by purchasing competitively from two suppliers rather than one supplier.

Jacky Naegelen—Reuters

After the failure of its first launch in 1996, the Ariane 5 vehicle successfully lifts off from the launch pad on Oct. 30, 1997. Investigation of the failed first launch revealed that the rocket's guidance system had been adapted from the Ariane 4 design without proper modifications.

Consequently, the Air Force selected both the Boeing Co., which offered the Delta III and IV vehicles, and the Lockheed Martin Co., which offered a variant of its Atlas II series.

Boeing also moved forward with its plans to develop the Sea Launch system. The command and control ship was launched and outfitted, and shore facilities at the former U.S. Navy base at Long Beach, Calif., were opened in October 1997. The first launch was scheduled for 1998. A Russian-built Zenit 3SL rocket was to be transported by the command ship from St. Petersburg to Long Beach. The stages were to be integrated in the command ship, and the vehicle, complete with satellite payload, was to be loaded onto the launch platform. The ship would then sail to the central Pacific Ocean south of Hawaii, where the rocket, loaded with propellant, would be launched from the platform. The concept relied heavily on simplified and automated launch procedures that had been developed by the former Soviet Union.

During the past year Russia launched two START-1 rockets, so named for the Strategic Arms Reduction Talks treaty, which banned the use of the SS-25 ballistic missile as a weapon. Russia was allowed, however, to convert the SS-25 ballistic missile for use as a booster rocket, and it launched the Zeya military cartography satellite on March 4 and the EarlyBird spacecraft on December 24. In like manner, Lockheed Martin succeeded in introducing its Athena rocket, which was constructed from Minuteman I ballistic missile stages. Athenas then launched the Lewis remote sensing satellite and the Lunar Prospector craft.

Only four launch failures were recorded during 1997. A Delta 2 carrying a Global Positioning System satellite exploded on January 17. The fourth stage of a Russian Proton K launcher failed on December 24, leaving the Asiasat communications satellite in a useless orbit. Another Russian failure was a Zenit 2, which destroyed a military satellite on May 20. Brazil's Satellite Launch Vehicle (VLS) was destroyed shortly after liftoff on November 2 when one of its four first-stage solid rocket motors failed to ignite.

On November 14 ground was broken near Haystack Butte on Edwards Air Force Base in California to start construction of the launch facility for the X-33 Advanced Technology Demonstrator. Beginning in 1999 the X-33 was to make 15 suborbital flights in order to demonstrate new designs and technologies for a single-stage-to-orbit Reusable Launch Vehicle that should revolutionize space transportation in the 21st century. The X-33 ultimately would reach 13 times the speed of sound (Mach 13) in unmanned flights. The speed goal had originally been Mach 15, but engineers lowered their sights when the vehicle's weight increased. Earlier in the year the X-33 program had passed its critical design review, in which virtually all plans and details were approved for construction of the flight vehicle. A test model of the X-33's linear aerospike engine successfully operated while carried atop an SR-71 supersonic jet. This was the first time that an aerospike engine had been operated in flight. The tests provided valuable data on how the engine performs in the bumpy transition from subsonic to supersonic flight.

—Dave Dooling

Ric Feld—AP/Wide World

TRANSPORTATION

During the past year all modes of transportation made significant capital investments in advanced technologies in order to improve their infrastructures. Information- and computer-based systems were seen as integral to improving access and mobility for people and goods. Both the public and private sectors recognized the importance of continuing to integrate electronic communications into the planning, design, and operations of transportation improvements. Several noteworthy infrastructure projects contributed to the advancement of a seamless multimodal transportation system.

Intelligent transportation systems

Intelligent transportation systems (ITS) emerged during the year as the centerpiece of future transport systems. The increased use of sophisticated communication networks was expected to improve traffic operations, reduce traveler delays, enhance overall safety, and minimize the environmental impacts of ever-increasing travel demands. Recent ITS deployments included the construction of advanced traffic control management centers in major metropolitan areas, the presence of on-call traveler information devices, and a demonstration of "driverless" highway vehicles.

Advanced traffic management systems (ATMS) detect the movement of highway vehicles and transmit the current traffic conditions to a traffic control center. Prior to the 1996 Olympic Games in Atlanta, Ga., an ATMS was constructed to monitor incidents in the Atlanta area. The system's capabilities provided a showcase for the potential to detect traffic crashes quickly, dispatch appropriate emergency response teams, and clear accidents to regain traffic

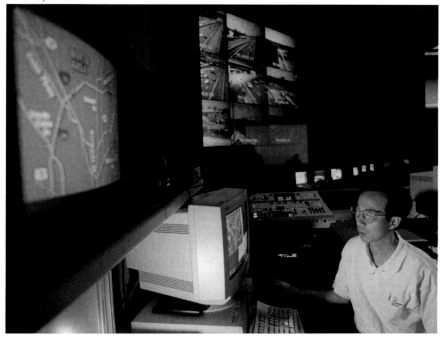

A software engineer inputs traffic information at the Transportation Management Center in Atlanta, Ga., in preparation for the 1996 Olympic Games. Atlanta's successful project showcased the potential of advanced traffic management systems to deal effectively with accidents and reestablish traffic flow.

flow. More than 300 video cameras continuously observed real-time vehicle operations. Changeable roadside message signs informed motorists of current conditions and provided instructions for taking alternative routes.

In addition to the ATMS in Atlanta, an advanced traveler information system (ATIS) was installed by the Georgia Department of Transportation. Its $14 million program, called the Traveler Information Showcase, was funded by the Federal Highway Administration (FHWA), the Federal Transit Administration (FTA), and state and local agencies and deployed six major technologies. First, more than 200 electronic information ("smart") kiosks were placed throughout downtown Atlanta and at the Hartsfield-Atlanta International Airport. These kiosks had the unique ability to provide real-time traffic and transit information. In addition to the kiosks, the showcase utilized handheld personal communication devices (PCDs). The PCD was a wireless communication device with a touch screen that enabled drivers to access real-time traffic information, electronic yellow pages, and mass transit schedules. In-vehicle navigation systems provided

motorists with the ability to request directions and the best route to a destination from a computer. Each of three on-line computer information services—cable television, interactive television, and Internet web pages—provided users with real-time traffic, speed, and accident data. These computer services were primarily used as a pretrip planning tool and allowed motorists to make route choices on the basis of time. Using all of these devices, Atlanta residents and visitors to the city were able to acquire information about congested areas, parking availability, and highway maintenance sites.

Chicago implemented a traffic signal master plan that used fiber-optic cable for communications and computers to monitor and supervise the system. The plan would improve the coordination and synchronization of the city's 2,700 signalized intersections. The ATMS connected each traffic signal to a central computer site, where operations were monitored and malfunctions detected. The total cost of implementation was estimated at $189 million, a savings of nearly 300% when compared with the estimated cost of almost $550 million to upgrade the current system.

The Port Authority of New York and New Jersey recently awarded an $18.5 million contract to design, install, and maintain an ATMS for the George Washington Bridge, which crosses the Hudson River to join New York City with its New Jersey suburbs. The new system was to include variable message signs, an automatic vehicle location (AVL) system for tracking vehicle locations relative to the bridge system, and an extensive vehicle detection system for sensing vehicle presence at specific locations. These advanced technologies were expected to increase the throughput of the bridge and also reduce operator fatigue and goods movement delays. The system would utilize an automated video detection device to determine the ideal Port Authority response vehicle, weather information, and travel advisories.

The "Travlink" operational test in the St. Paul–Minneapolis, Minn., area utilized an ATIS to provide real-time bus transit scheduling and a variety of real-time traffic reports. Travlink also used a computer-aided dispatch and AVL system to improve fleet management. Using smart kiosks, electronic signboards, and video display monitors, real-time traffic information was provided to travelers regarding the status of the 80 buses operating on Interstate 394, a major commuter corridor nearly 20 km (12 mi) long that connects major suburban areas of Minneapolis. Connected to a central computer, the ATIS tracked vehicles continuously to detect schedule and route deviations. Transit users could also access this information by using smart kiosks strategically located in three downtown business centers. The kiosks provided color graphics that mapped real-time bus locations and estimated arrival times.

During the year Japan was developing an advanced safety vehicle (ASV) prototype. The aim of the ASV project was to equip vehicles with sensors that could detect roadway surface conditions in order to avoid accidents. Also included in the ASV prototype were automatic steering and braking systems to lessen the damage resulting from collisions. It was estimated that ASVs might save more than 3,000 lives each year.

Four basic technologies were applied to the ASV prototype. The first, preventive safety technologies, detected driver drowsiness. This technology would have the capability to awaken a driver, and if the driver was not in the proper condition to control the vehicle, the automatic braking system would become operational. The second, accident avoidance technologies, monitored the vehicle's surrounding environment. If an accident was imminent, the driver would be warned. If conditions did not improve, the automatic braking system would be applied. The third and fourth technologies were designed to reduce collision and postcollision damage to both passengers and pedestrians. Using scanning radar, the system would warn drivers of nearby pedestrians. A warning message would be sounded to alert the driver, and if no action took place, the automatic braking system would be applied. High-performance scanning radar would be able to detect pedestrians at night at a distance of up to 45 m (148 ft).

The National Automated Highway System Consortium (NAHSC), a group comprising researchers from government, industry, and academia, proved the technical feasibility of full vehicle automation. The NAHSC indicated that an automated highway system (AHS) could reduce driver stress, pollution, congestion, and accidents. Entitled Demo '97, the international demonstration occurred in August 1997 along a 12.2-km (7.6-mi) stretch of Interstate 15 (I-15) in San Diego, Calif. Using platoons of automatically controlled Buick LeSabres and Honda Accords, researchers from the consortium gave live public demonstrations of these vehicles. Each car's speed and directional heading were controlled not by a driver but by onboard computers.

More than 92,000 magnets were installed into the roadway surface to provide guidance to the cars. Equipped with magnetic sensors that enabled them to determine their positions on the highway, the cars were able to travel exactly 6.4 m (21 ft) apart at 97 km/h (60 mph). Such a system had the potential to double roadway throughput capacity from 2,200 vehicles per hour per travel lane to more than 4,400 vehicles per hour per lane.

One car was programmed to demonstrate obstacle detection and avoidance as it merged into the platoon of vehicles on I-15. The programmed car broke away from the platoon, changed lanes, and rejoined the platoon from the rear. Vehicle-to-vehicle communication systems broadcast radio signals at a rate of 50 times per second to permit the automatic vehicle control. Each car in the platoon utilized the radar to report speed and acceleration rates to the vehicle behind it.

As of 1998, motor carriers traveling across the United States were required to receive shipment credentials from appropriate agencies in each state. During 1996, however, Maryland and Virginia had been selected by the FHWA to preview the Commercial Vehicle Information Systems and Networks (CVISN) project, which was being designed to provide the efficient movement of goods and services throughout North America. No longer would motor carriers have to stop in every state at inspection stations. Government agencies would be able to access and share electronically information related to motor carrier permits. By 1998 most states had the technology to implement such a project.

CVISN would include electronic credentialing, clearance, and roadside inspection technologies and the communications link connecting them. Data networks would be interconnected by a standard protocol. Users would have the ability to gather information related to a specific motor carrier identification, assemble it in standard form, and present the required information to the investigating agency. The computer-based credentialing system would allow carriers to submit hazardous materials permits, tax reports, and oversize/overweight permits to many state agencies simultaneously. The electronic

clearance system would allow compliant carriers to bypass weigh stations by using a transponder that would be interconnected to the station's computer. If a vehicle was not compliant, the transponder would trigger a red light that would signal the driver to pull into the weigh station for an inspection check.

A significant aspect of CVISN would be its ability to enhance public safety. Enforcement officials could effectively target those motor carriers who had unfavorable safety records. Using handheld computer units, law-enforcement personnel would be able to take a "snapshot" of the carrier's history from various databases that would include relevant credentialing and safety information. The public benefit from such a system would be the improvement in highway safety.

Road transport

Boston's Central Artery/Tunnel Project (CA/T), the "Big Dig," was the largest and

most complex highway infrastructure project ever to take place in the heart of a major American city. The construction was expected to take more than 10 years to complete, and the cost was now forecast at $10.8 billion for approximately 12.1 km (7.5 mi) of urban expressway. The project's goal was to depress the existing Interstate 93 (I-93) through downtown Boston and increase traffic capacity to minimize the 10-hour-long traffic jams that often occurred. I-93 (the Central Artery) was built in the 1950s to handle about 75,000 cars per day, but by 1998 it was accommodating approximately 190,000. Current projections indicated that this section of highway could be used by as many as 220,000 vehicles per day with 14 to 15 hours of congestion. The new expressway was to be an 8–10-lane highway located below ground level via a series of cuts and tunnels through the heart of downtown Boston.

One of the major construction feats of the CA/T was the Ted Williams Tunnel, a 2.6-km (1.6-mi) immersed tube cut-and-cover tunnel constructed under Boston Harbor. The project was completed in December 1995 as the first milestone of the CA/T and won the Outstanding Civil Engineering Achievement award for 1996. The project was estimated to be 40% complete by the end of 1997 and was expected to be fully completed by 2004.

Triple trailer trucks by 1998 were legal in 16 states of the U.S. The trucks could be a maximum of 33.6 m (110 ft) long, with most being 32 m and weighing about 115 tons, depending on load and cargo. A demonstration project in California explored the use of triple trailer trucks on the interstate highways in California between

During a demonstration of an automated highway system in San Diego, Calif., a Honda employee displays a hands-free driving technique while traveling at 89 km/h (55 mph). The speed and directional heading of each car in the demonstration were controlled not by a driver but by onboard computers.

Denis Poroy—AP/Wide World

southern California and Las Vegas, Nev. This led to a debate on triple trailer truck safety and functionality. Critics of lifting the freeze contended that triple trailer trucks compromise safety and damage the roads on which the trucks travel. They maintained that the extra hinge point of the triple trailer truck makes them more susceptible to jackknifing and loss of control. These critics also contended that the heavier loads of the triples would cause even more damage to the already suffering highway system.

Proponents of the triples offered statistics that showed that triples are no more dangerous than any other truck on the highway. In Nevada, for example, there were 50,045 accidents involving cars, 2,182 involving normal commercial vehicles, and only 6 accidents involving triples. Also, in Arizona no accidents involving triple trailers were reported. It is important to note that the number of triple trailer trucks in those states was relatively small and that most stayed on limited low-traffic highways.

Rail transport

Transportación Ferroviaria Mexicana (TFM) was engaged in revamping the Mexican rail industry during the past year. Jointly owned by Kansas City Southern Industries and Transportación Maritima Mexicana, TFM bid $1.4 billion to operate the 4,200-km (2,600-mi) Northeast Railroad of Mexico for 50 years. It was the first privatization of the Mexican railroad industry. Some of the most experienced American railroaders from such companies as Conrail and Santa Fe were enlisted to manage the system.

The goals of the privatization were to achieve a smooth transition between systems and to become comparable to the U.S. railroads. Among the driving forces of the rail industry in Mexico, accounting in large part for its increased profitability, were the lack of roads and the delays associated with overland trucking. The increasing efficiency of the Mexican rail system could be attributed to the mix of experienced rail people, the influx of necessary capital, and enhanced management strategies.

Collisions between trains and vehicles whose drivers had ignored rail crossing gates and other warning devices at highway-railroad grade crossings had by 1998 become the leading cause of fatalities within the railway industry. In an effort to address this problem, a $5.1 million project entitled "Sealed Corridor" was under way along the 280-km (174-mi) Raleigh–Greensboro–Charlotte rail line in North Carolina. This stretch of track, which was controlled by the Norfolk Southern Corp., had 130 public and 35 private railroad grade crossings. It was also designated a potential high-speed (train speeds of 145 km/h [90 mph]) rail corridor. To improve the grade crossings in the corridor, the project leaders were employing several technologies and strategies, including driver behavior studies by means of video surveillance and data collection; analyses of violator demographics; the use of median barriers, long gate arms, and four-quadrant gates; and the use of improved signs. The project was a partnership that included the North Carolina Department of Transportation, Norfolk Southern's Innovative Research Group, the Federal Railroad Administration (with in-

put from NASA's Jet Propulsion Laboratory), and the ITS Joint Program Office.

Air transport

During 1997 Logan International Airport in Boston handled more than 25 million passengers and 337,000 kg (743,000 lb) of cargo. It had become apparent, however, that the airport needed to be revamped in order to be able to handle the increased traffic and cargo of the 21st century. The airport was originally constructed to accommodate 50,000–60,000 passengers per day, but by 1998 the daily total exceeded 65,000. As of 1998, approximately $1 billion was to be invested in the infrastructure and systems of the airport. A new airport transfer connector to improve the intermodal capabilities of the airport was part of the planned improvements. It would provide bus and commuter rail connections to the airport as well as to the Ted Williams Tunnel and the South Boston Transit way. The connector was scheduled to be completed in three phases, with the first using existing roadways, the second separating the transit buses from the automobile traffic, and the third replacing the buses with an automated transit system within the airport.

First opened in 1974, the international facility at Logan was one of the biggest and most efficient of its kind. It was originally built to accommodate 600 passengers per hour, and upgrading completed in 1980 increased that number to 1,600. By 1998 approximately 1,700–1,900 passengers per hour traveled through the facility during peak periods. The new expanded facility was planned to accommodate 3,000 passengers per hour.

A new airport being constructed on Hong Kong's Chek Lap Kok Island is designed to have a capacity of 87 million passengers per year and a cargo capacity of 8.9 million metric tons per year. The total cost of the airport and its extensive supporting transportation projects is estimated at about $20 billion.

The new airport being constructed on Chek Lap Kok Island to serve Hong Kong was designed to have a capacity of 87 million passengers per year and an estimated cargo capacity of 8.9 million metric tons per year. The total estimated cost of the airport and its extensive supporting transportation projects was about $20 billion. The Airport Core Programme, as it was called, consisted of five major highway projects, a new railway, several kilometers of tunnels, a large suspension bridge, a viaduct, and an airport facility constructed on a 1,248-ha (3,084-ac) platform partially reclaimed from the sea. The highways were to navigate the harbor crossing by means of dual three-lane immersed road tunnels. There would also be a railway tunnel of an immersed tube design; it was to be 1,250 m (4,100 ft) long and 23 m (75 ft) below sea level. This tunnel was to be constructed of reinforced-concrete sections each weighing 20,000 tons. The railway itself was to be 34 km

(21 mi) long and would connect Chek Lap Kok with Hong Kong by means of 130-km/h (80-mph) train service at the rate of 35 trains per hour in each direction during peak hours. Other concerns about the construction of the tunnels included the coordination with harbor traffic and shipping lanes, which had to remain open and unobstructed during the construction process.

The Tsing Ma suspension bridge was built to provide the link for the two sections of highway and railway systems being constructed. The bridge was the longest double-deck single-span suspension bridge in the world. With cables consisting of 130,000 cu m (4,591,000 cu ft) of concrete and 47,000 tons of reinforcing bars, it was built to sustain typhoon winds of 300 km/h (185 mph). The main deck of the bridge weighed approximately 60,000 tons and was 41 m (134.5 ft) wide and 7.3 m (23.9 ft) deep. The deck had two levels, with the top level carrying an open twin three-lane highway and the enclosed bot-

tom level carrying the airport express railway and a twin two-lane highway to be used when winds were too high for the open top level to be used. The Lantau Link, which, in addition to the Tsing Ma bridge, comprised the Ma Wan viaduct and the Kap Shui Mun bridge, officially opened in April 1997. The airport itself was to have two 3,800-m (12,467-ft)-long runways. Early in 1998 it was on schedule for opening and operation in July 1998.

Marine transport

The dramatic increase in the liquefied natural gas (LNG) market led to an increase in size of the ships and of the fleets of carriers shipping LNG. In 1997 there were about 100 vessels transporting approximately 10.7 million cu m of LNG, equivalent to about 4.5 million tons. The newest ship in the fleet could transport 137,000 cu m (4,838,000 cu ft) of LNG. It transported its first load, of 60,000 tons, to Japan.

Fireworks explode over the Tsing Ma suspension bridge at its official opening on April 27, 1997. The 2.2-km (1.4-mi)-long bridge links the Hong Kong mainland to Chek Lap Kok and Lantau islands. The bridge is the longest double-deck single-span suspension bridge in the world.

Franki Chan—AP/Wide World

The ships used to transport LNG are unique in their requirements. Internal tanks are composed of thin stainless or high-nickel-content steel backed by a secondary barrier of rigid insulation. The LNG can be transported at a temperature of $-163°$ C ($-261.4°$ F); it must be insulated and could evaporate quickly. The vessels that transport LNG also are faster than other tankers (17–20 knots, compared with 14–16 knots) because of their comparatively lightweight cargo.

Legislation

In November 1997 the U.S. Congress agreed to a short-term extension of the Intermodal Surface Transportation Efficiency Act. The reason for doing so was that Congress could not agree to the funding levels to be appropriated for the nation's transportation infrastructure. Congress was expected to make further decisions on a long-term transportation reauthorization bill in 1998. The U.S. Department of Transportation identified eight goals for the reauthorized bill: (1) promote intermodalism, (2) improve planning and public participation, (3) empower state and local officials, (4) strengthen partnerships, (5) encourage performance management, (6) promote innovative financing, (7) encourage new technologies, and (8) encourage better infrastructure investment and management.

The reauthorization bill, referred to as BESTEA (Building Efficient Surface Transportation and Equity Act of 1997), would provide six years of surface transportation funding to include the following: fiscal year 1998, $24.9 billion for highways and highway safety and $5.4 billion for transit; fiscal year 1999, $28.5 billion for highways and highway safety and $5.9 billion for transit; fiscal years 2000, 2001, 2002, and 2003, $32 billion per year for highways and highway safety and $6.4 billion per year for transit.

Sustainable transportation

Limited public-sector financing, much of which would be applied to competing interests, justified new strategies for addressing the challenge of providing adequate and efficient transportation in future years. To ensure the public's desired level of travel, accessibility, and safety, information infrastructure was becoming a necessary supplemental transportation network. National and international telecommunication systems were becoming crucial for sustaining transportation services. The application of well-designed information technologies should help mitigate urban traffic congestion, improve safety, reduce environmental impacts, and increase economic productivity for all transportation users.

—John M. Mason

SCIENTISTS OF THE YEAR

NOBEL PRIZES

The 1997 Nobel Prizes were announced in Stockholm and Oslo on October 6–15. In the fields of chemistry, physics, and physiology or medicine, the awards recognized a striking diversity of individual achievements, including groundbreaking discoveries about enzymatic mechanisms underlying the synthesis and breakdown of adenosine triphosphate (ATP), a critical energy-carrying molecule in living cells; the development of methods to cool and trap atoms with laser light; and the controversial research of disease-causing agents, called prions, that could potentially lead to treatments for Alzheimer's disease. The following article describes the prizewinners and their work in detail.

NOBEL PRIZE FOR CHEMISTRY

A Dane, a Briton, and an American shared the 1997 Nobel Prize for Chemistry for discoveries about ATP synthase, an enzyme responsible for making ATP, the universal energy carrier in living cells. By means of energy-rich chemical bonds, the molecule ATP captures the chemical energy released from food and makes it available to cells for muscle contraction, transmission of nerve impulses, construction of cell components, and other processes. It serves this critical function, often described as the energy currency of cells, in living things ranging from microbes to humans.

The Royal Swedish Academy of Sciences awarded half of the $1 million prize to Paul D. Boyer of the University of California, Los Angeles (UCLA), and John E. Walker of the Medical Research Council (MRC) Laboratory of Molecular Biology, Cambridge, Eng. They were honored for research conducted independently that explained the way ATP synthase works as a catalyst in cells to promote the synthesis of ATP. The other half of the prize went to Jens C. Skou of Aarhus University, Århus, Den., for discovery of the first molecular pump in cells. Powered by ATP, molecular pumps are protein molecules that transport ions, or electrically charged atoms, through cell membranes. Skou discovered sodium, potassium-ATPase, a special enzyme that functions as such a pump by degrading ATP and using the released energy to power the transport process.

When Boyer began his research on ATP formation in the early 1950s, scientists knew that it was the energy carrier in living cells. ATP consists of a molecule of adenosine linked to a chain of three phosphate groups by high-energy bonds. Removal of a phosphate group releases the stored energy for use by cells. In the process ATP becomes adenosine diphosphate (ADP). With help from chemical energy in food, a phosphate can be added to ADP, producing more ATP. In the late 1970s Boyer proposed the "binding-change hypothesis," a detailed elucidation of the mechanism by

Sharing the 1997 Nobel Prize for Chemistry were John E. Walker (left), Paul D. Boyer (center), and Jens C. Skou (right).

which ATPase catalyzes synthesis of ATP from ADP and phosphate.

"Walker's work complements Boyer's in a remarkable manner," the Swedish Academy stated. Walker, who began studies on ATP synthase in the early 1980s, verified that the mechanism proposed by Boyer was valid. In the 1980s Walker deciphered the sequence, or linear arrangement, of the amino acid building blocks of ATP synthase. He added further evidence in the 1990s by obtaining the first high-resolution crystal structure of the active part of ATP synthase. All of Walker's structural clarifications were consistent with Boyer's mechanism.

Skou was honored for research that he had done in the late 1950s. He established sodium, potassium-ATPase as the first enzyme known to promote transport of ions through cell membranes. Such transport maintains normal concentrations of sodium, potassium, and other chemicals in cells. Sodium concentration inside cells is lower than outside, and potassium concentration is higher inside than out. When, for example, a nerve cell transmits an impulse, sodium ions pour into the cell, increasing their internal concentration. They must be transported out of the cell for it to fire again. That transport requires energy, which sodium, potassium-ATPase acquires by detaching phosphate groups from ATP molecules.

Other researchers later discovered more ion pumps with similar structures and functions. A calcium pump, for instance, helps to control muscle contraction, and a hydrogen pump produces hydrochloric acid in the stomach. Popular drugs used to treat stomach ulcers and gastritis work by inhibiting action of the pump enzyme.

Boyer was born on July 31, 1918, in Provo, Utah, and received a doctoral degree in biochemistry from the University of Wisconsin at Madison. After joining UCLA in 1963, he directed the institution's Molecular Biology Institute (1965–83) and became professor emeritus of chemistry and biochemistry (1990). Walker was born on Jan. 7, 1941, in Halifax, Eng., and received a Ph.D. from the University of Oxford. In 1982 he became senior scientist at the MRC Laboratory of Molecular Biology. Skou, born on Oct. 8, 1918, in Lemvig, Den., trained in medicine at the University of Copenhagen and earned a Ph.D. from Aarhus University, where he became professor of physiology (1963). In 1977 he was made professor of biophysics at Aarhus.

NOBEL PRIZE FOR PHYSICS
The 1997 Nobel Prize for Physics was awarded to two American scientists and a French colleague for developing techniques for using laser light to cool and trap atoms so that they can be studied in detail. Other scientists extended the methods in 1995 to achieve a new state of matter termed a Bose-Einstein condensate and in 1997 to make an atom laser.

Additional applications "are just around the corner," stated the Royal Swedish Academy of Sciences, which awarded the prize. It cited superior atomic clocks for more accurate determinations of position on Earth and in space and new ways of making very small electronic components. "The new methods ... have contributed greatly to increasing our knowledge of the interplay between radiation and matter," the Nobel citation added.

The prize was shared by Steven Chu of Stanford University, William D. Phillips of the National Institute of Standards and Technology, Gaithersburg, Md., and Claude N. Cohen-Tannoudji of the Collège de France and the École Normale Supérieure, Paris. Chu was born on Feb. 28, 1948, in St. Louis, Mo. He graduated from the University of Rochester, N.Y., in 1970. He received a doctoral degree in physics in 1976 from the University of California, Berkeley, and in 1990 he became a professor at Stanford. Phillips, born on Nov. 5, 1948, in Wilkes-Barre, Pa., received a doctoral degree in physics (1976) from the Massachusetts Institute of Technology. Cohen-Tannoudji was born on April 1, 1933, in Constantine, Alg. He was educated at the École Normale, receiving a doctoral degree in physics in 1962.

The three physicists worked independently, each moving the technology farther ahead. In 1985 Chu and his co-workers at Bell Laboratories, Holmdel, N.J., developed the original method for cooling atoms. The techniques were needed because atoms and molecules in gases move so fast—e.g., 4,000 km/h (2,500 mph) for atoms and molecules in air at room temperature—that detailed observations are difficult. Scientists knew that lowering the temperature could reduce the speed of the particles. To slow atomic and molecular motion enough for detailed study, intense chilling to temperatures near absolute zero (0 K, or −273.15° C, or −459.67° F) was needed. At such cold temperatures, however, gases normally condense and freeze.

Chu and associates made an apparatus that allowed gases to be chilled to within a fraction of a degree of absolute zero without freezing. It consisted of six laser beams that bombard the gas's constituent particles from all directions, slowing their motion. The laser light acts much like an extremely thick liquid, which has been dubbed optical molasses, that slows movement of the particles. Individual atoms thus can be studied in great detail, and scientists can get glimpses of their inner structure, the Royal Academy observed.

The apparatus created a glowing pea-sized cloud containing about one million chilled atoms. In the initial experiments Chu's group cooled atoms to a temperature of about 240 μK (microkelvins), or 240 millionths of a degree above absolute zero. Atoms at that temperature were slowed to a speed of about 30 cm (12 in) per second. Subsequent addition of magnetic coils to Chu's device allowed scientists to trap the atoms so that they could be studied or used for experiments.

Phillips and his associates designed a similar experiment, developing several new methods for measuring temperature. By 1988 his group had achieved temperatures of 40 μK. Between 1988 and 1995 Cohen-Tannoudji and his colleagues made further advances, finally cooling atoms to a temperature within 1 μK, which corresponded to a speed of only 2 cm (0.8 in) per second.

"Intensive development is in progress concerning laser cooling and the capture of neutral atoms," the Academy noted. "Among other things, Chu has constructed an atomic fountain, in which laser-cooled atoms are sprayed up from a trap like jets of water." Chu visualized the device as the basis of a new generation of ultraprecise atomic clocks. Existing atomic clocks are accurate to about one second in 32 million years. Chu's work could make them accurate to one second in three billion years.

NOBEL PRIZE FOR PHYSIOLOGY OR MEDICINE

An American scientist who discovered an entirely new kind of disease-causing agent, called a prion, won the 1997 Nobel Prize for Physiology or Medicine. Prions are believed to cause a number of degenerative brain diseases in humans and other animals. They include bovine spongiform encephalopathy (BSE), or "mad cow" disease, which forced wide destruction of

cattle herds in the U.K. beginning in the late 1980s, and Creutzfeldt-Jakob disease (CJD) in humans. Recent evidence suggested that a newly discovered variant of CJD can be transmitted from cows with BSE to humans.

The Nobel Assembly of the Karolinska Institute, Stockholm, awarded the prize to Stanley B. Prusiner of the University of California, San Francisco. It was the first time since 1987 that the prize had gone to a single scientist. Nobel Prizes often have recognized originators of unpopular theories who were finally vindicated after years of struggle against opposition from colleagues. As of 1997, however, the prion controversy showed little sign of ending, with skeptics questioning whether prions exist

Winning the 1997 Nobel Prize for Physics were Steven Chu (left), William D. Phillips (below left), and Claude N. Cohen-Tannoudji (below right).

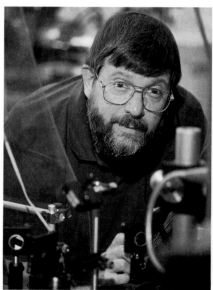

and with some insisting that BSE, CJD, and other diseases actually are caused by still-undiscovered viruses.

"Stanley Prusiner has added prions to the list of well-known infectious agents including bacteria, viruses, fungi and parasites," the Nobel Assembly stated. "[His] discovery provides important insights that may furnish the basis to understand the biological mechanisms underlying other types of dementia-related diseases, for example Alzheimer's disease, and establishes a foundation for drug development and new types of medical treatment strategies."

Born on May 28, 1942, in Des Moines, Iowa, Prusiner grew up in Cincinnati, Ohio, and was educated at the University

Stanley B. Prusiner won the 1997 Nobel Prize for Physiology or Medicine.

of Pennsylvania (A.B., 1964; M.D., 1968). He spent four years in biochemical research before becoming (1972) a resident in neurology at the University of California, San Francisco, School of Medicine. Prusiner joined the faculty there in 1974 and became a professor of neurology and biochemistry. While a neurology resident, he was in charge of a patient who died of CJD, a rare brain disease that results in dementia. Other scientists had established that CJD, and related conditions termed kuru and scrapie, could be transmitted in brain tissue. Kuru occurred among cannibalistic people in Papua New Guinea who ate the brains of tribesmen who had been infected with kuru. Scrapie is a brain disease in sheep that causes the animals to scratch and scrape off their skin. Nevertheless, no conventional agent could be isolated from infected tissue. The tissue remained infectious despite treatment that would have destroyed the DNA or RNA of any viruses or bacteria present.

Scientists had proposed several theories about the kind of agent responsible for these diseases. Some blamed an unusual, slow-acting virus. In the 1960s British scientists Tikvah Alper and J.S. Griffith proposed that an infectious agent lacking nucleic acid could cause scrapie. "[It was] a sensational hypothesis since at the time all known infectious agents contained the hereditary material DNA or RNA," the Nobel Assembly explained.

Prusiner and his associates embraced this idea. By 1982 they had announced discovery of a protein in the brains of scrapie-infected hamsters that was not present in healthy animals. To describe this infectious particle, Prusiner coined the term *prion*. Whereas "the scientific com-

munity greeted this discovery with great skepticism," the Assembly stated, "an unwavering Prusiner continued the arduous task to define the precise nature of this novel infectious agent."

Prusiner's group later showed that humans and other animals have a gene that specifies the production of prion protein. The protein's amino acid chain can fold into two distinct forms with different three-dimensional structures. One is a tightly coiled, unstable, normal form that does not cause disease. The other is an unwound, more stable, abnormal form. Prusiner's research indicated that the abnormal protein causes CJD, scrapie, and other prion diseases by a catalytic process in which it, on contact with the normal protein, causes the latter to change its structure and become abnormal. In a chain reaction ever more of the abnormal protein is produced, and after months or years it finally accumulates to levels that cause obvious brain damage.

Prusiner's work could help scientists understand Alzheimer's disease and other more common brain disorders. For example, some researchers believed that Alzheimer's disease is caused by a structural change in certain nonprion proteins, which leads to the accumulation of abnormal deposits in the brain. His research also suggested possible ways of treating and preventing prion diseases in humans and animals. Prusiner's group, for instance, was trying to develop drugs that attach to normal prion protein and stabilize it, so that the protein resists unwinding. As a preventive approach Prusiner also suggested breeding sheep and cows that lack the prion gene, which did not seem essential for normal life.

—Michael Woods

OBITUARIES

Cousteau, Jacques-Yves
June 11, 1910—June 25, 1997

French oceanographer, filmmaker, and inventor Jacques Cousteau popularized the study of marine environments through numerous books, films, and television programs that chronicled his undersea investigations. Though not formally trained as a scientist, Cousteau was drawn to undersea exploration by his love both of the ocean and of diving. After graduating from France's naval academy in 1933, he was commissioned a second lieutenant. His plans to become a navy pilot were undermined by an almost fatal automobile accident in which both of his arms were broken. During his convalescence he discovered goggle diving, and his fascination with the sport inspired him to design, with Émile Gagnan, the aqualung, also known as scuba (self-contained underwater breathing apparatus), which became commercially available in 1946. Cousteau helped to invent many other tools useful to oceanographers, including the diving saucer—a small, easily maneuverable submarine for seafloor exploration—and a number of underwater cameras. He served in World War II as a gunnery officer in France and was also a member of the French Resistance. He later was awarded the Legion of Honour for his espionage work. Cousteau's experiments with underwater filmmaking began during the war, and when the war ended, he continued this work by founding and heading the French navy's Undersea Research Group. To expand his work in marine exploration, he founded numerous marketing, manufacturing, engineering, and research organiza-

Jacques Cousteau

tions, which were incorporated (1973) as the Cousteau Group. In 1950 Cousteau converted a British minesweeper into the *Calypso,* an oceanographic research ship aboard which he and his crew carried out numerous expeditions. He gained international recognition with the publication of *The Silent World* (1953), the first of many books. Two years later he adapted the book into a documentary film that won both the Palme d'Or at the 1956 Cannes International Film Festival and an Academy Award in 1957, one of three Oscars his films received. Cousteau retired from the navy in 1956 with the rank of captain and served as director of the Oceanographic

Institute and Museum in Monaco. In the early 1960s he conducted experiments in underwater living in undersea laboratories called Conshelf I, II, and III. Cousteau produced and starred in many television programs, including "The Undersea World of Jacques Cousteau" (1968–76). In 1974 he formed the Cousteau Society, a nonprofit environmental group. His last book, *Man, the Octopus, and the Orchid,* was published posthumously.

Dicke, Robert Henry
May 6, 1916—March 4, 1997

American physicist Robert Dicke worked in such wide-ranging fields as microwave physics, cosmology, and relativity and was noted as both an inspired theorist and a successful experimentalist. Dicke earned an A.B. (1939) from Princeton University and a Ph.D. in physics (1941) from the University of Rochester, N.Y. After graduation he joined the Radiation Laboratory at the Massachusetts Institute of Technology, where during World War II he made significant contributions to radar technology and microwave-circuit systems. Through high-precision gravitational experiments, Dicke confirmed a concept integral to Einstein's general theory of relativity, the equivalence principle, which states that the gravitational mass of a body is equal to its inertial mass. Dicke was an early proponent of the big-bang theory of the origin of the universe, and in the 1960s he and several colleagues proposed that a remnant of that explosive origin should pervade the universe in the form of detectable radiation of microwave wavelengths. Before Dicke was able to confirm this hypothesis through observation, two other investigators, Robert Wilson and Arno Penzias, detected the microwave background radiation, a discovery for which they eventually were awarded the Nobel Prize for Physics in 1978. Dicke joined the faculty of Princeton in 1946, rose to full professor in 1957, and was appointed Albert Einstein professor of science in 1975, becoming professor emeritus in 1984. Dicke was elected to the National Academy of Sciences in 1967 and received its Comstock Prize in 1973. Among other numerous awards he received in recognition of his scientific achievements were the National Medal of Science (1971) and NASA's Exceptional Scientific Achievement Medal (1973). His writings include *Principles of*

Sir John Eccles, with his wife

Microwave Circuits (1948; with Carol G. Montgomery and Edward M. Purcell) and *Gravitation and the Universe* (1970).

Eccles, Sir John Carew
Jan. 27, 1903—May 2, 1997

Australian neurophysiologist Sir John Eccles discovered many aspects of the vertebrate nervous system, notably how nerve impulses are transmitted between neurons, or nerve cells, work for which he shared the 1963 Nobel Prize for Physiology or Medicine with Alan L. Hodgkin and Andrew F. Huxley. Eccles's prizewinning research showed that one neuron communicates with a closely adjacent neuron by releasing chemicals into the synapse, the narrow space between the two cells. The chemicals, called neurotransmitters, cross the synapse and bind to the second cell, either activating or inhibiting it. His findings resolved a long-standing debate over

whether nerve cell communication occurs through chemical or electrical means. Eccles studied biology and medicine at Melbourne University (M.B. and B.S.; 1925), where he qualified for a Rhodes scholarship. At the University of Oxford, he studied with leading neurophysiologist Sir Charles Scott Sherrington. After graduating (1929; Ph.D.) Eccles taught and conducted research at Oxford until 1937, when he returned to Australia to become director of the Kanematsu Memorial Institute of Pathology, Sydney. During World War II he was a medical consultant to the Australian army. Eccles then served (1944–51) as professor of physiology at the University of Otago, Dunedin, N.Z., before heading (1952–66) the physiology department at the Australian National University, Canberra. Facing mandatory retirement, he left Australia and continued his work (1966–68) at the Institute for Biomedical Research, Chicago, and the State University of New York at Buffalo, where he was distinguished professor of physiology (1968–75). He was elected (1941) to the Royal Society of London and received (1962) the Royal Medal. He served as president of the Australian Academy of Science (1957–61) and was knighted in 1958. In addition to the more than 500 scientific papers that he published, Eccles was the author of a number of books, including the purely scientific *The Physiology of Nerve Cells* (1957) and the philosophical *Facing Reality: Philosophical Adventures by a Brain Scientist* (1970).

Essen, Louis
Sept. 6, 1908—Aug. 24, 1997

British physicist Louis Essen built the cesium-beam atomic clock, a device that ultimately changed the way time is measured. Atomic clocks measure the passage of time by using a device that counts the extremely regular waves of electromagnetic radiation emitted from atoms. This new method of timekeeping generated a more accurate time scale than was previously possible and eventually, in 1967, replaced the astronomical methods used until then to determine the international time standard. Essen developed the clock in 1955 with his collaborator J.V.L. Parry at the National Physical Laboratory in Teddington, Middlesex, Eng. Essen began working at the laboratory in 1929, not long after receiving his B.Sc. in physics (1928) from the University of London, where he also earned a Ph.D. (1941) and D.Sc. (1948). There he began his career-long focus on the physics of frequency generation and measurement. In 1938 he developed the Essen quartz ring clock, a highly stable timepiece that allowed measurement of the seasonal variations in the Earth's rate of rotation. During World War II Essen devised a number of instruments to measure radio waves, such as the cavity resonance wavemeter, and after the war he used these devices to measure the velocity of light. In 1946 his measurements, carried out with A.C. Gordon-Smith, showed that light travels 16 km (10 mi) per second faster than the value accepted at the time. Essen's expertise in measuring time and velocity led him to question some aspects of Einstein's theories, criticisms he detailed in his paper *The Special Theory of Relativity: A Critical Analysis*. Essen received numerous honors, including the A.S. Popov Gold Medal from the U.S.S.R. Academy of Sciences in 1959, the same year he was made an O.B.E. In 1960 he was elected a fellow of the Royal Society of London.

Frankl, Viktor
March 26, 1905—Sept. 2, 1997

Austrian psychiatrist and psychotherapist Viktor Frankl developed the psychological approach known as logotherapy, widely recognized as the "third school" of Viennese psychotherapy after the "first school" of Sigmund Freud and the "second school" of Alfred Adler. The basis of Frankl's theory was that the primary motivation of an individual is the search for meaning in life and that the primary purpose of psychotherapy should be to help the individual find that meaning. As a teenager he entered into a correspondence with Freud, who asked permission to publish one of his papers. After graduating from the University of Vienna Medical School in 1930, Frankl joined the staff of the Am Steinhof psychiatric hospital in Vienna. By 1938 he had become chief of neurology at Vienna's Rothschild Hospital. Anti-Semitism was on the rise, however, and in 1942 Frankl and his family were sent to the concentration camps, where his mother, father, and wife perished. As he observed the brutality and degradation around him, Frankl theorized that those inmates who had some meaning in their lives were more likely to survive. Following liberation, Frankl returned to Vienna, where he became head of the neurological department at the Polyclinic Hospital. He also produced the classic book *Man's Search for Meaning* (1946), which he dictated to a team of assistants in nine days and which went on to sell some nine million copies in 26 languages. Frankl also taught at the University of Vienna until 1990 and held chairs at a number of American universities. A few months before his death, he published *Man's Search for Ultimate Meaning and Recollections: An Autobiography*.

Fukui, Kenichi
Oct. 4, 1918—Jan. 9, 1998

Japanese theoretical chemist Kenichi Fukui applied a variety of concepts in physics to research that revolutionized the understanding of how chemical reactions take place. His work was based on a mathematical analysis of the actions of electrons as they are exchanged between atoms and molecules during a chemical reaction. Applying principles of quantum physics and using related mathematical treatments, he analyzed the properties that these electrons exhibit during and after reactions. Fukui theorized that in many chemical reactions it is the electrons in the outer or-

Svenskt Pressefoto/Archive Photos

Kenichi Fukui

bitals—those regions of space occupied by electrons farthest from the atomic nuclei—that determine the pathway of the reaction and its final products. To the crucial configurations in which electrons in these outer orbitals participate during reactions, Fukui gave the name *frontier orbitals*. Although he had first set forth his theory in a 1952 paper and went on to publish more than 270 papers on frontier orbitals, his work received little initial notice owing to the obscurity of the English-language journals that carried most of his papers and the extremely complex nature of his calculations. He and Roald Hoffmann shared the 1981 Nobel Prize for Chemistry for their independent work on the theoretical analysis of chemical reactions. Fukui's theories have enabled scientists to predict chemical reaction pathways more precisely and have led to many advances in the pharmaceutical and chemical-synthesis industries.

Fukui was awarded (1948) a doctorate from Kyoto University, where he served as a professor of physical chemistry (1951–82). He was the president of the Kyoto Institute of Technology from 1982 to 1988. In 1981 Fukui was elected a foreign member of the U.S. National Academy of Sciences, and he was also the recipient of the Japanese Order of Culture.

Hershey, Alfred Day
Dec. 4, 1908—May 22, 1997

American biochemist Alfred Hershey was recognized as one of the founders of molecular genetics and shared the 1969 Nobel Prize for Physiology or Medicine with Salvador Luria and Max Delbrück, two other giants in the field. The three were honored for their enormous contributions to the understanding of genetic processes and of the fundamental role of nucleic acid in the transmission of inherited characteristics.

Alfred Hershey

Hershey carried out experiments primarily on bacteriophages or phages, viruses that infect bacteria. In the early 1940s Hershey, Luria, and Delbrück formed the core of the "phage group," an informal association of scientists from a variety of laboratories who collaborated in the study of bacteriophages. Hershey's research demonstrated the occurrence of such basic viral phenomena as the spontaneous mutation of genetic, heritable factors and the ability of genetic material from different viral particles to recombine—discoveries that helped other investigators devise methods to combat major disease-causing viruses. This work also led to a greater understanding of the molecular mechanisms by which all organisms, including humans, inherit genetic information. Hershey's best-known experiment was carried out in 1952 with his assistant Martha Chase at Cold Spring Harbor (N.Y.) Laboratory. Their work, of-

UPI/Corbis-Bettmann

ten referred to as the "blender experiment" in deference to the common household appliance they employed, demonstrated that DNA alone, and not protein, is the stuff of which genes are made. That discovery, together with James Watson and Francis Crick's elucidation of the structure of DNA the next year, paved the way for scientists to study the molecular basis of inheritance. After earning (1934) a doctorate in chemistry from Michigan State College, Hershey taught at Washington University School of Medicine, St. Louis, Mo., where he remained until 1950. That year he joined the research staff of the department of genetics (later renamed the Genetics Research Unit) of the Carnegie Institution of Washington at Cold Spring Harbor. He was named director of the unit in 1962 and retired in 1974. In addition to the Nobel Prize, Hershey was awarded the Albert Lasker Award (1958) and the Kimber Genetics Award (1965). He was also elected (1958) a member of the U.S. National Academy of Sciences.

Hill, Dorothy
Sept. 10, 1907—April 23, 1997

Australian paleontologist Dorothy Hill was a prominent geologist and achieved worldwide renown as an authority on fossil corals. One of the most highly regarded woman scientists of her era, she amassed an impressive list of firsts—among them, first woman fellow (1956) of the Australian Academy of Science, first woman professor (1959) at an Australian university, first Australian woman elected (1965) to the Royal Society, and first woman president (1970) of the Australian Academy of Science. Although as a geology student at the University of Queensland (B.Sc., 1928;

D.Sc., 1942), Hill specialized in paleontology partly because it was deemed a suitable field for a woman, she became fascinated with Paleozoic Era fossil corals after discovering a deposit during a visit to a small town in Queensland. She was awarded a scholarship to the University of Cambridge, where she received a Ph.D. in 1932. Continuing her research there, she compared her Australian fossils with those of the same age found in the U.K. and then reviewed and thoroughly revised the descriptions of the British fossils. In 1937 Hill returned to the University of Queensland, and except for World War II service in the Women's Royal Australian Naval Service (1942–45), she spent the remainder of her career there, becoming research professor of geology in 1959 and achieving emeritus status in 1973. In the 1940s and '50s she helped establish the Great Barrier Reef Committee's research efforts. Hill's work, which included over 100 scientific papers, contributed immensely to knowledge of not only invertebrate paleontology but also Queensland's stratigraphy and geology, and this in turn brought about an increase in mineral exploration. She was created C.B.E. in 1971; the following year the Dorothy Hill Chair in Palaeontology and Stratigraphy was established in her honor at the University of Queensland.

Kendrew, Sir John Cowdery
March 24, 1917—Aug. 23, 1997

British biochemist Sir John Kendrew deduced the structure of the muscle protein myoglobin, and for this work he was awarded the 1962 Nobel Prize for Chemistry along with colleague Max Perutz, who worked out the structure of the related protein, hemoglobin. Kendrew's work was

groundbreaking because it was the first time that the three-dimensional conformation of a protein had been solved, and this knowledge led to the understanding of how myoglobin binds and transports oxygen in muscles. He studied physical chemistry at Trinity College, Cambridge (B.A.; 1939), but his studies were interrupted by World War II. Kendrew joined the Air Ministry to work on airborne radar and then served as scientific adviser to the Allied Air Command, eventually finishing his wartime service in Southeast Asia. There he met the physicist and X-ray crystallographer J.D. Bernal, who stimulated his interest in the study of proteins. Kendrew began working at the Cavendish Laboratory in Cambridge with Perutz, who was using X-ray crystallographic techniques to unravel protein structure. Kendrew received a doctorate in physics in 1949, whereupon he turned his attention to myoglobin. By 1959, as the result of laborious studies of the patterns into which crystallized samples of myoglobin diffracted X-ray beams, he had elucidated the protein's structure. After receiving the Nobel Prize, Kendrew shifted from laboratory work to administration. He served as deputy chairman of the department at Cambridge that he and Perutz created, the Medical Research Council Unit for Molecular Biology (now called the Laboratory of Molecular Biology). His influence led to the creation of the European Molecular Biology Laboratory in Heidelberg, Ger., where he served (1975–82) as director. In 1981 he was appointed president of St. John's College, Oxford. Kendrew became a fellow of the Royal Society in 1960, was knighted in 1963, and received the Royal Medal in 1965. He founded the *Journal of Molecular Biology* in 1959 and served as its editor in chief until 1987. He was the author of *The Thread of Life: An Introduction to Molecular Biology* (1966).

Porter, Keith Roberts
June 11, 1912—May 2, 1997

Canadian-born American cell biologist Keith Porter was one of the founding fathers of modern cell biology and pioneered the use of the electron microscope to observe biological cells and the fine structures within them. While working in the 1940s at the Rockefeller Institute (later Rockefeller University), New York City, Porter developed a technique called whole-mount electron microscopy, by which images of single, complete cells, magnified about 100,000 times, were produced. The procedure provided a window through which scientists were able to view the internal organization of the cell in detail for the first time. As an undergraduate, Porter studied biology at Acadia University, Wolfville, N.S., and he went on to receive a doctorate in biology (1938) from Harvard University. After graduation he moved (1939) to the Rockefeller Institute, where during the 1940s and '50s he and colleague George Palade, along with other scientists, made many significant contributions to the study of cell structure, including the understanding that cells are divided and, in large part, organized by highly convoluted networks of skeletal-like microtubules and membranous sacs. In 1961 Porter returned to Harvard, and he later (1965–67) served as chairman of the biology department. He moved on in 1968 to establish and head the department of molecular, cellular, and developmental biology at the University of Colorado at Boulder. After relinquishing the chairmanship in 1975, Porter worked for several years as part-time director of the Marine Biological Laboratory at Woods Hole, Mass. He helped organize the American Society for Cell Biology and the Tissue Culture Association and also was instrumental in starting the *Journal of Biophysical and Biochemical Cytology,* now the *Journal of Cell Biology.* Porter was elected to the U.S. National Academy of Sciences in 1964 and received a number of prestigious awards, including the National Medal of Science (1977). In addition to writing more than 200 scientific papers, he published several books, notably *An Introduction to the Fine Structure of Cells and Tissues* (1963; with Mary Bonneville).

Prelog, Vladimir
July 23, 1906—Jan. 7, 1998

Swiss chemist Vladimir Prelog pioneered research in several areas of molecular structure and function and made important discoveries about the way that atomic arrangements determine the chemical properties of many biological molecules. Along with John Warcup Cornforth, he was awarded the 1975 Nobel Prize for Chemistry for his work on the molecular architecture of cholesterol, antibiotics, and antimalarial alkaloids. Six years after earning a doctorate (1929) from the Institute Technical School of Chemistry in Prague, Prelog became a lecturer at the University of Zagreb, Croatia, but fled to Switzerland in 1942 to escape German occupation. There he accepted an offer to work at the Swiss Federal Institute of Technology, Zürich, with his mentor, 1939 Nobel Prize winner Leopold Ruzicka, whose research helped establish the field of stereochemistry, which examines the properties of chemical compounds on the basis of the three-dimensional arrangement of their atoms. Prelog focused on chirality—functional differences based on the mirror-image relationship, or left- and right-handedness, of otherwise identical chemical structures—and helped establish the chiral nomenclature system. His work with steroids, antibiotics, and antimicrobial chemical structures, including nonactins and rifamycin, facilitated a variety of pharmaceutical advances. A well-traveled and internationally acclaimed lecturer, Prelog was elected a foreign member of the U.S. National Academy of Sciences in 1961 and became a member of the Royal Academy of Britain in 1962. He served as director (1957–65) of the Swiss Federal Institute of Technology's laboratory of organic chemistry, where he continued to teach until his retirement in 1976.

Purcell, Edward Mills
Aug. 30, 1912—March 7, 1997

American physicist Edward Purcell shared the 1952 Nobel Prize for Physics with Felix Bloch for having independently developed nuclear magnetic resonance (NMR), a method used to detect and measure the magnetic fields of atomic nuclei and a powerful tool for investigating molecular structures and chemical interactions. Purcell's work formed the basis of spectroscopic and imaging techniques with applications ranging from chemical analysis and radio astronomy to medical diagnosis. He studied electrical engineering as an undergraduate at Purdue University, West Lafayette, Ind., during which time he developed an interest in physics. After graduation (B.S., 1933) he spent a year at the Technische Hochschule in Karlsruhe, Ger., studying physics as an international exchange student. On returning to the United States, he enrolled at Harvard University, receiving a master's degree (1935) and doctorate (1938) in physics. Purcell, who spent most of his career at Harvard, served as an instructor there until 1941 and as a full professor from 1949 until his retirement in 1980. He took a brief leave of absence from the university during World War II, however, when he contributed to the war effort as a member of a research team investigating shortwave radar at the Massachusetts Institute of Technology. He returned to Harvard in 1946 and soon thereafter developed NMR methodology for measuring magnetic fields in atomic nuclei. In 1951 Purcell applied the principles of this discovery to detecting the wavelengths of radiation emitted from neutral hydrogen clouds in space. His research proved useful to astronomers attempting to map galactic structures in the universe. Purcell wrote a number of classic books on microwaves, electricity, and magnetism, including *Physics: For Science and Engineering Students* (1952), which he co-authored, and *Electricity and Magnetism* (1965). He was elected to the National Academy of Sciences in 1951 and received the National Medal of Science from the National Science Foundation in 1978.

Rossi, Aldo
May 3, 1931—Sept. 4, 1997

Italian architect Aldo Rossi created simple yet powerful works by using such geometric shapes as cones, cylinders, and squares and by making skillful use of light and shadow. Rossi was educated at the Milan Polytechnic and following graduation (1959) went to work for the design magazine *Casabella*, becoming its editor in 1964. In 1966 he set forth his architecture theories in *L'architettura della città* (*The Architecture of the City*, 1982), which established his reputation as a theorist and became an influential classic. He later published the manifesto *Architettura razionale* (1973) and *A Scientific Autobiography* (1981). Considered Rossi's most famous design was the Cemetery of San Cataldo in Modena, Italy (1971–77), in which a simple cube-shaped ossuary is surrounded by an apparently unending colonnade. Other well-known works were the Teatro del Mondo, created for the 1980 Venice Biennale; the Museum of Maastricht, Neth.; and the Hotel Il Palazzo in Fukuoka, Japan. In 1990 Rossi was honored with the Pritzker Prize, architecture's highest award.

Rudolph, Paul
Oct. 23, 1918—Aug. 8, 1997

American architect Paul Rudolph became one of the most eminent postwar Modernist architects in the U.S. before fading into relative obscurity in the 1970s. Rudolph studied with German Modernist Walter Gropius at the Harvard Graduate School of Design, where he earned (1947) a master's degree in architecture. One year later he established his own architectural firm in Sarasota, Fla. His designs for a series of spare, airy houses in the Siesta Key area earned him a reputation as a virtuoso composer of space, form, and light. His renown quickly spread, and in 1957 Rudolph was named chairman of Yale University's prestigious architecture school, a position he held until 1965. During his tenure he completed one of the most defining commissions of his career—the 10-story Art and Architecture Building on the Yale campus. Never simply a slavish disciple of European Modernism, Rudolph, it was said, "broke the Atlantic sound barrier, creating designs that were more than the sum of their European influences." Anchored by poured-in-place concrete towers, the Yale building's exterior formed a lively collage of interlocking geometric shapes. In con-

Archive Photos

Paul Rudolph

trast to this monumental street presence, the interior appeared seamless, flowing, and shot with light, an illusion Rudolph created by using a complex assemblage of 37 different levels divided by glass walls. The building, however, became the target of student protesters who set fire to it in 1969. By then, Rudolph's reputation had begun to decline in the United States, and his abstract Modernist aesthetic was soon eclipsed by the growing popularity of Postmodernism's revival of historical styles

413

and ornamentation. He continued, however, to find an audience for his work in Asia. Working from his historic brownstone on Beekman Place in New York City, famous in design circles for the architect's controversial Modernist renovation in the 1960s, Rudolph drafted monolithic highrise projects for such cities as Hong Kong, Singapore, and Jakarta, Indon.

Sager, Ruth
Feb. 7, 1918—March 29, 1997

American geneticist Ruth Sager conducted groundbreaking research on where genetic material is found in cells; her findings changed the way that biologists view cell heredity. Later in her career she studied the genetic mechanisms related to cancer. Sager entered the University of Chicago at age 16, sampling the liberal arts before a chance encounter with a survey course on biology ignited her interest in the field. She graduated with a B.S. in 1938. Graduate work in plant physiology followed at Rutgers University, New Brunswick, N.J., where she received an M.S. in 1944. She continued graduate studies in genetics at Columbia University, New York City, earning a doctorate in 1948. Sager joined the research staff at the Rockefeller Institute (now Rockefeller University), New York City, as an assistant in 1951. There she challenged the prevailing theory that inherited characteristics are transmitted exclusively by the genes in the chromosomes, which are found in a cell's nucleus. In studying heredity in *Chlamydomonas* alga, she discovered that a gene located outside the chromosomes also transmits inherited characteristics. Nonchromosomal genes were later shown to be ubiquitous in living organisms. In 1955 Sager joined Columbia

University's zoology department, where she expanded her understanding of how nonchromosomal genes work. She served as a professor of biology at Hunter College, New York City, from 1966 through 1975, when she was appointed professor of cellular genetics at Harvard University and

Ruth Sager

head of Harvard's Dana-Farber Cancer Institute. Sager's extensive research into the mechanisms associated with cancer involved tumor suppressor genes, breast cancer, and the genetic means by which cancer multiplies. Her many prizes included the Gilbert Morgan Smith Medal, the National Cancer Institute's Outstanding Investigator Award, and a Guggenheim fellowship.

Schramm, David Norman
Oct. 25, 1945—Dec. 19, 1997

American theoretical astrophysicist David Schramm integrated subatomic-particle

physics with cosmology, which led to a greater understanding of the composition, structure, and origin of the universe during the big bang. After earning degrees in physics from the Massachusetts Institute of Technology (S.B., 1967) and the California Institute of Technology (Ph.D., 1971), he became (1972) an assistant professor at the University of Texas at Austin. In 1974 he joined the faculty of the University of Chicago and the university's Enrico Fermi Institute for Nuclear Studies as an associate professor. He later became (1995) vice president of research at the University of Chicago. Schramm helped to explain that the universe was created within the first few seconds following the big bang— much nearer to the event than previously believed. In particular he helped to explain the creation of the three lightest chemical elements—hydrogen, helium, and lithium. Schramm also helped describe the composition of matter in the universe. Theorizing that all existing deuterium, an isotope of hydrogen, was created during the big bang, Schramm used the amount of deuterium in existence to calculate that the universe consists mostly of unknown "exotic" or "dark" matter. Schramm was also known for having predicted that only three or four families of fundamental particles exist—a view once controversial but later accepted. Schramm was elected to the U.S. National Academy of Sciences in 1986. He died when the plane he was piloting crashed near Denver, Colo.

Schwarzschild, Martin
May 31, 1912—April 10, 1997

German-born American astronomer Martin Schwarzschild studied the structure and evolution of stars and pioneered the use of balloons to carry scientific equipment into the stratosphere for solar research. Schwarzschild, whose father, Karl, was also a renowned astronomer, earned a Ph.D. (1935) from the University of Göttingen, Ger. As a professor (1947–79) at Princeton University, he helped establish the school as a world leader in theoretical astrophysics, studying the presence and effects of discontinuities in the chemical compositions of stars by developing digital electronic computers (the first used for scientific research) to calculate numerical equations of stellar structure. Schwarzschild discovered previously unknown instabilities, such as shell flashes, late in the lifetime of stars and was the first to explain the development of red giant stars. In 1952 he teamed with Allan Sandage to study the growth of red giants after the point at which the core of the star begins to contract gravitationally owing to the consumption of hydrogen at its center by nuclear fusion. The pair created an evolutionary sequence of numerical models to demonstrate the increase of the star's luminosity concurrent with the cooling of its surface and an increase in its total volume. Schwarzschild later studied evolutionary processes of stars in globular clusters and published *Structure and Evolution of the Stars* (1958). He was also recognized for his theoretical studies of the dynamics of galactic structure. He was perhaps best known for his 1957 Project Stratoscope I, in which a balloon lifted a telescope 25 km (15 mi) above the Earth's atmosphere and obtained sharp images of the solar surface. In 1959 he sent up Stratoscope II to take pictures of the outer planets and galactic nuclei. Schwarzschild was elected (1956) to the National Academy of Sciences and

was president (1970–72) of the American Astronomical Society. His numerous honors included the Henry Draper Medal of the National Academy of Sciences (1961), the Gold Medal of the Royal Astronomical Society (1969), and, posthumously, the National Medal of Science (1997).

Shoemaker, Eugene Merle
April 28, 1928—July 18, 1997

American planetary geologist Eugene ("Gene") Shoemaker was hailed as one of the chief founders of planetary geology and considered by many scientists to be the consummate sky gazer of the 20th century. Throughout much of his long career, Shoemaker worked closely with his wife and colleague, Carolyn Spellman Shoemaker. Between them they identified 32 comets and 1,125 asteroids, missing by only 5 the world comet record set by 19th-century astronomer Jean-Louis Pons. Their most spectacular find, Comet Shoemaker-Levy 9, was discovered with amateur astronomer David Levy. The comet dazzled the world in July 1994 as its 21 glowing fragments tore into Jupiter's southern hemisphere, the largest chunks exploding with a force comparable to several million megatons of TNT. This was not the first time that Shoemaker had made headlines. In 1948 after graduating at age 20 with a master's degree in geology from the California Institute of Technology (Caltech), he surveyed craters in the landscape of the American Southwest. The young geologist rocked the scientific world in the late 1950s by supplying confirmation of the origin of Meteor Crater near Winslow, Ariz. Following his discovery of coesite, a form of silica created under the high pressure of meteoric impacts, Shoemaker theorized that the

1,200-m (4,000-ft)-wide bowl-shaped pit was formed when a meteorite crashed into the Earth's surface more than 50,000 years ago. His research lent credence to the theory that the bombardment of the Earth and other planets with celestial debris played an important role in the history of planetary evolution. He later supported the hypothesis that an object from outer space may have been responsible for the cataclysmic changes on Earth that led to the extinction of the dinosaurs and other life forms 65 million years ago. Shoemaker warned of the possibility of other such devastating encounters with the Earth and favored the development of technology that would intercept threatening astral projectiles before impact. During his tenure with the U.S. Geological Survey from 1948 to his retirement in 1993, he established the agency's Center of Astrogeology in Flagstaff, Ariz., where he served as chief scientist. While also teaching at Caltech from 1962 to 1985, Shoemaker found time to pursue one of his lifelong interests—the geologic history of the Moon. As principal investigator for NASA's Apollo Moon project in the 1960s, he used a telescope to map lunar craters and studied rock specimens retrieved from the Moon's surface, as well as helping to train NASA astronauts in lunar geology, a discipline that he was credited with inventing. Shoemaker received the U.S. National Medal of Science in 1992.

Spitzer, Lyman, Jr.
June 26, 1914—March 31, 1997

American astrophysicist Lyman Spitzer advanced knowledge of the physical processes occurring in interstellar space and pioneered efforts to harness nuclear fusion as a source of clean energy. After Spitzer earned a B.A. from Yale University in 1935, he spent a year as a graduate fellow at the University of Cambridge. He received a Ph.D. in astrophysics from Princeton University in 1938 and shortly thereafter began teaching at Yale. During World War II he was recruited by the U.S. Navy for the Division of War Research at Columbia University, New York City, where he assisted in the development of sonar. Spitzer's interest in the study of star formation took him in 1947 to Princeton as a professor of astronomy and the director of the observatory there. In 1946 he had begun urging the United States government to launch an orbiting space telescope to record astronomical phenomena without interference from the Earth's atmospheric effects. His efforts resulted in the construction and launch in 1990 of the Hubble Space Telescope in addition to other orbiting observatories. In the early 1950s his study of the ionized gases (plasmas) that are crucial to aspects of stellar formation and energy production led to the organized study of plasma physics. Hoping to find a new source of power for peaceful applications, he persuaded the U.S. Atomic Energy Commission in 1951 to fund the development of his "stellarator," a device that theoretically could achieve controlled thermonuclear fusion in ionized gas contained in a magnetic field. Despite decades of experimentation at Princeton's Plasma Physics Laboratory, the device and later fusion machines at Princeton were never completely successful. Funds for the project were cut off by Congress just days before Spitzer's death. Spitzer wrote a number of influential books, including *Physics of Fully Ionized Gases* (1956),

Diffuse Matter in Space (1968), and *Dynamical Evolution of Globular Clusters* (1987). Among Spitzer's numerous awards was the National Medal of Science, bestowed in 1979.

Wald, George
Nov. 18, 1906—April 12, 1997

American biologist and biochemist George Wald was a co-winner, with Haldan K. Hartline of the U.S. and Ragnar Granit of Sweden, of the 1967 Nobel Prize for Physiology or Medicine for the research he carried out on the chemistry of vision. He was also outspoken in his opposition to the Vietnam War, nuclear weapons proliferation, and human rights abuses and was proud of the fact that his name had been included on Pres. Richard M. Nixon's "enemies list." Wald, who received a bachelor's degree (1927) in zoology from Washington Square College, New York University, and a doctorate (1932) from Columbia University, New York City, was

George Wald

conducting research in Berlin on a National Research Council fellowship (1932–33) when he identified the presence of Vitamin A in the pigments in the retina and thus its importance to the maintenance of vision. He continued his research in Heidelberg, Ger., and the Universities of Zürich, Switz., and Chicago before joining (1934) the faculty of Harvard University, where he spent the following 43 years, becoming professor emeritus in 1977. At Harvard, often in collaboration with Ruth Hubbard—whom he married in 1958—and Paul Brown, he made further discoveries regarding the means by which images are transmitted from the eye to the brain and the role of vitamin A in this process. Besides the Nobel, Wald's many awards included the Eli Lilly Award of the American Chemical Society (1939), the Lasker Award of the American Public Health Association (1953), and the Rumford Medal of the American Academy of Arts and Sciences (1959).

Philippot—Sygma

RECENT BOOKS OF SCIENCE

The following list encompasses 91 recent books published in English in 1997 that have been judged significant contributions to learning in their respective areas of science. Each citation includes a few lines of commentary to indicate the tenor of the work. The citations are organized by broad subject area, using the appropriate parts of *Encyclopædia Britannica*'s Propædia as an outline.

Matter and Energy

Michael Hawkins, *Hunting Down the Universe: The Missing Mass, Primordial Black Holes, and Other Dark Matters,* an account of the author's 20-year odyssey of discovery that led to provocative new conclusions about the universe.

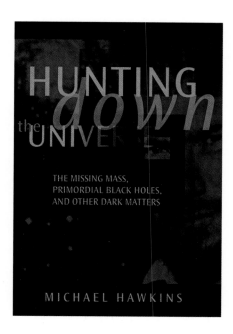

Richard Morris, *Achilles in the Quantum Universe,* a historical study of the concept of infinity and the philosophers and mathematicians who have explored its meaning.

Michael Springford (ed.), *Electron: A Centenary Volume,* essays by 11 physicists on the form and function of the electron, whose discovery by J.J. Thomson in 1897 has influenced scientific research from molecular biology to astrophysics.

Alexander Y. Grosberg and Alexei R. Khokhlov, *Giant Molecules: Here, There, and Everywhere...,* a description of the class of giant molecules of which natural substances such as DNA and synthetic polymers are composed, explaining their place in science, industry, and the human body.

Nickolas Solomey, *The Elusive Neutrino: A Subatomic Detective Story,* a discussion of the neutrino, whose detection has given astronomers and physicists stunning insights into the beginnings of the universe.

Helga Nowotny and Ulrike Felt, *After the Breakthrough: The Emergence of High-Temperature Superconductivity as a Research Field,* a study of the influence of the revolutionary breakthrough in superconductivity on social and economic behavior.

Alfred K. Mann, *Shadow of a Star: The Neutrino Story of Supernova 1987A,* a scientist's eyewitness account of a stellar explosion (the first one seen since 1604), explaining the event and its aftermath and what was learned about the composition of the star.

David Park, *The Fire Within the Eye: A Historical Essay on the Nature and Meaning of Light,* an essay on the spiritual, natural, and scientific preeminence of light as scientists and philosophers past and present have sought to understand it and its concomitant phenomenon, vision.

Timothy Ferris, *The Whole Shebang: A State-of-the-Universe(s) Report,* an overview of recent scientific depictions of the universe, detailing current research that may point to the existence of multiple universes, each governed by its own physical laws.

Alan H. Guth, *The Inflationary Universe: The Quest for a New Theory of Cosmic Origins,* a theory of the universe that attempts to explain the origin, nature, and indestructibility of matter.

Martin Rees, *Before the Beginning: Our Universe and Others,* a discussion of black holes, dark matter, nucleosynthesis of the elements, and related astrophysical phenomena.

Lee Smolin, *The Life of the Cosmos,* a reflection on the possibility of constructing a single unified theory that would successfully merge Einstein's theory of relativity with quantum theory.

James B. Kaler, *Cosmic Clouds: Birth, Death, and Recycling in the Galaxy,* a description of cosmic evolution and the life cycle and chemistry of heavenly bodies.

Barry E. DiGregorio, with Gilbert V. Levin and Patricia Ann Straat, *Mars: The Living Planet,* an account of the science of exobiology and its relation to research studies in Antarctica, taking as its principal focus the hunt for evidence of life on Mars.

Piers Bizony, *The Rivers of Mars: Searching for the Cosmic Origins of Life,* a work that examines the question of whether the chemical essentials for life on Earth were sown from space and whether they also exist on other heavenly bodies, particularly Mars.

The Earth

Ann Vileisis, *Discovering the Unknown Landscape: A History of America's Wetlands,* a social and environmental history of wetlands in the U.S.

Paul Schullery, *Searching for Yellowstone: Ecology and Wonder in the Last Wilderness,* a history of the oldest, the largest, and probably the best-known national park in the U.S.

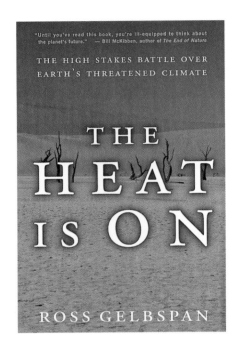

Ross Gelbspan, *The Heat Is On: The High Stakes Battle over Earth's Threatened Climate,* an examination by a Pulitzer Prize-winning journalist of the political and economic forces influencing the global-warming debate.

Ernest Zebrowski, Jr., *Perils of a Restless Planet: Scientific Perspectives on Natural Disasters,* case studies of catastrophic natural events, employing scientific methodology for developing theories, technologies, and public policy to minimize damage and possibly predict occurrences.

Joanna Burger, *Oil Spills,* a historical survey of oil spills, their effect on the biosphere, and efforts to contain or prevent them.

William J. Broad, *The Universe Below: Discovering the Secrets of the Deep Sea,* a firsthand account of deep-sea exploration and how the release of previously

secret technologies has accelerated the pace and scope of biological discoveries and recovery of sunken treasure.

Walter A. Lyons, *The Handy Weather Answer Book,* an explanation of weather and related phenomena in a question-and-answer format.

Richard V. Fisher, Grant Heiken, and Jeffrey B. Hulen, *Volcanoes: Crucibles of Change,* a study of volcanoes, enumerating their types and causes as well as events that foreshadow volcanic activity, with firsthand accounts of eruptions.

Thomas Fairchild Sherman, *A Place on the Glacial Till: Time, Land, and Nature Within an American Town,* a geologic, archaeological, and paleontological overview of an area near Oberlin, Ohio.

Life on Earth

Richard Nelson, *Heart and Blood: Living with Deer in America,* essays on the natural history of deer from their role in

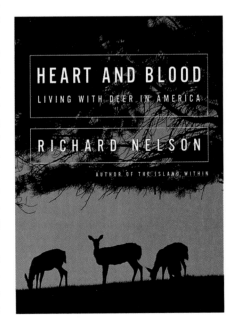

Native American culture to their effects on modern suburban landscapes.

John R. Horner and Edwin Dobb, *Dinosaur Lives: Unearthing an Evolutionary Saga,* a paleobiological study of several prehistoric species, presenting evidence from fossil remains that the mass extinction of dinosaurs had an earthly, not extraterrestrial, cause.

Vicki Croke, *The Modern Ark: The Story of Zoos; Past, Present and Future,* an inquiry into the moral and ethical implications of animal captivity.

Karl J. Niklas, *The Evolutionary Biology of Plants,* a review of major themes in the evolution of plants.

Elio Schaechter, *In the Company of Mushrooms: A Biologist's Tale,* a learned look at the natural history of fungi.

Ronald Orenstein, *Songbirds: Celebrating Nature's Voices,* a natural history of songbird behavior.

Walter Alvarez, *T. Rex and the Crater of Doom,* a theory about the mass extinction of dinosaurs that occurred 65 million years ago, pointing to geologic evidence for a comet or asteroid impact off the Yucatán Peninsula.

Lionel R. Milgrom, *The Colours of Life: An Introduction to the Chemistry of Porphyrins and Related Compounds,* a biochemical discussion of colors, explaining why grass is green and blood is red and exploring pigments at the molecular level.

Jared Diamond, *Why Is Sex Fun? The Evolution of Human Sexuality,* a speculation on whether the development of such exclusively human sexual behaviors as preference for sex in private may have given humans an evolutionary advantage over other mammals.

Boyce Rensberger, *Life Itself: Exploring the Realm of the Living Cell,* an introduction to the fundamentals of cellular biology and the study of genes via a voyage into the interior of the cell to observe its many components.

Frans de Waal and Frans Lanting, *Bonobo: The Forgotten Ape,* a study of the bonobo, contrasting its social behavior with that of the chimpanzee and making a case for the existence of pacifist egalitarianism within at least one species of primate.

Amotz Zahavi and Avishag Zahavi, with Naama Zahavi-Ely and Melvin P. Ely, *The Handicap Principle: A Missing Piece of Darwin's Puzzle,* a discussion of an adjunct to the process of natural selection, asserting that the behavior that proclaims an individual animal's superior strength or speed will gain the animal an advantage over its competitors for mates or food.

Michael Sims, *Darwin's Orchestra: An Almanac of Nature in History and the Arts,* brief essays, in one-a-day format, on aspects of natural history, ranging from a battle-halting eclipse in 585 BC to a method for studying the hearing of earthworms.

Susan Allport, *A Natural History of Parenting: From Emperor Penguins to Reluctant Ewes, a Naturalist Looks at How Parenting Differs in the Animal World and Ours,* a survey of the wide range of parenting behaviors throughout the animal kingdom.

Christopher McGowan, *The Raptor and the Lamb: Predators and Prey in the Living World,* a study of the symbiotic relationship between predator and prey that shows how an ingenious offense and a resourceful defense promote traits that contribute to the survival of both species.

Martha A. Strawn, *Alligators: Prehistoric Presence in the American Landscape,* a pictorial as well as verbal plea for protection of an ancient species, with photographs and essays depicting the habitat, life, and often violent death at human hands of the American alligator.

Stephen H. Schneider, *Laboratory Earth: The Planetary Gamble We Can't Afford to Lose,* a state-of-the-Earth report.

Linda Lear, *Rachel Carson: Witness for Nature,* a biography of the renowned 20th-century environmental scientist and writer Rachel Carson, whose books helped create a worldwide awareness of the dangers of environmental pollution.

Human Life

Roger Lewin, *Patterns in Evolution: The New Molecular View,* an account of the effect of molecular science on evolutionary studies, tracing the history of and the relationships between the disparate forms of life on Earth.

Milford Wolpoff and Rachel Caspari, *Races and Human Evolution: A Fatal Attraction,* a discussion of the "Eve" theory of human evolution (one common ancestor) as contrasted with multiregionalism, the hypothesis that posits diverse origins—possibly different species—for the variety of modern human races.

Noel T. Boaz, *Eco Homo: How the Human Being Emerged from the Cataclysmic History of the Earth,* a work relating early humans to their ecological setting and asserting that the evolutionary success of hominids arose in large part from their rapid response to extreme fluctuations in the prehistoric African climate.

Sherwin B. Nuland, *The Wisdom of the Body,* a physician's celebration of the complexity and delicate durability of the human body, with an anatomic tour and meditations on the mysteries of the body's spiritual and psychological architecture.

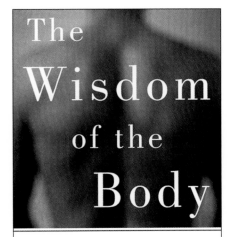

Eric J. Cassell, *Doctoring: The Nature of Primary Care Medicine,* a declaration in favor of returning the patient to the center of the physician's focus, making the impersonal rationalism of technology secondary to the doctor's trained yet sympathetic attention.

Stephen S. Hall, *A Commotion in the Blood: Life, Death, and the Immune System,* the story of immunology and immunotherapy in the treatment of various cancers as seen in the work and lives of principal researchers in the field.

Richard Rhodes, *Deadly Feasts: Tracking the Secrets of a Terrifying New Plague,* a work that predicts the spread of several virulent fatal contagious diseases that have already surfaced around the globe and urges prevention research and international public health measures.

Bernard J. Baars, *In the Theater of Consciousness: The Workspace of the Mind,* an examination of the way humans experience themselves and their world, with discussions on the phenomena of dreaming and sleeping and the way the brain processes signals.

Deborah Blum, *Sex on the Brain: The Biological Differences Between Men and Women,* an evolutionary approach to sexual differences that speculates on the influence of gender on aggressiveness, risk taking, and endurance.

Human Society

Robert Pool, *Beyond Engineering: How Society Shapes Technology,* a discussion of how historical, political, cultural, organizational, economic, and psychological factors have shaped technological developments.

Janine M. Benyus, *Biomimicry: Innovation Inspired by Nature,* a study of the new field of biomimicry, in which nature's designs and processes are imitated to solve human problems.

Jared Diamond, *Guns, Germs and Steel: The Fates of Human Societies,* a study of the development of early human cultures.

Gary Paul Nabhan, *Cultures of Habitat: On Nature, Culture, and Story,* a look at the relationship between biological diversity and human communities with close ties to the land.

George B. Dyson, *Darwin Among the Machines: The Evolution of Global Intelligence,* a history of the information revolution and the visionaries who helped to bring it about.

Richard Longstreth, *City Center to Regional Mall: Architecture, the Automobile, and Retailing in Los Angeles, 1920–1950,* a case study of Los Angeles, covering aspects of the city from downtown expansion to atrophy to the emergence of regional centers.

Robert Kuttner, *Everything for Sale: The Virtues and Limits of Markets,* a history of markets that makes the case for a mixed economy in which government acts as a stabilizer and expresses societal desires for progress and improved technology.

Art

George F. Thompson and Frederick R. Steiner (eds.), *Ecological Design and Planning,* essays on the latest thinking and practices in the art and science of ecological landscape design.

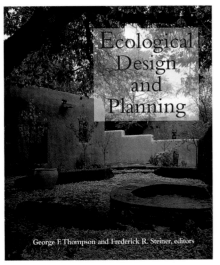

George F. Thompson and Frederick R. Steiner, editors

David Wiles, *Tragedy in Athens: Performance Space and Theatrical Meaning,* a study of Athenian performance and stagecraft, based on the archaeological evidence of vase paintings and the remains of altars, theaters, and other structures.

Steven L. Cantor, *Innovative Design Solutions in Landscape Architecture,* a description of 50 architectural projects by firms of various sizes.

Technology

Joseph B. Lambert, *Traces of the Past: Unraveling the Secrets of Archaeology Through Chemistry,* an examination of the ways in which cutting-edge scientific methods are yielding new insights into ancient life.

Robert McCormick Adams, *Paths of Fire: An Anthropologist's Inquiry into Western Technology,* a history of Western technology, arguing that technology has operated less as an isolated engine of change than as part of a broader pattern of social, cultural, and scientific information.

Janet H. Murray, *Hamlet on the Holodeck: The Future of Narrative in Cyberspace,* a discussion of the way computer technology is reshaping traditional narrative as new digital systems interact with conventional literature.

Bettyann Holtzmann Kevles, *Naked to the Bone: Medical Imaging in the 20th Century,* a consideration of X-ray technology and its influence on society.

Keith Wailoo, *Drawing Blood: Technology and Disease Identity in Twentieth-Century America,* an assertion that medical technology has changed the way diseases are diagnosed.

John D. Graham and Jennifer Kassalow Hartwell (eds.), *The Greening of Industry: A Risk Management Approach,* case studies of six industries showing the effect of risk management practices on controlling and preventing pollution.

Paul Bianchina, *Builder's Guide to New Materials and Techniques,* an introduction to new technologies that are profoundly influencing building design and construction.

Derek Phillips, *Lighting Historic Buildings,* an analysis of lighting and its relationship to changing concepts of interiors and exteriors of buildings, with remarks on the importance of minimizing anachronistic lighting in historic structures.

Steven Winter Associates, *Accessible Housing by Design: Universal Design Principles in Practice,* a collection of examples of housing designs for various types of disabled inhabitants in a wide range of climates and topographies in the U.S., with photographs and diagrams highlighting specific features.

Bert S. Hall, *Weapons & Warfare in Renaissance Europe: Gunpowder, Technology, and Tactics,* a history of military technology, describing the changes in weaponry and battle tactics associated with the development of gunpowder.

Ken Alder, *Engineering the Revolution: Arms and the Enlightenment in France, 1763–1815,* an examination of French politics and economics in light of the technology introduced by French military engineers who crafted the first interchangeable parts for gun and cannon manufacture.

Robert Geddes (ed.), *Cities in Our Future: Growth and Form, Environmental*

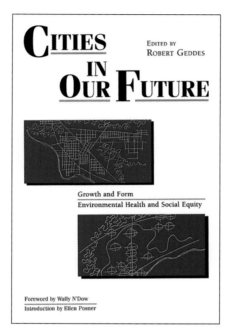

Health and Social Equity, an analysis of the history, physical terrain, and environmental issues facing five "city-regions" in North and Central America, with proposals for improving each.

Religion

Roald Hoffmann and Shira Leibowitz Schmidt, *Old Wine, New Flasks: Reflections on Science and Jewish Tradition,* a humanistic meditation on science and religion based on chemistry and Old Testament Judaism that explores humanity's domination of nature.

The History of Mankind

Michael White, *Isaac Newton: The Last Sorcerer,* a biography of the great English scientist Sir Isaac Newton.

Adrian Desmond, *Huxley: From Devil's Disciple to Evolution's High Priest,* a biography of the controversial 19th-century scientist Thomas Henry Huxley.

Mauro Ambrosoli (trans. Mary McCann Salvatorelli), *The Wild and the Sown: Botany and Agriculture in Western Europe, 1350–1850,* a history of the French, Italian, and English farmers, botanists, and landowners who together promoted new farming methods based on crop rotation and livestock raising.

Matthew H. Edney, *Mapping an Empire: The Geographical Construction of British India,* an account of mapmaking as a political and scientific undertaking in British India.

Jacques Roger (trans. Sarah Lucille Bonnefoi), *Buffon: A Life in Natural History,*

a biography of George-Louis Leclerc, comte de Buffon, the premier French scientist of the Enlightenment.

Jeremy Black, *Maps and History: Constructing Images of the Past,* a noted historian's comprehensive account of historical atlases, which, incorporating 90 black-and-white illustrations and 30 color plates, describes the evolution of maps from the classical world to the late 20th century, links historical atlases to politics, and considers the influence of modern imaging technology on mapmaking.

William J. Murtagh, *Keeping Time: The History and Theory of Preservation in America,* an account of historic preservation of objects, archaeological sites, and buildings, with guidelines and discussions of social, legal, ethical, and economic issues.

The Branches of Knowledge

J. François Gabriel (ed.), *Beyond the Cube: The Architecture of Space Frames and Polyhedra,* a description of a type of construction that consists of hollow geometric forms, enumerating the construction's properties, virtues, relationship to crystal formation, and future applications.

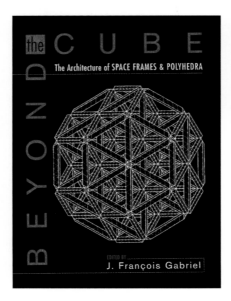

Ivan Amato, *Stuff: The Materials the World Is Made of,* a popular history of the material sciences.

Jan Gullberg, *Mathematics from the Birth of Numbers,* a history of numbers and their symbols, with discussions ranging from the four rules of arithmetic to calculus and differential equations as well as explanations of symbols and how they work.

Maurizio Forte and Alberto Siliotti (eds. and comps.), *Virtual Archaeology: Re-creating Ancient Worlds,* a collection of three-dimensional high-definition computer reconstructions, along with hundreds of full-color maps, diagrams, and photographs, providing readers with a

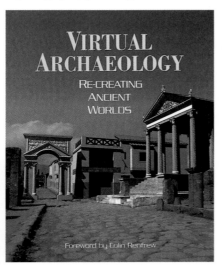

sense of how significant archaeological sites around the world once looked, including Pompeii, Giza, Troy, and Abu Simbel.

Martin W. Lewis and Kären E. Wigen, *The Myth of Continents: A Critique of Metageography,* an assertion that the fragmentation of the former Soviet Union demonstrates that the traditional nation-

state-continent approach to geography is outdated, and a zone system like the Pacific Rim is the wave of the future.

Sara Schechner Genuth, *Comets, Popular Culture, and the Birth of Modern Cosmology,* an account of the interrelated effects of comet lore and popular culture on early modern science, covering the influence of astrological studies on celestial mechanics and how changing perceptions of comets altered the view of nature and the world.

Colin Bruce, *The Strange Case of Mrs. Hudson's Cat and Other Science Mysteries Solved by Sherlock Holmes,* a whodunit approach to 12 of the most perplexing scientific conundrums of our time.

Ernst Mayr, *This Is Biology: The Science of the Living World,* a holistic approach to the history, philosophy, and methodology of the life sciences, emphasizing the ways in which biologists are developing increasingly precise information about the living world and how the life sciences compare with and differ from the physical sciences.

Terrence W. Deacon, *The Symbolic Species: The Co-evolution of Language and the Brain,* an investigation of the apparently unique relationship of mind and brain that has developed in humans and is expressed in the ability of humans to create and manipulate language symbols.

Michael D. Resnik, *Mathematics as a Science of Patterns,* a look at the philosophical underpinnings of mathematics as a science of patterns and at the relationship of mathematics to realism and empiricism.

—Jean S. Gottlieb

CONTRIBUTORS TO THE SCIENCE YEAR IN REVIEW

Richard A. Anthes

Earth Sciences: Atmospheric Sciences. President, University Corporation for Atmospheric Research, Boulder, Colo.

William A. Blanpied

Science Policy. Senior International Analyst, National Science Foundation, Washington, D.C.

Harold Borko

Electronics and Information Sciences: Computer Systems and Services. Professor Emeritus, University of California, Los Angeles.

John M. Bowen

Medical Sciences: Veterinary Medicine. Professor and Associate Dean Emeritus, College of Veterinary Medicine, University of Georgia.

Brandon R. Brown

Physics: Nuclear Physics. Intern, Science Communication Program, University of California, Santa Cruz.

Paul J. Campbell

Mathematics. Professor of Mathematics and Computer Science, Beloit (Wis.) College; Visiting Professor, University of Augsburg, Ger.

David L. Carlson

Anthropology. Associate Professor of Anthropology, Texas A & M University at College Station.

Kim Alan Chapman

Environment: Issues and Policy. Director of Science and Conservation, The Nature Conservancy of Minnesota.

David E. Collins

Materials Science and Engineering: Polymers. Graduate Research Assistant, School of Materials Engineering, Purdue University, West Lafayette, Ind.

Dave Dooling

Space Exploration. Owner, D^2 Associates, Huntsville, Ala.

Rolfe Erickson

Earth Sciences: Geology and Geochemistry. Professor of Geology, Sonoma State University, Rohnert Park, Calif.

David E. Farrell

Physics: Condensed-Matter Physics. Professor of Physics, Case Western Reserve University, Cleveland, Ohio.

Jean S. Gottlieb

Recent Books of Science. Freelance Editor; Bibliographer.

Robert Haselkorn

Life Sciences: Molecular Biology and Genetics. F.L. Pritzker Distinguished Service Professor, Department of Molecular Genetics and Cell Biology, University of Chicago.

Christopher T. Hill

Physics: Elementary-Particle Physics. Scientist II, Fermi National Accelerator Laboratory, Batavia, Ill.; Professor of Physics, University of Chicago.

Charles King Hoyt

Architectural and Civil Engineering. Principal, Charles King Hoyt Architect; Fellow, American Institute of Architects.

William A. Jensen

Life Sciences: Botany. Professor of Plant Biology, Ohio State University at Columbus.

John Patrick Jordan

Food and Agriculture: Agriculture (in part). Director, Southern Regional Research Center, USDA-ARS, New Orleans.

Ronald H. Kaitchuck

Astronomy. Professor of Physics and Astronomy, Ball State University, Muncie, Ind.

Allan P. Katz

Materials Science and Engineering: Ceramics. Technical Team Leader for Structural Ceramics, Air Force Research Laboratory, Materials and Manufacturing Directorate, Wright-Patterson Air Force Base, Ohio.

George B. Kauffman

Chemistry: Applied Chemistry. Professor of Chemistry, California State University at Fresno.

David B. Kitts

Earth Sciences: Paleontology. Professor Emeritus, Department of History of Science, University of Oklahoma.

Rebecca Kolberg

Medical Sciences: General Medicine. Senior On-Line Editor, Time Life Medical; Writer, "Healthweek," PBS.

Matthew John M. Krane

Materials Science and Engineering: Metals. Assistant Professor of Materials Engineering, Purdue University, West Lafayette, Ind.

Patricia Brazeel Lewis

Food and Agriculture: Agriculture (in part). Public Relations Consultant, New Jersey Agricultural Experiment Station, Rutgers University, New Brunswick, N.J.

Charles Lydeard
Life Sciences: Zoology. Assistant Professor of Biology, University of Alabama at Tuscaloosa.

John M. Mason
Transportation. Associate Dean of Graduate Studies and Research, College of Engineering, Pennsylvania State University.

Nicolas Mokhoff
Electronics and Information Sciences: Electronics. Executive Editor, *EE Times.*

Richard Monastersky
Earth Sciences: Oceanography. Earth Science Editor, *Science News,* Washington, D.C.

Charles S. Mueller
Earth Sciences: Geophysics. Geophysicist, U.S. Geological Survey, Golden, Colo.

Christopher Peterson
Psychology (in part). Professor of Psychology, University of Michigan at Ann Arbor.

Stuart L. Pimm
Life Sciences: Ecology. Professor of Ecology, University of Tennessee at Knoxville.

Marla Reicks
Food and Agriculture: Nutrition. Associate Professor, Department of Food Science and Nutrition, University of Minnesota at Minneapolis.

John Rhea
Defense Research. Washington Bureau Chief, *Military & Aerospace Electronics.*

C. Paul Robinson
Energy (in part). President and Laboratories Director, Sandia National Laboratories, Albuquerque, N.M.

Martin E.P. Seligman
Psychology (in part). Professor of Psychology, University of Pennsylvania.

Lawrence J. Shimkets
Life Sciences: Microbiology. Professor and Head of Microbiology, University of Georgia.

Ron Sims
Medical Sciences: Dentistry. Special Collections Librarian and Catalog/Reference Librarian, Galter Health Sciences Library, Northwestern University Dental and Medical Schools, Chicago.

Leslie Smith
Earth Sciences: Hydrology. Professor of Earth and Ocean Sciences, University of British Columbia.

Michael B. Smith
Chemistry: Organic Chemistry. Professor, Department of Chemistry, University of Connecticut.

Ben P. Stein
Physics: Atomic, Molecular, and Optical Physics. Science Writer, American Institute of Physics, College Park, Md.

Robert E. Stoffels
Electronics and Information Sciences: Telecommunications Systems. Consultant, St. Petersburg, Fla.

Bud Ward
Environment: Environmental Technology. Executive Director, Environmental Health Center, National Safety Council, Washington, D.C.

Philip R. Watson
Chemistry: Physical Chemistry. Professor, Department of Chemistry, Oregon State University.

Stephanie A. Weiss
Electronics and Information Sciences: Photonics and Optical Technology. Executive Editor, *Photonics Spectra.*

James D. Wilde
Archaeology. Archaeologist, Headquarters, Air Force Center for Environmental Excellence, San Antonio, Texas.

Charles H. Winter
Chemistry: Inorganic Chemistry. Associate Professor, Department of Chemistry, Wayne State University, Detroit.

Alexander Wolfe
Electronics and Information Sciences: Computers and Computer Science. Managing Editor, Computers and Communications, *EE Times.*

Joan B. Woodard
Energy (in part). Vice President, Energy, Environment, and Information Technology Division, Sandia National Laboratories, Albuquerque, N.M.

Michael Woods
Scientists of the Year: Nobel Prizes. Science Editor, Block News Alliance.

CONTRIBUTORS TO THE ENCYCLOPÆDIA BRITANNICA SCIENCE UPDATE

Gordon P. Bierwagen
Industrial Polymers (in part). Professor of Polymers and Coatings, North Dakota State University.

Tom D. Crouch
Orville and Wilbur Wright. Chairman, Department of Aeronautics, National Air and Space Museum, Smithsonian Institution, Washington, D.C.

Alan N. Gent
Industrial Polymers (in part). Dr. Harold A. Morton Professor Emeritus of Polymer Physics and Polymer Engineering, University of Akron, Ohio.

Joseph E. Hawkins
Sensory Reception (in part). Emeritus Professor of Otolaryngology (Physiological Acoustics), University of Michigan Medical School, Ann Arbor.

George B. Kauffman
Industrial Polymers (in part). Professor of Chemistry, California State University at Fresno.

J. Preston
Industrial Polymers (in part). Senior Research Scientist, Research Triangle Institute, Research Triangle Park, N.C.

Ferdinand Rodriguez
Industrial Polymers (in part). Professor of Chemical Engineering, Cornell University, Ithaca, N.Y.

Malcolm P. Stevens
Industrial Polymers (in part). Professor of Chemistry, University of Hartford, West Hartford, Conn.

INDEX

This is a three-year cumulative index. Index entries for review articles in this and previous editions of the *Yearbook of Science and the Future* are set in boldface type, *e.g.,* **Astronomy.** Feature articles appear under the article title and are identified as such. Entries to other subjects are set in lightface type, *e.g.,* radiation. Additional information on any of these subjects is identified with a subheading and indented under the entry heading. Subheadings in quotes refer to feature articles on that topic. The numbers following headings and subheadings indicate the year (boldface) of the edition and the page number (lightface) on which the information appears. The abbreviation "*il.*" indicates an illustration.

> **Astronomy 99**–250; **98**–252; **97**–276
> gamma-ray bursts **99**–393
> honors **98**–404; **99**–407
> "How Old Is the Universe?" **97**–32

All entry headings are alphabetized word by word. Hyphenated words and words separated by dashes or slashes are treated as two words. When one word differs from another only by the presence of additional characters at the end, the shorter precedes the longer. In inverted names, the words following the comma are considered only after the preceding part of the name has been alphabetized. Names beginning with "Mc" and "Mac" are alphabetized as "Mac"; "St." is alphabetized as "Saint." Examples:

> Lake
> Lake, Simon
> Lake Placid
> Lakeland